Second Canadian Edition

Human Evolution and PREHISTORY

William A. Haviland
University of Vermont

Gary W. Crawford
University of Toronto Mississauga

NELSON / EDUCATION

NELSON / EDUCATION

Human Evolution and Prehistory, Second Canadian Edition
William A. Haviland and Gary W. Crawford

Associate Vice President, Editorial Director:
Evelyn Veitch

Editor-in-Chief, Higher Education:
Anne Williams

Acquisitions Editor:
Scott Couling

Marketing Manager:
Heather Leach

Developmental Editor:
My Editor Inc.

Photo Researcher and Permissions Coordinator:
Indu Ghuman

Content Production Manager:
Susan Wong

Production Service:
GEX Publishing Service

Copy Editor:
Karen Rolfe

Proofreader:
GEX Publishing Service

Indexer:
Noeline Bridge

Manufacturing Coordinator:
Loretta Lee

Design Director:
Ken Phipps

Interior Design:
Dianna Little

Cover Design:
Dianna Little

Cover Image:
Joane Cardinal-Schubert RCA

Compositor:
GEX Publishing Service

Printer:
Courier Kendallville

Library and Archives Canada Cataloguing in Publication

Haviland, William A.
  Human evolution and prehistory / William A. Haviland, Gary W. Crawford. — 2nd Canadian ed.

Includes bibliographical references and index.

ISBN-13: 978-0-17-610280-7
ISBN-10: 0-17-610280-9

  1. Physical anthropology—Textbooks. 2. Ethnology—Textbooks. 3. Primates—Textbooks. 4. Archaeology—Textbooks. I. Crawford, Gary W. II. Title.

GN60.H39 2008
306
C2007-904016-0

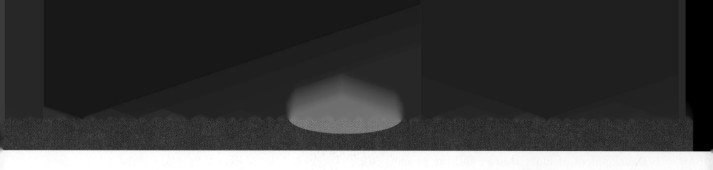

PURPOSE

Human Evolution and Prehistory, Second Canadian Edition, is a brief text that offers a straightforward, balanced presentation on views of human evolution, adaptation, and prehistory. It focuses on selected aspects of biological anthropology and archaeology as they relate to the origin of humanity, the origin of culture, and the development of human biological and cultural diversity. Haviland's commitment to challenging students' ethnocentrism is continued and reinforced in this new Canadian edition.

Designed for introductory anthropology courses that combine biological anthropology (also known as physical anthropology) and archaeology, Haviland and Crawford's *Human Evolution and Prehistory* presents the key concepts and terminology from biological anthropology and archaeology that apply to the interrelated subjects of human biology and cultural evolution. This text provides more of the biological background than one would get in an archaeology course alone. At the same time, it provides more of the cultural context than one would get in a course restricted to biological anthropology. The first and most obvious aim of the text, therefore, is to give students a comprehensive introduction to each subfield as it bears on the related topics of the origin of humanity, the origin of culture, and the development of human biological and cultural diversity. In the process, students will come to understand the ways human culture and biology are interdependent, with each having an impact on the other.

A secondary goal of the text is to persuade students to understand the true complexity of our evolution and that our presence is *not* the outcome of a process that led inexorably and predictably to where we are today. Indeed, "debunking" is an important function of anthropology, and questioning beliefs in the superiority of humans over other forms of life, farming over food foraging, or complex civilizations over cultures based on subsistence farming is something that anthropologists do especially well. Anthropology is, in this sense, a tool to enable students to rethink their place in the world and their responsibilities to it.

ORGANIZATION
A Unifying Theme

To provide students with a sense of the big picture, *Human Evolution and Prehistory* uses a theme that allows students to contextualize each part and each chapter, regardless of the order in which they are read. Accordingly, each part, as well as each chapter within the part, has been developed as a self-contained unit of study that may be used in any sequence by the instructor. There are four parts in *Human Evolution and Prehistory*:

Part I: The Study of Humankind introduces students to the discipline of anthropology in general and in Canada specifically. Many disciplines study humanity, but anthropology does so by including humans and their ancestors in all times and places. Part I explores the methods of anthropologists, with a particular focus in Chapter 2 on how the distant past is studied. Chapter 3 introduces the subject of human biology and the principles of evolution that are the foundation for discussions in subsequent chapters.

Part II: Primate Evolution and the Emergence of the Hominines sets out the current understanding of the development of the human lineage from the first tropical, apelike animals to the first recognizable direct human ancestors. Chapter 4 reviews modern primates to see how much humans are like other primates. In Chapter 5 the fossil record of early primates is examined. By using knowledge of modern primates and evolutionary theory, we can see how anthropologists discern which fossils are the likely ancestors to the human line and how these early primates behaved. The earliest true hominine, *Australopithecus*, is the subject of Chapter 6. This apelike human walked upright but still had apelike mental abilities.

Part III: Evolution of the Genus Homo and the Development of Early Human Culture examines the appearance of *Homo*, the genus to which humans are classified. Humans begin to rely more on culture than their biological makeup in order to adapt to new environmental situations. Chapter 7 looks at the first *Homo* and the developing reliance on meat in addition to plant gathering. At first meat was scavenged, then hunting became common. Stone tools became prevalent for the first time. Chapters 8, 9, and 10 explore the evolution of modern humans both biologically and behaviourally. Modern humans eventually move into temperate and arctic habitats as well as Australia, an accomplishment owed to their incredible ingenuity.

Part IV: Human Biological and Cultural Evolution Since the Old Stone Age continues with the development of food production and new forms of social and political organization. Macroevolutionary biological changes are no longer evident, but microevolutionary changes continue. New selective pressures were introduced with agriculture. Chapter 11 examines the shift to food production around the world. The shift began independently in many regions and had far-reaching consequences. Not all the consequences were beneficial, but food production provided subsistence security for longer periods compared to hunting and gathering. Food production provided for the first time a significantly expandable resource base and an important basis for the development of modern political institutions.

The first such institutions are explored in Chapter 12. Chapter 13 looks at what underlies modern human biological variation and why racial classification is an inappropriate concept. Human biological variation is a result of forces that have changed the frequencies of alleles in human gene pools. Many of these forces are a direct result of human cultural practices.

Many Messages, Many Media

Anthropology is arguably among the most naturally "multimedia" of all studies. Humans, as primates, rely heavily on visual input for information, and so it is not surprising that people today depend heavily on media other than print for much of their information. Moreover, in conveying descriptive information about a fossil, an artifact, or other archaeological features, a picture is often worth more than words alone. Given this, and our students' level of comfort with nonprint media, the art program is an important part of this second Canadian edition's narrative, and a selection of videos brings action and life to the ideas presented in the book, while weblinks build skills for analysis and research, and move the content of *Human Evolution and Prehistory* away from the standard linear textbook format to a multimedia package. The textbook's website also holds a wealth of information and quizzes in a virtual setting. PowerPoint slides bring the ideas and art of the text into the classroom. And, of course, the suggested readings, featuring many Canadian and international authors, and the bibliography continue to show the rich library of anthropological texts upon which students can draw. Thus, *Human Evolution and Prehistory* provides a broad set of instructional tools to expand the classroom.

SPECIAL FEATURES OF THE BOOK

Chapter Openers

Well-designed chapter openers act as previews that summarize the major concepts to be learned in each chapter. The inclusion of chapter outlines prepares students for the chapter's content.

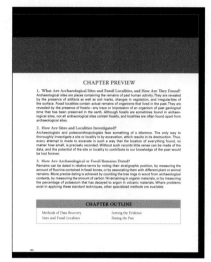

Maps, Photographs, and Illustrations

Colourful and eye-catching visuals are used to make important anthropological points and to clarify anthropological concepts. These have also proved to be valuable and memorable teaching aids.

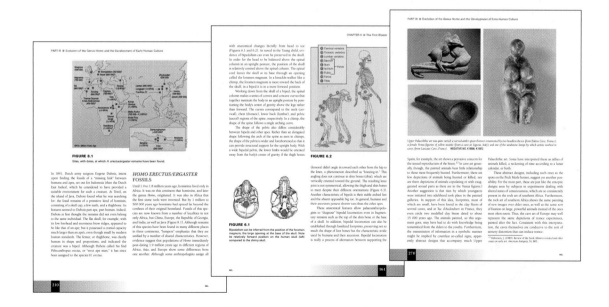

Original Studies

The Original Studies are excerpts, integrated within the flow of the text, from case studies and other original works by women and men in the field who have done, or are doing, work of anthropological significance. Found throughout the text, they bring important anthropological concepts to life, and show students how anthropologists study humankind, human culture, and biology, past and present.

Gender Perspectives

Along with integrated text coverage of gender, these special boxes delve into specific issues relating to gender.

Anthropology Applied

These boxes focus on applications of anthropology in a wide variety of biological and cultural contexts, as well as career opportunities outside academics.

Anthropologist Profiles

Eminent Canadian anthropologists are profiled in each chapter, working in a field relevant to the chapter.

Glossary

There is a running glossary in each chapter, and a cumulative glossary at the end of the text to aid student mastery of the language of the field.

Questions for Critical Thought

Questions are designed to encourage students to think critically and apply important concepts to contemporary issues.

Chapter Summary

These chapter review sections summarize the chapter's content and are designed to help students master the material.

Internet Resources

These features provide more resources to further explore the concepts within the chapter.

THIS SECOND CANADIAN EDITION

This second Canadian edition has been updated, edited, and fine-tuned to continue the Canadian perspective. The many changes are described below.

CHAPTER 1 Anthropology's relevance is illustrated with discussion of racism, the issue of same-sex marriage, and the common confusion of "nation" with "state." The unique history of Canadian archaeology and biological anthropology, as well as its institutional organization, is discussed. Sociocultural and linguistic anthropology have been significantly deemphasized. A new section on theoretical perspectives has been added. Includes Anthropology Applied box with Canadian emphasis, and Canadian biographies.

CHAPTER 2 Details the methods of studying the human past, providing many Canadian examples throughout and including a section on public archaeology in Canada. The discussion of archaeological methods has been expanded. Forensic anthropology field methods are now detailed in this edition. The section on Public Archaeology has been substantially revised. Includes Anthropology Applied box, Canadian biography, and Canadian Original Study box.

CHAPTER 3 New and updated coverage of human genetics and the evolutionary implications of the Human Genome Project. Speciation has been moved from Chapter 5 to Chapter 3 and integrated with new perspectives from genetics and evolution. Includes Anthropology Applied box, Canadian biography, and Original Study box.

CHAPTER 4 An updated discussion of chimpanzee culture and a section on Canadian research on primate behaviour. Primate classification has been revised. Includes Anthropology Applied box, Canadian biographies, Gender Perspectives box, and Original Study box.

CHAPTER 5 Includes an updated discussion of fossil primates. Speciation has been moved to Chapter 3. Includes biography of David Begun and Original Study box.

CHAPTER 6 Focuses more on the development of bipedalism. Updated discussion of *Australopithecus* and new material on the predecessors of *Australopithecus*. Early tool use among West African chimpanzees is discussed. Includes, Canadian biography, Gender Perspectives box, and Original Study box.

CHAPTER 7 Updated discussion of what membership in the genus *Homo* means as well as what constitutes early human behaviour. Includes Original Study box.

CHAPTER 8 Features a discussion of Acheulean tools, comparable technology in China, and implications of stone tool technology for language origins. The *Homo erectus* designation for all immediate post–*Homo habilis* fossils has been replaced with an emphasis on variation within the fossils assigned to *Homo erectus* in the previous edition. *Homo ergaster* is given more prominence in the revised discussion. The discussion of the expansion of the first human ancestors out of Africa has been revised. Includes Canadian biography, Gender Perspectives box, and Original Study box.

CHAPTER 9 The concept of Archaic *Homo sapiens* has been replaced by an updated classification of the post-*Homo erectus/ergaster* fossils. Neandertals are considered a separate species rather than a subspecies of modern human. An updated discussion on Neandertal DNA, the controversial "Neandertal flute," and Neandertals and the spoken language. Includes Canadian biography, Gender Perspectives box, and Original Study box.

CHAPTER 10 Emphasizes the difficulty of defining "anatomically modern." The *Homo floresiensis* controversy is introduced. Discussion of Upper Palaeolithic technology and adaptations are updated. Coverage of the peopling of the New World, including new information on Canada as well as the recent Kennewick Man controversy. Includes Anthropology Applied box, Canadian biography, Gender Perspectives box, and Original Study box.

CHAPTER 11 Begins with a discussion of the first post-glacial adaptations. A discussion of Archaic cultures in North America has been added. Updated material includes information on the Ohalo II and Abu Hureyra sites in the Near East section, the domestication of goats, and secondary agricultural origins, including the origins of agriculture in Ontario, Korea, and Japan. Also includes a Canadian biography, Gender Perspectives box, and Original Study box.

CHAPTER 12 New section on social complexity has been added as a counterpoint to the concept of "civilization." Detailed discussion of Çatalhöyük, examination of the so-called Classic Maya collapse, discussion of early writing, new material on genetic diseases (cystic fibrosis and Tay-Sachs). Includes Anthropology Applied box, Canadian biography, and Original Study box.

CHAPTER 13 A section on evolutionary medicine has been added. Examines modern human diversity and includes Canadian views on race. Includes Anthropology Applied box, Canadian biography, and Original Study box.

SUPPLEMENTS

Human Evolution and Prehistory, Second Canadian Edition, recognizes that anthropology is arguably among the most naturally "multimedia" of all studies. The selection of ancillaries accompanying this text reflects this need for teaching and learning tools to also be of many media.

For the Student:

Human Evolution and Prehistory Website (www.humanevolution2.nelson.com)

Revised by Nadia Ferrara of McGill University and available free to students, this powerful web-based supplement provides:

- Chapter-related true/false questions
- Chapter-related multiple-choice questions
- Chapter-related short questions
- Chapter-related Internet activities
- Chapter-related key term glossary
- Chapter summaries
- Crossword puzzles

- Anthropology weblinks
- Lecture notes in PowerPoint format
- Suggested readings
- *Anthropology News* link

Lecture Notes in PowerPoint Format

Chapter-by-chapter slideshow, created by Moira McLaughlin of St. Thomas University, provides an overview of chapter content and is available as a download on the website.

Anthropology Online: Wadsworth's Anthropology Resource Centre

This Resource Centre contains a wealth of additional resources, quizzes, and exercises for both students and instructors. Included on this website is a Virtual Tour of Applying Anthropology, a special section where students can find anthropologists at work, graduate student information, job boards, internships and fieldwork, and an essay on careers with video.

For the Instructor:

Instructor's Resource CD-ROM

Included on the CD-ROM are the key supplements designed to aid instructors:

Instructor's Manual

Revised by John Steckley of Humber College, this manual offers teaching objectives, lecture suggestions, and class activity suggestions that correspond to each chapter of the textbook.

Test Bank

Revised by Nadia Ferrara of McGill University, the Test Bank contains more than 1200 true/false and multiple-choice questions, 30 percent of them new or revised from the last edition.

Computerized Test Bank

The ExamView Computerized Testing Software contains all the questions in the printable Test Bank. This program is an easy-to-use test creation software compatible with Microsoft Windows. Instructors can add or edit questions, instructions, and answers, and can select questions by previewing them on the screen, selecting them randomly, or selecting them by number. Instructors can also create and administer quizzes online, whether over the Internet, a local area network (LAN), or a wide area network (WAN).

Lecture in PowerPoint Format

Chapter-by-chapter slideshow, created by Moira McLaughlin at St. Thomas University, providing an overview of chapter content, available as a download on the website:

Human Evolution and Prehistory Website
(www.humanevolution2.nelson.com)

Instructor supplements are available on the password-protected Instructor resource centre of the textbook's general website:

- Instructor's Manual
- Lecture Notes in PowerPoint Format

Also accessible to instructors are the student resources of extra quizzes, crossword puzzles, Internet activities, and so forth. Explore such resources as weblinks to the Canadian Museum of Civilization, Smithsonian Institution, the Archaeology Channel, and more.

Adapting a successful text to a new audience was not as straight forward as I thought it would be. Balancing the original text with Canadian content while updating the necessarily changing science requires the help and advice of researchers, students, and publishing professionals. As a result, I am indebted to many people for their assistance, patience, and encouragement throughout the ongoing development of this second Canadian edition of William A. Haviland's *Human Evolution and Prehistory*. First, a special thanks goes to William Haviland for his insight into what first-year students really need from an introductory anthropology course.

I am also grateful to all the reviewers for their comments and feedback in the preliminary discussions and the first-draft manuscript analysis. Without exception, their suggestions were thoughtful and relevant, and this Canadian edition is better as a result. Although I was not able to address all the comments, I did my best. Many thanks to:

Brian J. Given, Carleton University

Gary Tunnell, Malaspina University-College

Robert Adlam, Mount Allison University

Michael Plant, North Island College

Catherine Carlson, Simon Fraser University

Paul Erickson, St. Mary's University

Stan Freer, University of Manitoba

Mary Silcox, University of Winnipeg

Rosemarie Denunzio, University of Windsor

Kathryn Denning, York University

The following reviewers helped shape the previous edition of this textbook:

Sheila Greaves, Athabasca University

Patricia Peach, College of New Caledonia

Lorraine McNeil, Fanshawe College

Nadia Ferrara, McGill University

Andrew Martindale, McMaster University

Paul Erickson, St. Mary's University

Moira McLaughlin, St. Thomas University

Joseph So, Trent University

Owen Beattie, University of Alberta

David Pokotylo, University of British Columbia

Matthew Hill, University of Waterloo

Laird Christie, Wilfrid Laurier University

Special thanks go to Gyoung-Ah Lee who searched for resources and checked Internet sites. I also extend my gratitude to several friends, family members, and colleagues for their help in finding illustrations and photos: George Dei, Allison Dyaz, Steve Jaunzems, Heather Miller, Chen Shen, and David Smith; Anne Zeller graciously provided examples of her research and videos.

My son, Kyle, has been patient and understanding throughout every stage of this project, being a sounding board and subject of one of the illustrations.

To the staff of Nelson, I thank you for your diligence, patience, kindness, and enthusiasm for this project. I wish to offer special thanks to Nelson's acquisition editor, Scott Couling, for his constant support, and the My Editor Inc. team for their patient guidance and unswerving enthusiasm during the development process. Thank you to Nelson's photo editor, Indu Ghuman, and heartfelt thanks to Susan Wong, content production manager; Karen Rolfe, copy-editor; and Marisa Taylor, project manager, for their hard work in polishing this text. I also wish to express our appreciation to the skilled editorial, design, and production team who have produced a visually striking text.

Gary W. Crawford

ABOUT THE AUTHORS

Dr. William A. Haviland, Professor Emeritus at the University of Vermont, earned his B.A., M.A., and Ph.D. degrees at the University of Pennsylvania. He has published widely on archaeological, ethnological, and physical anthropological research carried out in Guatemala, Maine, and Vermont. Dr. Haviland is a member of many professional societies, including the American Anthropological Association and the American Association for the Advancement of Science.

One of Dr. Haviland's greatest loves is teaching, which originally prompted him to write *Cultural Anthropology*. He says he learns something new every year from his students about what they need from a first-year course in anthropology. In addition to writing *Cultural Anthropology*, Dr. Haviland has authored several other popular works for anthropology students.

Dr. Gary W. Crawford is a Fellow of the Royal Society of Canada and a professor of anthropology at the University of Toronto Mississauga, where he has been based since 1979. He is also a research associate at the Royal Ontario Museum in Toronto. Dr. Crawford received his doctorate in anthropology from the University of North Carolina at Chapel Hill. He has published and lectured on the archaeology and palaeoethnobotany of Japan, China, Korea, the Great Lakes region, and Kentucky. Dr. Crawford also co-authored the Canadian supplement *Canadian Perspectives on Archaeology and Biological Anthropology*. Among his professional memberships are affiliations with the Society for American Archaeology, the Canadian Archaeological Association, and the Society for Economic Botany.

Introductory anthropology has been one of Dr. Crawford's key teaching interests over the years. He has been gratified by the success of many of his students, whose life and career choices have been influenced by their study of anthropology.

BRIEF CONTENTS

CONTENTS

Part III
Evolution of the Genus Homo and the Development of Early Human Culture

CHAPTER 12
The Rise of Cities and Civilization 334

CHAPTER 13
Modern Human Diversity 368

To our students, past, present, and future

Cartography (the craft of mapmaking as we know it today) had its beginnings in 13th-century Europe, and its subsequent development is related to the expansion of Europeans to all parts of the globe. From the beginning, there have been two problems with maps: the technical one of how to depict a three-dimensional, spherical object on a two-dimensional, flat surface, and the cultural one of whose worldview they reflect. In fact, the two issues are inseparable, for any projection inevitably makes a statement about how one views one's own people and their place in the world. Indeed, maps often shape our perception of reality as much as they reflect it.

In cartography, a projection refers to the system of intersecting lines (of longitude and latitude) by which part or all of the globe is represented on a flat surface. There are more than 100 different projections in use today, ranging from polar perspectives to interrupted "butterflies" to rectangles to heart shapes. Each projection causes distortion in size, shape, or distance in some way or another. A map that shows the shape of land masses correctly will of necessity misrepresent the size. A map that is accurate along the equator will be deceptive at the poles.

Perhaps no projection has had more influence on the way we see the world than that of Gerhardus Mercator, who devised his map in 1569 as a navigational aid for mariners. So well suited was Mercator's map for this purpose that it continues to be used for navigational charts today. At the same time, the Mercator projection became a standard for depicting land masses, something for which it was never intended. Although an accurate navigational tool, the Mercator projection greatly exaggerates the size of land masses in higher latitudes, giving about two-thirds of the map's surface to the northern hemisphere. Thus, the lands occupied by Europeans and European descendants appear far larger than those of other people. For example, North America (19 million square kilometres) appears almost twice the size of Africa (30 million square kilometres), while Europe is shown as equal in size to South America, which actually has nearly twice the land mass of Europe.

A map developed in 1805 by Karl B. Mollweide was one of the earlier equal-area projections of the world. Equal-area projections portray land masses in correct relative size, but, as a result, distort the shape of continents more than other projections. They most often compress and warp lands in the higher latitudes and vertically stretch land masses close to the equator. Other equal-area projections include the Lambert Cylindrical Equal-Area Projection (1772), the Hammer Equal-Area Projection (1892), and the Eckert Equal-Area Projection (1906).

The Van der Grinten Projection (1904) was a compromise aimed at minimizing both the distortion of size in the Mercator and the distortion of shape in equal-area maps such as the Mollweide. Although this projection is an improvement, the lands of the northern hemisphere are still emphasized at the expense of the southern. For example, in the Van der Grinten, the Commonwealth of Independent States (the former Soviet Union) and Canada are shown at more than twice their relative sizes.

The Robinson Projection, which was adopted by the National Geographic Society in 1988 to replace the Van der Grinten, is one of the best compromises to date between the distortion of size and shape. Although an improvement over the Van der Grinten, the Robinson Projection still depicts lands in the northern latitudes as proportionally larger at the same time that it depicts lands in the lower latitudes (representing most developing nations) as proportionally smaller. Like European maps before it, the Robinson Projection places Europe at the centre of the map with the Atlantic Ocean and the Americas to the left, emphasizing the cultural connection between Europe and North America, while neglecting the geographical closeness of northwestern North America to northeast Asia.

The following pages show four maps that each convey quite different "cultural messages." Included among them is the Peters Projection, an equal-area map that has been adopted as the official map of UNESCO (the United Nations Educational, Scientific, and Cultural Organization), and a map made in Japan, showing us how the world looks from "the other side."

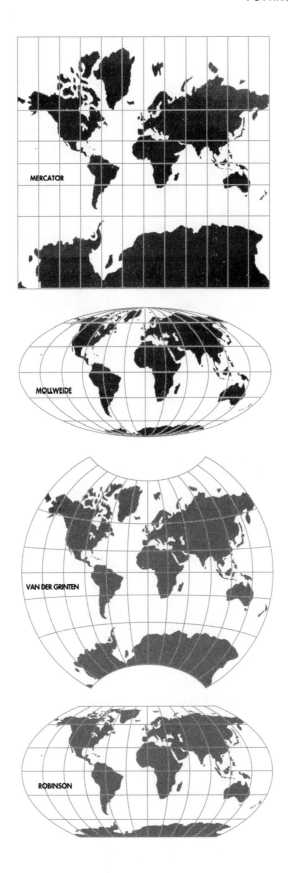

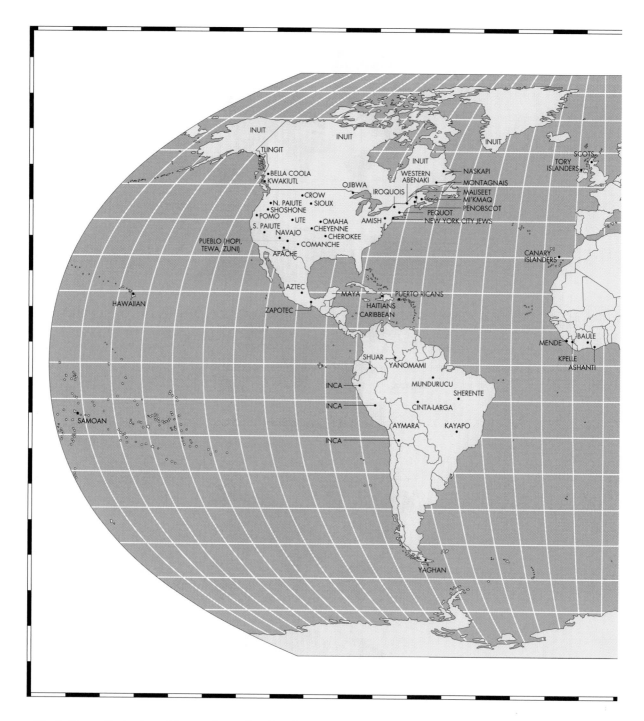

The Robinson Projection   *The map above is based on the Robinson Projection, which is used today by the National Geographic Society and Rand McNally. Although the Robinson Projection distorts the relative size of land masses, it does so to a much lesser*

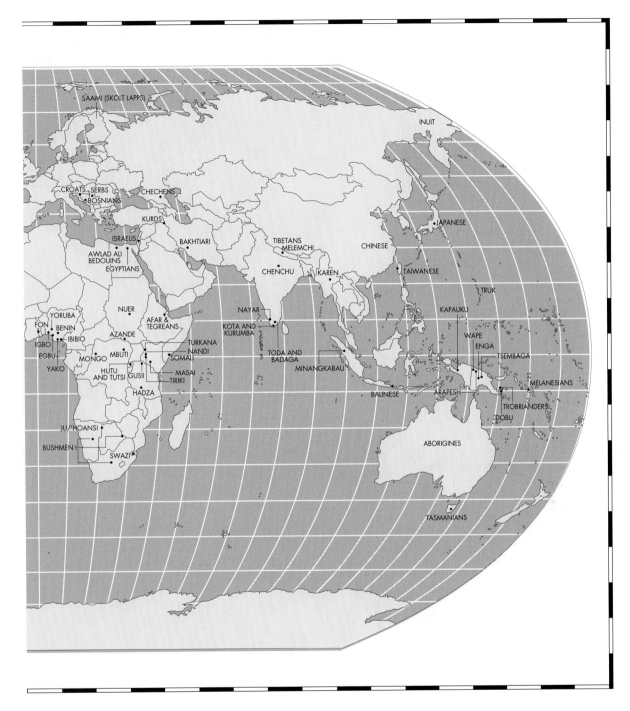

degree than most other projections. Still, it places Europe at the centre of the map. This particular view of the world has been used to identify the location of many of the cultures discussed in this text.

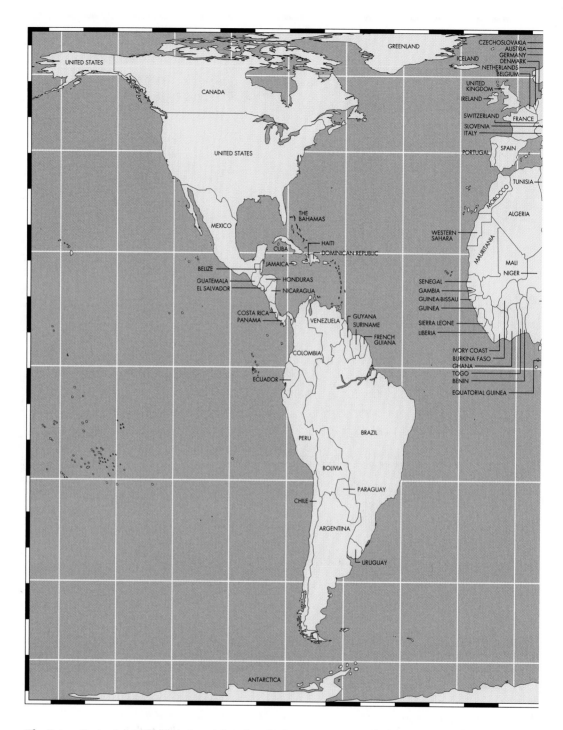

The Peters Projection   *The map above is based on the Peters Projection, which has been adopted as the official map of UNESCO. While it distorts the shape of continents (countries near the equator are vertically elongated*

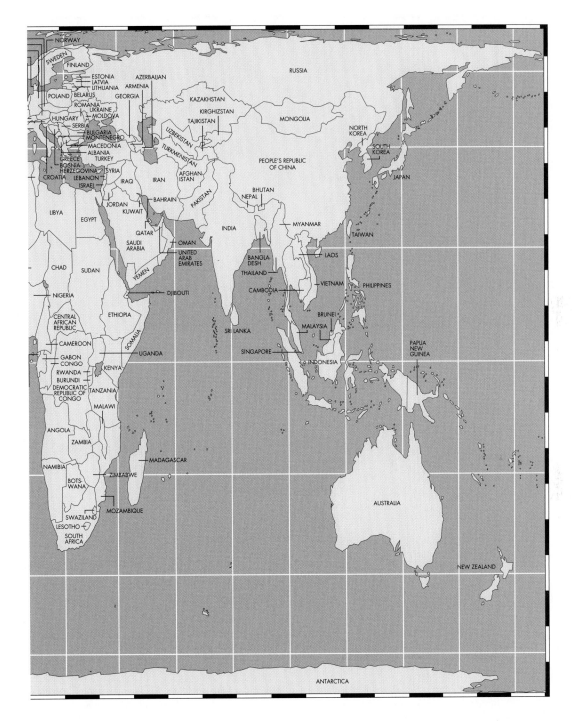

by a ratio of two to one), the Peters Projection does show all continents according to their correct relative size. Though Europe is still at the centre, it is not shown as larger and more extensive than the developing countries.

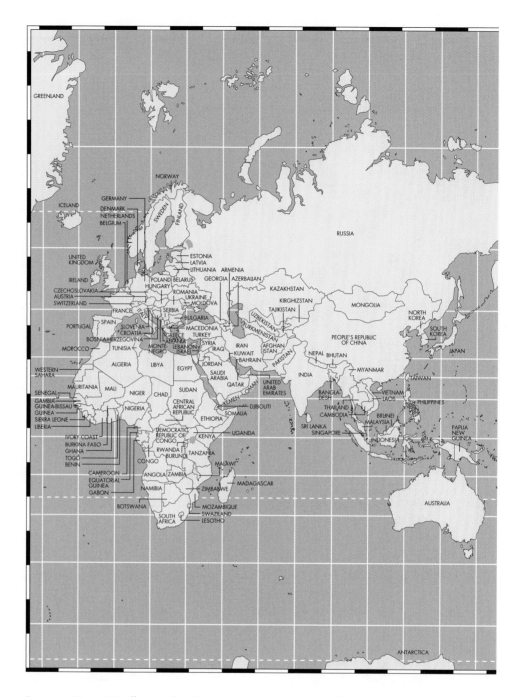

Japanese Map *Not all maps place Europe at the centre of the world, as this Japanese map illustrates. Besides reflecting the importance the Japanese attach to themselves in the world, this map has the virtue*

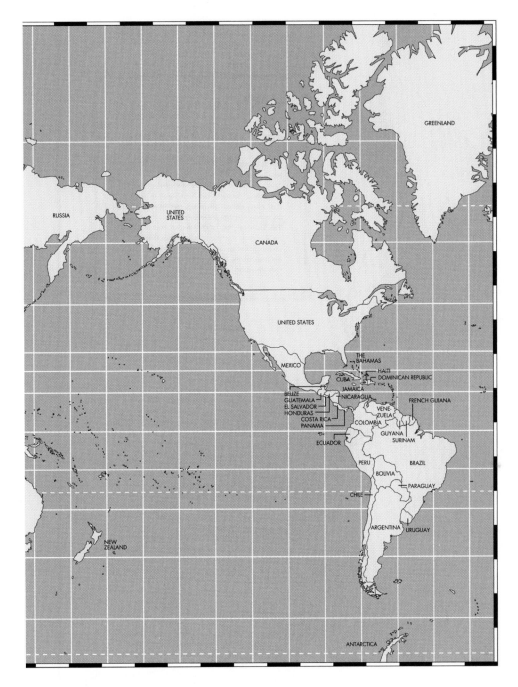

of showing the geographic proximity of North America to Asia, a fact easily overlooked when maps place Europe at their centre.

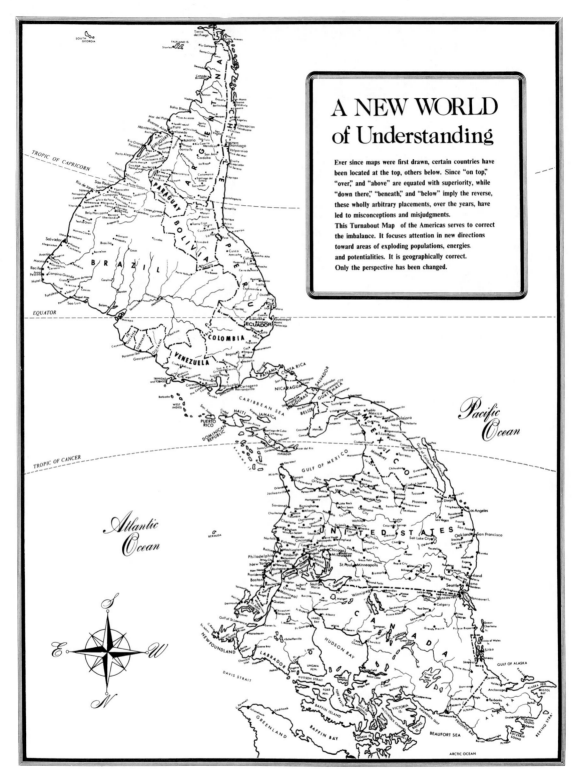

A NEW WORLD of Understanding

Ever since maps were first drawn, certain countries have been located at the top, others below. Since "on top," "over," and "above" are equated with superiority, while "down there," "beneath," and "below" imply the reverse, these wholly arbitrary placements, over the years, have led to misconceptions and misjudgments.

This Turnabout Map of the Americas serves to correct the imbalance. It focuses attention in new directions toward areas of exploding populations, energies, and potentialities. It is geographically correct. Only the perspective has been changed.

The Turnabout Map *The way maps may reflect (and influence) our thinking is exemplified by the "Turnabout Map," which places the South Pole at the top and the North Pole at the bottom. Words and phrases such as "on top," "over," and "above" tend to be equated by some people with superiority. Turning things upside down may cause us to rethink the way North Americans regard themselves in relation to the people of Central America.* © 1982 by Jesse Levine Turnabout Map™ —Dist. by Laguna Sales, Inc., 7040 Via Valverde, San Jose, CA 95135

Second Canadian Edition

Human Evolution

and

PREHISTORY

CHAPTER

1

The Nature of Anthropology

Humans are just one of 10 million species. But among these, including 4000 fellow mammals, we humans are the only ones capable of studying ourselves and the world around us. We do this not only because we are curious, but also because knowledge helps us make adjustments necessary for survival. Adaptations based on knowledge are essential in every culture, and culture is our species' ticket to survival. The comprehensive study of human development and cultures, past and present, is the business of anthropology.

©JODI COBB/NATIONAL GEOGRAPHIC IMAGE COLLECTION, ©ANUP AND MANOJ SHAH, ©JAMES L. STANFIELD/NATIONAL GEOGRAPHIC IMAGE COLLECTION, ©GEORGE H. HUEY/CORBIS.

CHAPTER PREVIEW

1. What Is Anthropology?

Anthropology, the study of humankind everywhere, throughout time, seeks to produce reliable knowledge about people and their behaviour, both about the things that make them different and the things they all have in common.

2. What Do Anthropologists Do?

Biological anthropologists (also called physical anthropologists) trace the evolutionary development of humans as biological organisms and look at biological variations within the species, past and present. They also study the physical and behavioural nature of our closest biological relatives: nonhuman primates such as monkeys and apes. Archaeologists seek to explain human behaviour by studying material culture of past cultures and, in certain cases, of living people. Linguistic anthropologists study the way language is used as a resource for practising, developing, and transmitting a culture. Sociocultural anthropologists are concerned with recent and contemporary human cultures, as they have been observed, experienced, and discussed with people whose culture they seek to understand.

3. How Do Anthropologists Do What They Do?

Anthropologists, in common with other scientists, are concerned with explaining observed phenomena. Most anthropological investigation involves fieldwork. Biological anthropologists and archaeologists most often conduct excavations of sites where evidence of the past is found. Linguistic anthropologists study how people use language to relate to one another, usually living for brief periods with the people whose language they are studying. Sociocultural anthropologists immerse themselves in a contemporary culture by living with the people, participating in their daily activities, and observing, firsthand, how they live.

The Development of Anthropology

Canadian Anthropology

A Note about Terminology

Anthropology and the Other Sciences

The Discipline of Anthropology

Anthropology and Science

Risks of Culture-Bounded Science

Theoretical Perspectives

Comparison in Anthropology

Anthropology and the Humanities

Anthropology's Contributions to Other Disciplines

Questions of Ethics

Impacts on Contemporary Life

For as long as they have been on earth, people have sought answers to questions about who they are, where they come from, and why they act as they do. Throughout most of their history, though, people relied on myth and folklore for their answers to these questions, rather than the systematic testing of data obtained through careful observation. Anthropology, over the last 200 years, has emerged as a scientific approach to answering these questions. Simply stated, **anthropology** is the study of humankind in all places and in all times.

Other disciplines also are concerned with human beings. Some, such as anatomy and physiology, study humans as biological organisms. The social sciences are concerned with the distinctive forms human relationships can take, while the humanities examine the great achievements of human cultures. Anthropologists are interested in all of these aspects of humanity; the difference is they are concerned with *everything* that has to do with humans. It is this unique, broad perspective that equips anthropologists to deal with that elusive thing called human nature.

Anthropology is the most liberating of all the sciences. Not only has it exposed the fallacies of racial and cultural superiority, but also its devotion to the study of all peoples, regardless of where and when they live, has cast more light on human nature than all the reflections of sages or the studies of laboratory scientists. Indeed, anthropological knowledge and understanding of the past and the present may even help humankind deal with its future.

THE DEVELOPMENT OF ANTHROPOLOGY

Although works of anthropological significance have a considerable antiquity—two examples are the accounts of other peoples by the Greek historian Herodotus (written in the 5th century B.C.) or by the North African scholar Ibn Khaldun (written in the 14th century A.D.)—anthropology as a distinct field of inquiry is a relatively recent product of Western civilization. The Division of Anthropology within the Geological Survey of Canada was created in 1911, for example, and it wasn't until 1925 that the first lecturer in anthropology was appointed in Canada. If people have always been concerned about themselves and their origins, and those

of other people, why then did it take such a long time for the systematic discipline of anthropology to appear? The answer to this question is as complex as human history. In part, it relates to the limits of human technology. Throughout most of their time on earth, people have been restricted in their geographical horizons. Without the means of travelling to distant places, observation of cultures and peoples far from one's own was a difficult—if not impossible—venture. Extensive travel was usually the exclusive domain of an elite few; the study of foreign peoples and cultures was not likely to flourish until adequate modes of transportation and communication could be developed.

This is not to say that people were unaware of the existence of others in the world who looked and acted differently from themselves. The Old and New Testaments of the Bible, for example, are full of references to diverse peoples, among them Jews, Egyptians, Hittites, Babylonians, Ethiopians, Romans, and so forth. However, the differences between these peoples pale by comparison to those between any of them on the one hand and, for example, indigenous people of Australia, the Amazon forest, or arctic North America. With the means to travel to truly faraway places, it became possible to meet for the first time such radically different people. It was the encounter with hitherto unknown peoples, which came as Europeans sought to extend their trade and political domination to all parts of the world, that focused attention on human differences in all their glory.

Another significant element that contributed to the slow growth of anthropology was that Europeans only gradually came to recognize that beneath all the differences, they shared a basic humanity with people everywhere. Cultural groups that did not share the fundamental cultural values of Europeans were labelled "savage" or "barbarian." It was not until the mid-18th century that a significant number of Europeans considered the behaviour of such people to be at all relevant to an understanding of themselves. This growing interest in human diversity, coming at a time when there were increasing efforts to explain things in terms of natural laws, cast doubts on the traditional explanations based on authoritative texts such as the Torah, Bible, or Qu'ran.

Anthropology. The study of humankind in all times and places.

BIOGRAPHY

Father Joseph-François Lafitau (1681–1746)
Sir Daniel Wilson (1816–1892)

In Canada, anthropological studies began in the 18th and 19th centuries with the help of dedicated scholars interested in the study of human culture. Two early contributors to Canadian anthropology, neither of whom were academic anthropologists, were Father Joseph-François Lafitau and Sir Daniel Wilson.

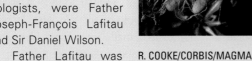

R. COOKE/CORBIS/MAGMA

Father Lafitau was a Jesuit missionary who lived with the Iroquois near Montreal from 1715 to 1720. Although Father Lafitau is most often credited with discovering wild ginseng in North America, his firsthand observations and scholarly writings provided valuable insight into the plants, animals, and people of the region. He noted a possible connection between Asian peoples, who used ginseng over 15 000 years ago, and North American aboriginal peoples. Among his literary works, Father Lafitau wrote *Customs of the American Indians Compared with the Customs of Primitive Times* (Toronto: Champlain Society, 1974).[1]

Sir Daniel Wilson was born in Edinburgh, Scotland, and educated at the University of Edinburgh. He moved to Canada in 1853, to become the

UNIVERSITY OF TORONTO ARCHIVES/A73-0026/517(99)

first professor of history and English literature at the University of Toronto, and in 1881 he became the first president of the University of Toronto. Wilson's contributions to science and education are many; he is described as an educator and administrator, archaeologist, artist, and anthropologist. Most notably, he recognized the importance of cultural studies, and is credited with founding the first anthropology courses at a Canadian university, nearly 150 years ago. Among his scholarly works, Wilson wrote *The Archaeology and Prehistoric Annals of Scotland*, which laid the groundwork for scientific inquiry in archaeology and introduced the term "prehistoric" to the scientific community.[2] Wilson was a significant influence on the development of professional anthropology and archaeology in Canada.

_____

[1] Progenix Corporation. (1998). *The history of ginseng in the United States*. Retrieved March 12, 2001, from the World Wide Web: http://progenixcorp.com/ushistory.html.

[2] Kelley, J.H., & Williamson, R.F. (1996, January). The positioning of archaeology within anthropology: A Canadian historical perspective. *American Antiquity, 61* (1), 5–20.]

Although anthropology originated within the context of Western civilization, it has long since gone global. Today, it is an exciting, transnational discipline whose practitioners are drawn from diverse societies all across the globe. Cultures that have long been studied by European and North American anthropologists—several First Nations peoples of Canada, for example—have produced anthropologists who continue to make their mark on the discipline. Their distinctive

perspectives help shed new light not only on their own cultures, but also on those of others, including Western societies.

CANADIAN ANTHROPOLOGY

Canadian anthropology owes its development and continued growth to several noteworthy individuals, many of whom are profiled in this book, and the institutions in which they worked. Three main influences are evident in the development of Canadian anthropology: museums, academic departments, and applied research. The National Museum of Canada in Ottawa played a major role in the direction of early Canadian anthropology. Anthropologists with the museum—such as Edward Sapir, head of the anthropology division of the Geological Survey of the National Museum of Canada (now the Museum of Civilization), French-Canadian Marius Barbeau, David Boyle, and Diamond Jenness conducted ethnographic, linguistic, and archaeological research into aboriginal cultures. Besides their academic pursuits, these scholars, along with other staff at the museum, were early advocates for aboriginal rights to religious and cultural freedom. This tradition of advocacy has remained an integral component of Canadian anthropology to the present day.[1]

In the mid-1800s, no professional archaeologists worked in the United States or Canada, but by the early 1800s in Europe, archaeology as a profession was well on its way. A number of key events influenced the field in Canada. In 1819, the collections in the Danish National Museum were organized into Stone, Bronze, and Iron ages. In the early 1830s, geological principles had been elucidated, and artifacts found in certain geological layers were for the first time deemed to be of great antiquity. Charles Darwin published *On the Origin of Species* in 1859. In 1846, the founding of the Smithsonian Institution in the United States had a profound impact on North American archaeology. The Canadian Institute, founded in 1849 in Toronto, was intended to be Canada's Smithsonian. A proposed science museum was to include aboriginal North American antiquities.[2] Daniel Wilson (see profile) arrived in Toronto from Scotland in 1853 to join the Canadian Institute. He would have a profound impact on Canadian archaeology and what would become the field of biological or physical anthropology. Following these developments was the creation of the Division of Anthropology within the Geological Survey of Canada in 1911. The University of Toronto became the next centre of anthropology in the country, but it would take many years before Canada was training its own museum curators and university professors.

In 1925, Thomas F. McIlwraith was appointed lecturer in anthropology at the University of Toronto.[3] Under McIlwraith's guidance, anthropology at the University of Toronto continued to grow in importance

until, in 1936, the first academic department of anthropology at a Canadian university was created. After World War II, academic departments of anthropology were established at other universities, most notably McGill and the University of British Columbia. Academic departments became another stronghold for Canadian anthropology and remain so today.

Although Daniel Wilson did not teach biological anthropology at a university, others—such as J.C.B. Grant and his student, James Anderson (see profile)—would soon do so. In many ways, biological anthropology in Canada was developing its own traditions, having been initially rooted in the medical world, before anthropology departments were common in Canada. Most anthropology departments in Canada were created in the 1960s and 1970s, a time when many new universities were also created in the country. Contrasting with biological anthropology, all the first archaeologists at universities in Canada were hired from abroad, particularly the United States. Some were U.S.–trained Canadians such as Bruce Trigger (see profile).[4]

While Daniel Wilson was investigating aboriginal physical variation in the late 1800s, the field of somatology, as biological anthropology was then called, was becoming established in the United States. The formal study of biological anthropology was started in North America by Ales Hrdlicka.[5] He carried out his research first at the American Museum of Natural History and then went to work at the Smithsonian Institution for four decades, and was responsible for the largest collection of human bone in North America. He was the first to hypothesize that aboriginal peoples came from Asia. Frederick Putnam, with whom Hrdlicka had worked early in his career, was another key figure in

[1] Hedigan, E.J. (1995). *Applied anthropology in Canada: Understanding aboriginal issues.* Toronto: University of Toronto Press.

[2] Killen, G. (1998). Toward a scientific archaeology: Daniel Wilson, David Boyle and the Canadian Institute. In D.H. Mitchell & P.J. Smith (Eds.), *Bringing back the past: Historical perspectives on Canadian archaeology* (pp. 15–24). Canadian Museum of Civilization, Mercury Series, Hull, Quebec.

[3] University of Toronto. (2001). *A brief history of anthropology at the University of Toronto.* Retrieved June 20, 2001, from the World Wide Web: www.chass.utoronto.ca/ anthropology/history.htm.

[4] Simonsen, B.O. (2002). *The Canadian Archaeological Association and the development of archaeology in Canada.* Retrieved November 30, 2002, from the World Wide Web: http://canadianarchaeology.com/history/bjorn.lasso.

[5] Brace C.L. (1982). The roots of the race concept in physical anthropology. In F. Spencer (ed.), *A History of American physical anthropology, 1930–1980.* New York: Academic Press.

North American anthropology. Putnam was appointed Professor of American Archaeology and Ethnology at Harvard University in 1886 and in 1890 was asked to orchestrate the anthropology exhibits at the World Columbian Exposition that eventually was the foundation for the Field Museum in Chicago. The first Ph.D. dissertation produced by Harvard was a study of "Eskimo" (Inuit) crania completed in 1898. Although this marked an academic first, Daniel Wilson's book on cranial types among First Nations of North America[6] had appeared and in 1884 he had published a detailed study of the Huron.[7] Evolution was controversial in the late 1800s and was not part of the subject matter of biological anthropology. The field was mainly descriptive through the 1930s and scholars were concerned more with reinforcing the concept of human races. Through the 1930s and 1940s researchers' interest in the typology of races declined and populations studies developed. At the same time scholars became interested in environmental influences on biological variation. Primate field studies by biological anthropologists blossomed in the 1950s. The evolution of the brain was inspired by Davidson Black's work in China where the first casts from inside skulls (endocasts) were made. Molecular anthropology had begun as early as 1962.

Although Daniel Wilson did not teach biological anthropology at a university, others would soon do so. The first true physical anthropologist in Canada is probably J.C.B. Grant. Grant was an anatomy professor who taught a young man, James Anderson, from Perth, Ontario. Anderson graduated in 1953 as a medical doctor rather than an anthropologist. Grant had studied the variation of First Nations communities, and Anderson followed his example. In 1958 Anderson became the first biological anthropologist in the Department of Anthropology at the University of Toronto. His legacy is still felt throughout Canada. One of Anderson's innovative contributions was the study of discrete traits combined with the collection of metric data.[8] His study of single traits and their variation had a considerable influence on future generations of researchers.

A NOTE ABOUT TERMINOLOGY

Many of the names assigned to aboriginal peoples, usually by European explorers and colonial governments, were not the terms used by the people to refer to themselves. Oftentimes, these European names had

Anthropologists represent a cross-section of human diversity. George Dei of OISE/UT and the Department of Anthropology, University of Toronto, is investigating minority students' education strategies, schooling in Ghana, inclusive schooling, and racism, among other issues. **COURTESY OF GEORGE DEI, UNIVERSITY OF TORONTO**

derogatory connotations, such as Eskimo, which means "eater of raw meat." Today, concerted efforts are being made to use the names actually chosen by the people. In Canada we use the terms "First Nations," "Inuit," and "Métis" to identify aboriginal people collectively, and their chosen names to identify distinctive cultural groups (e.g., Kwakwaka'wakw instead of Kwakiutl, Dane-zaa instead of Beaver).

In a text such as this one, where we refer to indigenous peoples around the world, the issue becomes even more problematic. In the United States, "Native American" or "Indian" are the preferred terms, and in South and Central America "Indian" is used. From a Canadian perspective, none of these labels seems appropriate; therefore, the term "aboriginal peoples" will be used to refer to indigenous groups in the Americas. When a more specific reference is meaningful, "First Nations" is used to specifically refer to people who were once known in Canada as "Indians." The term does not normally include Inuit or Métis. In other parts of the world, the term "indigenous peoples," or more preferably, their own name, will be used. For

[6] Wilson D. 1858. *On the supposed prevalence of one cranial type throughout the American aborigines.* Edinburgh: s.n.

[7] Wilson D. (1884). *The Huron-Iroquois of Canada: A typical race of American aborigines.* Ottawa: Transactions of Royal Society of Canada.

[8] Jerkic S.M. (2001). The influence of James E. Anderson on Canadian Physical Anthropology. In L. Sawchuck and S. Pfeiffer (eds.)., *Out of the past: The history of human osteology at the University of Toronto.* Toronto: CITD Press, University of Toronto at Scarborough. http://citdpress .utsc.utoronto.ca/osteology/pfeiffer.html.

other regions of the world every effort will be made to use the people's preferred name. For example, the Ju/'hoansi of the Kalahari Desert in Africa, a cultural group discussed extensively in this text, used to be called the perjorative "bushmen"; later they were called the !Kung; and today we use their own name, Ju/'hoansi (meaning "genuine people"). Yet whichever terms are used, the decision will not satisfy everyone; indeed, the whole issue of terminology is complicated and highly sensitive, especially since even within aboriginal groups a consensus regarding appropriate labels has not been achieved, and some confusion remains among nonaboriginal peoples as to which names are preferred. Nonetheless, this attempt to use sensitive, culturally appropriate terms is one small step in the right direction.

ANTHROPOLOGY AND THE OTHER SCIENCES

It would be incorrect to conclude from the foregoing that serious attempts were never made to analyze human diversity before the 18th century. Anthropologists are not the only scholars who study people. In this respect they share their objectives with the other social and natural scientists. Anthropologists do not think of their findings as something quite apart from those of psychologists, economists, sociologists, or biologists; rather, they welcome the contributions these other disciplines have to make to the common goal of understanding humanity, and they gladly offer their own findings for the benefit of these other disciplines. Anthropologists do not expect, for example, to know as much about the structure of the human eye as anatomists or as much about the perception of colour as psychologists. As synthesizers, however, they are better prepared to understand how these relate to colour-naming behaviour in different human societies than any of their fellow scientists. Because they look for the broad basis of human ideas and practices without limiting themselves to any single social or biological aspect, anthropologists can acquire an especially broad and inclusive overview of the complex biological and cultural organism that is the human being.

THE DISCIPLINE OF ANTHROPOLOGY

Anthropology is traditionally divided into four fields: biological anthropology, archaeology, linguistic anthropology, and sociocultural anthropology. **Biological anthropology** is concerned primarily with humans as biological organisms. **Archaeology** explores the human past primarily through the excavations of past human habitations. **Sociocultural anthropology** deals with humans as cultural animals. A number of Canadian anthropologists received their training at British schools, while others were educated at American institutions. In the British tradition, the term "social anthropology" is preferred to "cultural anthropology." To accommodate both traditions, we use the term "sociocultural anthropology." Archaeology, too, investigates cultural behaviour, by reconstructing the lives of people who lived in the past. Linguistic anthropology is the study of human languages of the past and present, as a means for people to relate to each other and to develop and communicate ideas about each other and the world. These fields are closely related; we cannot understand what people do unless we know what people are. We also want to know how biology does and does not influence culture, as well as how culture affects biology. **Applied anthropology** has become increasingly important, and today is often considered a fifth field that intersects with the other fields of anthropology (Figure 1.1). Applied anthropologists attempt to use their expertise to solve the practical problems of humanity, using the methods and knowledge of anthropology. Americanist anthropology takes the

---

Biological anthropology. The systematic study of humans as biological organisms.

Sociocultural anthropology. The branch of anthropology that focuses on humans as a culture-making species.

Archaeology. The study of material remains and cultural features, usually from the past, to describe and explain human behaviour.

Applied anthropology. Applying the knowledge and methods of anthropology to solve practical problems.

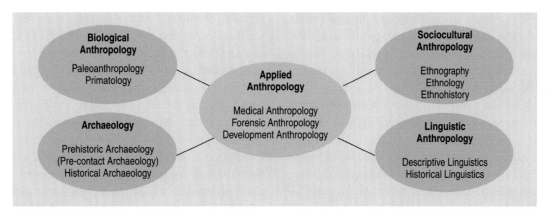

FIGURE 1.1 The subfields of anthropology

position that the subfields are integrated to a significant degree. Archaeology, for example, examines cultural behaviour from the perspective of the content of archaeological sites. Linguistic relationships in a region can inform the archaeological record by suggesting ancient migration patterns. Biological anthropology needs account for the interaction of human behaviour and biology. The spread of HIV is one example. Another example in Chapter 3 examines how a form of anemia in people is related to agricultural practices in Africa where malaria is prevalent.

Biological Anthropology

Biological anthropology (or, alternatively, physical anthropology) is the branch of anthropology that focuses on humans as biological organisms, and one of its many interests is human evolution.

Within biological anthropology, the subfield of **palaeoanthropology** studies fossil remains of our ancestors, in an attempt to reconstruct the course of human biological evolution. Several generations of the Leaky family (East Africa), Davidson Black (China, see Chapter 8), Donald Johanson (also east Africa), David Begun (early primates), Alan Walker (*Homo erectus*), Eric Trinkaus and many others have made an extraordinary impact on our understanding of human evolution. Whatever distinctions people may claim for themselves, they are mammals—specifically, primates—and, as such, they share a common ancestry with other primates, most specifically apes and monkeys. **Primatology** is the study of the biological and social nature of our closest relatives,

prosimians, monkeys, and apes. Well-known primatologists Dian Fossey (gorillas), Jane Goodall (chimpanzees), Biruté Galdikas of Simon Fraser University (orangutans), and Linda Fedigan of the University of Calgary (monkeys and prosimians in general) have provided us with startling new insights into the complex social behaviour of nonhuman primates. Through analysis of fossils and observation of living primates, biological anthropologists try to reconstruct the ancestry of the human species in order to understand how, when, and why we became the kind of animal we are today. Human **skeletal biology** is the analysis and interpretation of human bones, generally from archaeological sites. Such remains help understand such issues as the age and sex structure of a population, health and diet issues, and interment patterns. **Forensic anthropology,** as described in the box

Paleoanthropology. The study of fossil remains with the goal of reconstructing human biological evolution.

Primatology. The study of nonhuman primates, their biology, adaptation, and social behaviour.

Skeletal biology. In anthropology, the analysis and interpretation of human bones, normally from archaeological sites.

Forensic anthropology. A field of applied biological anthropology and archaeology that specializes in the identification of human skeletal remains for legal purposes.

on page 9, is a relatively new and exciting field within biological anthropology and archaeology with an applied concentration. It is also a leading specialization in the new field of forensic science. The field has been popularized by television and books by authors such as Kathy Reichs who is also a professor at the University of North Carolina, and works for the Office of the Chief Medical Examiner in North Carolina and for the Laboratoire de Sciences Judiciaires et de Médecine Légale for the province of Quebec. The reality of forensics is quite different from the popular accounts, with investigations every bit as slow-paced, meticulous, and with as little or as much drama as other scientific research.

Biological anthropologists study present-day human variation. Although we are all members of a single species, we differ from each other in many obvious and not so obvious ways. We differ not only in such visible traits as the colour of our skin or the shape of our nose, but also in such biochemical factors as our blood type and our susceptibility to certain diseases. The biological anthropologist applies all the techniques of modern molecular biology to achieve fuller understanding of human variation and the ways in which it relates to the different environments in which people have lived and to different cultural practices.

Forensic Anthropology

Forensic anthropologists, who are specialists in human osteology and archaeology, become part of a larger team of scientists (e.g., forensic odontologists, forensic pathologists, and law enforcement officers) working to identify and contextualize human remains for legal purposes. This legal element is what separates forensic anthropology from all other fields of biological anthropology and to some extent differentiates it completely from anthropology. The connection with anthropology came about initially because of the expertise biological anthropologists, particularly osteologists, can bring to an investigation. The work of forensic anthropologists is challenging; they are often called on by law enforcement authorities and medical examiners to help recover and identify the decomposed bodies of murder victims and missing persons, bodies burned beyond recognition, and commingled remains (more than one skeleton mixed together). Following the terrorist attacks on the World Trade Center and the U.S. Pentagon on September 11, 2001, forensic anthropologists helped identify the human remains found among the debris. On occasion, forensic anthropologists must exhume and examine skeletal remains discovered in mass graves, such as in Rwanda after the 1994 massacres. When forensic anthropologists investigate human remains, they want to answer several crucial questions: Is this a human skeleton (indeed are the remains actually bone)? How many individuals are represented? Was a crime committed in the death of this individual? Can a *biological identity* be established (sex, age, stature, race or ancestral origin)? Can a *personal identity* be established (name of the individual)? The forensic anthropologist's analysis might also reveal diseases or trauma (e.g., broken bones) present at the time of death, as well as the diet and nutritional state, and general health of the deceased.

In Canada, forensic anthropologists do not determine race from skeletal remains, but they are concerned with ancestry.[9] In contrast, their U.S. counterparts will classify an individual set of remains according to census categories and will often use the term "race." The whole issue of race (see Chapter 13) is problematic, since it is more of a sociopolitical or cultural construct than a biological reality, and despite new measurement systems, is highly subjective at best. The problem is amplified because anthropologists and anatomists gave up the study of race decades ago, and for good reason (see Chapter 13). Yet the community will identify an individual according to a socially defined race, such as African, aboriginal, East Asian, or European descent. The Canadian Police Information Centre (CPIC) database for missing persons identifies individuals as "White" or "Non-white." South Asians are listed as Non-white in the database but the ancestry of South Asian skeletal remains are difficult to distinguish from those of Europeans, although it is possible. [10] Some general morphological traits, such as blood type, body shape, limb length, face shape (e.g., nose), hair forms (e.g., oblong, round), wear patterns on teeth, and morphology of incisors can tell forensic anthropologists much about the ancestry of the remains.[11,12]

---

9 Rogers T. (1999). *The attribution of ancestry for European and India (South Asian) individuals within a forensic context.* Burnaby, B.C.: Simon Fraser University.

10 Ibid.

11 Nafte M. (2000). *Flesh and bone: An introduction to forensic anthropology.* Durham, N.C.: Carolina Academic Press.

12 Rhine S. (1998). *Bone voyage: A journey in forensic anthropology.* Albuquerque: University of New Mexico Press.

ANTHROPOLOGY APPLIED

Forensic Anthropology

Dr. Owen Beattie, University of Alberta

Well-known Canadian forensic anthropologist. Owen Beattie has conducted more than 100 forensic investigations for coroners, police departments, and medical examiners across Canada in the past 20 years. Currently, Beattie teaches biological and forensic anthropology at the University of Alberta in Edmonton and serves as consultant in physical anthropology for the Office of the Chief Medical Examiner in Alberta.

As a forensic anthropologist, Beattie has become increasingly involved in the investigation of human rights violations around the world. In the mid-1990s, he served as part of a United Nations international team that exhumed and analyzed victims of the 1994 Rwandan massacres. Beattie has also used his considerable forensic expertise to help solve some of the most fascinating mysteries of the Arctic north. He is most famous for his work on the remains of members of the doomed 1845–48 Franklin Expedition to find the Northwest Passage. His two award-winning books, *Frozen in Time and Buried in Ice,* examine the mysterious fate of Sir John Franklin's crew. In 1999, Beattie supervised removal of the frozen remains of a 15th-century hunter discovered in a remote glacier in Tatshenshini-Alsek National Wilderness Park, British Columbia. (See the Original Study in Chapter 2.) The ancient hunter and the artifacts associated with the body have elicited great interest within the scientific and First Nations communities.

Currently, Beattie is completing a project on the 1719 disappearance of Captain James Knight's ships, the *Albany* and the *Discovery,* on their way to explore Hudson Bay.

Biological anthropologists do not study only fossil skulls. Shown here is Dr. Owen Beattie from the University of Alberta, whose specialty is forensic anthropology. Dr. Beattie is widely known for his work on the fate of the 1845–48 Franklin Expedition.

COURTESY OF UNIVERSITY OF ALBERTA

Sources: Young Alberta Book Society. (1998). *Owen Beattie.* Retrieved October 16, 2000, from the World Wide Web: www.culturenet.ucalgary.ca/yabs/beattieo.html.

Eighth Annual Young Scientist Conference. (n.d.). *Owen Beattie.* Retrieved October 16, 2000, from the World Wide Web: http://ftp.ei.edduc.ab.ca/dept/ins/beattie/html.

Archaeology

Archaeology is the study of material remains and cultural features in order to describe and explain human behaviour. A primary goal of anthropological archaeology is to explain past human behaviour. Classical archaeology is interested in Greek and Roman history, both of which are rarely studied by anthropologists. Other fields such as fine art history, medieval studies, and Egyptology use archaeological methods but central to their subject matter is the history of particular peoples. Practitioners of these types of archaeology are usually not found in anthropology departments.

Traditionally, archaeologists have focused on people who lived before us, for material products and traces of human practices, rather than practices themselves, are all that survive of the past. Archaeologists study the tools, pottery, and other enduring features such as hearths, pits, structures, and settlements that remain as the legacy of earlier cultures. Such objects, and the way they were left in the ground, reflect aspects of human behaviour. For example, shallow, restricted concentrations of charcoal that include oxidized earth, bone fragments, and charred plant remains, and near which are pieces of fire-cracked rock, pottery, and tools suitable for food preparation, are indicative of cooking and associated food processing at a First Nations site. From such remains much can be learned about a people's diet and subsistence practices. Thus, **prehistoric archaeologists** can find out about human behaviour in the distant past, far beyond the mere 5000 years historians are limited to by their dependence on written records. In Canada, the term **"precontact"** rather than "prehistoric" has recently come into use when referring to the ancestors of contemporary First Nations, Inuit, and Métis cultures, to avoid the suggestion that people living in North America before Europeans arrived did not have a history. This, of course, is not true; aboriginal peoples possess diverse and vibrant cultural histories spanning thousands of years before Europeans arrived in Canada. Archaeologists are not limited to the study of prehistoric or precontact societies; **historic archaeologists** study those cultures with historic documents available in order to supplement the material remains people left behind. In Canada, for example, the archaeology of fur trade sites is common. In most literate societies, written records are associated with governing elites, rather than people at the "grass-roots" level. Thus, although documents can tell archaeologists much they might not know from archaeological evidence alone, it is equally true that archaeological remains can tell historians much about a cultural group that is not apparent from its written records. John Cotter sees the advantage of adding archaeology to historical research as "the ability of archaeological evidence to add a third dimension to historical research which will bring into clearer focus the familiar, everyday life of the past, no matter in what period."[13]

The discovery of a War of 1812 American cemetery in Ontario provides previously unknown details of life and death during the U.S. occupation of Fort Erie from July to November 1814. The soldiers were large, young men who show signs of malnutrition and chronic back injuries, among other ailments. The middle individual's left leg was amputated, an all-too-common procedure at the time.

ARCHAEOLOGICAL SERVICES, INC.

Although archaeologists have concentrated on the human past, significant numbers of them are concerned with the study of material objects in contemporary settings. One example is the University of Arizona's Garbage Project, which, by a carefully controlled study of household waste, continues to produce information about contemporary social issues. Among its accomplishments, the project has tested the validity of interview-survey techniques, upon which sociologists, economists,

[13] Cotter J.L. (1978). Symposium on Role of Archaeology in Historical Research, Summary and Analysis. In: R. L. Schuyler (ed.), *Historical archaeology: A guide to substantive and theoretical contributions* (pp. 18–19). Farmingdale, N.Y.: Baywood Publishing.

> **Prehistoric/precontact archaeology.** The study of ancient cultures that did not possess writing systems to record their history.
>
> **Historic archaeology.** The study of the material remains of past societies that also left behind historical documentary evidence. This subfield of archaeology studies the emergence, transformation, and nature of the Modern World.

and other social scientists and policymakers rely heavily for their data. The tests clearly show a significant difference between what people say they do and what garbage analysis shows they actually do. In 1973, a questionnaire was administered to determine the rate of alcohol consumption in Tucson. In one part of town, 15 percent of respondent households affirmed consumption of beer, but no household reported consumption of more than eight cans a week. Analysis of garbage from the same area, however, demonstrated that some beer was consumed in over 80 percent of households, and 50 percent discarded more than eight empty cans a week. Another interesting finding of the Garbage Project is that when beef prices reached an all-time high in 1973, so did the amount of beef wasted by households (not just in Tucson, but in other parts of the United States as well). Although common sense would lead us to suppose just the opposite, high prices and scarcity correlate with more, rather than less, waste. Such findings show that ideas about human behaviour based on conventional interview-survey techniques alone can be seriously in error. Likewise, they show that what people actually do does not always match what they think—or say—they do.

In 1987, the Garbage Project began a program of test excavations in landfills in different parts of the United States. From this work came the first reliable data on what materials actually go into landfills and what happens to them there. And once again, common beliefs turn out to be at odds with the actual situation. For example, biodegradable materials such as newspapers take longer to decay when buried in deep, compacted landfills than anyone previously expected. Needless to say, this kind of information is vital if North America is ever to solve its waste-disposal problems.

The previous discussion should not lead students to believe that archaeologists are concerned only with material culture—the physical evidence of past cultures. The artifacts are merely a means to interpret and reconstruct human history. Robert McGhee, curator of Arctic archaeology at the Canadian Museum of Civilization, dismisses the value of artifacts as objects themselves; rather, he uses these artifacts to learn about the people who used and then discarded them. Using archaeological evidence, McGhee has highlighted the important role the Arctic has played in human history and how

the Inuit have interacted with other cultures, such as Norsemen, Basques, and Asians.

In the 21st century, most academic archaeologists in North America who research nonliterate and some literate cultures are appointed to anthropology departments, with the exceptions, in Canada, of Simon Fraser University, the University of Calgary, and the University of Saskatchewan where there are separate archaeology departments. Archaeologists are also appointed to departments of Classics, Egyptology, Near Eastern Studies, and Celtic Studies to name a few other specialties. These areas focus more on history and languages although individual scholars may also study anthropology. Biological anthropology, although usually found in anthropology departments, is not always associated with anthropology either; however, there are no stand-alone biological anthropology departments in Canada. Outside North America, anthropology is often only physical or biological anthropology. The North American affiliation of archaeology with anthropology is unusual from a world perspective. Archaeology is a set of tools, a way to explore the past, so we would expect to find the tools used in a variety of disciplines concerned with the past. What archaeologists *do* with those tools differentiates the style of archaeology in different countries. In China, for example, archaeology is usually affiliated with history. In a way, archaeological research is dependent on the culture in which it is practised, and to some extent, the same may be said about biological anthropology.

Anthropology provides a broad foundation for archaeology, but maybe it is not broad enough. Archaeological problems are probably best resolved in an interdisciplinary context. Psychology, evolutionary biology, and even fire investigation can all contribute to understanding the past. Another way to approach this issue is to ask whether archaeology can make unique contributions to understanding anthropological problems. In universities, archaeology might be better situated so that it has working relations with many departments, rather than strictly anthropology. Will archaeology continue its alliance with anthropology in the future? Probably, but the situation is constantly changing. Due to the legal and ethical necessity of rescuing archaeological sites ahead of development projects, many archaeologists are now working in the private sector rather than in museums or universities. Some archaeologists feel the connection to anthropology is restrictive.

Sociocultural, Linguistic, Applied, and Medical Anthropology

In order to understand the work of the sociocultural anthropologist, we must clarify what we mean when we speak of culture. **Culture** is the fundamental organizing concept in anthropology yet ask an anthropologist to define "culture" and you will get many answers. Culture is as fundamental to the subject matter of anthropology as the concept of time is to the physicist but is equally elusive. Culture is thought to be the fundamental characteristic tat makes humans unique so having a clear definition would seem important. In its earliest use, culture was thought by Edward Tylor in the 19th century to be a stage on an evolutionary scale. Today we recognize the plurality of cultures. One common definition is to think of culture as the often unconscious standards by which societies—structured groups of people—operate. These standards are socially learned rather than acquired through biological inheritance. Because they determine, or at least guide, the day-to-day behaviour of the members of a society, human behaviour is, above all, cultural behaviour. These behaviours are also thought to form an integrated whole but it is not clear that cultures can actually be described as integrated wholes; that is, culture may not be a "thing" whose every part is connected to all other parts Culture may be a dynamic entity that is more action than things. For example, for many anthropologists culture is the ability to communicate symbolically, particularly with language. The manifestations of culture may vary considerably from place to place, but no person is "more cultured" in the anthropological sense than any other. Other anthropologists view language as the way to define culture. To archaeologists, cultures are societies at particular times and places, and recognized by their material culture.

Just as biological anthropology is closely related to the other biological sciences, sociocultural anthropology is closely related to the other social sciences. The one to which it has most often been compared is sociology, since the business of both is the description and explanation of behaviour of people within a social context. Sociologists, however, do not examine cultural and biological factors together. Moreover, they have concentrated heavily on studies of people living in industrialized North American and European societies, thereby increasing the probability that their theories of human behaviour will be **culture-bound**: that is, based on assumptions about the world and reality that are part of the sociologists' own Western culture. Since sociocultural anthropologists, too, are largely products of the culture with which they grew up, they are also vulnerable to culture-bound theorizing. However, they constantly seek to minimize the problem of bias by studying the whole of humanity in all times and places and do not limit themselves to the study of recent Western peoples; anthropologists have found that to fully understand the complex of human ideas and behaviour, all humans, past and present, must be studied. More than any other feature, the cross-cultural and long-term historical perspective distinguishes sociocultural anthropology from the other social sciences. It provides anthropology with a far richer body of data than that of any other discipline that studies humankind, and it can also be applied to any current issue.

The emphasis sociocultural anthropology places on studies of ancient and more recent non-Western cultures has often led to findings that run counter to existing beliefs derived from Western studies. Thus, sociocultural anthropologists were the first to demonstrate "that the world does not divide into the pious and the superstitious; that there are sculptures in jungles and paintings in deserts; that political order is possible without centralized power and principled justice without codified rules; that the norms of reason were not fixed in Greece, the evolution of morality not consummated in England. ... We have, with no little success, sought to keep the world off balance; pulling out rugs, upsetting teatables, setting off firecrackers. It has

Culture. The often unconscious standards by which societies—structured groups of people—operate. These standards are socially learned rather than acquired through biological inheritance

Culture-bound. Based on the assumptions and values of one's own culture.

The discovery by geologists in the 18th and 19th centuries that the world was far older than most Europeans thought paved the way for the anthropological exploration of past cultures and peoples. ROGER RESSMEYER/CORBIS

been the office of others to reassure; ours to unsettle."[14] Although the findings of sociocultural anthropologists have often challenged the conclusions of sociologists, psychologists, and economists, anthropology is absolutely indispensable to them, as it is the only consistent check against culture-bound assertions. In a sense, anthropology is to these disciplines what the laboratory is to physics and chemistry: an essential testing ground for their theories.

Perhaps the most distinctive feature of humanity is its ability to speak. Language is what allows us to preserve and transmit our culture from generation to generation. Humans are not alone in the use of symbolic communication. Studies have shown that the sounds and gestures made by some other animals—especially by apes—may serve functions comparable to those of human speech; yet no other animal has developed a system of symbolic communication as complex as that of humans.

The branch of cultural anthropology that studies human languages is called **linguistic anthropology.** Linguistic anthropologists study the way language is used as a resource for practising, developing, and transmitting culture. They examine how people use language and other means of expression to develop relationships with one another and to maintain social distinctiveness. **Historical linguistics** is of considerable interest to archaeologists because it focuses on the history of languages (the way languages develop and change one another with the passage of time). By working out the genealogical relationships among languages and examining the distributions of those languages, linguistic anthropologists may estimate how long the speakers of those languages have lived where they do. By identifying those words in related languages that have survived from an ancient ancestral tongue, they can also suggest both where and how the speakers of the ancestral language lived.

---

[14] Geertz, C. (1984). Distinguished lecture: Anti anti-relativism. *American Anthropologist, 86,* 275.

Linguistic anthropology. The branch of cultural anthropology that studies human language.

Historical linguistics. The study of language origins, language change, and the relationships between languages.

Applied anthropology is a veritable gold mine of cultural knowledge that, when put to practical use, can help solve or at least alleviate some of the social problems that humans in many cultures experience. The Anthropology Applied boxes found throughout this book feature some of the specialized services applied anthropologists provide. Besides academic settings, applied anthropologists often work within government bureaus, private corporations, and international development agencies. More often than not, they function as mediators between the members of a cultural group and some government or private agency. Canadian applied anthropologists provide fundamental background information for First Nations land claim negotiations. Indeed, as mentioned earlier, applied anthropologists have played a prominent role in the development of Canadian anthropology as a discipline.

Applied archaeologists work in cultural resource management (CRM), assessing and, at times, excavating archaeological sites threatened by human activity, such as dam building. One of the largest excavations of this type was at the Draper site in Pickering, Ontario, in the 1970s as part the ill-fated Pickering airport development. In Canada, CRM is the main type of archaeology. Public archaeologists, as part of the applied nature of CRM, have also worked alongside First Nations and Inuit groups to develop cultural awareness programs that introduce the public to the value of heritage sites and the history they recount. As you have already seen, forensic anthropology is an excellent example of applied research in biological anthropology. Applied linguistic anthropologists are becoming increasingly involved in language retention among First Nations groups and serve as advisers for bilingual education. Applied medical anthropologists work closely with traditional healers to reconcile traditional medical practices with modern medicine.

Medical Anthropology

In part due to the growing importance of global health organizations, which face a wide cross-cultural array of healing traditions and practices, medical anthropology has emerged as a significant specialization within the discipline of anthropology. In the past, medical anthropologists were individuals trained as physicians and ethnographers who investigated health beliefs and practices of people in exotic places while also providing

them with "Western" medicine. Medical anthropologists during this early period translated local experiences of sickness into the scientific language of Western biomedicine. Following a re-evaluation of this ethnocentric approach in the 1970s, medical anthropology emerged as a unified discipline that incorporated theories and practices of anthropology. Today, medical anthropology is defined as a specialization that brings theoretical and applied approaches from cultural and biological anthropology to the study of human health and disease. Medical anthropologists study medical systems as cultural systems similar to any other social institution. They use cross-cultural and scientific models drawn from biological anthropology to understand and improve human health. They have also turned their attention toward biomedicine, contributing a wide-ranging perspective to the social and cultural aspects of health care in their own societies. Their work sheds light on the connections between human health and political and economic forces, both globally and locally. Many of the Biocultural Connections featured throughout this text present the work of medical anthropologists.

Ethnography

Whenever possible, the anthropologist becomes **ethnographer** by going to live among the people under study. Through **participant observation**—eating a people's food, speaking their language, and personally experiencing their habits and customs—the ethnographer creates an **ethnography** or a description of a culture by seeking to understand their way of life to a far greater extent than any nonparticipant anthropologist or other social scientist ever could; one learns a culture best by learning how to behave acceptably in the society in which one is doing fieldwork.

Ethnographer. An anthropologist who studies cultures from a comparative or historical point of view, utilizing ethnographic accounts.

Participant observation. In ethnography, the technique of learning a people's culture through direct participation in their everyday life for an extended period of time.

Ethnography. The systematic description of a particular culture based on firsthand observation.

In Cartagena, Columbia, an ethnographer interviews local fishermen. **1996 RICHARD LORD**

He or she must be a careful observer in order to be able to get an in-depth overview of a culture without placing undue emphasis on one of its parts at the expense of another. Only by discovering how all cultural institutions—social, political, economic, religious—relate to one another can the ethnographer begin to understand the cultural system. Anthropologists refer to this as the **holistic perspective,** and it is one of the fundamental principles of anthropology.

When participating in unfamiliar cultures, the ethnographer does not just blunder about blindly but enlists the assistance of individual **informants.** These are members of the society in which the anthropologist as ethnographer is working, with whom he or she develops close relationships, and who help the anthropologist as a newcomer in the community unravel whatever activities are taking place. As a child learns proper behaviour from its parents, so do informants help the anthropologist in the field unravel the mysteries of what is, at first, a strange culture.

Although ethnographic fieldwork is basic to ethnology, it is not the sole occupation of the ethnologist. Largely descriptive in nature, ethnography provides the basic data the **ethnologist** (who is more theoretically oriented) may then use to study one particular aspect of a culture by comparing it with that same aspect in others. Anthropologists constantly make such cross-cultural comparisons, and this is another hallmark of the discipline.

ANTHROPOLOGY AND SCIENCE

The foremost concern of all anthropologists, regardless of specialization, is the detailed and comprehensive study of humankind. Anthropology has been called a social or a behavioural science by some, a natural science by others, and one of the humanities by still others. Can the work of the anthropologist properly be labelled scientific? What exactly do we mean by the term "science"?

Science is a carefully honed way of producing knowledge to explain or understand the underlying logic, the structural processes, that make the world tick. Science is a creative endeavour that seeks testable explanations for observed phenomena, ideally in terms of the workings of universal and immutable principles, or laws. Two basic ingredients are essential for this: imagination and skepticism. Imagination, though capable of leading

Holistic perspective. A fundamental principle of anthropology, that the various parts of culture must be viewed in the broadest possible context to understand their interconnections and interdependence.

Informants. Members of a society in which the ethnographer works who help interpret what he or she sees taking place.

Ethnologyist. Someone who analyzes ethnographic data.

BIOGRAPHY

David Boyle (1842–1911)
James Anderson (1926–1995)
Bruce G. Trigger (1937–2006)

David Boyle, a teacher and naturalist, was the first professional archaeologist in Canada. He actively worked on producing the Ontario site inventory at the Canadian Institute and published many archaeological reports. Scholars in Canada such as Boyle did not work in isolation.

An influential figure in Canadian biological anthropology was James Anderson of Perth, Ontario. He graduated in 1953 as a medical doctor, but one of his professors at the University of Toronto was J.C.B. Grant. Grant had studied the biological variation of several First Nations communities, and Anderson was determined to follow his example. By 1958, Anderson was the first biological anthropologist in the Department of Anthropology at the University of Toronto, and his legacy is still felt throughout Canada. One of Anderson's innovations was the study of discrete traits along with metric data. His study of single traits and their variations had a considerable influence on future generations of researchers.

Bruce G. Trigger was been a pivotal force in anthropological archaeology since the early 1960s. As a student, Trigger became interested in the study of archaeological settlement patterns. His Ph.D. dissertation examined the factors that influenced changing population size and distribution of population in Lower Nubia, from the beginnings of agriculture (ca 4000 B.C.) until the end of the Christian period (ca A.D. 1500).

In 1963, Trigger began teaching at McGill University, where he was Professor in the Department of Anthropology until his death in 2006. Trigger trained archaeologists interested in the Iroquoian prehistory of southern Ontario. These researchers focused on understanding Iroquoian development in terms of economic, social, and political change in individual communities. Trigger also produced major historical and ethnohistorical works on the eastern woodlands peoples, in particular the Huron. His historical publications helped expand and define the goals of ethnohistory and aligned pre-contact archaeology with history.

In the 1980s, Trigger focused his studies on the history of archaeology in an effort to understand the changing ideas that have shaped archaeologists' understanding of the past. His book, *A History of Archaeological Thought*, is used as a textbook on the history of archaeology in many countries.

Trigger devoted his last years to discerning the factors that shape human behaviour and the archaeological record. He conducted a comparative study of early civilizations that seeks to explore those factors that account for the cross-cultural similarities and differences that have evolved independently in cultures in various parts of the world. Trigger concluded that in addition to ecological constraints on cultural traditions, culture is shaped by the specific psychological and cognitive needs of human beings that are a product of their biological evolution. Inevitably, his research will have implications for general theory construction in anthropology and will provide a basis for critiquing processual (see page 6) and postmodern approaches in archaeology.

Throughout his career, Trigger attempted to use archaeological data to avoid narrow or simplistic explanations and to understand human behaviour in its full complexity. He was also interested in using archaeological findings to refute ethnic stereotypes, especially as these relate to aboriginal peoples of North America. Trigger has often encouraged First Nations students to become archaeologists, and to become involved in interpreting their own history.

us astray, is required in order that we may recognize unexpected ways phenomena might be ordered and think of old things in new ways. Without it, there can be no science. Skepticism is what allows us to distinguish **fact** from fancy, to test our speculations, and to prevent our imaginations from running away with us.

In their search for explanations, scientists do not assume that things are always as they appear on the surface. After all, what could be more obvious than that the earth is a stable entity, around which the sun travels every day? And yet, it isn't so. Scientists reject religious and metaphysical explanations, as well as all explanations and appeals to any authority that are not supported by strong empirical (observational) evidence. Because explanations are constantly challenged by new observations and novel ideas, science is self-correcting; that is, inadequate explanations are sooner or later shown up as such, to be replaced by more reliable explanations.

The scientist begins with several **hypotheses** or possible explanations for the relationship among certain observed facts. Various kinds of data relevant to these hypotheses are then collected. Using the additional information, the scientist tries to disprove each hypothesis. Ideally one hypothesis will not be disproven, and it becomes the strongest explanation, or **theory**. Thus, a theory, contrary to popular use of the term, is more than mere speculation; it is a carefully checked-out explanation of observed reality. Even so, no theory is ever considered to be beyond challenge. Truth in science is not considered to be absolute but rather a matter of varying degrees of probability; what is considered to be true is what is most probable. This is just as true in anthropology as it is in biology or physics. But while nothing, except perhaps in mathematics, can be proved to be absolutely true, incorrect assumptions can be proved false. Indeed, if a theory (or hypothesis) is not potentially falsifiable, it cannot be considered scientific. So it is that, as our knowledge expands, the odds in favour of some theories over others are generally increased, even though old "truths" sometimes must be discarded as alternative theories are shown to be more probable.

To illustrate how scientific methodology works, the Original Study (p. 20) presents a famous case from physical anthropology.

RISKS OF CULTURE-BOUNDED SCIENCE

Straightforward though the scientific approach may seem, there are serious difficulties in its application in anthropology. One problem is that once one has stated a hypothesis, one is strongly motivated to verify it, and this can lead to unwittingly overlooking negative evidence, as well as other mistakes. This is a familiar problem in science; as palaeontologist Stephen Jay Gould puts it: "The greatest impediment to scientific innovation is usually a conceptual lock, not a factual lock."[15] In anthropology there is a further difficulty: In order to arrive at useful theories concerning human behaviour, one must begin with hypotheses that are as objective and as little culture-bound as possible. And here lies a major—some people would say insurmountable—problem: It is difficult for someone who has grown up in one culture to frame hypotheses about others that are not culture-bound.

As one example of this sort of problem, we may look at attempts by archaeologists to understand the nature of settlement in the Classic period of Maya civilization. This civilization flourished between A.D. 250 and 900 in what is now northern Guatemala, Belize, and adjacent portions of Mexico and Honduras. Today much of this

[15] Gould, S.J. (1989). *Wonderful life.* New York: Norton (p. 226).

Fact. An observation verified by several observers skilled in the necessary techniques of observation.

Hypotheses. Tentative explanations of the relations among certain phenomena.

Theory. In science, an explanation of natural phenomena, supported by a reliable body of data.

ORIGINAL STUDY

The Strange Case of "Piltdown Man"

In 1910, parts of a human skull and an almost intact lower jaw were found in the Piltdown gravels in Sussex, England. Although the gravels were thought to be quite ancient, the skull was remarkably modern in appearance. The jaw, however, was exceedingly apelike. The find, Piltdown I, was named *Eoanthropus dawsoni,* Dawson's "dawn man," after its discoverer Charles Dawson, an amateur archaeologist, palaeontologist, and practising lawyer. In 1913 an apelike canine tooth was found to go with the jaw, and in 1915 Piltdown II, fragments of skull plus a molar tooth, were found 3.2 kilometres from Piltdown I. So much for the facts, but what to make of them? Two hypotheses come to mind. The first is that the remains are just what they seem: an ape jaw found in proximity to human skull remains. The other is that skulls and jaw belong to some kind of "missing link" with a modern-sized human brain but primitive, apelike jaws. It was the second hypothesis, even though it aroused occasional dissention, that was generally accepted until the early 1950s.

The reasons for widespread acceptance of hypothesis 2 are as follow. With the publication in 1859 of Darwin's theory of evolution by natural selection, intense interest developed in finding traces of prehistoric human ancestors. Accordingly, predictions

were made as to what those ancestors looked like. Darwin himself, on the basis of his knowledge of embryology and the comparative anatomy of living apes and humans, suggested in his later book *The Descent of Man* that early humans had, among other things, a large brain and an apelike face and jaw.

Although the tools made by prehistoric peoples were forthcoming, their bones were not. To be sure, a few Neandertal and Cro-Magnon skeletons came to light in Europe, but they weren't at all like the predicted missing link. Moreover, more ancient and primitive *H. erectus* fossils found in Java were the subject of a heated debate. Their discoverer reacted to this controversy by burying the fossils beneath his dining room floor, where no one could examine them. Given this state of affairs, the Piltdown finds could not have come at a better time. Here at last was the long-awaited missing link, and it was almost exactly as predicted. Even better, so far as English-speaking scientists were concerned, it was found in English soil!

In the context of the evidence available in the early 1900s, the idea of an ancient human with a large brain and an apelike face could become widely accepted as valid. A reexamination of this theory, however, was forced by the discovery of more and more fossils, primarily in Africa, China, and Java. These seemed to show that modern-looking human jaws preceded the development of large-sized brains, rather than the other way around. Thus, the Piltdown remains became more and more of a problem. This led one physical anthropologist, J.S. Weiner, to reconsider the Piltdown fossils, and this is what he found:

1. The only actual human characteristic of the jaw was the apparent tooth wear; otherwise, it was just like the jaw of an ape.
2. The muscle attachments indicate an apelike arrangement of jaw muscles, which would not produce a human wear pattern.
3. The heavy wear of the canine tooth is inconsistent with other features of the tooth that clearly indicate it came from an immature individual.

4. The parts of the jaw that would give it away as surely that of an ape were missing.

5. When drilling for a dentine sample from a tooth, it was found that this was pure white beneath a thin surface stain—not what one would expect in an ancient fossil.

On the basis of these findings, Weiner returned to the first of our two original plausible hypotheses—that the remains were human skulls and an ape jaw. But now there was a corollary hypothesis that someone had faked the evidence, causing widespread acceptance of the "big-brained human with apelike jaws" hypothesis. Specifically, Weiner proposed that someone had stained the jaw of an ape, destroyed the parts that would give it away for what it was, filed the teeth, and then planted them together with the human skull parts in the Piltdown gravels.

He and two of his colleagues then devised a series of appropriate procedures to test the logical consequences of his hypothesis. For example, microscopic examination revealed the presence of abrasion on the teeth, as would be produced by filing. Chemical tests revealed significant differences in chemical content between jaw and skull; these would be expected if they were from different sources but not if they belonged together. In short, Weiner and his colleagues were able to conclusively falsify the "big-brained human with apelike jaws" hypothesis and to confirm Weiner's version of the "ape jaw with human skull" hypothesis.

Source: Based on Weiner, J.S. (1955). *The Piltdown forgery.* New York: Oxford University Press.

---

region is covered by a dense tropical forest of the sort that people of European background find difficult to manage. In recent times this forest has been inhabited by a few people, who sustain themselves through slash-and-burn farming. (After cutting and burning the natural vegetation, crops are grown for two years or so before fertility is exhausted and a new field must be cleared.) Yet numerous archaeological sites featuring temples sometimes as tall as modern 20-story buildings, other sorts of monumental architecture, and carved stone monuments have been found there. Because of their cultural bias against tropical forests as places to prosper and against slash-and-burn farming as a means of raising sufficient food, North American and European archaeologists asked the question: How could the Maya have maintained large, permanent settlements on the basis of slash-and-burn farming? The answer seemed self-evident: They couldn't; therefore, the great archaeological sites must have been ceremonial centres inhabited by few, if any, people. Periodically a rural peasantry, living scattered in small hamlets over the countryside, must have gathered in these centres for rituals, or to provide labour for their construction and maintenance.

This view dominated for several decades, and it was not until 1960 that archaeologists working at Tikal,

one of the largest of all Maya sites, decided to ask the simplest and least biased questions they could think of: Did anyone live at this particular site on a permanent basis? If so, how many, and how were they supported? Working intensively over the next decade, with as few preconceived notions as possible, the archaeologists were able to establish that Tikal was a large settlement inhabited on a permanent basis by tens of thousands of people, who were supported by forms of agriculture more productive than slash-and-burn alone. It was this work at Tikal that proved wrong the older culture-bound ideas and paved the way for a new understanding of Classic Maya civilization.

By recognizing the potential problems of framing hypotheses that are not culture-bound, anthropologists have relied heavily on a technique that has proved successful in other fields of the natural sciences. As did the archaeologists working at Tikal, they immerse themselves in the data to the fullest extent possible. By doing so, they become so thoroughly familiar with the minute details that they can begin to see patterns inherent in the data, many of which might otherwise have been overlooked. These patterns are what allow the anthropologist to frame hypotheses, which then may be subjected to further testing.

THEORETICAL PERSPECTIVES

Biological anthropologists and archaeologists develop new knowledge primarily by applying a scientific approach, but this is not the whole story. Within each subfield, the intellectual context in which their science is approached has an impact on how results are interpreted. So while obvious culture-bound interpretations need to be avoided, informed explanations are still made within a set of assumptions that form a **theoretical perspective**. If our theoretical perspective is evolutionary, then we work in a framework in which organisms adapt to their environment, new species develop, and others become extinct. In biological anthropology, the primary theoretical perspective is set in a model of evolution but this has not always been the case. Earlier in this chapter we saw that in the 19th and early 20th century biological anthropologists were interested in describing human variation in the context of race research. Evolution played almost no role in their thinking. When the mechanisms of evolution were better understood race disappeared as a fundamental concept and was replaced by a concept of human biological variation informed by evolutionary theory. As we will see later in this text, there is more than one way to view the evolution of species. How we understand species development affects how fossils are classified. New developments in how we understand human genetics in turn affect the way we view evolution in general and the evolution of humans in particular. For example, if we expect species to develop gradually, certain fossils would be considered "transitional" or "missing links." If one accepts a view of sudden change (that evolution is not gradual) then no fossils are missing links, and searching for such fossils is an exercise in futility.

Theoretical perspectives abound in archaeology. The scientific approach in North America came into popularity only in the middle of the 20th century. In the late 1800s through the early 1900s archaeology was descriptive, much like biological anthropology was. Archaeologists were preoccupied with describing artifacts and figuring out to what culture they belonged and how old they might be. So archaeology was mainly a kind of history to the extent that working out the particulars of what was going in what period was enough. In some countries like China and Japan this is still the main purpose of archaeology. Innovative ideas developed in one place and then diffused from one culture to another. Agriculture, for example, was thought to have developed first in the Near East with the idea then spreading from there. Archaeologists had no data to demonstrate this, but it seemed reasonable and was an acceptable explanation for agriculture becoming established around the world.

Evolution did not go unnoticed and some scholars thought that societies might have evolved like organisms did. If life developed from simple to complex with humans as the result then societies might have evolved with the end result being civilization. The foundation had been established by European archaeologists such as Christian Thomsen who organized the National Museum of Denmark's collections into Stone, Bronze, and Iron Ages. In China scholars had proposed a similar model nearly 2000 years ago. Others embellished the concept and although Thomsen's model is not useful today because it was a vast oversimplification and he did not have the knowledge that archaeologists today have, it established the groundwork for understanding that technology, just like species, changed over time and that some logical ordering was possible. The results of ethnographic work around the world told archaeologists that there were societies that likely represented forms that existed in earlier times. Lewis Henry Morgan, for example, investigated the Iroquois First Nation in New York state.[16] Based on his observations of a relatively egalitarian society with subsistence farming in which women had a strong role, he proposed that the original human societies were similar. He called this stage "savagery" and the subsequent stage "barbarism." The final stage was civilization. To Morgan, this was a primitive state of communism and so his work influenced people such as Marx and Engels. Until 15 to 20 years ago, Chinese archaeologists working in their communist political setting were still

---

[16] Morgan L.H. (1877). *Ancient society: or, Researches in the lines of human progress from savagery, through barbarism to civilization.* Chicago: C.H. Kerr.

Theoretical perspective. In archaeology, the set of assumptions that form a model or theory.

interpreting the early farming societies there according to Morgan's model.

The unilineal model of cultural evolution ran into some trouble when scholars investigating aboriginal cultures in the Americas became aware that cultural variation seemed to correlate with environmental variables. There were desert and woodland cultures for example. Julian Steward looked to the environment and ecology to help explain cultural variation.[17] This theoretical perspective is known as **cultural ecology.** Archaeologists took notice and began to make a concerted effort to collect environmental data from their sites. **Settlement archaeology** developed in order to understand how people organized themselves in particular settings by studying the arrangement of sites in the landscape.

The world entered the nuclear age after World War II. Radiocarbon dating was an outgrowth of nuclear research and soon archaeologists could rapidly acquire dates for objects and sites instead of spending their time making educated guesses. In the 1950s and 1960s science was the way to enlightenment in developed countries. The space race was on and by 1969 people had landed on the moon. Archaeologists, too, turned to a more explicit scientific approach. They turned their efforts to understanding the processes of culture change and adaptation. **Processual archaeology**—a scientific approach to explaining the process of culture changes and adaptations, and a critical turning point in archaeology—was born. Now that dating and describing artifacts were so much easier this new form of archaeology (in fact, it is also known as the *new archaeology*) meant that archaeologists could turn to explaining the past. Processual archaeology is rooted in an explicitly scientific approach and focused on the processes of development of, for example, the origins of agriculture and social complexity as well as processes involved in their subsequent development. Although hypothesis testing is at the core of processual archaeology, some archaeologists have gone so far as to propose "laws" that might work like the laws of Newtonian physics.

The interest in explaining the past has challenged archaeologists to develop new theoretical perspectives and each has its own assumptions. Those dissatisfied with the scientific approach introduced an alternative model influenced by postmodern studies in other

disciplines. This approach is called **postprocessual** archaeology. Postprocessual is a diverse set of perspectives, all of which are in some way a reaction to processualism. To many archaeologists the laws that the processualists proposed were trivial, or as Kent Flannery called them, "Mickey Mouse laws."[18] Postprocessualists proposed that artifacts were not simply a reflection of what went on in a society but a result of deliberate thoughts and actions that can be investigated. **Agency theory** views the archaeological record as a result of the actions of individuals who are in turn part of the culture in which their actions take place. **Engendered archaeology** is set in feminist

---

[17] Steward J.H. (1955). *Theory of culture change: The methodology of multilinear evolution.* Urbana: University of Illinois Press.

[18] Flannery K. (1973). Archaeology with a capital "S." In C.I. Redman (ed.), *Research and theory in current archeology* (pp. 47–53). New York: J. Wiley and Sons.

Cultural ecology. The perspective that uses ecological and environmental factors to explain cultural variation; culture is the primary means by which people adapt to their environment.

Settlement archaeology. Research designed to describe the arrangement of occupations in the landscape in order to understand how people organized themselves in particular settings.

Processual archaeology. A scientific approach to explaining the process of culture changes and adaptations.

Postprocessual archaeology. A critique of processual archaeology that rejects scientific explanations of the archaeological record. It represents a diverse perspective encompassing social and cognitive aspects of human behaviour.

Agency theory. In postprocessual archaeology, the view that the archaeological record results from the actions of individuals who are part of a culture in which their actions take place.

Engendered archaeology. Set in feminist theory, it examines the roles gender plays in understanding the past, including the impact of gender bias in the profession of archaeology.

theory and examines the roles gender plays in understanding the past, including the impact of gender bias in the profession of archaeology. Other postprocessual archaeologists go so far as to say that archaeological interpretations cannot possibly be objective or scientifically based; the world view of the investigator inevitably colours their intepretation. This general discussion of theoretical perspectives in fact is making that point. The theoretical aspects of doing archaeology, that is, how we think about the things archaeologists recover, is for some just as interesting as excavating and reporting finds. This book can be read in terms of the place, time, and culture in which it was written and says as much about the archaeologists and biological anthropologists who are working in their respective fields as it does about the results of their research.

COMPARISON IN ANTHROPOLOGY

The end result of archaeological or ethnographic fieldwork, if properly carried out, is a coherent statement about a culture that provides an explanatory framework for understanding the ideas and actions of the people who have been studied. And this, in turn, is what permits the anthropologist to frame broader hypotheses about human behaviour. Plausible though such hypotheses may be, however, the consideration of a single society is generally insufficient for their testing. Without some basis for comparison, the hypothesis grounded in a single case may be no more than a historical coincidence. On the other hand, a single case may be enough to cast doubt on, if not refute, a theory that had previously been held valid. The discovery in 1948 that aborigines living in Australia's northern Arnhem Land put in an average workday of less than six hours, while living well above a bare sufficiency level, was enough to call into question the widely accepted notion that food-foraging peoples are so preoccupied with finding food that they lack time for any of life's more pleasurable activities. Even today, economists are prone to label such peoples as "backward," even though the observations made in the Arnhem Land study have since been confirmed many times over in various parts of the world.

Hypothetical explanations of cultural phenomena may be tested by the comparison of archaeological and/or ethnographic data for several societies found in a particular region. Carefully controlled comparison provides a broader context for understanding cultural phenomena than does the study of a single culture. The anthropologist who undertakes such a comparison may be more confident that the conditions believed to be related really are related, at least within the region that is under investigation; however, an explanation that is valid in one region is not necessarily so in another.

Ideally, theories in cultural anthropology are generated from worldwide comparisons. The cross-cultural researcher examines a worldwide sample of societies in order to discover whether or not hypotheses proposed to explain cultural phenomena seem to be universally applicable. Ideally the sample should be selected at random, thereby enhancing the probability that the conclusions of the cross-cultural researcher will be valid; however, the greater the number of societies being compared, the less likely it is that the investigator will have a detailed understanding of all the societies encompassed by the study. The cross-cultural researcher depends upon other ethnographers for data. It is impossible for any single individual personally to perform in-depth analyses of a broad sample of human cultures throughout the world.

In anthropology, cultural comparisons need not be restricted to ethnographic data. Anthropologists can, for example, turn to archaeological data to test hypotheses about cultural change. Cultural characteristics thought to be caused by certain specified conditions can be tested archaeologically by investigating situations where such conditions actually occurred. Also useful are data provided by the ethnohistorian. **Ethnohistory** is a kind of historical ethnography that studies cultures of the recent past through oral histories; through the accounts

> **Ethnohistory.** The study of cultures of the recent past through oral and written histories; accounts left by explorers, missionaries, and traders; and through analysis of such records as land titles, birth and death records, and other archival materials.

of explorers, missionaries, and traders; and through analysis of such records as land titles, birth and death records, and other archival materials. The ethnohistorical analysis of cultures, like archaeology, is a valuable approach to understanding change. By examining the conditions believed to have caused certain phenomena, we can discover whether or not those conditions truly precede those phenomena.

Ethnohistoric research is also valuable for assessing the reliability of data used for making cross-cultural comparisons. Anthropologists working with data from such resources as the Human Relations Area Files have sometimes concluded that among food foragers it is (and was) the practice for married couples to live in or near the household of the husband's parents (anthropologists call this *patrilocal residence*). To be sure, this is what many ethnographers reported. But most such ethnographies were done among food foragers whose traditional practices had been severely altered by pressures set in motion by the expansion of Europeans to all parts of the globe. For example, the Western Abenaki people of north-western New England are asserted to have practised patrilocal residence prior to the actual invasion of their homeland by English colonists. What ethnohistorical research shows, however, is that their participation in the fur trade with Europeans, coupled with increasing involvement in warfare to stave off foreign incursions, led to increased importance of men's activities and a change from flexible to patrilocal residence patterns.[19] Upon close examination, other cases of patrilocal residence among food foragers turn out to be similar responses to circumstances associated with the rise of colonialism. Far from wives regularly going to live with their husbands in proximity to the latter's male relatives, food-foraging peoples originally seem to have been far more flexible in their postmarital residence arrangements.

Though a valuable research tool, ethnohistory is not without its own set of problems and limitations. Early explorers, traders, and missionaries came to Canada with preconceived notions about First Nations peoples; many of the early accounts reflect these biases, and suffer from inaccuracies, misinterpretations, and distortions. As an example, ignorance and personal biases are rife in early accounts of practices such as the Sun Dance and potlatch ceremonies. Ethnohistorians must take into consideration the reliability and objective nature of their sources, and often rely on several forms of information to validate their findings.

ANTHROPOLOGY AND THE HUMANITIES

Although the sciences and humanities are often thought of as mutually exclusive approaches to learning, they share common methods for critical thinking, mental creativity, and innovation.[20] In anthropology, both come together, which is why, for example, anthropological research is funded not only by such science agencies as the Canadian Institutes of Health Research and the National Science and Engineering Research Council, but also by the Social Sciences and Humanities Research Council. To paraphrase Roy Rappaport, a past president of the American Anthropological Association, the combination of scientific and humanistic approaches is and always has been a source of tension. It has been crucial to anthropology because it truly reflects the condition of a species that lives and can live only in terms of meanings that it must construct in a world devoid of intrinsic meaning, yet subject to natural law. Without the continued grounding in careful observation that scientific aspects of our tradition provide, our interpretive efforts may float off into literary criticism and speculation. But, without the interpretive tradition, the scientific tradition that grounds us will never get off the ground.[21]

The humanistic side of anthropology is perhaps most immediately evident in its concern with other cultures' languages, values, and achievements in the arts and literature (including oral history among peoples who lack writing). Beyond this, anthropologists

[19] Haviland, W.A., & Power, M.W. (1994). *The original Vermonters* (Rev. and exp. ed.), pp. 174–175, 215–216, 297–299). Hanover, NH: University Press of New England.

[20] Shearer, R.R., & Gould, S.J. (1999). Of two minds and one nature. *Science, 286*, 1093.

[21] Rappaport, R.A. (1994). Commentary. *Anthropology Newsletter, 35*, 76.

remain committed to the proposition that one cannot fully understand another culture by simply observing it; as the term *participant observation* implies, one must *experience* it as well. Thus, ethnographers spend prolonged periods of time living with the people they study, sharing their joys and suffering their deprivations, including sickness and, sometimes, premature death. They are not so naive as to believe that they can be, or even should be, dispassionate about the people whose trials and tribulations they share. As Robin Fox puts it, "Our hearts, as well as our brains, should be with our men and women."[22] Nor are anthropologists so self-deceived as to believe that they can avoid dealing with the moral and political consequences of their findings. Indeed, anthropology has a long tradition of protecting and promoting the rights of indigenous peoples.

The humanistic side of anthropology is evident as well in its emphasis on qualitative, as opposed to quantitative, research. This is not to say that anthropologists are unaware of the value of quantification and statistical procedures; they do make use of them for various purposes. Nevertheless, reducing people and the things they do to numbers has a definite dehumanizing effect (it is easier to ignore the concerns of impersonal numbers than it is those of flesh-and-blood human beings) and keeps us from dealing with important issues less susceptible to numeration. For all these reasons, anthropologists tend to place less emphasis on numerical data than do other social scientists.

Given their intense involvement with other groups of people, it should come as no surprise that anthropologists have amassed as much information about human weakness and greatness—the stuff of the humanities—as any other discipline. Small wonder, too, that above all they intend to avoid allowing a coldly scientific approach to blind them to the fact that human groups comprise individuals with a rich assortment of emotions and aspirations that demand respect. Anthropology has sometimes been called the most human of the sciences, a designation that anthropologists embrace with considerable pride.

ANTHROPOLOGY'S CONTRIBUTIONS TO OTHER DISCIPLINES

Students often ask, "Why should we study anthropology?" To answer this question we need to examine the personal, academic, and professional benefits of an education in anthropology. For those of us who have ever wondered why people behave the way they do, believe in what they do, or look the way they do, anthropology can help answer these questions. Anthropologists can teach us about the different ways in which people organize their lives and can go a long way toward explaining human behaviour.

Regardless of their field of study, students can benefit academically from an anthropological education. For example, from an economic anthropology course, a student can learn about the myriad ways that people around the world organize their production, exchange, and consumption activities, and will come to understand that there are many meanings associated with economic activities. Anthropology also contributes to disciplines outside the social sciences; archaeological and ethnohistorical research has much to offer history and geology, and biological anthropology both benefits from and contributes to the science of biology. Thus, any student who studies anthropology, even briefly, receives a broader, more well-rounded education.

For students who decide to major in anthropology, there are numerous areas of specialization that prepare them for future careers. For example, urban anthropologists often work in areas of policy, planning, and development in urban settings. Medical anthropologists work alongside other health specialists to identify the beliefs, attitudes, and behaviours that affect health and illness.

As synthesizers, understanding colour-naming behaviour in different human groups is an appropriate subject for anthropologists to explore. For example, the Coast Salish languages of southwestern British Columbia

---

[22] Fox, R. (1968). *Encounter with anthropology*. New York: Dell, p. 290.

do not have separate words to distinguish blue from green, while Russian has a separate word for pale blue and another word for dark blue.[23] Since anthropologists look for broad explanations of human behaviour without limiting themselves to any single social or biological aspect of that behaviour, they can acquire an especially extensive overview of humans as complex biological and cultural organisms.

Researchers outside the field of anthropology are beginning to recognize the value of anthropology's unique methodology—that of immersion in a culture. Participant observation provides a research model for other disciplines, such as education, geography, and psychology. Thus, anthropology enhances the research and experience of other disciplines, disciplines that would be diminished if not for the knowledge and research methods of anthropology.

QUESTIONS OF ETHICS

The kinds of research carried out by anthropologists, and the settings within which they work, raise a number of important moral questions about the use and abuse of our knowledge. Who will make use of the findings of anthropologists, and for what purposes? Who, if anyone, will profit from them? In the case of a hostile minority, for example, will governmental or corporate interests use anthropological data to suppress that minority? And what of traditional communities around the world? Who is to decide what changes should or should not be introduced for community "betterment"? By whose definition is it betterment—the community's, that of some remote government, or an international agency like the World Bank? Then there is the problem of privacy. Anthropologists deal with people's private and sensitive matters, including things that people would not care to have generally known about them. How does one write about such matters and at the same time protect the privacy of informants? Not surprisingly, because of these and other questions, anthropologists must carefully consider the subject of ethics.[24] Canadian researchers

are guided by the Tri-Council Policy Statement (TCPS) on ethical conduct for research involving human subjects. The guidelines are very specific with regard to aboriginal peoples. Researchers need to carefully consider notions of private and public life, property, and language differences that may blur communications on issues such as consent.

Anthropologists recognize that they have obligations to three sets of people: those whom they study, those who fund the research, and those in the profession who expect us to publish our findings so that they may be used to further knowledge. Because fieldwork requires a relationship of trust between fieldworker and informants, the anthropologist's first responsibility clearly is to his or her informants and their people. Everything possible must be done to protect their physical, social, and psychological welfare and to honour their dignity and privacy. In other words, *do no harm*. The Canadian TCPS also points out that free and informed consent is essential as is the respect for vulnerable persons. Although early ethnographers often provided colonial administrators with the kind of information needed to control the "natives," ethnographesrs have long since ceased to be comfortable with such work and regard as basic a people's right to their own culture.

Archaeologists and biological anthropologists investigating ancient human remains and sites recognize their obligations to the archaeological record as well as to the descendants of the people represented in the record. The Canadian Archaeological Association has two sets of principles of ethical conduct. One relates to the archaeological heritage of Canada and the other to aboriginal peoples. The principles acknowledge that archaeological remains are irreplaceable, nonrenewable, and unique. Furthermore, considering

---

[23] For further discussion see Bonvillain, N. (2000). *Language, culture, and communication: The meaning of messages* (3rd ed.). Upper Saddle River, NJ: Prentice Hall.

[24] American Anthropological Association. (1998). Code of ethics of the American Anthropological Association. *Anthropology Newsletter, 39* (6), 19–20.

Ignorance of other cultures can have serious consequences. When President George W. Bush responded to attacks on targets in New York and the Pentagon, he spoke of a "crusade" against terrorism, which the U.S. Department of Defense dubbed "Operation Infinite Justice." These choices of language caused problems with Islamic countries, where the word crusade *reminds people of Christian invasions of Muslim lands, and where only Allah can dispense "infinite justice."* TODD HOLLIS/AP/WIDE WORLD PHOTOS

most archaeological heritage in Canada represents First Nations and Inuit peoples, principles of consultation, aboriginal involvement, sacred sites and places, and communication and interpretation have been established. Human remains and associated objects are considered especially significant. In addition are the results of the Task Force on Museums and First Peoples.[25] Museum collections must be handled and interpreted properly, recognizing the needs and aspirations of First Nations peoples. The Task Force set out principles and recommendations to aid in accurately

portraying cultural heritage. Central to the principles are partnerships between First Nations peoples and Canadian museums. Such guidelines help specialists meet their ethical obligations as both scholars and members of Canadian society.

IMPACTS ON CONTEMPORARY LIFE

The relevance of anthropological knowledge for the contemporary world may be illustrated by three quite different examples. In North America today, discrimination based on notions of race continues to be a serious problem affecting economic, political, and social relations. What anthropology has shown, as we shall see in Chapter 13, is the fallacy of racial categories themselves. Far from being the biological reality it is thought to be, the concept of race emerged in the 18th century as a device for justifying the dominance of Europeans and their descendants over Africans, North American aboriginal peoples, and other "people of colour." In fact, differences of skin colour are adaptations to differing amounts of ultraviolet radiation and have nothing to do with other abilities. Nor do they co-vary with other biological characteristics; a northern European, for example, may have more in common with a "black" from southern Africa than with someone from Greece or Italy, depending on what genetically based characters other than skin colour are considered. Moreover, one finds far more biological variation within any given human population than between them. In short, human races are nothing more than folk categories, and the sooner this is recognized, the better off we will all be.[26]

A second example involves the issue of same-sex marriage. As this is written, several countries have moved toward allowing such unions: Brazil, for example, by recognizing "stable unions" between same-sex partners, the Netherlands, Belgium, and

---

[25] First Nations and the Canadian Museums Association (1992). *Turning the page: Forging new partnerships between museums and First Peoples.* Ottawa.

[26] American Anthropological Association. (1998). Statement on "race." Available: www.aaanet.org/stmts/racepp.htm.

Canada (in Ontario, British Columbia, and Quebec). In the United States, California and Massachusetts are debating and Vermont has legalized "civil unions" between same-sex couples. Those opposed to same-sex unions frequently argue that marriage has always been between one man and one woman, and that only heterosexual relations are natural. Yet, neither assertion is true. Anthropologists have documented same-sex marriages in many human societies in various parts of the world, where they are regarded as perfectly acceptable under appropriate circumstances. As for homosexual behaviour, it is quite common in the animal world (see, for example, Chapter 4), including among humans.[27] The only difference between people and other animals is that human societies specify when, where, how, and with whom it is appropriate (just as they do for heterosexual behaviour).

In numerous ways, our ignorance about other peoples and their ways is a cause of serious problems. It is as true today as when Edwin Reischauer, a former ambassador, said it some years ago: "Education is not moving rapidly enough in the right directions to produce the knowledge about the outside world and attitudes toward other peoples that may be essential for human survival."[28] Anthropology, then, can contribute to contemporary life an understanding of and way of looking at the world's peoples that are nothing less than basic skills for survival in the modern world.

[27] Kirkpatrick, R.C. (2000). The evolution of human homosexual behavior. *Current Anthropology, 41,* 384.

[28] Quoted in Haviland, W.A. (1997). Cleansing young minds, or what should we be doing in introductory anthropology? In C.P. Kottak, J.J. White, R.H. Furlow, & P.C. Rice (eds.), *The teaching of anthropology: Problems, issues, and decisions.* Mountain View, CA: Mayfield, p. 35.

CHAPTER SUMMARY

Throughout human history, people have needed to know who they are, where they came from, and why they behave as they do. Traditionally, myths and legends provided the answers to these questions. Anthropology, as it has emerged over the last 200 years, offers another approach to answering the questions people ask about themselves.

Anthropology is the study of humankind. In employing a scientific approach, anthropologists seek to produce a reasonably objective understanding of both human diversity and those things all humans have in common. The five major branches of anthropology are biological anthropology, archaeology, linguistic anthropology, applied anthropology, and sociocultural anthropology. Biological anthropology focuses on humans as biological organisms. Biological anthropologists trace the evolutionary development of the human animal and study biological variation within the species today. Archaeologists study material objects, usually from past cultures, in order to explain human behaviour. Linguistic anthropologists, who study human languages, may deal with descriptions of languages, with histories of languages, or with how languages are used in particular social settings. Applied anthropologists put into practical use the knowledge and expertise of anthropology. Sociocultural anthropologists study humans in terms of their cultures in the present and recent past.

Ethnographers go into the field to observe and describe human behaviour; ethnologists do comparative studies of particular facets of a culture, such as religion or economic practices; and ethnohistorians study cultures of the recent past using oral histories and written accounts left by explorers, missionaries, and traders.

Anthropology is unique among the social and natural sciences in that it is concerned with formulating explanations of human diversity based on a study of all aspects of human biology and behaviour in all known societies. Thus, anthropologists have devoted much attention to the study of non-Western peoples.

Anthropologists are concerned with the objective and systematic study of humankind. The data sociocultural anthropologists use may be from a single society or from numerous societies that are then compared.

In anthropology, the humanities and sciences come together to create a genuinely human science. Anthropology's link with the humanities can be seen in its concern with people's beliefs, values, languages, arts, and literature—oral as well as written—but above all in its attempt to convey the experience of living as other people do. As both science and humanity, anthropology has essential skills to offer the modern world, where understanding the other people with whom we share the globe has become a matter of survival.

QUESTIONS FOR CRITICAL THOUGHT

1. To what extent are biological anthropology and archaeology related? How do the two complement each other?

2. Discuss the negative and positive aspects of archaeology and biological anthropology being associated with anthropology.

3. How might archaeology and biological anthropology be affected by the context and place where they develop? How do you think your education and choice of subjects is affected by the circumstances in which you are living?

INTERNET RESOURCES

Anthropologists at Work
www.nku.edu/~anthro/careers.html#careers
Discusses students' questions about anthropology careers and the type of work anthropologists do, and provides some excellent practical advice for newly graduated students.

www.canadianarchaeology.com/links.lasso
An extensive site by the Canadian Archaeological Association. Links Canadian anthropology departments, field schools, anthropology-related websites, etc.

www.sas.upenn.edu/~ekondrat/Dor.html

An interesting webpage featuring Tel Dor, an ancient city in Israel. Visit the site to learn about Dor's history, and the archaeology of the region. Offers vivid photographs and maps of the site. Learn how archaeologists conduct a huge, multidecade excavation.

Anthropology and Ethics

http://library.lib.binghamton.edu/subjects/anthro/ethics.html

Provides numerous links to anthropology associations, including the Canadian Archaeological Association. In each link the associations present their Codes of Professional Ethics and address issues such as professional responsibility.

Anthropology in the News

www.tamu.edu/anthropology/news.html

A collection of timely articles related to archaeology and physical anthropology.

Careers in Anthropology

www.utsc.utoronto.ca:80/~chan/capa/resources/Careers.html

An extensive site with numerous links that offer advice, suggestions, and testimonials about career opportunities in anthropology, both inside and outside academia. The site also links to a listing of international field school and research opportunities.

www.aaanet.org/careers.htm

American Anthropological Association site providing useful information on academic careers and related workshops. It also lists current job advertisements in anthropology worldwide.

www.museum.state.il.us/ismdepts/anthro/dlcfaq.html

Answers frequently asked questions about archaeology in the United States.

http://archaeology.about.com/library/univ/blggsa.htm

Contains the *Guide to Departments* published by the American Anthropological Association, providing information on institutions with anthropological programs, their faculty members, and the research focus of each member. Also included are their membership listings, statistical data, and a listing of Ph.D. dissertations in anthropology.

www.canadian-universities.net/Universities/Programs/Anthropology.html

A guide to Canadian anthropology programs.

www.saa.org/careers/academic.html

Lists four-year postsecondary institutions that have at least an archaeologist as a faculty member in Canada, the United States, and Latin America.

Field School Opportunities

www.archaeologyfieldwork.com/forums/index.php

Lists current field schools, volunteer opportunities in archaeology, and internships in museums and archaeology-related institutions. It also lists frequently asked questions about archaeological fieldwork.

Forensic Anthropology

www.forensicanthro.com

A list of descriptions of programs and degrees in forensic anthropology. Links tutorials and contains information about forensic anthropology, osteology and anatomy, archaeology, forensics, portal sites, anthropology, employment, and journals.

What Is Anthropology?

www.louisville.edu/a-s/anthro/whatis.htm

A fairly comprehensive explanation of anthropology and its subdisciplines.

www.anthropologie.net

A large compendium of news and information on anthropology with an emphasis on archaeology.

www.sha.org

The Society for Historic Archaeology, a U.S. organization, offers a wide range of resources to explore this active field.

SUGGESTED READINGS

For a list of suggested readings, visit the textbook's website at www.humanevolution2.nelson.com.

Methods of Studying the Human Past

This excavation is of an Ainu burial intruding into an archaeological site in Hokkaido, Japan. The nylon strings mark a grid that assists the excavator to accurately map the remains. The grid is also tied into a larger site-wide grid that allows the archaeologists to document the location of artifacts and their context. Without such meticulous records, the finds tell us nothing about the human past.

GARY CRAWFORD

CHAPTER PREVIEW

1. What Are Archaeological Sites and Fossil Localities, and How Are They Found?

Archaeological sites are places containing the remains of past human activity. They are revealed by the presence of artifacts as well as soil marks, changes in vegetation, and irregularities of the surface. Fossil localities contain actual remains of organisms that lived in the past. They are revealed by the presence of fossils—any trace or impression of an organism of past geological time that has been preserved in the earth. Although fossils are sometimes found in archaeological sites, not all archaeological sites contain fossils, and localities are often found apart from archaeological sites.

2. How Are Sites and Localities Investigated?

Archaeologists and palaeoanthropologists face something of a dilemma. The only way to thoroughly investigate a site or locality is by excavation, which results in its destruction. Thus, every attempt is made to excavate in such a way that the location of everything found, no matter how small, is precisely recorded. Without such records little sense can be made of the data, and the potential of the site or locality to contribute to our knowledge of the past would be lost forever.

3. How Are Archaeological or Fossil Remains Dated?

Remains can be dated in relative terms by noting their stratigraphic position, by measuring the amount of fluorine contained in fossil bones, or by associating them with different plant or animal remains. More precise dating is achieved by counting the tree rings in wood from archaeological contexts, by measuring the amount of carbon 14 remaining in organic materials, or by measuring the percentage of potassium that has decayed to argon in volcanic materials. Where problems exist in applying these standard techniques, other specialized methods are available.

CHAPTER OUTLINE

Methods of Data Recovery	Sorting the Evidence
Sites and Fossil Localities	Dating the Past

A popular stereotype of anthropologists is that they are concerned exclusively with the human past. This is not the case, as should now be evident; not even archaeologists and biological anthropologists, those most likely to be engaged in the study of the past, devote all of their time to such pursuits. As explained in Chapter 1, some archaeologists study the refuse of modern peoples, and many biological anthropologists engage in research on such issues as present-day human variation and adaptation. Nevertheless, the study of the human past is an important *part* of anthropology, given its concern with peoples in all places and times. Moreover, knowledge of the human past is essential if we are to understand what it was that made us distinctively human, as well as how the processes of change—both biological and cultural—affect the human species. Indeed, given the radical changes taking place in the world today, one may say that an understanding of the nature of change has never been more important. Although not their sole concern, archaeology and biological anthropology are the two branches of anthropology most involved in the study of the human past.

Archaeologists (apart from those engaged in the analysis of modern garbage) study things left behind by people who lived in historic or prehistoric times—tools, trash, traces of shelters, and the like. As the British archaeologist Stuart Piggot put it, "Archaeology is the science of rubbish."[1] Most of us are familiar with some kind of archaeological material: the coin dug out of the earth, the fragment of an ancient jar, the spear point used by some ancient hunter. The finding and cataloguing of such objects is often thought by laypeople to be the chief goal of archaeology. While this was true in the 19th century, the situation changed in the 20th. Today, the aim is to use archaeological remains to reconstruct human societies that can no longer be observed firsthand, in order to understand and explain human behaviour. Although it may look as if the archaeologist is digging up things, he or she is really digging up human behaviour.

The actual remains of our ancestors, as opposed to the things they lost or discarded, are the concern of biological anthropologists. Those biological anthropologists engaged in the recovery and study of the fossil evidence for human evolution, as opposed to those who study present-day peoples, are generally known as **palaeoanthropologists.** Unlike palaeontologists, who study all forms of past life, palaeoanthropologists confine their attention to humans, near humans, and other ancient primates, the group to which humans belong.

Just as the finding and cataloguing of objects was once the chief concern of the archaeologist, so the finding and cataloguing of human and other primate fossils was once the chief concern of the palaeoanthropologist. But, again, there has been a major change in the field; although recovery, description, and organization of fossil materials are still important, the emphasis since the 1950s has been on what those fossils can tell us about the processes at work in human biological evolution. It is not so much a case of what you find, but what you find out.

In Chapter 1, we surveyed at some length just what it is that anthropologists do and why they do it. We also looked briefly at the ethnographic methods used by anthropologists to study the cultures of living peoples. Other methods are required, however, when studying peoples of the past—especially those of the prehistoric past, before the existence of written records. The term **prehistoric** is a conventional one that, while not denying the existence of history, recognizes that *written* history is absent. In Canadian archaeology, **pre-contact** is an accepted alternative because it acknowledges a long First Nations oral history pertaining to times before European arrival in North America. Since the next two parts of this book are about the ancient past, in this chapter we shall look at how archaeologists and palaeoanthropologists go about their study of the human past.

METHODS OF DATA RECOVERY

Archaeologists, one way or another, work with **artifacts:** any object fashioned or altered by humans—a flint chip, a basket, an axe, a pipe, or such nonportable things

---

[1] Quoted in Fagan, B.M. (1995). The quest for the past. In L.L. Hasten (Ed.), *Annual editions 95/96, Archaeology* (p. 10). Guilford, CT: Dushkin.

Palaeoanthropologist. An anthropologist who studies human evolution from fossil remains.

Prehistoric. A conventional term used to refer to the period of time before the appearance of written records. Does not deny the existence of history, merely of *written* history.

Pre-contact. The period before European arrival in the Americas.

Artifact. Any object fashioned or altered by humans.

as house ruins or walls. An artifact expresses a facet of human culture. Because it is something that someone made, archaeologists like to say that an artifact is a product of human behaviour or, in more technical words, that it is a material representation of an abstract ideal.

Just as important as the artifacts themselves is the way they were left in the ground. What people do with the things they have made, how they dispose of them, and how they lose them also reflect important aspects of human behaviour. Furthermore, the context in which the artifacts were found tells us which objects were contemporary with which other objects, which are older, and which are younger. Without this information, the archaeologist is in no position at all even to identify, let alone understand, specific cultures of the past. This importance of context cannot be overstated; without context, the archaeologist in effect knows nothing! Unfortunately, such information is easily lost if the materials have been disturbed, whether by bulldozers or by the activities of relic collectors.

While archaeologists work with artifacts and non-fossilized human bone, palaeoanthropologists work with human or other primate fossils—the remains of past forms of life. And just as the context of a find is as important to the archaeologist as the find itself, so is the context of a fossil absolutely critical to the palaeoanthropologist. Not only does context tell which fossils are earlier or later in time than other fossils, but also by noting the association of human fossils with other non-human remains the palaeoanthropologist may go a long way toward reconstructing the environmental setting in which the human lived.

The Nature of Fossils

Broadly defined, a **fossil** is the remains of a once-living organism of past geologic time that has been preserved in the earth's crust. The term is usually reserved for the remains of organisms that lived more than 10 000 years ago.[2] Fossilization typically involves the hard parts of an organism because the soft parts usually disappear. Bones, teeth, shells, horns, and the woody tissues of plants are the most successfully fossilized materials. Although the soft parts of an organism are rarely fossilized, the casts or impressions of footprints, and even whole bodies, have sometimes been found. Because dead animals quickly attract meat-eating scavengers and bacteria that cause decomposition, they rarely

survive long enough to become fossilized; they must be covered by some protective substance soon after death.

Cases in which an entire organism of any sort, let alone a human, is preserved in a relatively unaltered state are especially rare. Fossils have usually been **altered** in some way. Fossils generally consist of such things as scattered teeth and fragments of bones found embedded

Fossils are not always found in the ground. In this picture, palaeoanthropologist Donald Johanson searches for fossils in a gully in Ethiopia. The fossils in the foreground were once buried beneath sediments on an ancient lake bottom, but rains in more recent times have eroded the sediments from around them so that they lie exposed on the surface. **DAVID L. BRILL**

---

[2] Allaby, A., & Allaby, M. (1999). *Dictionary of earth sciences*. Oxford: Oxford University Press.

> **Fossil.** The remains of a once-living organism, generally having lived more than 10 000 years ago.
>
> **Altered fossils.** Remains of plants and animals that lived in the past that have been altered, as by the replacement of organic material by calcium carbonate or silica.

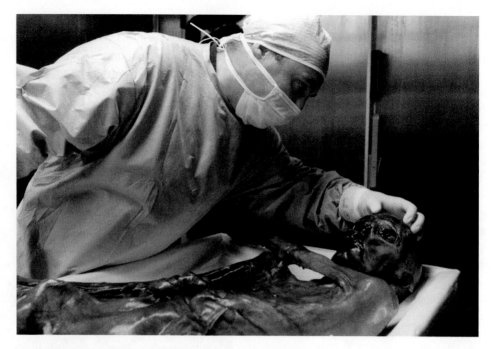

In rare circumstances, human bodies are so well preserved that they could be mistaken for recent corpses. Such remains are not actually fossils. This is the case of the 5200-year-old "Ice Man," exposed by the melting of an alpine glacier in northern Italy in 1991. AUGUSTIN OCHSENREITER/AP/WIDE WORLD PHOTOS

in the earth's crust as part of rock deposits. Thousands, and even millions, of years ago, the organisms died and were deposited in the earth; they may then have been covered by sediments and silt, or sand. These materials gradually hardened, forming a protective shell around the skeleton of the organism. The internal cavities of bones or teeth and other parts of the skeleton were generally filled in with mineral deposits from the sediment immediately surrounding the specimen. Then the external walls of the bone decayed and were replaced by calcium carbonate or silica.

Fossilization is most apt to occur among marine animals and other creatures that live near water, because their remains accumulate on shallow sea, river, or lake bottoms, away from waves and tidal action. These concentrations of shells and other parts of organisms are covered and completely enclosed by the soft waterborne sediments that eventually harden into shale and limestone.

Terrestrial animals that do not live near lakes, rivers, or the sea are less likely to be fossilized unless they happened to die in a cave, or their remains were dragged there by some other meat-eating animal. In caves, conditions are often excellent for fossilization,

as minerals contained in water dripping from the ceiling may harden over bones left on the cave floor. In northern China, for example, many fossils of *H. erectus* (discussed in Chapter 8) and other animals were found in a cave at a place called Zhoukoudian, in deposits consisting of consolidated clays and rock that had fallen from the cave's limestone ceiling. The cave had been frequented by both humans and predatory animals, who left remains of many a meal there.

Unless protected in some way, the bones of a land dweller, having been picked clean and often broken by predators and scavengers, are then scattered and exposed to the deteriorating influence of the elements. The fossil record for many primates, for example, is poor, because organic materials decay rapidly in the tropical forests in which they lived. The records are much more complete in the case of primates that lived on the grassy plains, or savannas, where conditions are far more favourable to the formation of fossils. This is particularly true in places where ash deposited from volcanic eruptions or waterborne sediments along lakes and streams could quickly cover over the skeletons of primates that lived there. At several localities in Ethiopia, Kenya, and Tanzania in

Waterlogged deposits (a bog) at the Red Bay site, Labrador, preserved a 16th-century Basque whaler's costume. Basque whalers set up whaling stations on the coast of Labrador during the late 16th and early 17th centuries. **JEREMY POWELL/CANADIAN CONSERVATION INSTITUTE/DEPARTMENT OF CANADIAN HERITAGE**

SITES AND FOSSIL LOCALITIES

Given that archaeologists and palaeontologists work with artifacts and fossils, the question is: Where are they found? Places containing archaeological remains of previous human activity are known as **sites.** Within a site, **features** are contiguous places that the archaeologist wishes to treat separately from other places within the site. Hearths, storage pits, or house floors are examples of features. There are many kinds of sites, and sometimes it is difficult to define their boundaries, for remains may be strewn over large areas. Some examples are hunting campsites, from which hunters went out to hunt game; kill sites, in which game was killed and butchered; village sites, in which domestic activities took place; and cemeteries, in which the dead, and sometimes their belongings, were buried.

Sometimes human fossil remains are present at archaeological sites. This is the case, for example, at certain early sites in East Africa. Sometimes, though, human remains are found at other localities. For example, in South Africa the fossil remains of early human ancestors have been found in rock fissures, where their remains were dropped by such predators as leopards and eagles. Such places are usually referred to as **fossil localities.**

Site and Locality Identification

Archaeological sites, particularly very old ones, frequently lie buried underground, and therefore the first task for the archaeologist is actually finding sites to investigate. How archaeologists find sites is partly determined by the reasons for the search. If an archaeologist is trying to determine how people regionally organized their settlements and the region is quite large, the

East Africa, numerous fossils important for our understanding of human evolution have been found near ancient lakes and streams, often sandwiched between layers of volcanic ash.

In certain cases, remains can be preserved without mineralization and the ancient organism will be relatively intact. The whole animal may be frozen in ice, like the famous mammoths found in Siberia, safe from the action of predators, weathering, and bacteria. Or it may be enclosed in a fossil resin such as amber. Specimens of spiders and insects dating back millions of years have been preserved in the Baltic Sea area, which is rich in resin-producing conifers. An entire organism may be preserved in the bottoms of lakes and sea basins or waterlogged deposits underground, where oxygen is limited. It may also be mummified or preserved in tar pits, peat, oil, or asphalt bogs, in which the chemical environment prevents the growth of decay-producing bacteria. Such **unaltered fossils**, although not common, are often quite spectacular and may be particularly informative.

Unaltered fossils. Remains of plants and animals that lived in the past and that have not been altered in any significant way.

Site. In archaeology, a place containing remains of previous human activity.

Feature. In archaeology, a place within a site that is treated separately from other places within the site.

Fossil locality. In palaeoanthropology, a place where fossils are found.

Some archaeological features are best seen from the air, such as this figure of a hummingbird made in prehistoric times on the Nazca Desert of Peru. **MIKE ANDREWS/ANCIENT ART & ARCHITECTURE**

archaeologist may survey only part of the region. These days most archaeology is part of cultural resource management. Local laws usually require an archaeological assessment before construction projects proceed, and the construction sites are surveyed in detail with no stone unturned, so to speak. In any case, most sites are revealed by the presence of artifacts. Chance may play a crucial role in the discovery. Usually, however, the archaeologist will have to survey a region in order to plot the sites. Thorough, systematic investigations involve a variety of techniques. The most common method is to walk a location and look for artifacts or signs of structures. In many parts of Canada the best time to survey for sites is in the spring before the vegetation develops or crops sprout. The archaeologist conducts a walking survey and looks for artifacts or other signs of human occupation. Next, the archaeologist will normally excavate a series of small test pits, each usually no larger than 50 centimetres on a side. The soil from the pit is passed through a screen and artifacts exposed in the screen are collected. The depth at which the artifacts are recovered is recorded and the soil is described. The location of the test pit is mapped. The locations of pits that have no artifacts in them are also important and by comparing the location of such pits with

artifact-containing pits the archaeologist can estimate the size of an occupation. A variation on this technique uses a coring device to sample soil from great depths. In areas such as the Huanghe (Yellow River) valley in North China sites are often covered in tens of meters of alluvium. Archaeologists use coring devices made from bamboo to penetrate the alluvium and check for buried walls, artifacts, and clues in the soil that indicate the presence of a human occupation.

Archaeologists may include interviews of local residents who usually know where artifacts or ancient structures can be found. L'Anse aux Meadows, an ancient Norse site in Newfoundland, was located this way. In addition to surveys from the ground, more and more use is made of remote sensing techniques, many of them byproducts of space-age technology. **Ground-penetrating radar** broadcasts radar waves into the soil and records the patterns of waves reflected back

Ground-penetrating radar. By transmitting electromagnetic pulses from surface antennas into the ground, and measuring the time lag between when the pulses are sent and when they are received back at the surface, patterns in soil density are recorded.

38

to the instrument. The reflections are characteristic of the surfaces from which they reflect. **Magnetometer** surveys detect minute, systematic fluctuations in the magnetic properties of the soil. Patterns in the magnetic properties can help reveal the location of buried architecture. Soil also varies in electrical conductivity because of the variable amount of water, metal, and soil compaction. By measuring the soil's resistance to electricity with a **soil-resistivity meter**, subsurface patterns can be found. Aerial photographs have been used off and on by archaeologists since the 1920s and are widely used today. Among other things, they were used for the discovery and interpretation of the huge geometric and zoomorphic markings on the coastal desert of Peru. More recently, use of high-resolution aerial photographs, including satellite imagery, resulted in the astonishing discovery of over 800 kilometres of prehistoric roadways connecting sites in the four-corners region (where Arizona, New Mexico, Colorado, and Utah meet) with other sites in ways that archaeologists had never suspected. This led to a new understanding of prehistoric Pueblo Indian economic, social, and political organization. Evidently, large centres like Pueblo Bonito were able to exercise political control over a number of satellite communities, mobilize labour for large public works, and see to the regular redistribution of goods over substantial distances.

On the ground, sites can be spotted by **soil marks,** or stains, that often show up on the surface of recently plowed fields. From soil marks, many Bronze Age burial mounds were discovered in northern Hertfordshire and southwestern Cambridgeshire, England. The mounds hardly rose out of the ground, yet each was circled at its core by chalky soil marks. Sometimes the very presence of certain chalky rock is significant. A search for Stone Age cave sites in Europe would be simplified with the aid of a geological map showing where limestone—a mineral necessary in the formation of caves—is to be found.

Some sites may be spotted by the kind of vegetation that grows on them. For example, the topsoil of ancient storage and refuse pits is often richer in organic matter than that of the surrounding areas, and so it grows a distinct vegetation. In China, buried city walls have the opposite impact, with vegetation growing poorly in the thin soil on top of buried walls. At Tikal, an ancient Maya site in Guatemala (Chapter 12), breadnut trees usually grow near the remains of ancient houses,

so that an archaeologist looking for the remains of houses at Tikal would do well to search where these trees grow. In England, a wooden monument of the Stonehenge type at Darrington, Wiltshire, was discovered from an aerial photograph showing a distinct pattern of vegetation growing where the ancient structure once stood.

Documents, maps, folklore—ethnohistorical data— are also useful to the archaeologist. Heinrich Schliemann, the famous (and controversial) 19th-century German archaeologist, was led to the discovery of Troy after a reading of Homer's *Iliad*. He assumed that the city described by Homer as Ilium was really Troy. Place names and local lore often are an indication that an archaeological site is to be found in the area. Archaeological surveys in North America depend a great deal upon amateur collectors who are usually familiar with local history.

Sometimes sites in eastern North America are exposed by natural agents, such as soil erosion or droughts. Many pre-contact First Nations sites have been exposed by the erosion of river banks. Several of the earliest agricultural sites in Ontario (A.D. 500–1000) were discovered because they were being eroded by the Grand River. During the long drought of 1853–54, a well-preserved prehistoric village was exposed when the water level of Lake Zurich, Switzerland, fell dramatically. In 1991, the mummified body of a man who lived 5200 years ago was found in the Tyrolean Alps, where it had been released by glacial melting. Similarly, in 2000, the remains of a young man nearly 500 years old were recovered from a British Columbia glacier.

Often, archaeological remains are accidentally discovered in the course of some other human activity. Plowing sometimes turns up bones, fragments of pots,

---

Magnetometer.   A device for detecting subsurface patterns by measuring the variation in magnetic-field strength of the soil.

Soil resistivity meter.   A device that detects subsurface patterns by passing electrical current through the ground and measuring the resistance of the soil to the current.

Soil marks.   Stains that show up on the surface of recently plowed fields that reveal an archaeological site.

Underground structures can often be revealed by surface vegetation growth patterns. The wheat in the foreground in this field in North China is stunted because of the poor soil conditions above a buried ancient city wall. **GARY CRAWFORD**

and other archaeological objects. Stone quarrying at Swanscombe, Kent, in England revealed an important site of the Old Stone Age, with human remains thought to be about 250 000 years old. In 1995, strip mining near the town of Schoningen in Germany led to the discovery of 400 000-year-old spears of **H. erectus** (see Chapter 8). So frequently do construction projects uncover archaeological remains that in many countries, including Canada, projects that require government approval will not be authorized unless measures are first taken to identify and protect archaeological remains on the construction site. Archaeological surveys in Canada are now routinely carried out as part of the municipal, provincial, and federal planning process for construction projects. One of the oldest sites in Canada, the Vermilion Lakes site, was found when the Trans-Canada highway was widened in Banff National Park, Alberta. The highway now goes around the site.

Conspicuous sites, such as the great mounds or "tells" of the Middle East, are easy to spot, for the country is open. The profusion of projectile point artifacts, and tipi rings and medicine wheel features, at Wanuskewin Heritage Park outside Saskatoon, Saskatchewan, clearly indicated the presence of pre-contact archaeological sites. But it is difficult to locate ruins, even those that are well above ground, where there is a heavy forest cover. Thus, the discovery of archaeological sites is strongly affected by local geography.

ORIGINAL STUDY

Kwäday Dän Ts'ínchi

Three men hunting sheep in northwestern British Columbia during the late summer, 1999, came across an unusual sight, the remains of a human and a number of artifacts melting from the edge of a glacier. What made this chance discovery so much more unusual was that it was in a relatively inaccessible wilderness region, over 50 kilometres south of the nearest modern settlement. The hunters had the presence of mind to take a few artifacts with them and reported it to the nearest authorities, the Champagne and Aishihik First Nations (CAFN) who co-manage the area with the B.C. government. With the hunters' story supported by the material evidence, members of the CAFN Heritage Program coordinated a first visit to the site, inviting both the Yukon and the B.C. Parks Branches' staff to join them. What they saw at the site left no doubt as to the significance of the discovery. The individual had not died there recently, but when and how the person died and just who he was could not be determined without a detailed investigation. Recognizing the person's likely ancient existence, CAFN community members named it Kwäday Dän Ts'ínchi or "long ago person found" in their Southern Tsutchone language. Time was of the essence because the body was exposed and at risk of quickly eroding away. Within days a team of experts consisting of archaeologists, a biological anthropologist, a glaciologist, and various government heritage experts flew by helicopter to the site to begin the investigation.

In many ways, this was as much a forensic investigation as it was an archaeological one. Investigators had a number of immediate concerns. What was the cause of death? What is the individual's sex? What was his/her age at the time of death? What was his/her state of health? What was his/her diet? What were his/her local kin associations? Where had he/she previously travelled? Investigators had to take care not to contaminate the site with their own DNA or anything else that might compromise the research. Personnel in direct contact with the remains wore sterile suits and gloves. Once removed from the ice and snow, the remains were wrapped in sterile sheets before being placed in plastic boxes. Everything had to be kept below freezing. This wasn't too difficult on site, but once the remains were taken back to the lab in Victoria, they needed to be kept in a climate-controlled walk-in freezer.

While members of the team worked on the human remains themselves, others surveyed the local area for other signs of ancient human presence. The glacier was well above the tree line so anything resembling wood was mapped and collected. Some or all might have belonged to Kwäday Dän Ts'ínchi. Oral history and historic records tell us that the area had a significant First Nations presence in the past. Trails passed through the area carrying traders between communities in the 19th century, but the specific location of the trails is unknown. Records of travels across glaciers by aboriginal peoples in the area exist, but the researchers acknowledge that much more research on oral history is required. Artifacts near Kwäday Dän Ts'ínchi may represent long-term travel through the area rather than having been on his/her person at the time of death. In fact, radiocarbon dating of the artifacts clearly indicates that many of the items found in the immediate area span a range of dates, suggesting others brought them there at different times. Many of the items, including two items of clothing, resulted in radiocarbon dates clustering in the 1400s. This is the best date for Kwäday Dän Ts'ínchi's death on the glacier.

Judging from the morphology of the pubic bone, among others, Kwäday Dän Ts'ínchi is a male. Other indicators on specific bones as well as a lack of degenerative arthritis indicate he was in his late teens or early 20s. Considerable soft tissue is preserved, but so far no signs of trauma have been found. His hair is long and black and the ends were cut. Lines of research include DNA analysis, parasitology, entomology, pathology, palaeobotany, palaeodiet, skeletal biology, and a host of others. Results of the research are not yet available. These studies take considerable time and must be conducted with utmost care.

(Continued)

Items found near him that appear to have been his include a brimmed, woven hat with a hide chinstrap. A possible knife in a hide or fur sheath was found on top of a fur garment associated with the body. Large fragments of clothing made from animal hide may form part of a robe. Other items associated with the body include a small hide bag with a strap that CAFN members identify as his personal medicine bag. Because of its private nature, the bag will not be opened. Fish remains, including scales, were found near the body and among the clothing fragments. The remains appear to be those of chum salmon, all from one individual aged about four years.

Much remains to be learned from this recent discovery. Significantly, researchers have yet to find a cause of death. Unable, for some reason, to continue on, he died in a prone position with his head resting on his wrist or hand. He froze quickly and was covered with snow, only to be exposed after nearly five centuries.

Source: Beattie, Owen, Apland, B., Blake, E.W., Cosgrove, J.A., Gaunt, S., Greer, S., Mackie A.P., Mackie, K.E., Straathof, D., Thorp, V., & Torffe, P.M. (2000). The Kwäday Dän Ts'ínchy discovery from a glacier in British Columbia. *Canadian Journal of Archaeology, 24(1)*, 129–147. Reprinted with permission.

Excavation of the Sakushu-Kotoni River site on the Hokkaido University campus in Sapporo, Japan, revealed the preserved remains of a 1200-year-old fish weir, used for trapping fish by ancestors of the Ainu. Although this part of the river was buried by silt, the sediments remained wet, thereby preserving the collapsed wooden structure. **COURTESY OF HOKKAIDO UNIVERSITY**

Although archaeological sites may be found just about anywhere, the same is not true for fossil localities. One will find fossils only in geological contexts where conditions are known to have been right for fossilization. Once the palaeoanthropologist has identified such regions, specific localities are identified in much the same ways as archaeological sites. Indeed, the discovery of ancient stone tools may lead to the discovery of human fossil remains. For example, it was the presence of very crude stone tools in Olduvai Gorge, East Africa, that prompted Mary and Louis Leakey to search there for the human fossils (discussed in Chapters 6 and 7) they eventually found.

Site and Locality Excavation

Before the archaeologist or palaeoanthropologist plans an excavation, he or she must ask the question, "Why am I digging?" Then he or she must consider the amount of time, money, and labour that can be committed to the enterprise. The recovery of archaeological and fossil material long ago ceased to be the province of the enlightened amateur, as it once was when any enterprising collector went out to dig for the sake of digging. A modern excavation is carefully planned and rigorously conducted; it should not only shed light on the human past but also help us to understand cultural and evolutionary processes in general.

Archaeological Excavation

Once a site is located that is likely to contribute to the solution of some important research problem, the next step is to plan and carry out excavation. To begin,

Sometimes archaeological sites are marked by dramatic ruins, as shown here. This temple called the Castillo stands at the heart of the ancient Maya city of Chichén Itzá. It was built in stages, one temple on another, by piling up rubble and facing each of the temple stages with limestone blocks held together with mortar. **GARY CRAWFORD**

the land is cleared, and the places to be excavated are plotted. This is usually done by means of a **grid system.** The surface of the site is divided into squares, with each square being numbered and marked with stakes. Each object found can then be located precisely in the square from which it came. (Remember, in archaeology, context is everything!) The starting point of a grid system may be a large rock, the edge of a stone wall, or an iron rod sunk into the ground. The starting point is also known as the reference or **datum point.** At a large site covering several square kilometres, this kind of grid system is not feasible because of the large size of the ruins. In such cases, the plotting may be done in terms of individual structures, numbered according to the square of a "giant grid" in which they are found (Figure 2.1).

In a gridded site, each square is dug separately with great care. Shovels and trowels are used to scrape the soil. By removing thin layers of soil, distinct differences in colour and texture of the soil can be recognized, which helps the excavator determine the location of ancient posts, pits, house floors, and other structures. Screens are used to sift all the loose soil so that even the smallest artifacts, such as flint chips or beads, are recovered. Pits and other special features are excavated separately from the surrounding soil. An archaeologist must become familiar with

the natural soil around the site so he or she knows how to distinguish archaeological deposits from naturally formed soil. When excavating a pit, for example, its boundaries are evident when the excavator reaches the natural soil that is expected at that depth. Pit soil is usually softer and darker in colour than the surrounding undisturbed soil.

If the site is **stratified**—that is, if the remains lie in layers one upon the other—each layer, or stratum, will be dug separately. Each layer, having been laid down during a particular span of time, will contain artifacts deposited at the same time and belonging to the same culture. In some cases, the structure of the layers can be studied and devices used to take continuous, small-diameter tubes of soil called cores. Aubrey Cannon at McMaster University, for example, studies complex shell midden sites in British Columbia in this manner. Culture

Grid system. A system for recording data from an archaeological excavation.

Datum point. The starting, or reference, point for a grid system.

Stratified. Layered; said of archaeological sites where the remains lie in layers, one upon another.

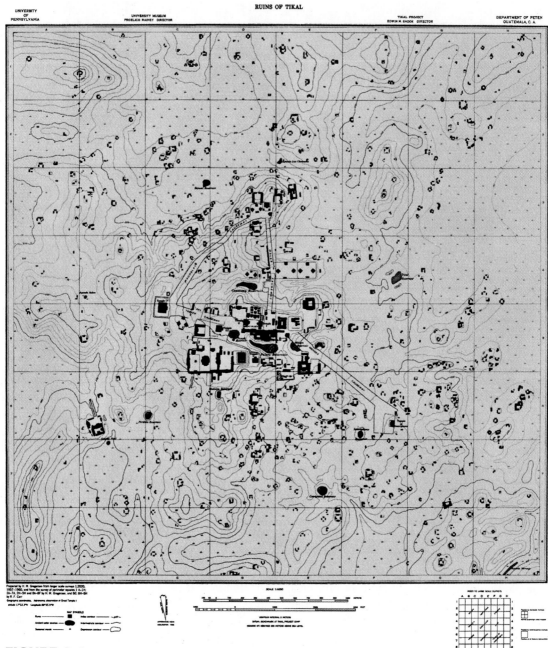

FIGURE 2.1

At large sites covering several square kilometres, a giant grid is constructed, as shown in this map of the centre of the ancient Maya city of Tikal. Each square of the grid is one-quarter of a square kilometre; individual structures are numbered according to the square in which they are found. UNIVERSITY MUSEUM, UNIVERSITY OF PENNSYLVANIA

ANTHROPOLOGY APPLIED

Cultural Resource Management (CRM)

Ever wonder what happens when an archaeological site or artifacts are discovered? Who owns the site, and who takes care of it? Do we have laws to protect ancient sites? What do we do if we find an artifact or if an archaeological site is discovered in the middle of a construction site? What can we learn from archaeological resources?

These questions and many others are the domain of cultural resource management (CRM), also known as heritage management. Although not everyone working in CRM is an archaeologist, many archaeologists are involved in CRM, most working at consulting agencies within the private sector. These archaeologists are charged with protecting, conserving, and documenting cultural resources that are threatened by human activities such as road construction, agricultural development, industrialization (e.g., dam building), and urbanization (e.g., housing developments).

Although the Canadian government has not established specific federal legislation to protect our cultural resources, virtually every province and territory now has heritage legislation and CRM programs (Williamson 2000) to protect archaeological and historical resources from looters, and various forms of development.

Within provincial legislation, archaeological resources are defined as any evidence of past human activity, and are protected by law from removal or disturbance. Archaeological excavations of these resources must be authorized, and in general, archaeologists must be issued a permit in order to excavate a site or collect any material from a site.

On federal lands, the Parks Canada Agency and the Department of National Defence have their own governing rules based on general federal policies (Parks Canada 2000).[1] Usually when an environmental impact assessment is conducted on federal land, an archaeological and palaeontological assessment is required as well. Parks Canada archaeologists maintain an inventory of the archaeological resources found within national parks. At newly discovered archaeological sites any activities that may endanger the site must be halted until archaeologists are called in to secure the site. If human remains are discovered, the police are notified. Everyone, including ordinary individuals, must be cautious during activities such as digging basements or breaking land, to avoid disturbing archaeological resources. It is everyone's responsibility to protect archaeological resources, and if a site is discovered, to report it to local officials.

This legislated requirement to conserve and protect archaeological resources has resulted in an explosion in consulting archaeology. Most archaeological projects conducted in Canada and the United States are under the auspices of CRM, and the majority of graduating students in archaeology become employees of private and governmental CRM agencies. These consultants have obligations to the resources they manage, to the public, who expect heritage sites to be adequately protected, and to the descendant communities, who are becoming increasingly involved in decision making regarding archaeological sites (Ferris 2000).[2]

---

[1] The URL addresses for provincial and territorial legislation can be found in the Internet Resources at the end of this chapter.

[2] Ferris, N. (2000). Warning—Steep grade ahead: Current directions in Canadian archaeology. *Canadian Journal of Archaeology, 24,* 182-186

change can be traced through the order in which artifacts were deposited. But, say archaeologists Frank Hole and Robert F. Heizer, "because of difficulties in analyzing stratigraphy, archaeologists must use the greatest caution in drawing conclusions. Almost all interpretations of time, space, and culture contexts depend on stratigraphy. The refinements of laboratory techniques for analysis are wasted if archaeologists cannot specify the stratigraphic position of their artifacts."[3] If no stratification is present, then the archaeologist digs by arbitrary levels. Each square must be dug so that its edges and profiles are straight; walls between squares are often left standing to serve as visual correlates of the grid system.

Many specialized techniques can be used to recover specific types of information. Soil samples can contain evidence of past vegetation. Stone tools may still have blood residues or starch grains from foods such as rice or potatoes. A technique employed when looking for very fine objects, particularly charred plant remains, fish scales or very small bones, is called **flotation.** Flotation consists of immersing soil in water, causing the particles to separate. Some will float, others will sink to the bottom, and the remains can be easily retrieved.

Excavation of Fossils

Excavating for fossils is in many ways like archaeological excavation, although there are some differences. The palaeoanthropologist must be particularly skilled in the techniques of geology, or else have ready access to geological expertise, because a fossil is of little value unless its temporal place in the sequence of rocks that contain it can be determined. In addition, the palaeoanthropologist must be able to identify the fossil-laden rocks, their deposition, and other geological details. In order to provide all the necessary expertise, palaeoanthropological expeditions these days generally comprise teams of experts in various fields in addition to physical anthropology. A great deal of skill and caution is required to remove a fossil from its burial place without damage. An unusual combination of tools and materials is usually contained in the kit of the palaeoanthropologist—pickaxes, enamel coating, burlap for bandages, and plaster of Paris.

To remove newly discovered bones, the palaeoanthropologist begins uncovering the specimen, using pick and shovel for initial excavation, then small camel-hair brushes and dental picks to remove loose and easily detachable debris surrounding the bones. Once the

Flotation allows archaeologists to routinely recover plant remains, small bone, and artifacts by immersing in water soil collected from sites. The lighter material, such as wood charcoal and seeds, floats in the water and is trapped in sieves as the water overflows the device. Heavier material is caught in a screen at the bottom of the flotation tank while the fine sediment passes through the screen and is discarded. **GARY CRAWFORD**

entire specimen has been uncovered (a process that may take days of back-breaking, patient labour), the bones are covered with shellac and tissue paper to prevent cracking and damage during further excavation and handling.

Both the fossil and the earth immediately surrounding it, or the matrix, are prepared for removal as a single block. The bones and matrix are cut out of the earth (but not removed), and more shellac is applied to the entire block to harden it. The bones are covered with burlap bandages dipped in plaster of Paris. Then the entire block is enclosed in plaster and burlap bandages, perhaps splinted with tree branches, and allowed to dry overnight. After it has hardened, the block is carefully removed from the earth, ready for packing and transport to a laboratory.

[3] Hole, F., & Heizer, R.F. (1969). *An introduction to prehistoric archeology* (p. 113). New York: Holt, Rinehart & Winston.

Flotation. An archaeological technique employed to recover very tiny objects by immersion of soil samples in water to separate heavy from light particles.

This photo shows a section through three pits at the Yagi site, a 5000-year-old Jomon site in northern Japan, and illustrates stratigraphy. The larger pit is the oldest. After the pit was no longer used, it filled with sediment, some of which was probably washed in during rainstorms or by melting snow. Later, another pit on the right was excavated by digging through the fill of the older pit. Finally, a shallow depression was created to make a fireplace. **GARY CRAWFORD**

Before leaving the discovery area, the investigator makes a thorough sketch map of the terrain and pinpoints the find on geological maps to aid future investigators.

Methods in Forensic Anthropology

Forensic anthropologists employ the methods, tools, and techniques of biological anthropologists and archaeologists. The first stage of forensic investigation is recovery. Like archaeologists, forensic anthropologists usually conduct a survey of a region, taking note of any unusual features or evidence that might suggest nearby human remains. Aerial photography may also be used to locate remains. If preliminary evidence warrants it, the forensic anthropologist will then excavate the site, going down one level at a time, carefully sifting all dirt for small items. Once the human remains are located, forensic anthropologists map and photograph the site, then carefully collect the evidence for transport to a laboratory. The site is also inspected for other evidence, such as fragments of clothing, body tissue or fluids, and personal effects like jewellery. In the second stage of the investigation, forensic anthropologists sort, catalogue, and analyze the remains.

This laboratory inventory becomes particularly important when determining the number of individuals found at the site, or whether there is commingling of human and nonhuman remains. Forensic anthropologists may also use dental records, X-rays, or other medical records that might help identify the remains.[4] Without these exacting procedures, the results of forensic research would be of questionable use in a criminal investigation. During the initial examination, forensic anthropologists must answer three questions.[5] *Are the remains bone?* Although this may seem straightforward enough, bone that has been chewed by animals, burned, or crushed in some way makes identification difficult. Materials such as melted foam insulation, tree roots, shell, and burned asbestos can resemble bone fragments. Forensic anthropologists examine these samples under a microscope to determine whether they are bone. *Are the remains human?* Scattered, perhaps damaged remains, especially incomplete limb and finger bones, and vertebra are difficult

---

[4] Rhine S. (1998). *Bone voyage: A journey in forensic anthropology.* Albuquerque: University of New Mexico Press.

[5] Nafte M. (2000). *Flesh and bone: An introduction to forensic anthropology.* Durham, N.C.: Carolina Academic Press.

to identify as human. As an example, defleshed fore and hind paws of bears appear very similar to human hand and foot bones. Fetal or infant skeletal material, which is undeveloped and has a different morphology than adult bones, can be easily mistaken for animal bones. Again, microscopic examination will answer this question. *Are the remains contemporary (less than 50 years), historical (50 to 500 years) or ancient (older than 500 years)?* Evidence at the site should provide clues to the age of the remains. If the remains are found in association with personal effects like a watch, then they are contemporary. On the other hand, if the skeleton is located in a remote area, wearing strange hand-sewn clothing or hides, and associated with rough-hewn wooden or stone tools, this increases the likelihood that the remains are historic or ancient. The state of decomposition also yields clues. If the skeleton still contains flesh and muscle, tufts of hair, or if there is a lot of insect activity, then the remains are likely quite recent. The presence of any orthodontic work or modern surgical procedures (e.g., hip replacement) also indicates that the remains are recent. Ancient bones are usually stained and more decayed from soil leeching. Answering this last question is crucial; if the remains are recent, they may become part of a criminal investigation. If the remains are historic or ancient, then they cease to be of forensic and legal significance; rather, the remains become an archaeological and heritage issue.

Forensic anthropologists use both qualitative and quantitative techniques in their analysis of human remains. They look for certain features or traits in the skeleton, keeping in mind variation within populations and between populations. Forensic anthropologists also take measurements and then, using comparative collections of skeletons, attempt to determine the biological identity of the remains. To establish the sex of the deceased, forensic anthropologists use both observation and measurement. Sexual dimorphism (differential size and shape between sexes) is most obvious in the pelvis and skull. To accommodate the relatively large head of human babies, a female has a pelvis that is rounder and wider than a male's. A female's skull is gracile and smooth, and she has less prominent brow ridges. In males the skull is larger, more robust, with rougher surface areas.[6] The mastoid bone behind the ear is larger in males than in females. Postcranially, males tend to be more robust than females within the same population. However, basing sex determination on size can be unreliable, particularly if specimens are from different populations. For example, East Indian skeletons tend to be more gracile than Europeans. Determining age is fairly straightforward in pre-adults since growth and development is relatively regular and predictable. Forensic anthropologists compare dental development, bone length, and fusion of growth centres to determine age. Fusion of different bones occurs at different times, thus forensic anthropologists can age the individual based on which epiphyses have fused. In individuals under the age of fifteen, dentition is the most reliable indicator of biological aging. In adults, forensic anthropologists examine wear and deterioration on bones and look for the presence of any age-related diseases, such as osteoporosis, which may begin as early as the 30s.

State of Preservation of Archaeological Evidence

What is recovered in the course of excavation depends upon the nature of the remains as much as upon the excavator's digging skills. Inorganic materials such as stone and metal are more resistant to decay than organic ones such as wood and bone. Often an archaeologist comes upon an assemblage—a collection of artifacts—made of durable inorganic materials, such as stone tools, and traces of organic ones long since decomposed, such as woodwork (Figure 2.2), textiles, or food.

State of preservation is affected by climate; under favourable climatic conditions, even the most perishable objects may survive over vast periods of time without being fossilized. For example, pre-dynastic Egyptian burials consisting of shallow pits in the sand often yield well-preserved corpses. Because these bodies were buried long before mummification was ever practised, their preservation can be the result only of rapid desiccation in the very warm, dry climate. The tombs of dynastic Egypt often contain wooden furniture, textiles, flowers, and papyri barely touched by time, seemingly as fresh looking as they were when deposited in the tomb 3000 years ago—a consequence of the dryness of the atmosphere.

The dryness of certain caves is also a factor in the preservation of human or animal feces. Sometimes called "coprolites" (fossilized feces), dry, unfossilized human feces are a source of information on prehistoric foods and can be analyzed for dietary remains. From such analysis

---

[6] Ibid.

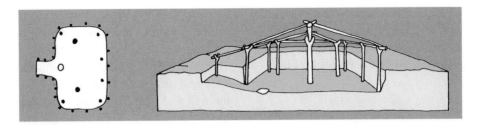

FIGURE 2.2

Although the wooden posts of a house may have long since decayed, their positions may still be marked by discoloration of the soil. The ancient posthole pattern of a palisade at the Auger site near Coldwater, Ontario, shows how complex Huron construction could get.

archaeologists can determine not only what the inhabitants ate but also how the food was prepared. Because many sources of food are available only in certain seasons, it is even possible to tell the time of year in which the food was eaten and the excrement deposited.

Certain climates can soon obliterate all evidence of organic remains. Maya ruins found in the very warm and moist tropical rain forests of Mesoamerica are often in a state of collapse—notwithstanding that many are massive structures of stone—as a result of the pressure exerted upon them by the heavy forest vegetation. The rain and humidity soon destroy almost all traces of

woodwork, textiles, or basketry. Fortunately, impressions of these artifacts can sometimes be preserved in plaster, and some objects made of wood or plant fibres are depicted in stone carvings and pottery figurines. Thus, even in the face of complete decay of organic substances, something may still be learned about them.

The cultural practices of ancient humans may also account for the preservation of archaeological remains. The ancient Egyptians believed that eternal life could be achieved only if the dead person were buried with his or her worldly possessions. Hence, tombs are usually filled with a wealth of artifacts. Many skeletal remains of Neandertals (Chapter 9) are known because they

This slipper from Mammoth Cave, Kentucky, is made of plant fibres. Over 2000 years old, this object survived only because of the dry condition of the cave in which it was found. **COURTESY OF WILLIAM CURTSINGE, CAVE RESEARCH FOUNDATION**

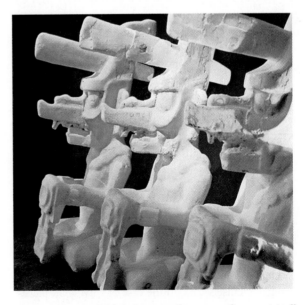

At the Maya site of Tikal, these manikin sceptre figures originally made of wood were recovered from a king's tomb by pouring plaster into a cavity in the soil, left when the original organic material decayed. **COURTESY OF THE UNIVERSITY MUSEUM, UNIVERSITY OF PENNSYLVANIA**

practised burial, perhaps because they, too, believed in some sort of afterlife. By contrast, skeletal remains of pre-Neandertal peoples are rare and when found usually consist of mere fragments rather than complete skeletons.

SORTING THE EVIDENCE

It cannot be stressed too strongly that the value of archaeological materials is virtually destroyed if an accurate and detailed record of the excavations is not kept. As one eminent anthropologist has put it:

> *The fundamental premise of excavation is that all digging is destructive, even that done by experts. The archaeologist's primary responsibility, therefore, is to record a site for posterity as it is dug because there are no second chances.*[7]

Excavation records include a scale map of all the features, the stratification of each excavated square, a description of the exact location and depth of every artifact or bone unearthed, and photographs and scale drawings of the objects. This is the only way archaeological evidence can later be pieced together so as to arrive at a plausible reconstruction of a culture. Although the archaeologist may be interested only in certain kinds of remains, every aspect of the site must be recorded, whether it is relevant to the particular investigation or not, because such evidence may be useful to others and would otherwise be permanently lost. One must remember that archaeological sites are nonrenewable resources, and that their destruction, whether by proper excavation or looting, is permanent.

After photographs and scale drawings are made, the materials recovered are processed in the laboratory. In the case of fossils, the block in which they have been removed from the field is cut open, and the fossil is separated from the matrix. Like the initial removal from the earth, this is a long, painstaking job involving a great deal of skill and special tools. This task may be done with hammer and chisel, dental drills, rotary grinders, or pneumatic chisels, and, in the case of very small pieces, with awls and tiny needles under a microscope.

Chemicals, such as hydrochloric and hydrofluoric acids, are also used in the separation process to dissolve the surrounding matrix. Some fossils require processing by other methods. For example, precise identification can be obtained by examining thin, almost transparent strips of some fossils under a microscope. Casts of the insides of skulls (**endocasts**) are made by filling the skull wall with an acid-resistant material, then removing the wall with acid. A skull may be cleaned out and the inside painted with latex. After the latex hardens, it is removed in a single piece, revealing indirect evidence of brain shape and outer appearance. Such endocasts are helpful in determining the size and complexity of ancient brains.

As a rule of thumb, archaeologists plan on at least three hours of laboratory work for each hour of fieldwork. In the lab, artifacts that have been recovered must first be cleaned and catalogued—often a tedious and time-consuming job—before they are ready for analysis. From the shapes of the artifacts and from the traces of manufacture and wear, archaeologists can usually determine their function. For example, Chen Shen of the Royal Ontario Museum in Toronto has been investigating tool function from wear patterns.[8] Using experiments and observations of microscopic wear patterns on stone artifacts from several archaeological sites in Ontario, he has been able to learn what materials (wood, hides, soft plant tissue, etc.) people were working, and the type of motions used (slicing, sawing, drilling, chopping, etc.). Shen discovered that many artifacts have unexpected uses. Stone cores, the block of stone that is the source of raw material for making tools, were also used occasionally for chopping, sawing, or drilling. Some tools such as arrow points show no evidence of having been used. This suggests that arrows may have been made for purposes other than shooting (honing tool-making skills, or for rituals), lost before they were used, or that once they were used, archaeologists don't find them because the used points were not discarded on-site.

Analysis of plant and animal remains provides clues about the environment and the economic activities

---

[7] Fagan, B.M. (1995). *People of the earth* (8th ed., p. 19). New York: HarperCollins.

[8] Shen, C. (2000). The tool use-patterning at the Grand Banks site of the Princess Point Complex, Southwestern Ontario. *Northeast Anthropology, 60,* 63–87.

> **Endocast.** A cast of the inside of a skull; helps determine the size and shape of the brain.

This shell mound in Kentucky, thousands of years old, shows signs of looting. Such looting is all too common and destroys irreplaceable evidence. GARY CRAWFORD

of the occupants of a site. **Palaeoethnobotany** and **archaeozoology** are subdisciplines of archaeology encompassing the analysis and interpretation of these remains. Such analysis may help clarify peoples' relationship to their environment and its influence upon the development of their **technology**—the knowledge they employ to make and use objects. For example, the occupants of the Wallace site, an Iroquoian village in Ontario, were agricultural and maintained a year-round presence at the community. Most of the crops and fruit were harvested in the fall but could be stored for extended periods. Leafy greens and strawberries would have been available earlier in the growing season. Most of the animals reported here are in the site area year-round. The few exceptions include the sandhill crane and common loon, which would have been in the area only during the spring and fall

migrations. The raven, a northern bird, may have been in the area during the winter, although it could have come to Wallace through trade. Resources came from the fields the Iroquois prepared, the habitats adjacent to the fields, and the nearby woodlands and wetlands (Figure 2.3). Few of the resources came from the deciduous and coniferous forests; the animals from those habitats are represented by only one or two individuals each. The nut and cherry trees are far more productive on forest edges than in the forest. Most of the resources came from close by. The bullheads, however, are from Lake Ontario, more than 40 kilometres away. Although this agricultural community had significantly altered the local environment, the results weren't particularly detrimental. After about 15 or 20 years, such villages were abandoned, perhaps having pushed the local environment to its limits.

Analysis of human skeletal material also provides important insights into ancient people's diets. Microscopic wear patterns on teeth, for example, may reveal whether abrasive plants were important foods. Similarly, people who eat more plants than meat will have a higher ratio of strontium to calcium in their bones. At the ancient Maya city of Tikal, analysis of human skeletons showed that elite members of society had access to better diets than lower-ranking members of society, allowing them to reach their full growth potential with greater regularity.

Important insights into life expectancy, mortality, and health status also emerge from the study of human skeletal remains. This subdiscipline of physical anthropology is **human osteology**. **Palaeopathology** is the study of disease in ancient populations, usually from evidence presented in bone. The examination of a 2800-year-old

Palaeoethnobotany. In archaeology, the analysis and interpretation of archaeological plant remains.

Archaeozoology. In archaeology, the analysis and interpretation of archaeological animal remains.

Technology. The knowledge that people employ to make and use objects.

Human osteology. The study of human skeletal remains.

Palaeopathology. The study of disease in ancient populations, usually from evidence presented in bone.

PLANT REMAINS	HABITAT	ANIMAL REMAINS	HABITAT
Cultigens		**Mammals (common)**	
common bean	1	beaver	5
corn/maize	1	bear	2, 3, 4
pumpkin/squash	1	deer	2, 3
sunflower	1	dog	—
tobacco	1	elk	2
Weedy Grains		**Mammals (rare)**	
chenopod	1, 2	eastern cottontail	3
grasses	1, 2	fisher	3, 4
knotweeds	1, 2	grey fox	2, 3
purslane	1, 2	grey squirrel	3
		marten	4
Fleshy Fruit		muskrat	5
American nightshade	1, 2	red squirrel	2, 3
blueberry	2	snowshoe hare	4
bramble	2		
cherry/plum	2, 3	**Birds**	
elderberry	1, 2	Canada goose	5
grape	2	hawk	1, 2, 3
ground cherry	1,2	passenger pigeon	3
hawthorn	2	raven	4
strawberry	1, 2	sandhill crane	4
		swan	5
Other Taxa		wild turkey	2, 3
bedstraw/cleaver	2		
cattail	5	**Fish**	
sumac	2	Atlantic salmon	5
wild rice	5	bullhead	5
		channel catfish	5
Nuts		sucker	5
acorn	2, 3		
butternut	2, 3	**Reptile**	
hickory	2, 3	frog/toad	5
		Amphibian	
		painted turtle	5

1: fields; 2: openings, forest edge; 3: deciduous forest; 4: coniferous forest; 5: aquatic

FIGURE 2.3

This is a simplified summary of plant and animal remains recovered from the Wallace site, an Iroquoian village in Ontario (A.D. 1500). The remains represent harvested, gathered, and hunted resources. All the plant remains are charred, while most of the animal bones are burned from cooking.

mummy on display at the Royal Ontario Museum in Toronto portrays a beautiful 35-year-old woman named Djed who was subjected to untold pain before her death. Nicholas Millet and Peter Lewin used a CT-scan of the mummified remains to avoid a destructive autopsy. They discovered dental pathologies that a normal examination might have missed. A large dental cyst in her jaw had deformed her face. It eventually burst, forcing pus through the bone into her body, poisoning her. They also found 13 smaller cysts and extensive gum disease. The enamel on her teeth was gone, probably having been eroded by the sand that was unavoidably present in the bread she ate. Any one of these maladies would have been intolerably painful.[9] Such studies have become

[9] Jack, Lee-Anne. (1995/96). The faces of Djed. *Rotunda, 28,* (3).

difficult to carry out, especially in the United States, as aboriginal communities demand (and federal law requires) the return of skeletons and associated artifacts from archaeological excavations for reburial. In Canada, there is no specific legislation requiring reburial, but anthropologists and First Nations have agreed to a protocol to be followed upon discovery of aboriginal human remains. Archaeologists find themselves in something of a quandary over this requirement; as scientists, they know the importance of the information that can be gleaned from studies of human skeletons, but as anthropologists, they are bound to respect the feelings of those whose ancestors those skeletons represent.

Public Archaeology

Archaeology not only studies the past for its own sake. The process of doing archaeology and the results of archaeology are relevant to people's lives today. Land entitlement, land development, local identity, tourism, and who has the right to museum collections are among the many issues that bring archaeology into the public eye. **Public archaeology** as a concept, particularly in North America, was first popularized in 1972 by Charles McGimsey who advocated for a state-sponsored archaeology program in order to preserve the archaeological record.[10] To McGimsey, all archaeology is public in the sense that everyone has a right to knowledge about the past. Today, public archaeology is any archaeological activity that interacts or has the potential to interact with the public[11] so in many ways it is a much larger discipline than academic or strictly research archaeology. Ultimately, public archaeology can serve as a vehicle to promote archaeology and conservation of heritage sites for future generations, and, most important of all, to make the past relevant to people of today.

One example of a sensitive public issue involving archaeology is the ownership and trade in artifacts and human remains. The issue is so important that international, national, and regional (e.g., provincial/state, municipal) policies and legislation have been developed. The UNESCO treaty of 1972, called the Convention Concerning the Protection of the World Cultural and Natural Heritage, seeks to encourage the identification, protection, and preservation of cultural and natural heritage around the world considered to be of outstanding value to humanity. Among its many purposes is to encourage international cooperation to preserve heritage and to support public awareness of heritage resources. NAGPRA (*The Native American Graves Protection and Repatriation Act*, 1990) in the United States provides a process for museums and federal agencies to return human remains, funerary objects, sacred objects, and objects of cultural patrimony to lineal descendants, culturally affiliated Indian tribes, and Native Hawaiian organizations. Canada does not have a law equivalent to NAGPRA but, as mentioned in the preceding section, Canadian archaeologists and First Nations follow a protocol similar to NAGPRA. Archaeological sites are protected by a variety of federal and provincial laws and regulations, all designed to preserve and manage archaeological sites and artifacts.

Repatriation of archaeological remains in Canada, especially burials, and collections of artifacts, has been an area where archaeologists and First Nations have had to come to terms. Returning materials of historical and spiritual significance in an appropriate fashion is an important goal of public archaeology. The Churchill River Diversion Archaeological Project: Post-Flood Survey demonstrates the way archaeologists and First Nations peoples can develop close working relationships.[12] When burials were recovered from the eroding shoreline of the Churchill River Diversion, project archaeologists consulted Nelson House First Nations elders on how to proceed. The burials were recovered according to the elders' wishes; a biological anthropologist was allowed to analyze the skeletal remains, and staff at the Manitoba Museum of Man and Nature illustrated, photographed, and made replicas of the recovered artifacts, then the skeletal remains and burial goods were returned for reburial. These activities have been augmented by frequent interpretive programs in the communities and the production of publications, such as *Kayasochi Kikawenow: Our Mother from Long*

---

[10] McGimsey C.R. (1972). *Public archeology*. New York: Seminar Press.

[11] Schadla-Hall T. (1999). Editorial: Public Archaeology. *European Journal of Archaeology*, 2, 147–158.

[12] Syms E.L. (1997). Increasing awareness and involvement of aboriginal people in their heritage preservation: Recent developments at the Manitoba Museum of Man and Nature. In G.P. Nicholas & T.D. Andrews, D. (Eds.) pp. 53–68. *At a crossroads: Archaeology and First Peoples in Canada*. Burnaby, B.C.: Archaeology Press.

Public archaeology. Any archaeological activity that interacts or has the potential to interact with the public.

Ago, an account of a young mother with her personal belongings who died in the late 17th century.

Generally, when First Nations and Inuit peoples become involved in archaeology, such as the Churchill River Diversion Archaeological Project, awareness of their cultural heritage increases dramatically, along with their concern for preserving it. Although the elders were saddened that the remains had been disturbed, they recognized the fortuitous opportunity to teach their young people more about ancient Cree heritage.

Leigh Syms, Curator of Archaeology at the Manitoba Museum of Man and Nature, makes the point that repatriation is not only about returning burials and sacred items to the descendant communities. It is also about building relationships based on mutual trust with First Nations peoples and providing educational opportunities, such as creating dynamic exhibits of original artifacts in educational exhibits, going into First Nations communities, and presenting educational workshops to students and teachers, thus bringing heritage to the people. Public archaeologists aim to distribute archaeological knowledge to a wide range of publics—descendant communities, aboriginal and nonaboriginal students, government agencies and authorities, businesspeople, developers, and the general public.

Treating the scientific and archaeological items as heritage items, by emphasizing their contribution to local heritage awareness, is another goal of public archaeology. Archaeologists make public the extraordinary level of skill required in manufacturing projectile points, producing ceramics, and creating works of art. Participatory action programs for First Nations peoples are also important in public archaeology, providing opportunities for First Nations peoples to train and work on excavations, develop and present interpretive programs, and identify conservation policies.

Museums are an important component of public archaeology—it is in museums that programs for restoring, exhibiting, and storing collections, as well as public education and outreach programs, are developed. At the Manitoba Museum of Man and Nature, staff provide numerous behind-the-scene tours in the archaeology lab that involve a large number of First Nations teachers and students, particularly adult students, in programs such as the Sharing Circle Training Program.

Besides interpreting cultural resources, a new endeavour, that of marketing and promoting unique

Some ancient societies devised precise ways of recording dates that archaeologists have been able to correlate with our own calendar. Here is the tomb of an important ruler, Stormy Sky, at the ancient Maya city of Tikal. The glyphs painted on the wall give the date of the burial in the Maya calendar, which is the same as March 18, A.D. 457, in our calendar. **UNIVERSITY MUSEUM, UNIVERSITY OF PENNSYLVANIA**

archaeological sites as tourism sites, has grown up over the last few decades. Two excellent examples of cultural tourism where First Nations peoples participated in the development of the interpretive programs and manage the centres are Head-Smashed-In Buffalo Jump, near Fort Macleod, Alberta, and Wanuskewin Heritage Park, near Saskatoon, Saskatchewan.

DATING THE PAST

With accurate and detailed records of their excavations in hand, archaeologists and palaeoanthropologists are able to deal with a question crucial to their research: the question of age. As we have seen, without knowledge of which materials are contemporary, older, or younger, no meaningful analysis is possible. How, then, are objects and events from the past reliably dated? Because archaeologists and palaeoanthropologists deal so often with peoples and events in times far removed from our own, the calendar of historic times is of little use to them. Therefore, they must rely on two kinds of dating: relative and "absolute." **Relative dating** consists simply of finding out if an event or object is younger or older than another. "**Absolute**" or (more properly) **chronometric dates** are dates based upon solar years and are reckoned in "years before the present" (B.P., with "present" defined as A.D. 1950). Many relative and chronometric techniques are available; here, there is space to discuss only the ones most often relied upon (others will be touched on as necessary in succeeding chapters). Ideally, archaeologists try to utilize as many methods as appropriate, given the materials available to work with and the funds at their disposal. By doing so, they significantly reduce the risk of arriving at erroneous dates.

Methods of Relative Dating

Of the many relative dating techniques available, **stratigraphy** is probably the most reliable. Stratigraphy is based on the simple principle that the oldest layer, or stratum, was deposited first (it is the deepest) whereas the newest layer was deposited last (in undisturbed situations, it lies at the top). Therefore, in an archaeological site the evidence is usually deposited in chronological order. The lowest stratum contains the oldest artifacts and/or fossils, whereas the uppermost stratum contains the most recent ones. Thus, even in the absence of precise dates, one knows the *relative* age of objects in one stratum compared with the ages of those in other strata.

Another common method of relative dating is **seriation.** Without knowing the actual ages of artifacts or groups of artifacts, they can be ordered using criteria such as complexity, decorations, or material that suggest a developmental sequence. Combined with stratigraphy to determine where to start the seriation, seriation can be a powerful tool.

Another method of relative dating is the **fluorine test.** It is based on the fact that the amount of fluorine deposited in bones is proportional to their age. The oldest bones contain the greatest amount of fluorine, and vice versa. The fluorine test is useful in dating bones that cannot be ascribed with certainty to any

particular stratum and cannot be dated according to the stratigraphic method. A shortcoming of this method is that the rate of fluorine formation is not constant, but varies from region to region.

Relative dating can also be done on the evidence of botanical and animal remains. A common method, known as **palynology,** involves the study of pollen grains. The kind of pollen found in any geologic stratum depends on the kind of vegetation that existed at the time that stratum was deposited. A site or locality can therefore be dated by determining what kind of pollen was found associated with it. In addition, palynology is also an important technique for reconstructing past environments in which people lived.

Another method, involving faunal analysis, relies on our knowledge of palaeontology. Sites containing the bones of extinct animal species are usually older than

---

[13] Fagan B.M., & Beck, C. (1996). *The Oxford companion to archaeology.* New York: Oxford University Press.

Relative dating. In archaeology and palaeoanthropology, designating an event, object, or fossil as being older or younger than another.

"Absolute" or chronometric dates. In archaeology and palaeoanthropology, dates for archaeological materials based on solar years, centuries, or other units of absolute time.

Stratigraphy. In archaeology and palaeoanthropology, the most reliable method of relative dating by means of strata.

Seriation. A method used to place artifacts in approximate chronological order based on the recognition of small-scale incremental changes in form or style. The method assumes that single artifacts or groups of artifacts that are most similar are closest to one another in time and space. Sequences based on seriation can be tied to absolute chronologies if one or more of the artifacts can be dated.[13]

Fluorine test. In archaeology or palaeoanthropology, a technique for relative dating based on the fact that the amount of fluorine in bones is proportional to their age.

Palynology. In archaeology and palaeoanthropology, a method of relative dating based on changes in fossil pollen over time.

sites in which the remains of these animals are absent. Very early North American First Nations sites have yielded the remains of mastodons and mammoths—animals now extinct—and on this basis the sites can be dated to a time before these animals died out, roughly 10 000 years ago. Even in the absence of extinct animal remains, faunal assemblages may provide clues to dating. Since the end of the Ice Age, climates have continued to change, in response to natural cycles as well as human activity. The resultant changes in ecology are reflected in the kinds of animal remains to be found. As one learns the sequence of changes, the presence or absence of particular animal species can give at least an approximate age for associated archaeological materials.

Methods of Chronometric Dating

One of the most widely used methods of "absolute" or chronometric dating is **radiocarbon analysis.** It is based on the fact that all living organisms absorb radioactive carbon (known as carbon 14), maintaining equilibrium with the level of this isotope in the atmosphere, and that this absorption ceases at the time of death. Carbon 14 is created in the atmosphere as a result of cosmic ray bombardment. Rapid mixing of the atmosphere means the amount of carbon 14 in the world is the same at any given time. It is possible to measure in the laboratory the amount of radioactive carbon left in even a few milligrams of a given organic substance, because radioactive substances break down or decay slowly and at a constant rate over a fixed period of time. Carbon 14 begins to disintegrate, returning to nitrogen 14, emitting radioactive (beta) particles in the process. At death, about 15 beta radiations per minute per gram of material are emitted. The rate of decay is known as "half-life," and the half-life of carbon 14 is 5730 years. This means that it takes 5730 years for one-half of the original amount of carbon 14 to decay into nitrogen 14. Beta radiation will be about 7.5 counts per minute per gram. In another 5730 years, one-half of this amount of carbon 14 will also have decayed. In other words, after 11 460 years, only one-fourth of the original amount of carbon 14 will be present. Thus the age of an organic substance such as charcoal, wood, shell, or bone can be measured by counting the beta rays emitted by the remaining carbon 14. The radiocarbon method can adequately date organic materials up to 70 000 years old and is the standard

method of dating such materials. Of course, one has to be sure that the association between organic remains and archaeological materials is valid. For example, charcoal found on a site may have arrived from a recent forest fire, rather than more ancient activity; or wood used to make something by the people who lived at a site may have been retrieved from some older context. Wood also grows annual rings, so if old wood from a 300-year-old tree, for example, is dated, the date will reflect a time several hundred years earlier, rather than the timing of the occupation. Hunted or domesticated animal bone and crops are the best items to date because they are the direct products of human activity and represent organisms with short lives. Selecting samples to radiocarbon-date has become easier since 1977, when a new technique for measuring the amount of carbon 14 in a sample was developed. The original radiocarbon-dating method was an estimate of the amount of carbon 14 in an organic sample. Using this method a sample is turned into a gas in a closed chamber and decays are counted, one by one. In order to know how much carbon 14 is left, the decay of nearly every remaining carbon 14 atom would need to be detected, but that is impossible. So an estimate based on the number of decays detected in a certain period is made. The estimate can be improved by using large amounts of organic material. Such a large amount is required that rarely is an actual artifact dated because it would be destroyed. What if we could directly measure the amount of carbon 14? Ted Litherland and his team at the University of Toronto helped develop a technique that can do just that. **Accelerator Mass Spectrometry (AMS)** dating is extremely sensitive because only about 50 milligrams of carbon is required to determine the

Radiocarbon analysis. In archaeology and palaeoanthropology, a technique for chronometric dating based on measuring the amount of radioactive carbon (C-14) left in organic materials found in archaeological sites.

Accelerator Mass Spectrometry. Also known as AMS dating, an innovation of regular mass spectrometry that determines the composition of a material by bombarding it with ions to separate and count the constituent atoms of a sample according to their mass. The quantity of carbon-14 can be directly measured using this technique.

The Accelerator Mass Spectrometer (AMS) system at the Isotrace laboratory, University of Toronto. The system is an innovation of regular mass spectrometry that determines the composition of a material by bombarding it with ions to separate and count the constituent atoms of a sample according to their mass. The AMS system is complex because it must accelerate ions to a much higher speed than in normal mass spectrometry in order to measure the extremely small amounts of carbon 14 found in ancient organic material. Using this technique, milligram samples of carbon such as found in grain seeds or threads in cloth can be dated. FROM HTTP://WWW.PHYSICS.UTORONTO.CA/~ISOTRACE/SEE "THE LAB" LINK IMAGE AT "THE AMS SYSTEM VIEWED FROM THE LOW ENERGY END"

mass of remaining carbon 14 using a nuclear accelerator. Small objects such as individual threads from clothing or small grains of crops can be dated.

Because there is always a certain amount of error involved, radiocarbon dates are not as absolute as is sometimes thought. This is why any stated date always has a plus-or-minus (±) factor attached to it. For example, a date of 5200 ± 120 years ago means that there is a 67 percent chance (a statistical standard) that the true date falls somewhere within the 240 years between 5080 and 5320 radiocarbon years ago. The qualification "radiocarbon years" is necessary, because we have discovered that radiocarbon years are not precisely equivalent to calendar years.

The discovery that radiocarbon years are not precisely equivalent to calendar years was made possible by another method of "absolute" dating, **dendrochronology.** First used in archaeology to date Pueblo Indian sites in the North American Southwest, this method is based on the fact that in the right kind of climate, trees add one (and only one) new growth ring to their trunks every year (Figure 2.4). The rings vary in thickness, depending upon the amount of rainfall received in a year, so that

> **Dendrochronology.** In archaeology, a method of chronometric dating based on the number of rings of growth found in a tree trunk.

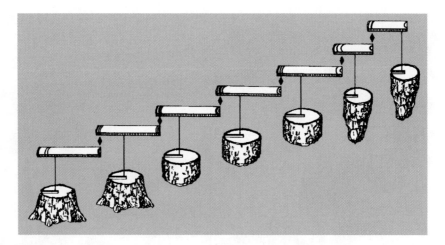

FIGURE 2.4

Chronometric dating based on tree rings is called *dendrochronology*. Starting with a sample of known age, ring patterns toward the inner part are matched with those from the outer part of the older sample, and so on, back in time.

climatic fluctuation is registered in the growth ring. By taking a sample of wood, such as a beam from a Pueblo Indian house, and by comparing its pattern of rings with those in the trunk of a tree known to be as old as the artifact, archaeologists can date the archaeological material. Dendrochronology is applicable only to wooden objects. Furthermore, it can be used only in regions in which trees of great age, such as the giant sequoias and the bristlecone pine, are known to grow. On the other hand, radiocarbon dating of wood from bristlecone pines that have been dated by dendrochronology allows us to correct carbon 14 dates so as to bring them into agreement with calendar dates. The cosmic rays that create carbon 14 are not constant over time, so radiocarbon dates need to account for the fluctuation of carbon 14 in the atmosphere and oceans over time. At 10 000 years ago, radiocarbon dates are as much as 2000 years off.

Potassium-argon analysis, another commonly used method of "absolute" dating, is based on a technique similar to that of radiocarbon analysis. It is used to date rock from the beginning of the earth up to about 100 000 years ago. Following intense heating, as from a volcanic eruption, radioactive potassium decays at a known rate to form argon, any previously existing argon having been released by the heating. The half-life of radioactive potassium is 1.3 billion years. Deposits that

are millions of years old can now be dated by measuring the ratio of potassium to argon in a given rock. Volcanic debris, such as at Olduvai Gorge and other localities in East Africa, is routinely dated by potassium-argon analysis; thus we know when the volcanic eruption occurred. If fossils or artifacts are found sandwiched between layers of volcanic ash, as they are at Olduvai and other sites in East Africa, they can therefore be dated with some precision. But as with radiocarbon dates, there are limits to that precision, and potassium-argon dates are always stated with a plus-or-minus margin of error attached.

Amino acid racemization dating, yet another chronometric technique, is of potential importance because it bridges a time gap between the effective ranges of the radiocarbon and potassium-argon methods. It is based on the fact that amino acids have left-handed and

Potassium-argon analysis. In archaeology and palaeoanthropology, a technique for chronometric dating that measures the ratio of radioactive potassium to argon in volcanic debris associated with human remains.

Amino acid racemization dating. In archaeology and palaeoanthropology, a technique for chronometric dating that measures the ratio of right- to left-handed amino acids.

In this photo, geologist Carl Swisher orients a rock sample for palaeomagnetic dating. This method of dating is based on the fact that the earth's magnetic pole has shifted over time. For example, magnetically charged particles in sediments between 1.8 and 1.6 million years old document a reversal, and fossils found in such sediments can be dated accordingly. **KENNETH GARRETT/NGS IMAGE COLLECTION**

right-handed forms. The amino acids trapped in organic materials gradually change, or "racemize" after death, from left-handed forms to right-handed forms. Thus, the ratio of left- to right-handed forms should indicate the specimen's age. Unfortunately, in substances like bone, moisture and acids in the soil can leach out the amino acids, thereby introducing a serious source of error. However, ostrich eggshells have proved immune to this problem, the amino acids being so effectively locked up in a tight mineral matrix that they are preserved for thousands of years. Because ostrich eggs were widely used as food, and the shells as containers in Africa and the Middle East, they provide a powerful means of dating sites of the middle part of the Old Stone Age (Palaeolithic), between 40 000 and 180 000 years ago.

Radiocarbon, potassium-argon, and amino acid racemization dating are only three of several high-tech dating methods that have been developed in the past few decades. Radiocarbon and potassium-argon, in particular, are the chronometric methods most heavily relied on by archaeologists and palaeoanthropologists; nevertheless, other methods are increasingly used as a check on accuracy and to supplement dates determined by other means. To cite one example, a technique called **electron spin resonance** measures the trapped electron population in bone or shell (the number of trapped electrons indicates the specimen's age). Because electron spin resonance dates derived from an important Middle Palaeolithic skull from Qafzeh, Israel (discussed in Chapter 9), agree with those based on amino acid racemization, we can have confidence that the dating is correct. Because other methods of chronometric dating are often complicated, they tend to be expensive; many can be carried out only on specific kinds of materials and, in the case of some, are so new that their reliability is not yet unequivocally established. It is for these reasons that they have not been as widely used as radiocarbon and potassium-argon analysis.

> **Electron spin resonance.** In archaeology and palaeoanthropology, a technique for chronometric dating that measures the number of trapped electrons in bone or shell.

BIOGRAPHY

Dr. David Meyer

Growing up on the Canadian plains, David Meyer acquired a permanent interest in the archaeology of the region. The subject of his master's thesis was a Palaeo-Inuit site in the Churchill, Manitoba, region. In the 1970s, he undertook ethnographic and historical research at Red Earth, a Plains Cree community in east central Saskatchewan. It later became his Ph.D. dissertation.

In 1974, Meyer directed the archaeology portion of the Churchill River Study, an early environmental impact study in northern Saskatchewan. This project resulted in a lasting research interest in the prehistory of the northern forests. The Churchill River work led, in 1976, to a permanent position as an archaeological consultant with the Saskatchewan Research Council. Over the next decade he worked on many archaeological projects, widely scattered from northernmost Saskatchewan south to the Montana border. One of the largest projects was the Nipawin Reservoir Heritage Study in 1981–85. During this time Meyer enlarged upon an early interest, the pre-contact pottery assemblages of the northern forests of Saskatchewan, Manitoba, and Ontario, developing this interest into a broader expertise in archaeological pottery. In particular, he researched and published on the late pre-contact Selkirk culture and its pottery.

In 1988, Meyer joined the faculty of the Department of Anthropology and Archaeology (now the Department of Archaeology) at the University of Saskatchewan. Since that time he has been involved in a number of field projects, including those at Cumberland House and southern Reindeer Lake. He has explored the social geography of boreal forest hunter-gatherers, especially the annual or biannual ingatherings. Of special interest has been the articulation of archival, ethnographic, and archaeological data in the identification and understanding of particular ingathering locales.

At present, Meyer is involved in a large, multiyear and multiuniversity research project involving the collaboration of nine researchers in four provinces and one state. His portion of the project involves the investigation of archaeological sites in the region of the confluence of the North and South Saskatchewan Rivers. Here, he has been directing the excavation of a 6000 B.P. occupation, and excavating sites dating from the last 2000 years. This work involves geoarchaeological and palaeoenvironmental studies, as well as archival research and consultation with Cree elders in this region.

CHAPTER SUMMARY

Archaeology and biological anthropology, though they do not neglect the present, are the two branches of anthropology most involved in the study of the human past. Archaeologists study material remains to describe and explain human behaviour; biological anthropologists called palaeoanthropologists study fossil remains to understand and explain the processes at work in human biological evolution. Each specialty contributes to the other's objectives, as well as its own, and the two share many methods of data recovery.

Artifacts are objects fashioned or altered by humans, such as a flint chip, a pottery vessel, or even a house. A fossil is any trace of an organism that lived over 10 000 years ago that has been preserved in the earth's crust. Fossilization typically involves the hard parts of an organism and is most apt to occur among animals and other organisms that live in or near water because of the likelihood that their corpses will be buried and preserved on sea, lake, and river bottoms. On land, conditions in caves or near active volcanic activity may be conducive to fossilization.

Places containing archaeological remains of previous human occupation are known as sites. Sometimes human fossils are present at archaeological sites, but they may occur by themselves at fossil localities. Sites and localities are generally located by a survey of a region. While fossil localities are revealed by the presence of fossils, archaeological sites are revealed by the presence of artifacts. Irregularities of the ground surface, unusual soil discoloration, and unexpected variations in vegetation type and colouring may also indicate the location of a site. Ethnohistorical data—maps, documents, and folklore—may provide further clues to the location of archaeological sites. Sometimes both fossils and archaeological remains are discovered accidentally, for example, in plowing, quarrying, or building construction.

Once a site or locality has been selected for excavation, the area is divided and carefully marked with a grid system; the starting point of the dig is called the datum point. Each square within the grid is carefully excavated, and any archaeological or fossil remains are recovered through employment of various tools and screens; for very fine objects, the method of flotation is employed. The location of each artifact when found must be carefully noted. Once excavated, artifacts and fossils undergo further cleaning and preservation in the laboratory with the use of specialized tools and chemicals.

The durability of archaeological evidence depends upon climate and the nature of the artifacts. Inorganic materials are more resistant to decay than organic ones. However, given a very dry climate, even organic materials may be well preserved. Warm, moist climates as well as thick vegetation act to decompose organic material quickly, and even inorganic material may suffer from the effects of humidity and vegetation growth. The durability of archaeological evidence is also dependent upon the social customs of ancient people.

Because excavation in fact destroys a site, the archaeologist must maintain a thorough record in the form of maps, descriptions, scale drawings, and photographs of every aspect of the excavation. All artifacts must be cleaned and classified before being sent to the laboratory for analysis. Often the shape and markings of artifacts can determine their function, and the analysis of vegetable and animal remains may provide information.

There are two kinds of methods for dating archaeological and fossil remains. Relative dating means determining the age of objects relative to one another and includes the methods of stratigraphy, based on the position of the artifact or fossil in relation to different layers of soil deposits, and seriation, which orders artifacts in a sequence. The fluorine test is based on the determination of the amount of fluorine deposited in the bones. The analysis of floral remains (including palynology) and faunal deposits is also widely employed. Methods of "absolute," or chronometric, dating include radiocarbon analysis, which measures the amount of carbon 14 that remains in organic objects; potassium-argon analysis, which measures the percentage of radioactive potassium that has decayed to argon in volcanic material; dendrochronology, dating based upon tree rings; and amino acid racemization, based on changes from left- to right-handed amino acids in organic materials, especially eggshells. Other chronometric methods exist, such as electron spin resonance, but are not as widely used, because of limited applicability, difficulty of application, expense, or (as-yet) unproven reliability.

QUESTIONS FOR CRITICAL THOUGHT

1. How does preservation affect our knowledge of the past?

2. What can we learn about a culture from the preserved remains of a single individual such as Kwäday Dän Ts'ínchi? What could be learned about our culture from the remains of one of us (you, for example)?

3. The desire for the repatriation of aboriginal artifacts has resulted in many requests to museums in Canada to return items to First Nations. Should museums return control of cultural items to the descendant communities? Should archaeologists excavate ancient burials? Why or why not?

4. Why are looted artifacts of little or no scientific value?

INTERNET RESOURCES

Anthropology in the News

www.tamu.edu/anthropology/news.html
A collection of timely articles on numerous archaeological and palaeoanthropological topics. Check this site regularly for new articles.

Archaeology of Arctic North America

http://watarts.uwaterloo.ca/ANTHRO/rwpark/ArcticArchStuff/ArcticIntro.html
This University of Waterloo site provides information on numerous topics, including the Arctic environment, fieldwork, the archaeological sequences of the Thule culture, and many links to other sites.

http://arcticcircle.uconn.edu/index.html
Introduces history, culture, and ethnography of the Arctic.

Archaeology of Canada (A selection)

www.sfu.ca/archaeology/museum
www.moa.ubc.ca
www.royalalbertamuseum.ca/human/archaeo/intro.htm
www.royalsaskmuseum.ca/index.shtml
www.manitobamuseum.mb.ca/mu_human_hist.html
www.uwo.ca/museum
www.virtualmuseum.ca/Exhibitions/Echo/html/e-echos-0402.html
www.gnb.ca/0131/archaeology/index-e.asp
http://museum.gov.ns.ca/arch
www.gov.pe.ca/peimhf/index.php3
www.nfmuseum.com/museum.htm
These websites provide access to local archaeological information throughout Canada.

ArchNet

http://archnet.asu.edu/regions/regions.php
A virtual library of archaeological resources. It provides links to academic departments, museums, journals, and various subjects, such as ceramics, archaeometry, botany, ethnohistory, ethnoarchaeology, geoarchaeology, and historic archaeology.

Bluefish Caves in Beringian Prehistory

www.civilisations.ca/academ/articles/cinq1_1e.html
Part site report, part historical examination, this site is a good example of the information that archaeological excavations can provide about people who lived in the past.

Canadian First Nations Ceramics

www.civilization.ca/archeo/ceramiq/cerart1e.html
An interesting and site that focuses on pre-contact pottery in Canada. It includes a virtual exhibit tour, an explanation of pottery-making techniques, and historical and ethnographic information on the First Nations peoples of Canada and their craft.

www.civilization.ca/cmc/archeo/ehome.htm
Learn about the efforts of museum archaeologists to broaden our understanding of the ancient history of Canada.

Canadian Museum of Civilization

www.civilization.ca/cmc/archeo/ouverte.html
Introduces students to the Archaeological Survey of Canada, the archaeology division of the Canadian Museum of Civilization, its history, current research, field reports, etc.

Head-Smashed-In Buffalo Jump

www.head-smashed-in.com

A comprehensive website that provides extensive archaeological information on Head-Smashed-In, designated a UNESCO world heritage site. Some of the links include legends, anatomy, history, recent excavations, and future plans for the site.

Human Evolution

www.talkorigins.org/faqs/homs/specimen.html

A listing of hominin fossils, with detailed discussion of their morphological and sometimes cultural features. A creationist argument is also presented for some of these specimens.

Iceman

www.bbc.co.uk/science/horizon/2001/iceman.shtml

A concise summary of research on the frozen remains of a man found in the mountains between Austria and Italy. The site has a transcript of a 2002 documentary on the discovery.

Legislation and Archaeology in Canada

www.pc.gc.ca/docs/r/pfa-fap/index_e.asp

Provides information about legislation relevant to archaeology on federal land in Canada.

Public Archaeology

http://archnet.asu.edu/topical/crm/crmint.html

A comprehensive listing of resources related to cultural protection and cultural resource management, including international legislation.

Underwater Archaeological Preserves

http://dhr.dos.state.fl.us/bar/uap

This site goes underwater to visit the State of Florida's Underwater Preserves. Visit the shipwrecked remains of battleships, steamers, and sailboats. Each shipwreck site contains a location map and a complete site plan as well as ways to become involved in Florida's Underwater Archaeology Program.

UNESCO (United Nations Educational, Scientific and Cultural Organization)

http://whc.unesco.org/en/about

A comprehensive look at World Heritage and the UNESCO Convention that is designed to protect important sites around the world.

University of Pennsylvania Museum of Archaeology and Anthropology

www.upenn.edu/museum

The award-winning interactive website of the University of Pennsylvania's Museum of Archaeology and Anthropology; experience the museum's fabulous collections. You can tour everything from virtual excavations being conducted by Penn faculty in places such as Mesoamerica and Central Asia, to the treasures housed in the Egyptian gallery, to virtual exhibits on the origins and ancient history of wine.

SUGGESTED READINGS

For a list of suggested readings, visit the textbook's website at www.humanevolution2.nelson.com.

CHAPTER 3

Biology and Evolution

Biology and its central theory, evolution, are vital for meeting the challenge of knowing ourselves as culture-bearing organisms. While human culture represents one of the most complex manifestations of life on earth, from a scientific standpoint, the evolution of humans is not a story of progressive improvement. Variations on the same genetic processes are shared across all organisms. The evolution of each species involves a unique history combining random events and adaptation to the local environment.

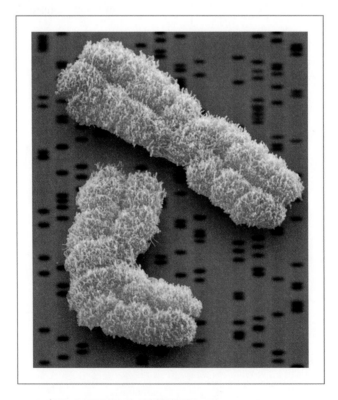

ANDREW SYRED/PHOTO RESEARCHERS, INC.

CHAPTER PREVIEW

1. What Forces Are Responsible for the Diversity of Primates in the World Today?

Although all primates—lemurs, lorises, tarsiers, monkeys, apes, and humans—share a common ancestry, they have come to differ through the evolutionary forces that have permitted them to adapt to a variety of environments in a variety of ways. Although biologists agree upon the fact of evolution, they are still unravelling the details of how it has proceeded.

2. What Is Evolution and How Does It Produce New Forms of Organisms?

Biological evolution is "descent with modification," as descendant populations come to differ from ancestral ones. Evolution happens as differential reproduction changes the frequency of a population's genetic variants from one generation to another over time. Evolution may proceed in a branching manner, when isolating mechanisms prevent gene flow between separated populations. Then drift and selection may proceed in different ways, leading to the appearance first of divergent subspecies and then of separate species. In the absence of isolation, a species as a whole may evolve in a linear manner through variational change in response to environmental changes. How new species arise is a matter of some controversy. Darwinian theorists propose that species arise through the gradual accumulation of changes while punctuated evolution proponents feel that new species arise quickly. Fossils can be assigned to the same or different species depending on how one views evolution proceeding.

3. What Are the Forces Responsible for Evolution?

Evolution works as mutation produces genetic variation, which is acted upon by drift (accidental changes in frequencies of gene variants in a population), gene flow (the introduction of new gene variants from other populations), and natural selection. Natural selection is the adaptive mechanism of evolution, favouring individuals with genetic variants that are adaptive and who produce more surviving offspring than those without.

CHAPTER OUTLINE

Humans have long had close contact with other animals. Some—such as dogs, horses, and cows—have lived close to people for so long that little attention is paid to their behaviour. We are interested only in how well they do what they were bred for—companionship, racing, milk production, or whatever. Domestic animals are so dependent on humans that they have lost many of the behavioural traits of their wild ancestors.

By contrast, wild animals, especially exotic ones, have always fascinated people, as the popularity of circuses and zoos attests. In cultures very different from those of the industrialized countries of the world—those of some First Nations peoples, for example—people can have a special relationship with particular animals, believing their fates to be intertwined. Such companion animals may be called upon for assistance to serve as messengers, or the person may be able to transfer his or her state of being into the animal's body.

A curious feature of this interest is the desire of humans to see animals as mirror images of themselves, a phenomenon known as **anthropomorphism.** Stories in which animals talk, wear clothes, and exhibit human virtues and vices go back to antiquity. Many children today learn of Mickey Mouse or Kermit the Frog and Miss Piggy; the animals created by Walt Disney, Jim Henson, and many others have become an integral part of contemporary North American culture. Occasionally one sees on television trained apes dressed like humans eating at a table, pushing a stroller, or riding a tricycle. They are amusing because they look so "human."

Over the ages, people have trained animals to perform tricks, making them mimic human behaviour. But in the Western world people never suspected the full extent of the relationship they have with animals. For centuries, Christianity—the dominant religion of the West—preached that humans and animals were quite separate from one another. Nevertheless, the close biological tie between humans and the other **primates**—the group of animals that, besides humans, includes lemurs, lorises, tarsiers, monkeys, and apes—is now better understood. The diversity of primates existing today is the product of **evolution,** defined by Darwin in his most famous book as *descent with modification*. Over time the operation of evolutionary forces permitted primates to adapt to environments in a variety of ways. These evolutionary forces are the subject of this chapter.

THE CLASSIFICATION OF LIVING THINGS

Crucial to our understanding of the place of humanity among animals was the invention by the 18th-century Swedish naturalist Carl von Linné of a system to classify living things. The problem the Linnaean system addressed was simply to create order in the great mass of confusing biological data that had accumulated in the wake of European exploration and exploitation of foreign lands. At the same time, discovering and naming the multitude of creatures was seen as a means of demonstrating the glory of God's creation.

Von Linné—or Linnaeus, as he is generally called—classified living things on the basis of overall similarities into small groups, or species. Modern classification, while retaining the structure of the Linnaean system, has gone beyond this by distinguishing superficial similarities among organisms—called **analogies**—from basic ones—called **homologies.** The latter are possessed by organisms that share a common ancestry; even though homologous structures may serve different functions (the hand of a human and the front paw of a dog, for instance), they arise in similar fashion and pass through similar stages in embryonic development prior to their ultimate differentiation. By contrast, analogous structures look similar and may serve the same purpose (the wings of birds and butterflies, for example), but they are built from different parts and do not pass through similar stages in embryonic development; nor do the organisms share a common ancestry.

Anthropomorphism.   The ascription of human attributes to nonhuman beings.

Primates.   The group of mammals that includes lemurs, lorises, tarsiers, monkeys, apes, and humans.

Evolution.   Descent with modification.

Analogies.   In biology, structures that are superficially similar; the result of convergent evolution.

Homologies.   In biology, structures possessed by two different organisms that arise in similar fashion and pass through similar stages during embryonic development.

Birds and butterflies exemplify analogy: Both have wings that are used for flight, but the wings are built differently. D. ROBERT & LORRI FRANZ/
CORBIS (LEFT), MICHAEL J. DOOLITTLE/THE IMAGE WORKS (RIGHT)

On the basis of homologies, as in Linnaeus's original system, groups of like **species** (a species is defined today as a population or group of populations capable of interbreeding that is reproductively isolated from other such populations) are organized into larger, more inclusive groups, called **genera** (the singular term is *genus*). The characteristics on which Linnaeus based his system were the following:

1. *Body structure:* A Guernsey cow and a Holstein cow are of the same species because they have identical body structure. A cow and a horse do not.
2. *Body function:* Cows and horses bear their young in the same way. Although they are of different species, they are closer than either cows or horses are to chickens, which lay eggs and have no mammary glands.
3. *Sequence of bodily growth:* Both cows and chickens give birth to—or hatch out of the egg—fully formed young. They are therefore more closely related to each other than either one is to the frog, whose tadpoles undergo a series of changes before attaining adult form.

Species are not arbitrary because they are breeding populations, and we can observe that species members reproduce only with members of the same species to produce fertile offspring. Exceptions to this are more common than one might think, particularly in the plant kingdom, but species is the only taxonomic category that is not based on interpretations of relationships. For example, all dogs belong to the same species, but a male Saint Bernard and a female Chihuahua would surely have trouble with the feat of copulation. On the other hand, Alaskan sled dogs are able to breed with wolves, even though they are of different species. In nature, however, wolves most often mate with their own kind. Although all species definitions are relative rather than absolute, the modern concept of species puts more stress on the question of whether breeding actually takes place in the wild than on the more academic question of whether breeding is technically feasible. After all, gibbons and siamangs, two different species of small apes, sometimes produce live offspring in captivity but none have been found in the wild. This species definition means that proposing a fossil species is an interpretation based on theorized relationships because reproduction patterns are not observable in the fossil record. Classification of fossils is based mainly on structure and, depending on the extent of the record, function and growth.

Modern taxonomy (scientific classification) is based on more than body structure, function, and growth. One must also compare chemical reactions of blood, protein structure, and the genetic material itself. Even comparison of parasites is useful, for they tend to show the same degree of relationship as the forms they infest.

Species. In biology, a population or group of populations that is capable of interbreeding but that is reproductively isolated from other such populations.

Genera; genus. In the system of plant and animal classification, a group of like species.

An example of homology: Fish have gills but humans do not. Gill structures do develop in the human embryo but then are modified to serve other purposes. From the rudimentary, gill-like structures are built such things as the jaw, bones of the inner ear, thymus, and parathyroid glands. CLEO PHOTOGRAPHY/PHOTO EDIT (LEFT), COLIN MILKINS, OXFORD SCIENTIFIC FILMS/ANIMALS ANIMALS/MAXX IMAGES (RIGHT)

Through careful comparison and analysis, Linnaeus and those who have come after him have been able to classify specific animals into a series of larger and more inclusive groups up to the largest and most inclusive of all, the animal kingdom. Table 3.1 shows the main categories of the Linnaean system applied to the classification of the human species, with a few of the more important distinguishing features noted for each category. (Other categories of primates will be addressed in Chapter 4.)

Notochord. A rod-like structure of cartilage that, in vertebrates, is replaced by the vertebral column.

TABLE 3.1   Classification of Humans

Kingdom	Animalia	Do not make their own food, but depend on intake of living food
Phylum	Chordata	Have at some stage gill slits as well as a **notochord** (a rod-like structure of cartilage) and nerve cord running along the back of the body
Subphylum*	Vertebrata	Notochord replaced by vertebral column ("backbone") to form internal skeleton along with skull, ribs, and limb bones
Class	Mammalia	Maintain constant body temperature; young nourished after birth by milk from mother's mammary glands
Order	Primates	Hands and feet capable of grasping; tendency to erect posture; acute development of vision rather than sense of smell; tendency to large brains
Superfamily	Hominoidea	Rigid bodies, broad shoulders, and long arms; ability to hang vertically from arms; no tail
Family	Hominidae	As above but 98% identical at genetic level
Subfamily	Homininae	Ground-dwelling with bipedal locomotion
Genus	*Homo*	Large brains; reliance on cultural, as opposed to biological adaption
Species	*sapiens*	Brains of modern size; relatively small faces

*Most categories can be expanded or narrowed by adding the prefix "sub" or "super." A family could thus be part of a superfamily, and in turn contain two or more subfamilies.

THE DISCOVERY OF EVOLUTION

As Linnaeus and his contemporaries went about their business of classification, no thought was given to the possibility that species might not be fixed and unchangeable. Rather, species were seen as being just as they had always been since the time of creation. Creationism has not gone away because all societies have creation explanations. This includes First Nations and the many religious traditions brought from around the world to North America. Some organized groups want a particular form of Judeo-Christian creationism taught in schools as a legitimate alternative to evolution. Creationism is *not* a subject to be dealt with in this text because it is based on a belief system rather than on scientific evidence. The most prominent opponents of evolution are fundamentalist Christians who feel that evolution contradicts their belief in the truth of the Bible. Throughout the centuries science has been viewed by many as an attack on the Christian faith. Galileo's support of the Copernican theory that the earth revolved around the sun and that the earth was not the centre of the universe is one example. Galileo's scientifically based model was considered such a challenge to the faith of his time that he was considered a criminal.

Douglas Futuyama has written extensively about the issue of modern opposition to evolution.[1] He focuses on the Creation Research Society (CRS), which has the most active group of critics. Members of the CRS must minimally have a Masters degree in a science and must also believe that the Bible is historically and scientifically accurate. The biblical perspective is that the earth was created in six days, each species was individually created, and all creatures were created for the benefit of people. Creation scientists are well aware that they must appear to be scientifically legitimate because religion is based on faith rather than empirical evidence. However, if their Christian faith can somehow be construed to appear scientific then they appear to be engaging evolutionary scholars on their own terms. But are they? Futuyama points out the creationists' position is that evolution cannot be proven. This is quite true because it capitalizes on a common misunderstanding of how science operates. In fact, scientists don't prove their propositions, they *test* them. If a proposition cannot be negated by the evidence, then it becomes stronger and can be called a theory. Creation scientists are not testing their own views because the Bible to

them is true, so they aren't practising science the way true scientists do. If they were, they would actually try to refute the Bible. Creation scientists respond to this issue by insisting that evolution is, in fact, a religion because evolution cannot be refuted by observations. In fact, it can. Futuyama points out that if a mammal fossil was found in Precambrian-age rocks, then the theory of evolution would be refuted. Creationism is a belief system grounded in faith in the Bible, so it is not a science. Being a Christian for many scientists is still compatible with doing science because the creation stories found in all societies are not meant to be taken literally.

Despite the fact that some people still prefer creationism as an explanation for our existence, the process of classification of organisms made naturalists increasingly aware of continuities among different forms of life. Such continuities were not surprising because in the 18th century Europeans commonly believed in a chain of being, a gradation of all things from God to the lowest and most material. This thinking actually facilitated consideration of the idea of evolution. But the concept of extinction was at odds with the concept of God because people thought that God would not let organisms disappear. Hiding fossils was simply God's way of having fun. Nevertheless, natural history was encouraged and comparative anatomy flourished. Inevitably, scholars such as Linnaeus (who was not an evolutionist) collected and organized information that would ultimately be fundamental to understanding evolution. At the same time, earth moving for construction and mining associated with developing industrialism brought to light all sorts of fossils of past life that had to be explained. With industrialization, the idea of progress became ever more prominent in European thought.

French naturalist Jean Baptiste Lamarck further influenced our thinking about species by proposing that they changed and that acquired characteristics could be inherited.[2] The changing needs of an organism, such as the need to get at leaves high in trees, led to the stretched neck of the giraffe. Each generation of giraffe inherited the stretched anatomy. George Cuvier, a geologist, was

---

[1] Futuyama D.J. (1995). *Science on trial: The case for evolution.* Sunderland: Sinauer Associates.

[2] Lamarck J.B. (1809). *Philosophie zoologique, ou, Exposition des considérations relative à l'histoire naturelle des animaux.* Paris: Chez Dentu [et] L'Auteur.

aware that different layers of sedimentary rock held different types of fossils.[3] This observation was consistent with a widely held view that layers of rock were a result of a series of divine catastrophes such as the biblical flood in the story of Noah's arc. Therefore, the layers of fossils were evidence of new acts of divine creation. This view has come to be known as **catastrophism**. Other geologists recognized gradual processes sculpting the landscape. Wind and rain slowly eroded rock, and such slow-acting processes were responsible for changes through time. The forces shaping the contemporary world were no different in the past. This view is known as **uniformitarianism**. Charles Lyell published a landmark book, *Principles of Geology*, in which he detailed the processes that formed the earth.[4] He was able to define certain geological epochs by using fossils. Charles Darwin was a fan of Lyell's work and they soon became friends.

In hindsight, it seems inevitable that someone would hit upon the idea of evolution. So it was that, by the start of the 19th century, many naturalists had come to accept the idea that life had evolved, even though they were not clear about how it happened. It remained for Charles Darwin, midway through the century, to discover how evolution worked. Interestingly, he was not alone in his discovery. A Welshman, Alfred Russell Wallace, independently came up with the same idea at the same time. That idea was **natural selection**, and it is based on two observations: All organisms display a range of variation, and all have the ability to expand beyond their means of subsistence. It follows that, in their "struggle for existence," organisms with advantageous variations for survival in a particular environment will do better than those without them, thereby

reproducing with greater success. Thus, as generation succeeds generation, nature selects the most advantageous variations, and species evolve. So obvious did the idea seem in hindsight that Thomas Huxley, one of the pillars of 19th-century British science, remarked, "How extremely stupid of me not to have thought of that."[5]

If Darwin's idea was so straightforward, why did it arouse such controversy? It wasn't so much that species were no longer seen as changeless entities that were set at the time of divine creation (as Linnaeus and his contemporaries thought); after all, emerging evolutionary ideas recognized that species were not fixed and immutable. But, before Darwin, evolution could still be seen as progressive, leading inexorably and predictably to humans, who stood at the pinnacle. After Darwin, this was no longer possible, as palaeontologist Stephen Jay Gould explains in the following Original Study.

[3] Cuvier G. (1812). *Recherches sur les ossemens fossiles de quadrupedes; ou, L'on rétablit les caractères de plusieurs espèces animaux que les révolutions du globe paroissent avoir détruites.* Paris: Chez Deterville.

[4] Lyell C. (1868). *Principles of geology.* New York: Appleton.

[5] Quoted in Durant, J.C. (2000, April 23). Everybody into the gene pool. *The New York Times Book Review,* p. 11.

Catastrophism. The view that layers of fossils were evidence of new acts of divine creation.

Uniformitarianism. The view that forces shaping the contemporary world were no different in the past.

Natural selection. The evolutionary process through which factors in the environment exert pressure that favours some individuals over others to produce the next generation.

ORIGINAL STUDY

The Unsettling Nature of Variational Change

The Darwinian principle of natural selection yields temporal change—evolution in the biological definition—by the twofold process of producing copious and undirected variation within a population and then passing along only a biased (selected) portion of this variation

to the next generation. In this manner, the variation within a population at any moment can be converted into differences in mean values (average size, average braininess) among successive populations through time. For this fundamental reason, we call such theories of change *variational* as opposed to the more conventional, and more direct, models of *transformational* change imposed by natural laws that mandate a particular trajectory based on inherent (and therefore predictable) properties of substances and environments. (A ball rolling down an inclined plane does not reach the bottom because selection has favoured the differential propagation of moving versus stable elements of its totality but because gravity dictates this result when round balls roll down smooth planes.)

To illustrate the peculiar properties of variational theories like Darwin's in an obviously caricatured, but not inaccurate, description: Suppose that a population of elephants inhabits Siberia during a warm interval before the advance of an ice sheet. The elephants vary, at random, and in all directions, in their amount of body hair. As the ice advances and local conditions become colder, elephants with more hair will tend to cope better, by the sheer good fortune of their superior adaptation to changing climates—and they will leave more offspring on average. (This differential reproductive success must be conceived as broadly statistical and not guaranteed in every case: In any generation, the hairiest elephant of all may fall into a crevasse and die.) Because offspring inherit their parents' degree of hairiness, the next generation will contain a higher proportion of more densely clad elephants (who will continue to be favoured by natural selection as the climate becomes still colder). This process of increasing hairiness may continue for many generations, leading to the evolution of woolly mammoths.

This little fable can help us understand how peculiar and how contrary to all traditions of Western thought and explanation the Darwinian theory of evolution, and variational theories of historical change in general, must sound to the common ear. All the odd and fascinating properties of Darwinian evolution—the sensible and explainable but quite unpredictable nature of the outcome (dependent upon complex and contingent changes in local environments), the

nonprogressive character of the alteration (adaptive only to these unpredictable local circumstances and not inevitably building a "better" elephant in any cosmic or general sense)—flow from the variational basis of natural selection.

Transformational theories work in a much simpler and more direct manner. If I want to go from A to B, I will have so much less conceptual (and actual) trouble if I can postulate a mechanism that will push me there directly than if I must rely upon the selection of "a few good men" from a random cloud of variation about point A, then constitute a new generation around an average point one step closer to B, then generate a new cloud of random variation about this new point, then select "a few good men" once again from this new array—and then repeat this process over and over until I finally reach B.

When one adds the oddity of variational theories in general to our strong cultural and psychological resistance against their application to our own evolutionary origin (as an unpredictable and not necessary progressive little twig on life's luxuriant tree), then we can better understand why Darwin's revolution surpassed all other scientific discoveries in reformatory power and why so many people still fail to understand, and may even resist, its truly liberal content. (I must leave the issue of liberation for another time, but once we recognize that the specification of morals and the search for a meaning to our lives cannot be accomplished by scientific study in any case, then Darwin's variational mechanism will no longer seem threatening and may even become liberating in teaching us to look within ourselves for answers to these questions and to abandon a chimerical search for the purpose of our lives, and for the source of our ethical values, in the external workings of nature.)

Source: Gould, S.J. (2000). What does the dreaded "E" word mean, anyway? *Natural History, 109* (1), 34–36. Copyright © the American Museum of Natural History.

In order for natural selection to occur, a vast length of time is necessary for gradual changes to accumulate, and it was not until the early 19th century that the idea of vast time took hold as the field of geology developed. It was this that made Darwin and Wallace's formulation possible. Still, there was a problem: No one knew how variation arose in the first place, nor were the mechanisms of heredity understood. This gave Darwin difficulty for the rest of his life, and by the end of his century, Darwin's theory was rejected by many. Ironically, the information he needed was available by 1865, when an obscure monk in what is now the Czech

The most important fossil site in the world is the Burgess Shale in the Canadian Rocky Mountains. The 530-million-year-old fossil bed discovered in 1909 contains the most comprehensive record of the Cambrian Explosion when multicellular marine animal life (there were no terrestrial animals at the time) evolved and diversified at a rate never seen before or since. Many species there do not fit into any known phyla, and numerous animal forms found there no longer exist. The Burgess Shale fossils tell us that evolution involves large-scale deletions followed by differentiation of the surviving life forms.

COURTESY OF UNIVERSITY OF CALGARY

Republic discovered the basic laws of heredity. Even so, it was not until well into the 20th century that genetics and Darwinian theory were reconciled. A fossil site in the Canadian Rocky Mountains also played a significant role in changing views on the immutability of species. Discovered in 1909, the Burgess Shale contains the best record of a time known as the Cambrian Explosion (figuratively speaking). During this extraordinary period between 525 and 545 million years ago, marine animal life (there were no terrestrial animals at the time) evolved and diversified at a rate never seen before or since.

HEREDITY

In order to understand how evolution works, one has to have some understanding of the mechanics of heredity, because heritable variation constitutes the raw material for evolution. Our knowledge of the mechanisms of heredity is fairly recent; most of the fruitful research into the molecular level of inheritance has taken place in the past five decades. Although some aspects remain puzzling, the outlines by now are reasonably clear.

The Transmission of Genes

Biologists call the actual units of heredity **genes**, a term that comes from the Greek word for "birth." The presence and activity of genes were originally deduced rather than observed by Augustine monk Gregor Mendel in the 19th century. Working at the time of publication of Darwin's theory of evolution, Mendel sought to answer some of the riddles of heredity by experimenting with garden peas to determine how various traits are passed from one generation to the next. Specifically, he discovered that inheritance was *particulate,* rather than *blending,* as Darwin and many others thought. That is, the units controlling the expression of visible traits retain their separate identities over the generations. This was the basis of Mendel's **law of segregation.** Another of his laws, that of **independent assortment,** was that what we now call genes, controlling different traits, are inherited independently of one another.

In the first half of the 20th century, much was learned about what genes did, but it was not until 1953 that James Watson and Francis Crick discovered that genes are actually portions of molecules of deoxyribonucleic acid, or **DNA**. DNA is a complex molecule with an unusual shape, rather like two strands of a rope twisted around

---

Genes.   Portions of DNA molecules that direct the synthesis of proteins. DNA molecules have the unique property of being able to produce exact copies of themselves.

Law of segregation.   Variants of genes for a particular trait retain their separate identities through the generations.

Law of independent assortment.   Genes controlling different traits are inherited independently of one another.

DNA.   The genetic material deoxyribonucleic acid; a complex molecule with information to direct the synthesis of proteins. DNA molecules have the unique property of being able to produce exact copies of themselves.

BIOGRAPHY

Charles R. Darwin (1809–1882)

Grandson of Erasmus Darwin (a physician, scientist, poet, and originator of a theory of evolution himself), Charles Darwin began the study of medicine at the University of Edinburgh. Finding himself unsuited for this profession, he then went to Christ's College, Cambridge, to study theology. Upon completion of his studies there, he took the position of naturalist and companion to Captain Fitzroy on the *HMS Beagle*, which was about to embark on an expedition to various poorly mapped parts of the world. The voyage lasted for close to five years, taking Darwin along the coasts of South America, over to the Galapagos Islands, across the Pacific to Australia, and then across the Indian and Atlantic oceans back to South America before returning to England. The observations he made on this voyage, his readings of Sir Charles Lyell's *Principles of Geology,* and the arguments he had with the orthodox and dogmatic Fitzroy had a powerful influence on the development of the ideas culminating in Darwin's most famous book, *On the Origin of Species,* which was published in 1859.

Contrary to what many people seem to think, Darwin did not "discover" or "invent" evolution. The general idea of evolution had been put forward by a number of writers, including his grandfather, long before Darwin's time. Nor is evolution a theory, as some people seem to believe, any more than gravity is a theory. To be sure, there are competing theories of gravity—the Newtonian and Einsteinian—that

BETTMANN/CORBIS

seek to explain its workings, but the evidence in favour of gravity is overwhelming. Similarly, the evidence in favour of evolution is overwhelming, so much so that evolution is now understood in biology as the organizing principle at all levels of life. But, as with gravity, there have been competing theories that seek to explain how evolution works.

Darwin's contribution was one such theory—that of evolution through natural selection. His was the theory that was best able to account both for change within species and for the emergence of new species in purely naturalistic terms. As is usually the case with pioneering ventures, there were weaknesses in Darwin's original theory. Ultimately, however, his basic ideas were vindicated, and modern biology has not only confirmed but (as with all good theories) extended and amplified those ideas. Today, we can say that the evidence in favour of natural selection is about as good as we had for the theory that the earth is spherical, until we were able to put up an astronaut who could see with his own eyes that this indeed is the case.

---

each another. These strands are formed by alternating sugars and phosphates and are connected by four base pairs: adenine, thymine, guanine, and cytosine (usually written as A, T, G, and C). The connections are between complementary bases: A with T and G with C (Figure 3.1). This confers upon genes the unique property of being able to make exact copies of themselves. This happens as a single strand attracts the appropriate bases—A to T, T to A, C to G, and G to C—and forms a new strand.

This new strand, by the same process, produces an exact copy of the original. As long as no errors are made in this replication process, new organisms will contain genetic material exactly like that in ancestral organisms.

The chemical bases of DNA constitute a recipe for making proteins. As science writer Matt Ridley puts it, "Proteins … do almost every chemical, structural, and regulatory thing that is done in the body: they generate energy, fight infection, digest food, form hair, carry

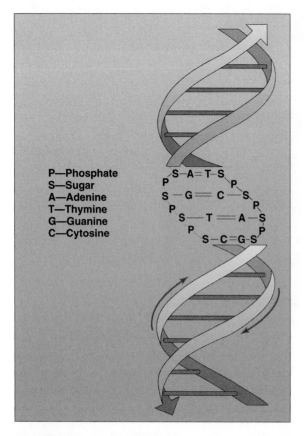

P—Phosphate
S—Sugar
A—Adenine
T—Thymine
G—Guanine
C—Cytosine

FIGURE 3.1

This diagrammatic representation of a portion of a deoxyribonucleic acid (DNA) molecule represents the double helix strands and the connecting nitrogenous base pairs. The helix strands are formed by alternating sugar and phosphate groups. The connection is produced by complementary bases—adenine with thymine, cytosine with guanine—as shown for a section of the molecule.

oxygen, and so on and on."[6] Almost everything in the body is made *of* or *by* proteins.

How is the DNA recipe converted into a protein? Through a somewhat complicated series of intervening steps, each three-base sequence of a gene, called a **codon,** specifies production of a particular amino acid, strings of which build proteins. Because DNA cannot leave the cell's nucleus, the directions for a specific protein are first converted into ribonucleic acid or **RNA** in a process called **transcription.** RNA differs from DNA in the structure of its sugar-phosphate backbone and in the presence of the base uracil rather than thymine. Next the RNA travels to the **ribosomes,** the cellular structure where **translation** of the directions found

in the codons into proteins occurs. For example, the sequence of CGA specifies the amino acid arginine, GCG alanine, CAG glutamine, and so on. There are 20 amino acids, which are strung together in different amounts and sequences to produce an almost infinite number of different proteins. This is the so-called **genetic code,** and it is the same for every living thing, whether it be a worm or a human being. Some simple living things without nucleated cells, such as the retrovirus that causes AIDS, contain their genetic information only as RNA.

Genes

A gene is a portion of the DNA molecule containing several base pairs that directs the production of a particular protein. Thus, when we speak of the gene for a human blood type in the A-B-O system, we are referring to the portion of a DNA molecule that is 1062 "letters" long—a medium-sized gene—that specifies production of an **enzyme,** a particular kind of protein that initiates and directs a chemical reaction. This particular enzyme causes molecules involved in immune responses to attach to the surface of red blood cells. Genes, then, are not really separate structures, as had once been imagined, but locations,

[6] Ridley, M. (1999). *Genome: The autobiography of a species in 23 chapters* (p. 40). New York: HarperCollins.

Codon. Three-base sequence of a gene that specifies production of an amino acid.

RNA. Ribonucleic acid; similar to DNA but with uracil substituted for the base thymine. Carries instructions from DNA to produce amino acids for protein building.

Transcription. Process of conversion of instructions from DNA into RNA.

Ribosomes. Structures in the cell where translation occurs.

Translation. Process of conversion of RNA instructions into proteins.

Genetic code. The sequence of DNA bases that specifies production of a particular amino acid.

Enzyme. Proteins that initiate and direct chemical reactions in an organism.

like dots on a map. These genes provide the recipe for the many proteins that keep us alive and healthy.

Interestingly, the human **genome**—the complete sequence of human DNA—contains 3 billion chemical bases, with about 30 000 functioning genes. This is a mere three times as many genes as in the lowly fruit fly. In fact, all multicellular organisms comprise the same types of cells and the same chemical structures. How the similarities on the one hand and the seemingly modest difference in numbers of genes can produce so much complexity in humans is an active area of research. One reason for the remarkable genetic similarities of all animals lies in the nature of the genes themselves. Two types of genes— structural and regulatory—are responsible for what organisms actually become. **Structural genes** contribute directly to the actual formation of a structure such as whether a person has brown or blue eyes. **Regulatory genes** control the expression or activity of other genes. **Homeobox genes** are the best-known group of regulatory genes and they were discovered only in the 1980s. These genes control such characteristics as whether an organism has fins or legs, is bipedal rather than quadrupedal, or bilaterally symmetrical or not. Homeobox genes do this by coding for proteins like structural genes but the proteins travel to other homeobox genes and activate or deactivate them at different times. These genes determine how a particular organism develops (humans for example) as well as how different organisms develop (fruit flies as opposed to humans).

Another reason for the differences between the fruit fly and humans can be suggested by the following analogy: A combination lock with two wheels can display almost 100 combinations, but a similar lock with six wheels—"only" three times as many—can generate just under 1 million.[7] Those 30 000 human genes account for only 1 to 1.5 percent of the entire genome. As Jerold Lowenstein puts it, our DNA, "like daytime television, is nine-tenths junk."[8] The genes themselves are split by long stretches of this "junk" DNA. The 1062 bases of the A-B-O blood group gene, for example, are interrupted by five such longish stretches. In the course of producing proteins, "junk" DNA is metaphorically "snipped out" and left on the "cutting room floor."

Some of this seemingly useless, noncoding DNA may actually be useful (see Anthropology Applied box, page 78) and was inserted by retroviruses; these are some of the most diverse and widespread infectious entities of vertebrates (they are responsible for many diseases that affect humans, such as immunodeficiencies—including AIDS—hepatitis, anemias, and some neurological disorders).[9] There are several thousand nearly complete viral genomes integrated into our own. Now inert or missing a gene, they account for 1.3 percent of the human genome. Other "junk" DNA consists of decaying hulks of once-useful but now functionless genes; damaged genes that have been "turned off" or stopped being used. All of this litter continues to exist because it is still very good at getting itself replicated. As it does so, mistakes are fairly frequently made, often adding or subtracting repeats of the four bases: A, C, G, and T. This happens with sufficient speed that it is different in every individual, but slowly enough that people mostly have the same repeat lengths of their parents. Because there are thousands of series, the result is a unique set of numbers for each person: his or her unique DNA fingerprint.

Chromosomes

Most DNA molecules do not float freely about in our bodies but are organized into structures called **chromosomes** found in the nucleus of each cell. Chromosomes, discovered early in the 20th century, are nothing more than

---

[7] Solomon, R. (2001, February 20). Genome's riddle. *The New York Times,* p. D3.

[8] Lowenstein, J.M. (1992). Genetic surprises. *Discover, 13*(12), 86.

[9] Amábile-Cuevas, C.F., & Chicurel, M.E. (1993). Horizontal gene transfer. *American Scientist, 81,* 338.

Genome. The complete sequence of DNA for a species.

Structural genes. Code for proteins that contribute directly to the actual formation of a structure such as whether a person has brown or blue eyes.

Regulatory genes. Control the expression or activity of other genes.

Homeobox genes. Regulatory genes that code for proteins that travel to other homeobox genes and activate or deactivate them at different times.

Chromosome. In the cell nucleus, long strands of DNA combined with a protein that can be seen under the microscope.

BIOGRAPHY

Gregor Mendel (1822–1884)

Johann Mendel, as he was christened, was raised on a farm in Moravia and attended the local grammar school. Having done well as a student, he became an Augustine monk in order to further his education. As Brother Gregor, he went on to serve as a parish priest but without much success. Since he had previously studied science at the University of Vienna, he thought of becoming a science teacher but failed the examination. So it was that he retreated to the monastery in Brno, in what is now the Czech Republic. There, he put to work two talents: a flair for mathematics and a passion for gardening.

As with all farmers of his time, Mendel had an intuitive understanding of biological inheritance. He went a step further, though, in that he recognized the need for a more systematic understanding. Thus, at age 34, he began carefully thought-out breeding experiments in the monastery garden, first with pea plants, then with others.

For eight years, Mendel worked, planting over 30 000 plants, controlling their pollination, observing the results, and figuring out the mathematics behind it all. This allowed him to predict the outcome of hybridization over successive generations. His findings were published in 1866 in a respected scientific journal found in all the best libraries of Europe. But despite Mendel's straightforward presentation, no one else picked up on the importance of his work until 1900. By then, understanding of cell biology had advanced to the point where rediscovery of Mendel's laws was inevitable, and in that year three European botanists, working independently of one another,

PHOTO RESEARCHERS, INC.

rediscovered not only the laws but also Mendel's original paper. With this rediscovery, the science of genetics took off. Still, it would be another 53 years before science understood the true nature of genes, the discreet units of inheritance, the existence of which Mendel had deduced from his experiments.

long strands of DNA combined with protein to produce structures that can be seen under a conventional light microscope. Each kind of organism has a characteristic number of chromosomes, which are usually found in pairs. For example, the body cells of the fruit fly each contain four pairs of chromosomes; those of humans contain 23 pairs; those of some brine shrimp have as many as 160 pairs. The two chromosomes in each pair contain genes for the same traits. The gene for one's A-B-O blood group, for instance, will be found on each chromosome

of a particular pair (Chromosome 9 in this instance), but there may be variant forms of these genes. There are three such variants of the A-B-O gene that determine whether one's blood type is A, B, AB, or O. Forms of genes that are located on paired chromosomes and that code for different versions of the same trait are called **alleles.** The difference between the A and B blood alleles is a mere seven chemical bases out of the total 1062.

Alleles.   Alternate forms of a single gene.

Cell Division

In order to grow and maintain good health, the body cells of an organism must divide and produce new cells. Cell division is initiated when the chromosomes, and hence the genes, replicate, forming a second pair that duplicates the original pair of chromosomes in the nucleus. To do this, the DNA metaphorically "unzips" between the base pairs—adenine from thymine and guanine from cytosine—following which each base on each now-single strand attracts its complementary base, reconstituting the second half of the double helix. Each new pair is surrounded by a membrane and becomes the nucleus that directs the activities of a new cell. This kind of cell division is called **mitosis**, and it produces new cells that have exactly the same number of chromosome pairs, and hence genes, as did the parent cell.

Like most animals, humans reproduce sexually. The reason sex is so popular, from an evolutionary perspective, is that it brings beneficial alleles together, purges the genome of harmful ones, and allows beneficial alleles to spread without being held back by the baggage of disadvantageous variants of other genes. Without sexual reproduction, we would lack genetic diversity, without which we would be more open to attack by various viruses than we already are. Nor would we be able to adapt to changing environments.

When new individuals are produced through sexual reproduction, the process involves the merging of two cells, one from each parent. If two regular body

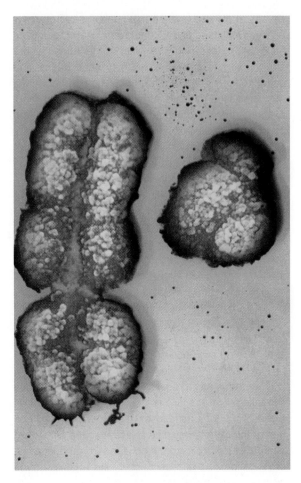

In humans as in all mammals, sex is determined by the male, as everyone inherits an X chromosome (left) from their mother, but has a 50-50 chance of inheriting an X or Y chromosome (right) from their father. Hence, about equal numbers of males and females are born. Compared to the other chromosomes, the Y is tiny and carries little genetic information, just the information required for maleness. The X carries a "normal" complement of genes.

BIOPHOTO ASSOCIATES/PHOTO RESEARCHERS, INC.

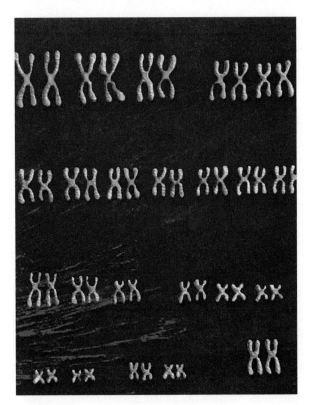

This is a photomicrograph of human chromosomes.

SUPERSTOCK

Mitosis. A kind of cell division that produces new cells having exactly the same number of chromosome pairs, and hence genes, as the parent cell.

ANTHROPOLOGY APPLIED

Evolutionary Implications of the Human Genome Project

The main motivation for financing the Human Genome Project (HGP) has been to identify the underlying causes of disease and the risks to humans from new energy resources and technologies.[1] Anthropologists have been following the HGP rather closely, but anthropology's interest has largely been ethical and policy related. There are billions of human genomes, of course, one for each human, and the project must examine the genomes of other organisms for the purpose of comparison. The human genome project has implications for biological anthropology's study of human diversity and evolution as well.

Among the roughly 30 000 genes estimated in the human genome, about 50 percent have known functions. To make matters even more complex, genes (the parts of DNA that code for proteins) are separated by repeated sequences of base pairs that do not code for proteins. These sequences comprise at least 50 percent of the human genome. This apparently useless DNA has been called "junk" DNA. But are these repeated sequences actually useless? Recent research indicates that they are not. They may have a significant role in increasing diversity and, thus, in evolution. One study indicates portions of junk DNA play a role in repairing damaged DNA. During the repair process rearrangement of genes can take place. The junk lies between genes so when a part of the junk transposes itself to a damaged portion of the DNA it may take adjacent genes with it. Yet another study points to the non-random, language-like organization of the base pairs. If the organization is language-like, there must be information encoded. Just what that information represents needs to be decoded. A great deal remains to be learned. Researchers are investigating issues such as gene regulation and function, DNA sequence organization, non-coding DNA functions, evolutionary conservation among organisms, and developmental genetics.

Further advances in understanding the human genome will result from comparisons to other organisms. Our closest living relative, the chimpanzee, has a genome remarkably similar to that of humans. Comparative genomics, the comparison of DNA sequence patterns among organisms, is a powerful strategy for identifying human genes and interpreting their functions. Among the few mammal genomes pieced together are the mouse, rat, and cat. Understanding variation among primates, the closest relatives of humans, is one issue, but what do we know about variation among mammals in general? By comparing different mammal orders, families, and genera we can come to a better understanding of the mechanisms underlying what makes mammals the mammals they are. Researchers have identified about 10 genes in mice that humans do not have, yet the number of genes in humans and mice is similar. Junk DNA seems to have stopped entering the human genome over 50 million years ago while the mouse has continued to add these sequences. In contrast, the transposable parts of the junk DNA that plays a role in repairing DNA and increasing diversity in the human genome are far more common in humans.

In 2005, the scientific world learned that a draft of the chimpanzee genome had been worked out.[2] The results confirm that humans and chimpanzee DNA differs by a small amount, and a major task will be to identify the evolutionary changes specific to humans.[3] For example, we may soon come to an understanding of the molecular basis of human language. Researchers have been aware for some time of a gene called FoxP2 in humans that is directly related to speech pathology, that is, problems with grammar and the physical articulation of words.[4] This gene differs only slightly in humans and chimpanzees. The slight differences mean that the selection pressure has affected the gene, and the differentiation is relatively recent. What does the difference represent? A comparison of the two genomes may tell us why humans have less muscular strength, less body hair, and delayed maturation compared to chimpanzees. Humans lack a chemical found on cell surfaces in chimpanzees. Could this be the basis for the difference in susceptibility to certain diseases in humans that chimpanzees are not susceptible to?[5] For example, we are aware that chimpanzees carry the HIV virus but rarely do chimpanzees have AIDS. So far, at least at the time of writing, the greatest divergence in the two genomes is found on the Y chromosome, present only in males. Recent duplication and insertions/deletions of DNA segments account for the main differences between the chimpanzee and human genomes. The main gene differences are ones that encode for proteins involved in immunity and reproduction, not proteins involved in cranial capacity, bipedalism and advanced brain function. These results so far still make it very difficult to determine what makes us human. For example, later in this chapter the potentially important role of regulatory genes in human evolution is discussed but the chimpanzee/human genome comparison cannot yet address regulatory genes because they are so difficult to identify.

In the future other primates may be the subject of genome analysis. Advocates of the rhesus macaque genome project note that the difference between the human and macaque genome sequences is about 5 to 7 percent.[6] Given the slightly larger difference between macaques and humans than between chimpanzees and humans, comparisons may be more informative.

Canadian scientists under the leadership of Tom Hudson at McGill University helped launch the International HapMap project in late October 2002.[7] (The term "HapMap" is derived from haplotype map; *haplotype* refers to the patterning of differences among individuals.) Canadian researchers are responsible for about 10 percent of the genome. The project involves a consortium of scientists from Canada, China, Japan, Nigeria, the United Kingdom, and the United States. Genetic differences among individuals are minor compared to the differences among the primates, but the differences number in the order of 10 million and form about 100 000 patterns. What this means is that there is no "normal" human genome so understanding its variation is crucial, but all 10 million differences cannot possibly be documented. By examining haplotypes instead of single gene mutations that underlie many rare diseases, variation in the human genome can be documented, and this will provide the basis for understanding many common diseases that are found in most human populations. The project is sampling DNA from 400 individuals from four ethnic groups. So far 270 individuals with Asian, African, and European ancestry have joined the study. When the project was announced fewer than 1.7 million variants or polymorphisms were known but by 2005 researchers had increased that number to more than 8 million. Investigators are now working on identifying the most important variants. With the current database, researchers can quickly and inexpensively investigate how patients with a particular genetically based health issue such as epilepsy may respond to a drug.

[1] (USDEHGP), U.S. Department of Energy Human Genome Project. (2001). *Genomics and its impact on medicine and society.* www.ornl.gov/sci/techresources/Human_Genome/publicat/primer2001/index.shtml.

[2] Gunter C., & Dhand, R. (2005). The chimpanzee genome. *Nature, 437,* 47–47.

[3] Li W.-H., & Saunders, M.A. (2005). News & views: The chimpanzee and us. *Nature, 437,* 50–51.

[4] Enard, W., Przeworski, M., Fisher, S.E., Lai, C.S.L., Wiebe, V., Kitano, T., Monaco, A.P., & Pääbo, S. (2002). Molecular evolution of FOXP2, a gene involved in speech and language. *Nature, 418,* 869–872.

[5] Cyranoski D. (2002). Almost human. *Nature, 418,* 910–912.

[6] Hastings A. (2001). Hardy-Weinberg Theorem. *Encyclopedia of Life Sciences.* Chichester: John Wiley & Sons, Ltd.

[7] Evenson, B. (2002, October 30). Canada to be at forefront of new genome research, *National Post,* A1.

cells, each containing 23 pairs of chromosomes, were to merge, the result would be a new individual with 46 pairs of chromosomes; such an individual surely could not survive. But this increase in chromosome number does not occur, because the sex cells that join to form a new individual are the product of a different kind of cell division, called **meiosis.**

Although meiosis begins like mitosis, with the replication and doubling of the original genes and chromosomes, it proceeds to divide that number into four new cells rather than two (Figure 3.2). Thus each new cell has only half the number of chromosomes with their genes found in the parent cell. Human eggs and sperm, for example, have only 23 single chromosomes (half of a pair), whereas body cells have 23 pairs, or 46 chromosomes.

> **Meiosis.** A kind of cell division that produces the sex cells, each of which has half the number of chromosomes, and hence genes, as the parent cell.

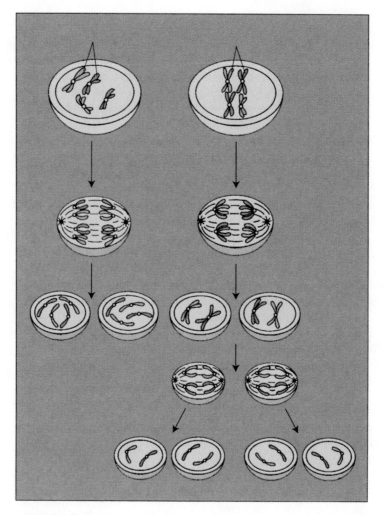

FIGURE 3.2

In cell division both mitosis (a) and meiosis (b) create new cells. However, in mitosis the new cell has the same number of chromosomes as the parent cell, whereas in meiosis there are half of the chromosomes. Chromosomes in blue originally came from one parent, those in pink from the other.

The process of meiotic division has important implications for genetics. Because paired chromosomes are separated, two different types of new cells will be formed; two of the four new cells will have one-half of a pair of chromosomes, and the other two will have the second half of the original chromosome pair. At the same time, corresponding portions of one chromosome may "cross over" to the other one, somewhat scrambling the genetic material compared to the original chromosomes. Of course, none of this will make any difference if the original pair was **homozygous**, possessing identical alleles for a specific gene. For example, if in both chromosomes of the original pair the gene for A-B-O blood type was represented by the allele for Type A blood, then all new cells will have the "A" allele. But if the original pair was **heterozygous**, with the "A" allele on one chromosome and the allele for Type O blood on the other, then half of the new cells will contain only the "O" allele; the

> **Homozygous.** Refers to a chromosome pair that bears identical alleles for a single gene.
>
> **Heterozygous.** Refers to a chromosome pair that bears different alleles for a single gene.

offspring have a 50-50 chance of getting either one. It is impossible to predict any single individual's **genotype,** or genetic composition, but (as Mendel originally discovered) statistical probabilities can be established.

What happens when a child inherits the allele for Type O blood from one parent and that for Type A from the other? Will the child have blood of Type A, O, or some mixture of the two? Many of these questions were answered by Mendel's original experiments.

Mendel discovered that certain alleles are able to mask the presence of others; one allele is dominant, whereas the other is recessive. This is his **law of dominance and recessiveness.** Actually, it is the traits that are dominant or recessive, rather than the alleles themselves; geneticists merely speak of dominant and recessive alleles for the sake of convenience. Thus, one might speak of the allele for Type A blood as being dominant to the one for Type O. An individual whose blood type genes are heterozygous, with one "A" and one "O" allele, will have Type A blood. In other words, the heterozygous condition (AO) will show exactly the same physical characteristic, or **phenotype,** as the homozygous (AA), even though the two have a somewhat different genetic composition, or genotype. Only the homozygous recessive genotype (OO) will show the phenotype of Type O blood.

The dominance of one allele does not mean that the recessive one is lost or in some way blended. A Type A heterozygous parent (AO) will produce sex cells containing both "A" and "O" alleles. (This is an example of Mendel's law of segregation, that alleles retain their separate identities.) Recessive alleles can be handed down for generations before they are matched with another recessive in the process of sexual reproduction and show up in the phenotype. The presence of the dominant allele simply renders the recessive allele inactive.

All of the traits Mendel studied in garden peas showed this dominant-recessive relationship, and so for some years it was believed that this was the only relationship possible. Later studies, however, have indicated that patterns of inheritance are not always so simple. In some cases, neither allele is dominant; they are both co-dominant. An example of co-dominance in human heredity can be seen also in the inheritance of blood types. Type A is produced by one allele; Type B by another. A heterozygous individual will have a phenotype of AB, because neither allele can dominate the other.

The inheritance of blood types points out another complexity of heredity. The number of alleles is by no means limited to two; certain traits have three or more allelic forms. Of course, only one allele can appear on each of the pairs of chromosomes, so each individual is limited to two alleles.

Another example of co-dominance is the alleles for normal **hemoglobin** (the protein that carries oxygen in the red blood cells) and the abnormal hemoglobin that is responsible for **sickle-cell anemia** in humans. The abnormality is caused by a change in a single base pair in the DNA of the hemoglobin gene, producing a single amino acid substitution in the protein. Individuals who are homozygous for this particular allele contract sickle-cell anemia, as their red blood cells take on a characteristic sickle shape, causing them to collapse and clump together, blocking the capillaries and so causing tissue damage. With their severe anemia, such individuals commonly die before reaching adulthood. The homozygous dominant condition (Hb^AHb^A; normal hemoglobin is known as hemoglobin A, not to be confused with blood Type A) produces only normal molecules of hemoglobin whereas the heterozygous condition (Hb^AHb^S) produces 50 percent normal and 50 percent abnormal molecules; except under low-oxygen or some other stressful conditions, such individuals suffer no ill effects. We shall return to the sickle-cell condition later, for we now know that under certain conditions the heterozygous condition is actually more advantageous than is the "normal" homozygous condition.

Genotype. The actual genetic makeup of an organism.

Law of dominance and recessiveness. Certain alleles are able to mask the presence of others.

Phenotype. The physical appearance of an organism that may or may not reflect a particular genotype because the latter may or may not include recessive alleles.

Hemoglobin. The protein that carries oxygen in the red blood cells.

Sickle-cell anemia. An inherited form of anemia caused by the red blood cells assuming a sickle or crescent shape.

Polygenetic Inheritance

So far, we have spoken as if the traits of organisms are single-gene traits—that is, the alleles of one particular gene determine one particular trait. Certainly this is the case with the A-B-O blood groups and some other things, but in humans, the most obvious traits are usually not ones controlled by a single gene. Skin colour, for example, is programmed by the action of many genes, each of which produces a small effect. In such cases, we speak of **polygenetic inheritance,** where two or more genes (as opposed to just two or more alleles) work together to effect one particular phenotypic character. Because so many genes are involved, each of which may have alternative alleles, it is difficult to unravel the genetic underpinnings of a trait like skin colour. Theoretically, the observed range of variation in human skin colour seems to require the presence of at least three, if not as many as six, separate genes, each of which produces a small additive effect. For this reason, characteristics controlled by multiple genes exhibit a continuous range of variation in their phenotype expression.

POPULATION GENETICS

At the level of the individual, the study of genetics shows how traits are transmitted from one generation to the next and enables a prediction about the chances that any given individual will display some phenotypic characteristic. At the level of the group, the study of genetics takes on additional significance, revealing mechanisms that support evolutionary interpretations of the diversity of life.

A key concept in genetics is that of the **population,** or a group of individuals within which breeding takes place. It is within populations that natural selection takes place, as some members produce more than their share of the next generation, while others produce less than their share. Thus, over a period of generations, the population shows a measure of adaptation to its environment as a consequence of this evolution.

The Stability of the Population

In theory, the characteristics of any given population should remain remarkably stable. And indeed, generation after generation, the bullfrogs in a farm pond, for example, look much alike, have the same calls, and

exhibit the same behaviour when breeding. Another way to look at this remarkable consistency is to say that the **gene pool** of the population—the genetic variants available to that population—seems to remain the same.

The theoretical stability of a population's gene pool is not only easy to observe; it is also easy to understand. As Mendel's experiments with garden peas revealed, and subsequent genetic experiments have confirmed, although some alleles may be dominant to others, the recessive alleles are not just lost or destroyed. Statistically, a heterozygous individual has a 50 percent chance of passing on to the next generation the dominant allele; he or she also has a 50 percent chance of passing on the recessive allele. The recessive allele may again be masked by the presence of a dominant allele in the next generation, but it is there nonetheless and will be passed on again.

Because alleles are not "lost" in the process of reproduction, the frequency with which certain ones occur in the population should remain exactly the same from one generation to the next. The **Hardy-Weinberg principle,** named for the English mathematician and the German physician who worked it out (in 1908) soon after the rediscovery of Mendel's laws, demonstrates algebraically that the percentage of individuals that are homozygous for the dominant allele, homozygous for the recessive allele, and heterozygous will remain the same from one generation to the next provided that certain specified conditions are met: that mating is entirely random; that the population is sufficiently large for statistical averages to express themselves; that no new variants

---

Polygenetic inheritance. When two or more genes work together to effect a single phenotypic character.

Population. In biology, a group of similar individuals that can and do interbreed.

Gene pool. The genetic variants available to a population.

Hardy-Weinberg principle. Demonstrates algebraically that the percentage of individuals that are homozygous for the dominant allele, homozygous for the recessive allele, and heterozygous should remain constant from one generation to the next, provided that certain specified conditions are met.

BIOGRAPHY

Esteban Parra

Esteban Parra is a molecular anthropologist at the University of Toronto. His Ph.D. is from the University of Santiago de Compostela, Spain. His research spans the subjects of genetic markers, human evolution, epidemiology, and forensic science. Topics he is pursuing include admixture, high-altitude adaptation, and the underlying mechanisms of human pigmentation. A main goal of his research is to characterize genetic variation within and between human populations. He is also interested in evaluating new technologies for DNA genotyping.

Parra's most recent study was the estimation of the European genetic contribution to 10 African-descent populations in the United States (Parra et al. 1998). Parra and his team discovered a sex-biased gene flow from Europeans to African Americans, the male contribution being substantially greater than the female contribution. There was no evidence of a significant maternal Amerindian contribution to any of the 10 populations (Parra et al. 1998). What makes this work of value from an anthropological perspective is the attempt to explore the social and political background of the patterns the researchers discovered. Parra is also concerned with developing methods to make the analysis of large samples of DNA more efficient. He believes that by developing more efficient analytical techniques we will be able to explore human genetic variation more effectively. The human genome project results are currently based on only a few people (five individuals in one project and 24 in another) so it is essential that we develop methods that will enable much larger samples of the genome to be obtained, or we will have little understanding of variation within the genome (HGMIS 2001, 4).

will be introduced into the population's gene pool; and that all individuals are equally successful at surviving and reproducing.[10] In real life, however, these conditions are rarely met, as geographical, physiological, or behavioural factors may favour matings between certain individuals over others; as populations—on islands, for example—may be quite small; as new genetic variants may be introduced through mutation, interspecies gene transfer, or gene flow; and as natural selection may favour the carriers of some alleles over others. Thus, changes in the gene pools of populations, without which there could be no evolution, can and do take place.

EVOLUTIONARY FORCES

Mutation

The ultimate source of change is **mutation** of genes. This happens when copying mistakes are made during cell division. It may involve a change in a single base of a DNA sequence, or at the other extreme, relocation of large segments of DNA. In any event, genes are altered, producing new alleles—ones not inherited from an ancestor, but heritable by descendants. The fact is, every second that you read this page, the DNA in each cell of your body is being damaged.[11] Fortunately, DNA repair enzymes exist that constantly scan DNA for mistakes, slicing out damaged segments and patching up gaps. Were it not for this repair mechanism, we would have diseases like cancer at a much higher frequency than we do, nor would we get a faithful copy of our parental inheritance (from an evolutionary perspective, the only mutations that count are those in sex cells). Not only would we not live long, but our species would not exist for long. But because the repair mechanism itself is not perfect, not all mistakes are corrected; otherwise, there would be no possibility for evolution to occur.

Geneticists have calculated the rate at which various types of mutant genes appear. In human populations, they run from a low of about five mutations per million

---

[10] http://en.wikipedia.org/wiki/Hardy-Weinberg theorem. Encyclopedia of Life Sciences. Chichester: John Wiley and Sons.

[11] Culotta, E., & Koshland, D.E., Jr. (1994). DNA repair works its way to the top. *Science, 266,* 1926.

Mutation. Chance alteration of a gene that produces a new allele.

Sickle-cell anemia is caused by an abnormal hemoglobin, called hemoglobin S. Those afflicted by the disease are homozygous for the allele S; heterozygotes are not afflicted. Shown here is a sickle cell among normal red blood cells.

MECKES/OTTAWA/PHOTO RESEARCHERS INC.

sex cells formed, in the case of a gene abnormality that leads to the absence of an iris in the eye, to a high of about 100 per million, in the case of a gene involved in a form of muscular dystrophy. (Note that the human male ejaculates hundreds of millions of sperm cells at a single time.) The average is about 30 mutants per million. Because of the repeated replication needed to supply fresh sperm throughout life, the mutation rate throughout the genome is five times higher in men than in women. Although mutations sometimes produce marked abnormalities, the great majority of them produce more subtle effects. Still, they are more often harmful than not.

Research with a variety of organisms indicates that certain factors increase the rate at which mutations occur. These include a number of chemicals, such as some dyes, certain antibiotics, and some chemicals used in the preservation of food. Another important cause of increased mutation rates is irradiation. The ultraviolet rays of sunshine are capable of producing mutations, as are X-rays and other radiation. In at least some organisms, there is even evidence stress can boost mutation rates, increasing the diversity necessary for selection if successful adaptation is to occur.[12]

In humans, as in all multicelled animals, the very nature of the genetic material itself ensures that mutations will occur. For instance, the fact that genes are split by stretches of "junk" DNA increases the chances that a simple editing mistake in the process of copying DNA will cause significant gene mutations. To cite one example, the gene for collagen (the main structural protein of the skin, bones, and teeth) is fragmented by no fewer than 50 segments of "junk" DNA. As a consequence, there are 50 chances for error each time the gene is copied. One result of this seemingly inefficient if not dangerous situation is that it becomes possible to shuffle the gene segments themselves like a deck of cards, putting together new proteins with new functions. Although individuals may suffer as a result (the French artist Henri Toulouse-Lautrec's growth abnormality resulted from a mutation of the collagen gene), it does make it possible for an evolving species to adapt more quickly to a new environment. Another source of genetic remodelling from within is the movement of whole DNA sequences from one locality or chromosome to another. This may disrupt the function of other genes or, in the case of so-called jumping genes, carry important functional messages of their own. In humans, about one in every 700 mutations is caused by "jumping genes," providing another mechanism for increasing diversity.

One recent finding is that humans have longer strings of repetitious DNA within and between genes than do other primates, so it is not surprising that we have a higher mutation rate. And a consequence of this is an increased incidence of such genetic disorders as Huntington's disease and Fragile X syndrome (a form of mental retardation).[13]

It is important to realize that mutations do not arise out of need for some new adaptation. Indeed, there is no tendency for the frequency of a particular mutation to correlate with the direction in which a population is evolving. Mutations are purely chance events; what

[12] Chicurel, M. (2001). Can organisms speed their own evolution? *Science, 292,* 1824–827.

[13] Glausiusz, J. (1995). Micro gets macro. *Discover, 16* (11), 40.

French artist Henri Toulouse-Lautrec, whose growth abnormality resulted from a mutation of the collagen gene.

TOPHAM/THE IMAGE WORKS

The 1998 Casitas Volcano mudslide in Nicaragua, triggered by the rains of Hurricane Mitch, buried a village, killing over 1200 people. This is one kind of accident that can produce chance alterations of allele frequency in human gene pools.

JOHN MOORE/AP/WIDE WORLD PHOTOS

happens once they occur depends on whether they happen (by chance) to enhance the survival and reproductive success of the individuals who carry them.

Genetic Drift

Each individual is subject to a number of chance events that determine life or death. For example, an individual squirrel in good health and possessed of a number of advantageous traits may be killed in a forest fire; a genetically well-adapted baby cougar may not live longer than a day if its mother gets caught in an avalanche, whereas the weaker offspring of a mother that does not die may survive. In a large population, such accidents of nature are unimportant; the accidents that preserve individuals with certain alleles will be balanced out by the accidents that destroy them. However, in small populations, such averaging out may not be possible. Because human populations today are so large, we might suppose that human beings are unaffected by chance events. Although it is true that a rock slide that kills five campers whose home community has a total population of 100 000 is not statistically significant, a rock slide that kills five hunters from a small group of food foragers could significantly alter frequencies of alleles in the local gene pool. The average size of local groups of historically known food foragers (people who hunt, fish, and gather other wild foods for subsistence) varies between about 25 and 50.

Another sort of chance event may occur when an existing population splits into two or more new ones, especially if one of these new populations is founded by a particularly small number of individuals. This amounts to a sampling error; in such cases, it is unlikely that the gene frequencies of the smaller population will duplicate those of the larger one. Even if a population does not split in this way, in a small population, the same sort of sampling error may occur as, by chance, parental alleles may not be passed on to the next generation in the same frequencies. If, for example, a person's genotype for blood type is AO, but he or she has only one offspring, only one of those alleles will be passed on.

The effect of chance events on the gene pool of small populations is called **genetic drift**. Genetic drift plays an important role in causing the sometimes striking characteristics found in isolated island populations. On the isolated island of Tristan de Cunha in the southern Atlantic Ocean, for example, over 20 percent of the human population have overt symptoms of asthma, despite living in an environment free of the pollution and other triggers that usually lead to asthma. Because asthma tends to run in families (regardless of what triggers asthma) and because the underlying biochemical events involved are the same, it is clear that an underlying genetic component exists. Thus, it appears that Tristan de Cunha was populated by descendants of an asthma-susceptible person.[14] Drift is also likely to have been an important factor in human evolution, because until 10 000 years ago all humans were food foragers who probably lived in relatively small, self-contained populations.

Gene Flow

Another factor that brings change to the gene pool of a population is **gene flow**, or the introduction of new alleles from nearby populations. Gene flow occurs when a population that was interbreeding and then was split into separate groups who had slightly different genetic makeups because of mutations, selection, or drift are once again able to interbreed, as, for example, when a river that once separated two populations of small mammals changes course. Migration of individuals or groups into the territory occupied by others may also lead to gene flow. This genetic change has been observed in several North American rodents that have been forced to leave their territory due to changes in environmental conditions. Gene flow has been an important factor in human evolution, both in terms of early human or near-human groups and in terms of current so-called racial variation. For example, the last 400 years have seen the introduction of alleles into Central and South American populations from both the Spanish colonists and the Africans whom Europeans imported as slaves. The result has been an increase in the range of phenotypic variation.

Interspecies Gene Transfer

A recent discovery is that the transfer of genes can occur between unrelated organisms. Unlike gene flow, however, it does not take place by interbreeding but through other means. Hence, like mutation, it is a source of random variation. Such **interspecies gene transfer** is well known between different kinds of bacteria, but seems to take place even among vertebrate animals. In some cases, the agent of transfer can be a retrovirus; the process is depicted in Figure 3.3.

Natural Selection

Although the factors discussed above may produce change in a population, that change would not necessarily make the population better adapted to its biological and social environment. **Adaptation** means both a process, by which organisms achieve a beneficial adjustment to an available environment, and the results of that process, the characteristics of organisms that fit them to the particular set of conditions of the environment in which they are generally found. Genetic drift, for example, often produces strange characteristics that have no survival value; mutant genes may be either

---

[14] Ridley, M. (1999). *Genome: The autobiography of a species in 23 chapters* (p. 71). New York: HarperCollins.

Genetic drift. Chance fluctuations of allele frequencies in the gene pool of a population.

Gene flow. The introduction of alleles from the gene pool of one population into that of another.

Interspecies gene transfer. Transfer of DNA as when retroviruses insert DNA into the cells of one species from another.

Adaptation. A process by which organisms achieve a beneficial adjustment to an available environment; also the results of that process—the characteristics of organisms that fit them to the particular set of conditions of the environment in which they are generally found.

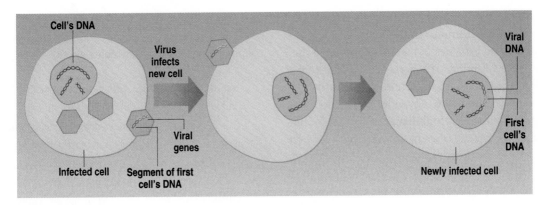

FIGURE 3.3

How viruses can transfer genetic material from one species to another.

helpful or harmful to survival, or simply neutral. So we return to the subject of natural selection, for it is this process that makes evolutionary change adaptive.

Natural selection refers to the evolutionary process through which the environment exerts pressure that selects some individuals over others to reproduce the next generation of the group. In other words, instead of a completely random selection of individuals whose traits will be passed on to the next generation, there is selection by the forces of nature. In the process, the frequency of genetic variants for harmful or maladaptive traits within the population is reduced while the frequency of genetic variants for adaptive traits is increased.

In popular writing, natural selection is often thought of as "survival of the fittest," a phrase coined by British philosopher Herbert Spencer but never used by Darwin. The phrase implies that the physically weak, being unfit, are eliminated from the population by disease, predation, or starvation. Obviously, the survival of the fittest has some bearing on natural selection; one need hardly point out that the dead do not reproduce. But there are many cases in which individuals survive, and even do quite well, but do not reproduce. They may be incapable of attracting mates, or they may be sterile, or they may produce offspring that do not survive after birth. For example, among the Uganda Kob, a kind of antelope native to eastern Africa, males that are unable to attract females form all-male herds in which they live out their lives. As members of a herd, they are reasonably well protected against predators, and so they may survive to relatively ripe old ages. They do not, however, pass on their genes to succeeding generations.

Change brought about by natural selection in the frequency with which certain genetic variants appear in a population is actually a very slow process. For example, the present frequency of the sickle-cell allele is 0.05 in the entire U.S. population. A 5 percent reduction per generation (about 25 years) would take about 2000 years to reach a frequency of 0.01, assuming complete selection against those homozygous for the allele. Yet given the great time span involved—life on earth has existed for 3 to 4 billion years—even such small and slow changes will have a significant cumulative impact on both the genotypes and phenotypes of any population.

Natural selection may act to promote change in frequencies of genetic variants, or act to promote stability, rather than change. **Directional selection** leads to a consistent change in some characteristic of a population through time. Selection may favour a particular allele,

> **Directional selection.** Natural selection that favours a single allele; therefore, allele frequency continuously shifts in one direction.

changing the frequency of that allele in the population. **Disruptive selection** on the other hand favours individuals at the extremes of the distribution and they produce more offspring. The population shifts from a continuous gradation with the centre of the distribution being the most common to a bimodal distribution with two types dominating. **Stabilizing selection** occurs in populations that are already well adapted or where change would be disadvantageous. In humans, for instance, there has been no significant change in brain size for the last 200 000 years or so. Stabilizing selection seems to be operating here, as the human birth canal is not adequate for the birth of larger-brained offspring. In cases where change is disadvantageous, natural selection will favour the retention of allele frequencies more or less as they are. The qualification "more or less" is necessary, as "stable" does not mean "static." Still, the evolutionary history of most forms of life is not one of constant change, proceeding as a steady, stately progression over vast periods of time; rather, it is one of prolonged periods of relative stability or gradual change punctuated by shorter periods of more rapid change (or extinction) when altered conditions require new adaptations or when a new mutation produces an opportunity to adapt to some other available environment. According to the fossil record, most species survive somewhere between 3 and 5 million years.[15]

Discussions of the action of natural selection typically focus on anatomical or structural changes, such as the evolutionary change in the types of teeth found in primates; ample evidence (fossilized teeth, for example) exists to interpret such changes. By extrapolation, biologists assume that the same mechanisms work on behavioural traits as well. It seems reasonable that individuals in a group of Vervet monkeys capable of warning one another of the presence of predators would have a significant survival advantage over those without this capability. Such situations have constituted an enigma for evolutionary biologists; individuals are typically seen as "survival machines," acting always selfishly in their own interest, but by giving an alarm call, an individual calls attention to itself, thereby becoming an obvious target for the predator. How, then, could the kind of behaviour evolve in which individuals place themselves at risk for the good of the group? One biologist's simple solution substitutes money for fitness to illustrate one way in which such cooperative behaviour may come about:

> *You are given a choice. Either you can receive $10 and keep it all or you can receive $10 million if you give $6 million to your next-door neighbor. Which would you do? Guessing that most selfish people would be happy with a net gain of $4 million, I consider the second option to be a form of selfish behavior in which a neighbor gains an incidental benefit. I have termed such selfish behavior benevolent.*[16]

Natural selection of beneficial social traits was probably a particularly important influence on human evolution, since in the primates, some degree of cooperative social behaviour became important for food getting, defence, and mate attraction. Indeed, anthropologist Christopher Boehm argues, "If human nature were merely selfish, vigilant punishment of deviants would be expected, whereas the elaborate prosocial prescriptions that favour altruism would come as a surprise."[17]

ADAPTATION

As a consequence of the process of natural selection, those populations that do not become extinct generally become well adapted to their environments. Anyone who has ever looked carefully at the plants and animals that survive in the deserts of the Western United

---

[15] Thomson, K.S. (1997). Natural selection and evolution's smoking gun. *American Scientist, 85*, 516.

[16] Nunney, L. (1998). Are we selfish, are we nice, or are we nice because we are selfish? *Science, 281*, 1619.

[17] Boehm, C. (2000). The evolution of moral communities. *School of American Research, 2000 Annual Report*, 7.

Disruptive selection. Natural selection that simultaneously favours individuals at both extremes of the distribution.

Stabilizing selection. Natural selection as it acts to promote stability, rather than change, in a population's gene pool.

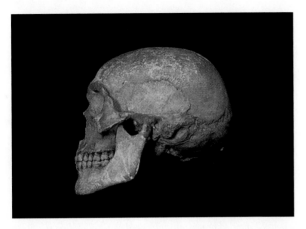

An example of stabilizing selection: The brain of the modern skull on the left is no bigger relative to body mass than that in the CA 50 000-year-old skull on the right, even though the outer appearance of the skulls has changed. **E.R. DEGGINGER/COLOR-PIC, INC.**

States, for example, can cite many instances of adaptation. Members of the cactus family have extensive root networks close to the surface of the soil, enabling them to soak up the slightest bit of moisture; they are able to store large quantities of water whenever it is available; they are shaped so as to expose the smallest possible surface to the dry air and are generally leafless as adults, thereby preventing water loss through evaporation; and a covering of spines discourages animals from chewing into the juicy flesh of the plant.

Desert animals are also adapted to their environment. The kangaroo rat can survive without drinking water, getting its water from the seeds it eats; many reptiles live in burrows where the temperature is lower; most animals are nocturnal or active only in the cool of the night. Many of the stories traditionally offered to explain observable cases of adaptation rely heavily on the purposeful acts of a world creator. The belief popular among Europeans early in the 19th century that God created each animal separately to occupy a specific place in a hierarchical ladder is one such example. Although the view is much less popular today, it is still held by many.

The adaptability of organic structures and functions, no matter how much a source of wonder and fascination, nevertheless falls short of perfection. This is so because natural selection can work with only what the existing store of genetic variation provides; it cannot create something entirely new. That exquisite design is

not the rule is illustrated by the pains of aching backs, the annoyances of hernias, and problems with hemorrhoids that we humans must endure because the body of a four-footed vertebrate, designed for horizontal posture, has been jury-rigged to be held vertically above the two hind limbs. And surely, truly intelligent design from scratch could have produced an eye without a blind spot. Yet, these defects have been perpetuated by natural selection, because they are outweighed by other aspects of human adaptation that enhance the reproductive success of the species as a whole.

The Case of Sickle-Cell Anemia

Among human beings, a particularly well-studied case of an adaptation paid for by the misery of many individuals brings us back to the case of sickle-cell anemia. This disorder first came to the attention of geneticists when it was observed that most North Americans who suffer from it are of African ancestry. Investigation traced the abnormality to populations that live in a clearly defined belt throughout central Africa (although brought to North America from central Africa, the condition also exists in some non-African populations, as will be noted below).

Geneticists were curious to know why such a deleterious hereditary disability persisted in these populations. The Hardy-Weinberg principle was at work, but the conditions maintaining the unusual balance

The moths shown in these two pictures are varieties of a single species. Although the mottled brown variant is well camouflaged on relatively clean tree trunks, it is readily visible on sooty tree trunks and is subject to increased predation. The reverse is true for the black variant, which became especially common when coal fuelled British industry. **E.R. DEGGINGER/COLOR-PIC, INC.**

of alleles were unknown. According to the theory of natural selection, any alleles that are harmful will tend to disappear from the group, because the individuals who are homozygous for the abnormality generally die—are "selected out"—before they are able to reproduce. Why, then, had this seemingly harmful condition remained in populations from central Africa?

The answer to this mystery began to emerge when it was noticed that the areas in which sickle-cell anemia is prevalent are also areas in which falciparum malaria is common (Figure 3.4). This severe form of malaria causes high fevers that significantly interfere with the reproductive abilities of those who do not actually die from the disease. Moreover, it was discovered that the same hemoglobin abnormalities are found in people living in parts of the Arabian Peninsula, Greece, Algeria, and Syria as well as in certain East Indians, all of whom also are native to regions where falciparum malaria is common.

Further research established that the abnormal hemoglobin was associated with an increased ability to survive the effects of the malarial parasite; it seems that the effects of the abnormal hemoglobin in limited amounts were less injurious than the effects of the malarial parasite.

Thus, selection favoured heterozygous individuals ($Hb^A Hb^S$). The loss of alleles for abnormal hemoglobin caused by the death of those homozygous for it (from sickle-cell anemia) was balanced out by the loss of alleles for normal hemoglobin, as those homozygous for it experienced reproductive failure.

This example also points out how adaptations tend to be specific; the abnormal hemoglobin was an adaptation to the particular parts of the world in which the malarial parasite flourished. When Africans adapted to that region came to North America, where falciparum malaria is unknown, what had been an adaptive characteristic became an injurious one. Where there is no malaria to attack those with normal hemoglobin, the abnormal hemoglobin becomes comparatively disadvantageous. Although the rates of sickle-cell trait are still relatively high among African Americans—about 9 percent show the sickling trait—this represents a significant decline from the approximately 22 percent who are estimated to have shown the trait when the first slaves were brought from Africa. A further decline over the next several generations is to be expected, as selection pressure continues to work against it.

This example also illustrates the important role culture may play even with respect to biological adaptation. In West Africa, falciparum malaria was not a significant problem until humans abandoned food foraging for farming a few thousand years ago. In order to farm, they had to clear areas of the natural forest cover. In the forest, decaying vegetation on the forest floor rapidly absorbed the heavy rainfall of the region. But once stripped of its natural vegetation, the soil lost this ability.

Furthermore, the forest canopy was no longer there to break the force of the rainfall, and so the impact of the heavy rains tended to compact the soil further. The result was that stagnant puddles commonly formed after rains, and these were perfect for the breeding purposes

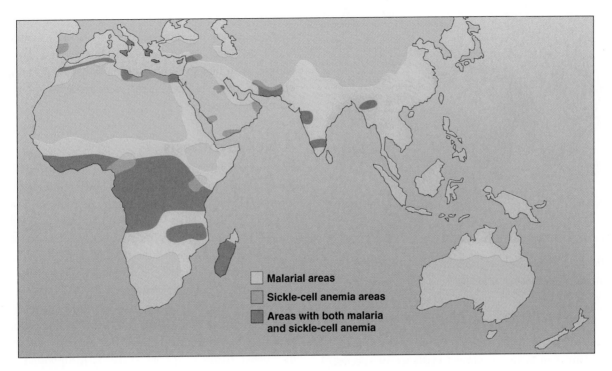

FIGURE 3.4

The allele that, in homozygotes, causes sickle-cell anemia makes heterozygotes resistant to falciparum malaria. Thus, the allele is most common in populations native to regions where this strain of malaria is common.

of the type of mosquito that is the host to the malarial parasite. These mosquitoes then began to flourish and transmit the malarial parasite to humans. Thus, humans unwittingly created the kind of environment that made a hitherto disadvantageous trait, the abnormal hemoglobin associated with sickle-cell anemia, advantageous.

Although it is true that all living organisms have many adaptive characteristics, it is not true that all characteristics are adaptive. All male mammals, for example, possess nipples, even though they serve no useful purpose. To female mammals, however, nipples are essential to reproductive success, which is why males have them. The two sexes are not separate entities, shaped independently by natural selection but are variants upon a single ground plan, elaborated in later embryology. Precursors of mammary glands are built in all mammalian fetuses, enlarging later in the development of females, but remaining small and without function in males.

Nor is it true that current utility is a reliable guide to historical origin. For one thing, nonadaptive characteristics may be co-opted for later utility. The unusually large size of a kiwi's egg, for example, enhances the survivability of kiwi chicks, in that they are particularly large and capable when hatched. Nevertheless, kiwi eggs probably did not evolve such large size because it is adaptive. Kiwis evolved from large, moa-sized ancestors, and in birds, egg size reduces at a slower rate than does body size. Therefore, the outsized eggs of kiwi birds seem to be no more than a developmental byproduct of a reduction in body size.[18] Similarly, an existing adaptation may come under strong selective pressure for some new purpose, as did insect wings. These did not arise so that insects might fly, but rather as gills that were used to "row," and later skim, across the surface of the water.[19] Later, the larger ones by chance proved useful for purposes of flight. In both these cases, what we see is natural selection operating as "a creative scavenger, taking what is available and putting it to new use."[20]

---

[18] Gould, S.J. (1991). *Bully for brontosaurus* (pp. 109–123). New York: Norton.

[19] Kaiser, J. (1994). A new theory of insect wing origins takes off. *Science, 266,* 363.

[20] Doist, R. (1997). Molecular evolution and scientific inquiry, misperceived. *American Scientist, 85,* 475.

This X-ray illustrates the unusually large size of a kiwi's egg.
OTOROHANGA ZOOLOGICAL SOCIETY

SPECIATION

The origin of distinct species is far more difficult to explain than is the continued existence of species. A species of cactus will survive as long as the conditions it needs to exist don't change. Variation within the species will help the species deal with perturbations in the local environment. If rainfall increases dramatically for example, the species may be wiped out if the variants cannot cope with the increased water. So maintaining species is relatively straightforward. The tough question is: how does novelty arise to form new species? Evolutionary biology, particularly human evolution studies, have been dominated by a Darwinian model of **gradualism**. Biologists define populations within species that are capable of interbreeding but may not regularly do so as **races,** or subspecies. The gradualist evolutionary model suggests that species evolve from subspecies through the accumulation of differences in the gene pools of the separated groups. This can happen, however, only in situations where one subspecies is isolated from others of its species for prolonged periods of time. There is nothing inevitable about races evolving into new species. Because they are by definition genetically open—that is, members of different races are capable of interbreeding—races are impermanent and subject to reamalgamation. This is precisely what happens as long as gene flow remains open.

In the case of humans, as we shall see in Chapter 13, the race concept cannot be applied. For one thing, the human propensity for gene flow makes it impossible to define races with any biological validity. To make matters worse, there has been a deplorable tendency to confuse cultural with biological phenomena under the heading of "race." As applied to humans, races are nothing more than social categories.

A New Synthesis

The problem with gradualism is that the fossil record has little evidence for it. Missing links showing in-between forms are difficult, if not impossible, to come by. Two graduate students, Niles Eldridge and Stephen J. Gould, noticed in their early 1970s study of trilobite fossils that trilobites changed little through time.[21] When changes occurred they were quick, at least in geological terms. After a dramatic change in the trilobites, the new species lasted for a long time with little significant change. Eldridge and Gould called this phenomenon **punctuated evolution.**[22] Since their initial study, the punctuated nature of speciation has been supported by many more studies. Jeffrey Schwartz, an evolutionary anthropologist, has written extensively on the role of these regulatory genes and the new synthesis of evolutionary change.[23,24] Schwartz points out that at the time of Eldridge and Gould's first study, the genetic basis for understanding this wasn't developed but today we have a much better knowledge of the potential biological basis for punctuated evolution. The relatively rapid appearance of novelty at the species level is set in

---

[21] Ibid.

[22] Eldredge N., & Gould S.J. (1972). Punctuated equilibria: An alternative to phyletic gradualism. In T.M. Schopf (Ed.), *Models in palaeobiology* (pp. 82–115). :Freeman Cooper.

[23] Schwartz J.H. (1999). *Sudden origins: Fossils, genes, and the emergence of species.* New York: John Wiley and Sons.

[24] Ibid.

Race. In biology, a subspecies; a population of a species that differs in allele frequencies from other such populations. Humans cannot be divided into racial categories that have any biological validity.

Punctuated evolution. A new species appears after a relatively quick and dramatic change then lasts for a long time with little significant change.

Gradualism. The perspective that species evolve through the accumulation of differences in the gene pools of subspecies that become isolated.

Although horses and donkeys (two separate species) can mate and produce live offspring (mules, pictured here), sterility of mules maintains the reproductive isolation of the parental species. **DON COUCH PHOTOGRAPHY**

developmental biology and the discovery of homeobox genes discussed earlier in this chapter.

Homeobox genes are the genes involved with the chain of events that take place after fertilization. Cells divide and multiply, differentiate and take on specific roles, and in turn interact with each other as they produce bone, muscle, and other tissues. Mice, chimpanzees, and humans, for example, have the same homeobox genes, so why are they so different from each other? Given that the homeobox genes are giving and receiving different instructions in different species, these regulatory genes are likely a powerful source of novelty leading to species differentiation. Schwartz surmises that mutations affecting gene regulation and expression are behind species evolution. These mutations would have been a result of radiation, temperature, or some other factor and would have no adaptive significance. He writes that "if a novelty doesn't kill you, you retain it, whether or not it will ever do you or your descendents any good."[25] Natural selection may fine-tune the novel feature and contribute to a species' longevity but it has nothing to do with its origin. Further research on evolution and the origin of species will need to carefully investigate the roles of selection, adaptation, and regulatory interaction and expression.

Isolating Mechanisms

Certain factors, known as **isolating mechanisms,** separate breeding populations, leading to the appearance first of divergent races and then divergent species. This happens as mutations may appear in one of the isolated populations but not in the other, as genetic drift affects the two populations in different ways, and as selective pressures may come to differ slightly in the two places. Because isolation prevents gene flow, changes that affect the gene pool of one population cannot be introduced into the gene pool of the other.

[25] Schwartz J.H. (2005). *The red ape: orangutans and human origins.* Cambridge, MA: Westview Press.

> **Isolating mechanisms.** Factors that separate breeding populations, thereby preventing gene flow, creating divergent subspecies and ultimately (if maintained) divergent species.

Regulator genes turn other genes on and off, and a mere change in their timing can cause significant evolutionary change. This may have a played a role in differentiating chimps and humans; for example, adult humans retain the flat facial profile of juvenile chimps.
DAVID BYGOTT/KIBUYU PARTNERS (LEFT), KAREN BAUMANN (RIGHT)

Some isolating mechanisms are geographical—preventing contact, hence gene flow, between members of separated populations. Anatomical structure can also serve as an isolating mechanism, as we saw in the case of the Saint Bernard and the Chihuahua. Other physical isolating factors include early miscarriage of the offspring; weakness or presence of maladaptive traits that cause early death in the offspring; or, as in the case of horses and donkeys, sterility of the hybrid offspring (mules).

Although physical barriers to reproduction may develop in geographical isolation, as genetic differences accumulate in the gene pools of separate populations, they may also result from accidents as cells undergo meiosis. In the course of such accidents genetic material may be broken off, transposed, or transferred from one chromosome to another. Even a relatively minor mutation, if it involves a gene that regulates the growth and development of an organism, may have a major effect on its adult form. In this way, a kind of instantaneous genetic isolation may occur.

Isolating mechanisms may also be social rather than physical. Speciation due to this mechanism is particularly common among birds. For example, cuckoos (birds that do not build nests of their own but lay their eggs in other birds' nests) attract mates by mimicking the song of the bird species whose nests they usurp; thus cuckoos that are physically capable of mating may have different courtship behaviour, which effectively isolates them from others of their kind.

Social isolating mechanisms are thought to have been important factors in human evolution. They continue to play a part in the maintenance of so-called racial barriers. Although there are no physical barriers to mating between any two mature humans of the opposite sex, awareness of social and cultural differences often makes the idea distasteful, perhaps even unthinkable; in India, for example, someone of an upper caste would not think of marrying an "untouchable." This isolation results from the culturally implanted concept of a significant difference between "us" and "them." Yet, as evidenced by the blending of human populations—even hostile ones—that has so often taken place in the world, people are also capable of suspending or even reasoning away social isolating mechanisms that would, in the case of other animals, lead separate populations to evolve into separate species. Such speciation is extremely unlikely in *Homo sapiens.*

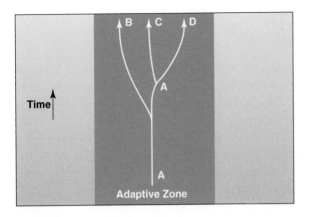

FIGURE 3.5

Divergent evolution occurs as different populations of an ancestral species become reproductively isolated. Through drift and differential selection, the number of descendant species increases.

Divergence and Convergence

As just described, isolation may cause a single ancestral species to give rise to two or more descendant species. Such **divergent** or **branching evolution** (Figure 3.5) is probably responsible for much of the diversity of life to be observed today. This has happened repeatedly, for example, as the platelike segments of the earth on which the continents ride have shifted position, separating once adjacent land masses.

Sorting out evolutionary relationships may be complicated by a phenomenon called **convergence** in which two distant forms—birds and bats, for example—develop greater similarities because their structures serve similar functions. Among the primates, an example is hind-leg dominance in both lemurs and humans. In most primates, the hind limbs are either shorter or of the same length as the forelimbs. Lemurs and humans are not closely related to each other, but both have longer hind limbs due to aspects of their locomotion. Humans are bipedal while lemurs use their long legs to push off and propel them from tree to tree. Convergent evolution takes place in circumstances where an environment exerts similar pressures on different organisms,

so that unrelated species become more like one another. Because the analogies produced by convergent evolution are not always easy to distinguish from the homologies that result from shared ancestry, it is often difficult to reconstruct the evolutionary history of any given species. As a case in point, humans and orangutans both have thick enamel on their molars, but African apes do not. Yet, molecular evidence reveals a closer human relationship to African apes than to orangs. Thus, thick molar enamel may be a case of analogy, rather than homology. Alternatively, thin enamel could have evolved separately in chimps and gorillas, and the presence of this feature in orangutans and humans could be retained from the ancestral condition.

CONCLUSION

As primatologist Frans de Waal notes, "Evolution is a magnificent idea that has won over essentially everyone in the world willing to listen to scientific arguments."[26] We will return to the topic in Chapter 5, as we look at how the primates evolved to produce the many species in the world today. First, however, we will survey the living primates (in Chapter 4) in order to understand the kinds of animals they are, what they have in common, and what distinguishes the various forms.

---

[26] de Waal, F. (2001). Sing the song of evolution. *Natural History, 110* (8), 77.

Divergent or branching evolution. An evolutionary process in which an ancestral population gives rise to two or more descendant populations that differ from one another.

Convergence. A process by which unrelated populations develop similarities to one another.

CHAPTER SUMMARY

In the 18th century, Carl von Linné (Linnaeus) devised a system to classify the great variety of living things then known. On the basis of similarities in body structure, body function, and sequence of bodily growth, he grouped organisms into small groups, or species. Modern taxonomy still uses his basic system but now looks at such characteristics as chemical reactions of blood, protein structure, and the makeup of the genetic material itself. Although Linnaeus regarded species as fixed and unchangeable, this idea was challenged by the finding of fossils, the idea of progress, and the many continuities among different species.

Evolution may be defined as descent with modification, which occurs as genetic variants in the gene pool of a population change in frequency. Genes, the actual units of heredity, are segments of molecules of DNA (deoxyribonucleic acid), and the entire sequence of DNA is known as the genome. DNA is a complex molecule resembling two strands of rope twisted around each other. Connecting the two strands are four chemical bases, adenine always pairing with thymine and guanine with cytosine. The sequence of these bases along the molecules are recipes that direct the production of proteins. These in turn direct the development of such identifiable traits as blood type. Just about everything in the human body is made of or by proteins, and human DNA provides the instructions for the thousands of proteins that keep us alive and healthy. DNA molecules have the unique property of being able to produce exact copies of themselves. As long as no errors are made in the process of replication, new organisms will contain genetic material exactly like that in ancestral organisms.

DNA molecules are located on chromosomes, structures found in the nucleus of each cell. Each kind of organism has a characteristic number of chromosomes, which are usually found in pairs. Humans have 23 pairs. Genes that are located on paired chromosomes and coded for different versions of the same trait are called alleles.

Mitosis, one kind of cell division, begins when the chromosomes (hence the genes) replicate, forming a second pair that duplicates the original pair of chromosomes in the nucleus. The process results in new cells with exactly the same number of chromosome pairs as the parent cell. Meiosis, a different kind of cell division, is involved in sexual reproduction. It begins with the replication of original chromosomes, but these are divided into four cells, each containing 23 single chromosomes.

The Augustine monk Gregor Mendel studied the mechanism of inheritance with garden peas. He discovered the particulate nature of heredity and that some alleles are able to mask the presence of others. They are called dominant. The allele not expressed is recessive. The allele for Type A blood in humans, for example, is dominant to the allele for Type O blood. Alleles that are both expressed when present are termed *co-dominant*. An individual with the alleles for Type A and Type B blood has the AB blood type.

Phenotype refers to the physical characteristics of an organism, whereas genotype refers to its genetic composition. Two organisms may have the same phenotype but different genotypes.

A key concept is that of population, or a group of individuals within which most breeding takes place. It is populations, rather than individuals, that evolve. The total number of different alleles of genes available to a population is called its gene pool. The frequency with which certain alleles occur in the same gene pool theoretically remains the same from one generation to another; this is known as the Hardy-Weinberg principle. Nonetheless, change does take place in gene pools as a result of several factors.

The ultimate source of genetic variation is mutation. These are accidents that cause changes in sequences of DNA. Although mutations are inevitable given the nature of cellular chemistry, extrinsic factors—such as heat, certain chemicals, or various kinds of radiation—can increase the mutation rate. Another source of variation is interspecies gene transfer, as retroviruses can introduce DNA from one species into the genome of another.

The effects of chance events (other than mutations and interspecies transfer) on the gene pool of a small population is called genetic drift. Genetic drift may have been an important factor in human evolution because until 10 000 years ago all humans probably lived in relatively small populations. Another factor that brings change to the gene pool of a population is gene flow, or the introduction of new variants of genes from nearby populations. Gene flow occurs when previously separated groups are able to breed again.

Natural selection is the force that makes evolutionary change adaptive. It reduces the frequency of alleles for harmful or maladaptive traits within a population and increases the frequency of alleles for adaptive traits. The term "adaptation" means both the process by which organisms achieve a beneficial adjustment to an available environment and the results of the process—the characteristics of organisms that fit them to the particular set of conditions of the environment in which they are generally found. A well-studied example of adaptation through natural selection in humans is inheritance of the trait for sickling red blood cells. The sickle-cell trait, caused by the inheritance of an abnormal form of hemoglobin, is an adaptation to life in regions in which falciparum malaria is common. In these regions, the sickle-cell trait plays a beneficial role, but in other parts of the world, the sickling trait is no longer advantageous, while the associated sickle-cell anemia remains injurious. Geneticists predict that as malaria is brought under control, within several generations, there will be a decline in the number of individuals who carry the allele responsible for sickle-cell anemia.

Over time, evolutionary forces act to produce new species from old ones. A species is a population or a group of populations that is capable of interbreeding. The concept of species is relative rather than absolute; whether breeding actually takes place in the wild or not is more important than the academic question of whether it is technically feasible. Biologists define populations within species that are capable of interbreeding but do so to a limited extent as subspecies or races. Although species are reasonably discreet and stable units in nature, races are impermanent and subject to reamalgamation. Among humans, it is not possible to define races with any biological validity.

Isolating mechanisms serve to separate breeding populations, creating first divergent races and then (if isolation continues) divergent species. Isolating mechanisms can be geographical; physical, as in the differing anatomical structures of the Saint Bernard and Chihuahua; or social, such as in the caste system of India.

As evolution proceeds it may be divergent (branching) or linear. The latter occurs as selection over time favours some variants over others, causing a change in a population's average characteristics. Convergence occurs when two unrelated species come to resemble each other owing to functional similarities.

Evolution is not a ladder of progress leading in a predictable and determined way to ever more complex forms. Rather, it has produced, through a series of accidents, a diversity of enormously varied designs that subsequently have been restricted to a lesser number of still less-than-perfect forms.

QUESTIONS FOR CRITICAL THOUGHT

1. How can the Human Genome Project help us understand human evolution?

2. Science fiction and fantasy authors have occasionally predicted a number of possible scenarios for future human evolution. Discuss the validity of making any such predictions.

3. Should we use our knowledge of genetics to manage our future biological makeup? Why or why not?

INTERNET RESOURCES

Blazing a Genetic Trail

www.hhmi.org/genetictrail

Learn how the genetics revolution is changing the practice of medicine. This site describes the story of the hunt for a cure for the genetic disease cystic fibrosis through gene therapy and also features a great tutorial in genetics.

Creationism

http://plato.stanford.edu/entries/creationism

The *Stanford Encyclopedia* has a detailed evaluation of creationism.

Darwinism
www.talkorigins.org/faqs/darwinism.html
Read a variety of quotes and discussions related to Darwinian evolution.

Genomes Programs of the U.S. Department of Energy Office of Science
www.doegenomes.org
Maintained by the U.S. Department of Energy, this information-packed site includes all the latest research about the Human Genome Project, including the ethical, legal, and social issues.

www.ncbi.nlm.nih.gov/genome/guide/chimp
This National Center for Biotechnology Information website provides an up-to-date source of information on the ongoing chimpanzee genome project.

www.hapmap.org
The International Hapmap Project website includes background information on the project as well as data and access to relevant publications.

www3.nationalgeographic.com/genographic
The genographic project is attempting to map the human genome geographically by creating a mitochondrial and Y-chromosome DNA database. Ten laboratories around the world are collecting DNA samples representing as many populations as possible. Individuals can also voluntarily submit a DNA sample; the project tells the donor the haplotype she belongs to. The donor is also provided with a history of her haplotype.

Hardy-Weinberg Principle
http://anthro.palomar.edu/synthetic/synth_2.htm
A useful site on the discussion of the Hardy-Weinberg principle.

Program in Evolutionary Biology, University of Montreal
www.bch.umontreal.ca/ciar/resources.html
This site has a variety of links to important evolution-related websites.

Punctuated Evolution
www.talkorigins.org/faqs/punc-eq.html
Read details about the alternative to Darwinian evolution. Problems with species determination in the fossil record, among other topics, are discussed.

SUGGESTED READINGS

For a list of suggested readings, visit the textbook's website at www.humanevolution2.nelson.com.

4

Monkeys, Apes, and Humans: The Modern Primates

Other primates have long fascinated humans, owing to our many shared anatomical and behavioural characteristics. By studying our closest living relatives, we address the challenge of knowing ourselves. The living primates provide us with important clues about human origins and the biological basis for human behaviour.

AUSTIN J. STEVENS/ANIMALS, ANIMALS

CHAPTER PREVIEW

1. What Is the Place of Humanity among the Other Animals?

Humans are classified by biologists as belonging to the primate order, a group that also includes lemurs, lorises, tarsiers, monkeys, and apes. They are so classified on the basis of shared characteristics of anatomy, physiology, protein structure, and even the genetic material itself. Among the primates, humans most closely resemble apes.

2. What Are the Implications of the Shared Characteristics between Humans and the Other Primates?

The similarities on which the modern classification of animals is based are indicative of evolutionary relationships. Therefore, by studying the anatomy, physiology, and molecular structure of the other primates, we can gain a better understanding of what human characteristics we owe to our general primate ancestry and what traits are uniquely ours as humans. Such studies indicate that many of the differences between apes and humans are differences of degree rather than kind.

3. Why Do Anthropologists Study the Social Behaviour of Monkeys and Apes?

By studying the behaviour of monkeys and apes living today—especially those most closely related to us—we may find essential clues from which to reconstruct the adaptations and behaviour patterns involved in the emergence of our earliest ancestors.

CHAPTER OUTLINE

The Primate Order

Primate Characteristics

Modern Primates

The Social Behaviour of Primates

The Question of Culture

All living creatures—be they great or small, fierce or timid, active or inactive—face a fundamental problem in common: that of survival. Simply put, unless they are able to adapt themselves to some available environment, they cannot survive. Adaptation requires the development of behaviour patterns that will help an organism utilize the environment to its advantage—to find food and sustenance, avoid hazards, and, if the species is to survive, reproduce. In turn, organisms need to have the biological equipment that makes possible the development of appropriate patterns of behaviour. For the hundreds of millions of years that life has existed on earth, biological adaptation has been the primary means by which the problem of survival has been solved. This is accomplished through natural selection as those organisms of a particular species whose biological equipment is best suited to a particular way of life produce more offspring than those whose equipment is not so adapted. In this way, advantageous characteristics become more common in succeeding generations, while less advantageous ones become less common.

In this chapter, we will look at the biological equipment possessed by the primates, the group of animals to which humans belong. By doing so, we will gain a firmer understanding of those characteristics we share with other primates, as well as those that distinguish us from them and make us distinctively human. We shall also sample the behaviour made possible by the biological equipment of primates. The study of that behaviour is important in our quest to understand something of the origins of human culture and the origin of humanity itself.

Providing milk to young via the mammary glands distinguishes mammals and other animals. Nursing young individuals is an important part of the general mammalian tendency to invest high amounts of energy into rearing relatively few young at a time. The pattern in reptiles is to lay many eggs that hatch independently, with the young fending for themselves. © MCGUIRE/ANTHRO-PHOTO

THE PRIMATE ORDER

The primate order (see Table 4.1) is only one of several mammalian orders, such as rodents, carnivores, ungulates (hoofed mammals), and so on. As such, primates share a number of **ancestral traits** with other mammals. Generally speaking, mammals are intelligent animals, having more in the way of brains than reptiles or other sorts of vertebrates. In most species, the young are born live, the egg being retained within the womb of the female until the embryo achieves an advanced state of growth. Once born, the young are nourished by their mothers with milk provided from the mammary glands, from which the class Mammalia gets its name. During this period of infant dependency, young mammals are able to learn some of the things that they will need for survival as adults. Overall, these characteristics make for more flexible behaviour than found among nonmammal vertebrates.

Mammals are also active animals. This is made possible by their relatively constant body temperature, an efficient respiratory system featuring a separation between the nasal and mouth cavities (allowing them to breathe while they eat), a diaphragm to assist in drawing in and letting out breath, and an efficient four-chambered heart that prevents mixing of oxygenated

> **Ancestral trait.** A characteristic that is shared widely, such as mammary glands in mammals, and is considered to have been shared by a common ancestor.

TABLE 4.1   The Primate Order

ORDER	SUBORDER	INFRAORDER	SUPERFAMILY	FAMILY	SUBFAMILY
Primates	Strepsirhini	Lemuriformes	Lemoroidea	Five families of lemurs and lemur-like animals	
			Lorisoidea	Three families of lorises	
	Haplorhini	Tarsii	Tarsioidea	One family, represented solely by tarsiers	
		Platyrrhini	Ceboidea	Three families of New World Monkeys	
		Catarrhini	Cercopithecoidea	One family with two subfamilies of Old World Monkeys	
			Hominoidea	Hylobatidae (small apes, gibbons, siamang)	
				Hominidae (apes, humans, and near humans)	Ponginae (Asian ape: orangutan)
					Homininae (African apes, humans and their immediate ancestors)

Hands that grasp and eyes that see in three dimensions enable primates, like these South American monkeys, to live effectively in the trees. JAMES MOORE/ANTHRO-PHOTO

and deoxygenated blood. Activity is facilitated as well by a skeleton in which the limbs are positioned beneath the body, rather than out at the sides, for ease and economy of movement. The bones of the limbs have joints constructed so as to permit growth in the young while simultaneously providing strong, hard joint surfaces that will stand up to the stresses of sustained activity.

Two classificatory systems exist for dividing the primate order into two suborders. The older system, dating back to the time of Linnaeus, divides primates into two groups: the Prosimii (from the Latin for "before monkeys"), which includes lemurs, lorises, and tarsiers, and the Anthropoidea (from the Greek for "human-like"), which includes monkeys, apes, and humans. This division was based on the overall similarity of the body plans within each group, a phenomenon biologists refer to as a grade. The prosimians have also been called the "lower primates" because they resemble the earliest fossil primates. In Asia and Africa, all prosimians are nocturnal (nighttime active) arboreal (tree-dwelling) creatures—again, like the fossil primates. The isolated but large island of Madagascar, off the coast of Africa, however, is home to a variety of diurnal (daytime active) ground-dwelling prosimians. In the rest of the world, the daytime active primates are all anthropoids. This group is sometimes called the "higher primates" due

to appearing later in evolutionary history and to a lingering belief that the group including humans was more "evolved." But from a contemporary biological perspective, no species is more evolved than any other. On the whole, prosimians are cat-sized or smaller, although some larger forms existed in the past. The prosimians also retain certain features common among nonprimate mammals, such as claws and moist, naked skin on their noses, not retained by the anthropoids.

The anthropoid suborder is further divided into two infraorders; the Platyrrhini, or New World monkeys; and the Catarrhini, consisting of the superfamilies Cercopithecoidea (Old World monkeys) and Hominoidea (apes). Although the terms "New World" and "Old World" reflect a Eurocentric vision of history (whereby the Americas were considered new only to European explorers and not to the indigenous people and animals already living there), these terms have evolutionary and geological relevance with respect to primates as we will see in Chapter 5. Old World monkeys and apes, including humans, have a 40-million-year shared evolutionary history in Africa distinct from the course taken by anthropoid primates in the tropical Americas. "Old World" in this context represents the evolutionary origins of anthropoid primates rather than a political or historical focus on Europe.

TABLE 4.2   Primate Anatomy Variation and Specialization

SUBORDER, INFRAORDER, SUPERFAMILY	SKULL AND FACE	DENTAL PATTERN AND SPECIALIZATIONS	LOCOMOTOR PATTERN AND MORPHOLOGY	TAIL AND OTHER SKELETAL SPECIALIZATIONS
Strepsirhini	Complete ring of bone around eye orbit	2-1-3-3	Hind-leg dominance for vertical clinging and leaping	Tail present
Lemuriformes		Dental comb for grooming		"Toilet claw" for grooming
Lorisiformes	Upper lip bound down to gum			
Haplorhini	Forward-facing orbit fully enclosed in bone Free upper lip Shorter snout			
Tarsiiformes Tarsiers		2-1-3-3	Hind leg dominance	Tail present
Platyrrhini New World Monkeys		2-1-3-3	Quadrupedal	Prehensile tail
Catarrhini Old World Monkeys		2-1-2-3 4-cusped molars	Quadrupedal	Tail present
Apes		2-1-2-3 Y5 molars	Suspensory hanging apparatus	No tail

Note: The dental pattern is a formula describing the number of incisors, canines, premolars, and molars on each side of the jaw, top and bottom. Apes have 2 incisors, 1 canine, 2 premolars, and 3 molars.

The genetic discoveries discussed in Chapter 2 led to the proposal of a new, primate taxonomy (see Table 4.1). A close genetic relationship was discovered between the tarsiers—animals resembling lemurs and lorises in their outward appearance and behaviour, as nocturnal tree dwellers—and monkeys and apes. The taxonomic scheme reflecting this genetic relationship places lemurs and lorises in the suborder Strepsirhini (from the Greek for "turned nose"). Tarsiers are placed with monkeys and apes in the suborder Haplorhini (from the Greek for "simple nose"). Although this classi-

ficatory scheme accurately reflects genetic relationships, it is still useful to make comparisons between "grades" or general levels of organization reflected in the older prosimian and anthropoid classification.

One final note of confusion in the primate classification system is what to do with humans.[1] The Hominoidea can be subdivided on the basis of genetic comparisons that indicate the orangutan is distantly

[1] Goodman, M., Bailey, W.J., Hayasaka, K., Stanhope, M.J., Slighton J., & Czelusniak, J. (1994). Molecular evidence on primate phylogeny from DNA sequences. *American Journal of Physical Anthropology, 94,* 7.

related to the African apes and humans. Following this reasoning, some anthropologists subdivide the Hominoidea into the Ponginae (the only living member of which is the orangutan) and the Homininae, which includes the African apes and humans. Humans and their closest fossil relatives are referred to as Hominini, the chimps and bonobos as Paninini, and the gorillas as Gorillini. A term still popular in human evolution research is "hominid," which has essentially the same meaning as "**hominin**."

PRIMATE CHARACTERISTICS

Although the living primates are a varied group of animals, they do have a number of features in common (Table 4.2). We humans, for example, can grasp, throw things, and see stereoscopically because we are primates. Primate features are, however, displayed in varying degree by the different members of this order; in some they are barely detectable, while in others they are greatly elaborated. The differences such as trait elaboration among primates are considered to be **derived traits**, that is, traits evolved and changed from characteristics in the common ancestor. Primates having similar derived traits are considered to have a very close evolutionary relationship. The minor differences in the molecular biology of humans and chimps are derived. All are useful in one way or another to **arboreal**, or tree-dwelling, animals, although (as any squirrel knows) they are not essential to life in the trees. For animals preying upon the many insects living on the fruit and flowers of trees and shrubs, however, such primate characteristics as manipulative hands and keen vision would have been enormously adaptive. Probably, it was as arboreal animals relying on visual predation of insects that primates got their start in life.

The Primate Brain

By far the most outstanding characteristic of primate evolution has been the enlargement of the brain among members of the order. Primate brains tend to be large, heavy in proportion to body weight, and very complex. The cerebral hemispheres (the areas of conscious thought) have enlarged dramatically and, in catarrhines, completely cover the cerebellum, which is the part of the brain that coordinates the muscles and maintains body equilibrium.

The reasons for this important change in brain size are many, but it likely began as the earliest primates, along with many other mammals, began to carry out their activities in daylight. Prior to 65 million years ago, mammals seem to have been nocturnal in their habits, but with the extinction of the dinosaurs, inconspicuous, nighttime activity was no longer the key to survival. With the change to diurnal or daytime activity, the sense of vision took on greater importance, and so visual acuity was favoured by natural selection. Unlike reptile vision, where the information-processing neurons are in the retina, mammalian vision is processed in the brain, permitting integration with information received by hearing and smelling.

If the evolution of visual acuity led to larger brains, it is likely that the primates' insect predation in an arboreal setting also played a role in enlargement of the brain. This would have required great agility and muscular coordination, favouring development of the brain centres. Thus it is of interest that much of the higher mental faculties are apparently developed in an area alongside the motor centres of the brain.[2]

Another related hypothesis that may help account for primate brain enlargement involves the use of the hand as a tactile organ to replace the teeth and jaws or snout. The hands assumed some of the grasping, tearing, and dividing functions of the snout, again requiring development of the brain centres for more complete coordination. Thus, while the skull and brain expanded, the teeth and jaws grew smaller. Certain areas of the brain became more elaborate and intricate. One of these areas is the cortex, considered to be the centre of an animal's intelligence; it receives impressions from the animal's various sensory receptors, analyzes them, and sends responses back down the motor nerves to the proper receptor.

The enlarged cortex not only served the primates well in the daily struggle for survival but also gave them the

---

[2] Romer, A.S. (1945). *Vertebrate paleontology* (p. 103). Chicago: University of Chicago Press.

Hominin. Hominoid tribe (between family and genus) to which all human species, including those that are extinct, are assigned.

Derived trait. A characteristic shared narrowly among organisms; it shows that organisms have a close evolutionary relationship.

Arboreal. Tree dwelling.

basis for more complex cerebration, or thought. Flexibility of thought probably played a decisive role in the evolution of the primates from which human beings emerged.

Primate Sense Organs

Catching insects in the trees, as the early primates did and many still do, demands quickness of movement and the ability to land in the right place without falling. Thus, early primates had to be adept at judging depth, direction, distance, and the relationships of objects in space—abilities that remain useful to animals that travel through the trees (as most primates still do today), even though they may have given up most insect eating in favour of fruits and leaves. In the haplorhines, these abilities are provided by **binocular vision** and three-dimensional **stereoscopic vision,** the ability to see the world in three dimensions—height, width, and depth. It requires two eyes set apart from each other on the same plane, so that each eye views an object from a slightly different angle (binocular vision). In addition, nerve fibres from each eye go to each side of the brain. The result is that the object assumes a three-dimensional appearance, indicating spatial relationships. Stereoscopic vision is one of the most important factors in primate evolution, for it evidently led to increased brain size in the visual area and a great complexity of nerve connections.

Visual acuity, however, varies throughout the primate order. Although all primates have forward-facing eyes that allow binocular and stereoscopic vision, monkeys and apes have better binocular vision than do the Lemuriformes. Forward-facing eyes also provide better visual clarity.[3] Matt Cartmill has proposed that binocular vision was an adaption to tracking insect prey by sight and seizing them in their hands.[4]

The primates' emphasis on visual acuity came at the expense of their sense of smell. One reason is that smell is processed in the snout, and a large protruding snout may interfere with stereoscopic vision. But smell is an expendable sense to tree-dwelling animals in search of insects; they no longer needed to live a "nose-to-the-ground" existence, sniffing close to the ground in search of food. The haplorhines especially have the least-developed sense of smell of all land animals. Strepsirhines still rely on it to a degree, scent marking objects in their territories.

Primates' sense of touch also became highly developed as a result of arboreal living. Primates found useful an effective feeling and grasping mechanism to grab their insect prey, and to prevent falls while moving through the trees. The primitive mammals from which primates descended possessed tiny tactile hairs that provided extremely sensitive tactile capacities. In primates, these hairs were replaced by informative pads on the tips of the animals' fingers and toes.

Primate Dentition

Although they have added things other than insects to their diets, primates have retained less specialized teeth than other mammals. According to primatologist W.E. LeGros Clark:

> An arboreal life obviates the necessity for developing highly specialized grinding teeth, since the diet available to most tree-living mammals in the tropics, consisting of leaves, shoots, soft fruits, and insects, can be adequately masticated by molar teeth of relatively simple structure.[5]

In most primates (humans included), on each side of each jaw, in front, are two straight-edged, chisel-like broad teeth called incisors (Figure 4.1). Behind the incisors is a canine, which in many mammals is large, flaring, and fanglike and is used for defence as well as for tearing and shredding food. Among some catarrhines the canine is somewhat reduced in size, especially in females, though it is still large in males. In humans, though, incisors and canines are practically indistinguishable,

---

[3] Barton R.A. (2004). Binocularity and brain evolution in primates. *PNAS, 101,* 10113–10115.

[4] Cartmill M. (1992). New views on primate origins. *Evolutionary Anthropology: Issues, News, and Reviews, 1,* 105–111.

[5] LeGros Clark, W.E. (1966). *History of the primates* (5th ed., p. 271). Chicago: University of Chicago Press.

Binocular vision. Vision with increased depth perception from two eyes set next to each other allowing their visual fields to overlap.

Stereoscopic vision. Complete three-dimensional vision from binocular vision plus visual connections from each eye to both sides of the brain allowing nerve cells to integrate the images derived from each eye.

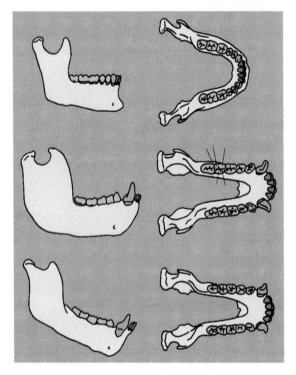

FIGURE 4.1

In this depiction of the lower jaws of a human, a gorilla, and a chimpanzee, incisors are shown in blue, canines in red, and premolars and molars in yellow. On one of the gorilla molars, the cusps are numbered to facilitate their identification.

Humans owe their flat facial profile and erect posture to their catarrhine ancestry. JIM LEACHMAN

although the canine has an oversized root, suggestive of larger canines some time back in our ancestry. Behind the canines are the premolars. Last come the molars, usually with four or five cusps, used mostly for crushing or grinding food. This basic dentition contrasts sharply with that of nonprimate mammals.

Comparative anatomy and the fossil record point to the existence of an early primate ancestor that possessed three incisors, one canine, five premolars, and three molars (expressed as the dental formula 3-1-5-3) on each side of the jaw, top and bottom, for a total of 48 teeth. In the early stages of primate evolution, four incisors (one on each side of each jaw) were lost. This change differentiated the primates, with their two incisors on each side of each jaw, from other mammals. The canines of most primates develop into long, daggerlike teeth that enable them to rip open tough husks of fruit and other foods. In a combat situation, male baboons, apes, and other primates flash these formidable teeth at their enemies, intending to scare them off. Only

infrequently, when this bluffing action fails, are teeth used to inflict bodily harm.

Other evolutionary changes in primate dentition involve the premolar and molar teeth. Over the millennia, three premolars became smaller and eventually disappeared altogether, while the two remaining premolars grew larger with the addition of a second pointed projection, or cusp, thus becoming "bicuspid." In humans, all eight premolars are bicuspid, but in apes, the lower first premolar is not. Instead, it is a specialized, single-cusped tooth with a sharp edge to act with the upper canine as a shearing mechanism. The molars, meanwhile, evolved from a three-cusp pattern to one with four and even five (in apes and humans) cusps. This kind of molar economically combined the functions of grasping, cutting, and grinding in one tooth.

The evolutionary trend for primate dentition has generally been toward economy, with fewer, smaller, more efficient teeth doing more work. Thus, our own 32 teeth (a 2-1-2-3 dental formula shared with the Old World monkeys and apes) are fewer in number than those of some, and more generalized than those of most, primates. Indeed, the absence of third molars in many individuals indicates that the human dentition is undergoing further reduction.

The Primate Skeleton

The skeleton gives an animal its basic shape or silhouette, supports the soft tissues, and helps protect the vital internal organs. In primates, for example, the skull protects the brain and the eyes. A number of factors are responsible for the shape of the primate skull as compared with those of most other mammals: changes in dentition, changes in the sensory organs of sight and smell, and increased brain size. The primate brain case, or **cranium**, tends to be high and vaulted. A solid partition exists in most primate species (including humans) between the eye and the temple, affording maximum protection to the eyes from the contraction of the chewing muscles positioned directly next to the eyes.

The **foramen magnum** (the large opening in the skull through which the spinal cord passes and connects to the brain) is an important clue to evolutionary relationships. In most mammals, as in dogs and horses, this opening faces directly backward, with the skull projecting forward from the vertebral column. In humans, by contrast, the vertebral column joins the skull toward the centre of its base, thereby placing the skull in a balanced position as required for habitual upright posture. Other primates, though they frequently cling, sit, or hang with their bodies upright, are not as fully committed to such posture as humans, and so their foramen magnum is not as far forward.

In most primates, the snout or muzzle portion of the skull has grown smaller as the acuity of the sense of smell declined. The smaller snout offers less interference with stereoscopic vision; it also enables the eyes to be placed in the frontal position. As a result, primates have flatter faces than other mammals. Below the primate skull and the neck is the **clavicle,** or collarbone, a holdover from primitive mammal ancestors. Though reduced in quadrupedal primates like monkeys, in apes and humans it serves as a strut that prevents the arm from collapsing inward when brought across the front of the body. It allows for great manoeuvrability of the arms, permitting them to swing

Humans are able to grasp and throw things as they do, in this case extremely accurately, because of characteristics of their hands and shoulders inherited from ape ancestors. **GARY CRAWFORD**

sideways and outward from the trunk of the body. The clavicle also supports the **scapula** (shoulder blade) and allows for the muscle development that is required for flexible, yet powerful, arm movement, particularly in hominoids, whose shoulders are especially broad. This shoulder and limb structure is associated with considerable acrobatic agility and, in the case of all apes and a few New World monkeys, the ability to **brachiate**—use their arms to swing and hang beneath the branches of trees with the body in a vertical (upright) position.

Primates have retained also the characteristic, found in early mammals, of **pentadactyly**. Pentadactyly, which means possessing five digits, is an ancient characteristic that proved to be of special advantage to tree-dwelling primates. Their grasping feet and hands (Figure 4.2)

Cranium. The brain case of the skull.

Foramen magnum. A large opening in the skull through which the spinal cord passes and connects to the brain.

Clavicle. The collarbone.

Scapula. The shoulder blade.

Brachiate. To use the arms to move from branch to branch, with the body hanging suspended beneath the arms.

Pentadactyly. Possessing five digits (fingers and toes).

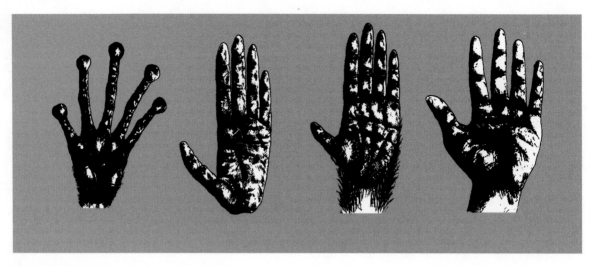

FIGURE 4.2

The hands of primates are similar. However, human hands are distinguished by prominent thumbs that can be used in opposition to the fingers. The highly specialized hands of the brachiators (gibbons and chimpanzees) are characterized by long fingers and less prominent thumbs.

have sensitive pads at the tips of their digits, backed up (except in some strepsirhines) by flattened nails. This unique combination of pad and nail provides the animal with an excellent **prehensile** (grasping) device for use when moving from branch to branch. The structural characteristics of the primate foot and hand make grasping possible; the digits are extremely flexible, the big toe is fully opposable to the other digits in all but humans and their immediate ancestors, and the thumb is opposable to the other digits to varying degrees.

Hindsight indicates that the flexible, unspecialized primate hand was to prove a valuable asset for future evolution of this group. Had they not had generalized grasping hands, early hominines (members of the human subfamily) would not have been able to manufacture and utilize tools and thus embark on the new and unique evolutionary pathway that led to the revolutionary ability to adapt through culture.

Reproduction and Care of Young

The breeding of most mammals occurs once or twice a year, but many primate species are able to breed at any time during the course of the year. Generally, the male is ready to engage in sexual activity whenever females are in **estrus,** around the time of ovulation. The female's receptivity is cyclical, corresponding to her period of estrus, which occurs once each month.

This is not to say that females are receptive regularly each month. Rather, the average adult female monkey or ape spends most of her time either pregnant or nursing, at which times she is not sexually receptive. But after her infant is weaned, she will come into estrus for a few days each month, until she becomes pregnant again. Because this can happen at any time, it is advantageous to have males present throughout the year. This is promoted in some species by lack of visual signs of estrus. Thus, sex plays a role in keeping both sexes constantly together, except among some orangutans, among whom adults may come together only when females are in estrus. In most species, however, sex is not the only, or even the most important, cause of males and females remaining together.

Among primates, as among some other mammals, females give birth to few offspring at a time. In the case of lemurs, the primates closest to the ancestral condition, two or three young are produced at each birth. By contrast, catarrhines (humans included), usually produce but a single offspring at a time. Natural selection may have favoured single births among primate tree dwellers because the primate infant, which has a highly developed grasping

Prehensile.   Having the ability to grasp.

Estrus.   In primate females, the time of sexual receptivity during which ovulation takes place.

110

ability (the grasping reflex can also be seen in human infants), must be transported about by its mother, and more than one clinging infant would seriously encumber her as she moved about the trees (where twinning is seen, fathers as well as mothers transport offspring). Moreover, a female pregnant with a large litter would be unable to lead a very active life as a tree dweller.

Because primates bear few young at a time, they must devote more time and effort to their care if the species is to survive. This usually means a longer period during which the infant is dependent upon its mother. As a general rule, the more closely related to humans the species is, the smaller, more helpless, and more immature the newborn offspring tend to be. For example, a lemur is dependent upon the mother for only a few months after birth; an ape, for four or five years; and a human for more than a decade. Prolonged infancy is typically associated with an increase in longevity (Figure 4.3). If the breeding life of primates had

not extended, the lengthened infancy could have led to a decrease in numbers of individuals. Something approaching this can be seen in the great apes: A female chimpanzee, for example, does not reach sexual maturity until about the age of 10, and once she produces her first live offspring, there is a period of five or six (on average 5.6) years before she will bear another. Furthermore, a chimpanzee infant cannot survive if its mother dies before it reaches the age of four at the very least. Thus, assuming that none of her offspring die before adulthood, a female chimpanzee must survive for at least 20 or 21 years just to maintain the size of chimpanzee populations at existing levels. In fact, chimpanzee infants and juveniles do die from time to time, and not all females live full reproductive lives. This is one reason apes are far less abundant in the world today than are monkeys.

The young of catarrhine, and especially hominoid, species are born with relatively underdeveloped nervous systems; moreover, they lack the social knowledge that guides behaviour. Thus, they depend upon adults not only for protection but also for instruction, as they must learn how to survive. The longer period of dependence in these primates makes possible a longer period of learning, which appears to be a distinct evolutionary advantage.

Establishing Evolutionary Relationships

Most of the primate characteristics discussed so far are present at least in a rudimentary sort of way in the strepsirhines, but all are seen to a much greater degree in the haplorhines. The differences between humans and the other haplorhines, especially catarrhines, are rather like those between strepsirhines and haplorhines. In humans many of the characteristic primate traits are developed to a degree not realized by any other species. Among some strepsirhines, some of the distinctive primate traits are missing, whereas others are clearly present, so that the borderline between primate and nonprimate becomes blurred, and the difference is one of degree rather than kind. All of this is fully expectable, given an evolutionary history in which early primates having a rough resemblance to today's strepsirhines developed out of some other mammalian order and eventually gave rise to early haplorhines; from these emerged the catarrhines and, ultimately, hominins.

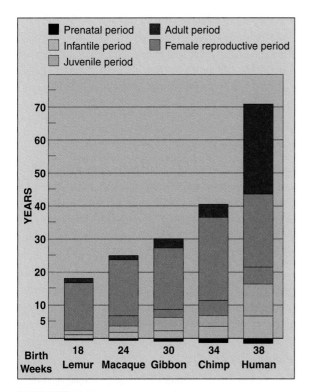

FIGURE 4.3

Primates are born at earlier stages of development than many other animals. Humans are born at a particularly early stage because of their larger brain; if born later, the baby's head would be too large for the mother's pelvis.

Similar though our appearance is to other primates, just how close our evolutionary relationship is to them is indicated most dramatically by molecular evidence. There is a striking similarity in blood and protein chemistry among the hominoids especially, indicating close evolutionary relationships. On the basis of tests with blood proteins, it has been shown that the bonobo, chimpanzee, and gorilla are closest to humans; next comes the orangutan; then the smaller apes (gibbons and siamangs); Old World monkeys; New World monkeys; and finally the strepsirhines. Measurements of genetic affinity confirm these findings, providing further evidence of humanity's close kinship to the great apes, especially those of Africa (Figure 4.4). The modern classification of humans, two species of genus *Pan* (bonobos and chimpanzees), and gorillas together in the subfamily Homininae, distinct from the Ponginae, reflects the fact that the three genera are more closely related to one another than any is to the orangutan.

At the genetic level, humans, bonobos, and chimpanzees are between 98 and 99 percent identical. The differences are that bonobos and chimps (like gorillas and orangs) have an extra pair of chromosomes; in humans, two medium-sized chromosomes have fused together in Chromosome 2 (the second largest of the human chromosomes). Of the other pairs, 18 are virtually identical between humans and the genus *Pan*, whereas the remaining ones have been reshuffled. Overall, the differences are fewer than those between gibbons (with 44 chromosomes) and siamangs (50 chromosomes),

which, in captivity, have produced live hybrid offspring. Studies of molecular similarities have suggested a closer relationship between *Pan* and humans than either has to gorillas. Fossil evidence also supports this view.[6] Others disagree, and the safest course at the moment is to regard all three genera as having an equal degree of relationship (the two species of genus *Pan* are, of course, more closely related to each other than either is to gorillas or humans).[7]

To sum up, what becomes apparent when humans are compared to other primates is how many of the characteristics we think of as distinctly human are no such thing; rather, they are variants of typical primate traits. The fact is, we humans look the way we do *because* we are primates, and the differences between us and others of this order—especially the apes—are more differences of degree than kind.

MODERN PRIMATES

The modern primates are mostly restricted to warm areas of the world. As already noted, they are divided into two suborders: Strepsirhini and Haplorhini. Strepsirhines are small Old World animals that do a lot of leaping and clinging; haplorhines include tarsiers, monkeys, apes, and humans.

Strepsirhines

The strepsirhines, the most primitive primates (that is, closest to the ancestral condition), are represented by the single infraorder Lemuriformes, within which are the lemurs and lorises. Although lemurs are restricted to the island of Madagascar (off the east coast of Africa), lorises range from Africa to southern and eastern Asia. Only on Madagascar, where there was no competition from other primates until humans arrived, are lemuriformes diurnal; lorises, by contrast, are all nocturnal. All these animals are small, with none larger than a good-sized dog. In general body outline, they resemble rodents and insectivores, with short pointed snouts, large pointed ears, and big eyes. In the anatomy of the upper lip and snout, lemuriformes resemble nonprimate mammals, in

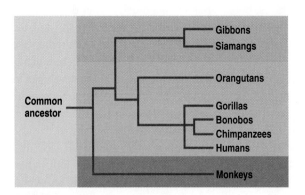

FIGURE 4.4

Based on molecular similarities and differences, a relationship can be established among various catarrhine primates. Present thinking is that the split between the human and African ape lineages took place between 5 and 8 million years ago.

[6] Begun, D. (1992). Miocene fossil hominids and the chimp-human clade. *Science, 257,* 1929–1933.

[7] Rogers, J. (1994). Levels of the genealogical hierarchy and the problem of hominid phylogeny. *American Journal of Physical Anthropology, 94,* 81.

Modern strepsirhines represent highly evolved variants of an early primate model. AP/WIDE WORLD PHOTOS (LEFT), DAVE AGEE/ ANTHRO-PHOTO (RIGHT)

that the upper lip is bound down to the gum and the naked skin on the nose around the nostrils is moist. They also have long tails, with that of a ring-tail lemur somewhat like the tail of a raccoon.

In brain structure, lemuriformes are clearly primates, and they have characteristically primate "hands," although they use them in pairs, rather than one at a time. Their legs are longer than their forelimbs, and when they move on all fours, the forelimbs are in a "palms down" position. They also leap and cling in near-vertical positions to branches. Although they retain a claw on their second toe, which they use for scratching and grooming, all other digits are equipped with flattened nails. Also for grooming is a structure unique to lemuriformes: a dental comb made up of the lower incisors and canines, which project forward from the jaw. With their distinctive mix of characteristics, strepsirhine primates appear to occupy a place between the haplorhines and insectivores (the mammalian order that includes moles and shrews).

Haplorhines

The suborder Haplorhini is divided into three infraorders: the Tarsii (tarsiers), Platyrrhini (New World monkeys), and Catarrhini (Old World monkeys, apes, and humans). Most haplorhines are bigger than the strepsirhines and are strikingly humanlike in appearance. Actually, it is more accurate to say that humans are remarkably like monkeys, but even more like apes, in appearance. The defining traits of the primates—large cranium, well-developed brain, acute vision, chisel-like incisors, prehensile digits—are especially evident in the haplorhines. Most haplorhines generally move on all four limbs but sit with the body erect, and many stand erect to reach fruit hanging in trees: Some apes even walk occasionally on two feet. Monkeys are often highly arboreal, and New World species have prehensile tails that wrap around a tree branch, freeing the forelimbs to grasp food. A few New World monkeys brachiate; Old World monkeys never do.

All apes may once have been fully arboreal brachiators, but among modern apes, only the gibbon and siamang still are. The larger bonobo, chimpanzee, and gorilla spend most of their time on the ground but sleep in the trees and may also find food there. Orangutans, too, spend time down on the ground, but are more arboreal than the African apes. When on the ground, they move mostly on all fours.

Tarsiers

Tarsiers are the haplorhine primates most like the lemuriformes, and in the past they were usually classified in the same suborder with them. Appearances can be deceiving, however; molecular evidence indicates a closer relationship to the other haplorhines. The head, eyes, and ears of these kitten-sized arboreal creatures are huge in proportion to the body. Tarsiers have the remarkable ability to turn their heads 180 degrees, so they can see where they have been as well as where they are going. Their digits end in plate-like, adhesive discs. Tarsiers are named for the elongated tarsal, or foot bone, that provides leverage for jumps of 2 metres or more. Tarsiers are mainly nocturnal insect eaters. In the structure of the nose and lips, and the part of the brain governing vision, tarsiers resemble monkeys.

Tarsiers are distinctive for their large eyes, adapted for their nocturnal habitat. MICHAEL DICK/ANIMALS, ANIMALS/MAXXIMAGES.COM

New World Monkeys

New World monkeys live in forests and swamps of South and Central America. They are characterized by flat noses with widely separated, outward-flaring nostrils, from which comes their name of platyrrhine (platy = flat; rhine = nose) monkeys. All are arboreal, and some have long, prehensile tails by which they hang from trees. These features and a 2-1-3-3 dental formula (three, rather than two, premolars on each side of each jaw) distinguish them from the Old World monkeys, apes, and humans. Platyrrhines walk on all fours with their palms down and scamper along tree branches in search of fruit, which they eat sitting upright. Spider monkeys are accomplished brachiators as well. Although other New World monkeys spend much of their time in the trees, they rarely hang or swing from limb to limb by their arms and have not developed the extremely long forelimbs and broad shoulders characteristic of brachiators.

Old World Monkeys

Old World, or catarrhine, monkeys are characterized by noses with closely spaced, downward-pointing nostrils, a 2-1-2-3 dental formula (two, rather than three, premolars on each side of each jaw), and their lack of prehensile tails. They may be either arboreal or terrestrial. The

E.R. DEGGINGER/COLOR-PIC, INC.

arboreal species include the guereza monkey, the Asiatic langur, and the strange-looking proboscis monkey. Some are equally at home on the ground and in the trees, such as the macaques, of which some 19 species range from Gibraltar (the misnamed "Barbary ape") to Japan.

Several species of baboons are largely terrestrial, living in the savannas, deserts, and highlands of Africa. They have long, fierce faces and move quadrupedally, with all fours in the palms-down position. Like all monkeys, their forelimbs and hindlimbs are of equal length. Their diet consists of leaves, seeds, insects, and lizards, and they live in large, well-organized troops consisting of related females and adult males that have transferred out of other troops. Because baboons have abandoned trees (except for sleeping and refuge) and live in environments like that in which humans may have originated, they are of great interest to primatologists.

Gibbons and orangutans are Southeast Asian apes. Gibbons are brachiators that use their long arms and hands to swing through the trees. Although orangutans sometimes brachiate, their legs move like arms and their feet are like hands; thus, much of their movement is by four-handed climbing. PETER DROWNE/ COLOR-PIC, INC.

Small and Great Apes

The apes are the closest living relatives we humans have in the animal world. Their general appearance and way of life are related to their semierect posture. In their body chemistry, the position of their internal organs, and even their diseases, they are remarkably close to humans'. They are arboreal to varying degrees, but their generally greater size and weight are obstacles to swinging and jumping as freely as monkeys. The exception is the small, lithe gibbon, which can both climb and swing freely through the trees and so spends virtually all of its time in them. At the opposite extreme are gorillas, who climb trees, using their prehensile hands and feet to grip the trunk and branches. Their swinging is limited to leaning outward as they reach for fruit, clasping a limb for support. Most of their time is spent on the ground.

The apes, like humans, have no external tail. Also shared with us are broad shoulders, unlike the narrow ones of monkeys. But, unlike humans, apes' arms are longer than their legs, indicating that their ancestors specialized for arboreal brachiation in a way that our own did not. In moving on the ground, the African apes "knuckle-walk" on the backs of their hands, resting their weight on the middle joints of the fingers. They stand erect when reaching for fruit, looking over tall grass, or in any activity where they find an erect position advantageous. The semierect position is natural in apes when on the ground because the curvature of their vertebral column places their centre of gravity, which is high in their bodies, in front of their hip joint. Thus, they are both "top heavy" and "front heavy." Furthermore, the structure of the ape pelvis is not well suited to support the weight of the torso and limbs easily. Nor do apes have the arrangement of leg muscles that enables humans to stand erect and swing their legs freely before and behind.

Gibbons and siamangs, which are native to Southeast Asia and Malaya, have compact, slim bodies with extraordinarily long arms compared to their short legs, and stand about a metre high. Although their usual form of locomotion is brachiation, they can run erect, holding their arms out for balance. Gibbons and siamangs resemble monkeys in size and general appearance more than the other apes.

Chimpanzees and gorillas are African apes. MIRIAM SILVERSTEIN/ANIMALS, ANIMALS/MAXXIMAGES .COM (LEFT), DAVID WATTS/ANTHRO-PHOTO (RIGHT)

Orangutans are found in Borneo and Sumatra. They are somewhat taller than gibbons and siamangs and are much heavier, with the bulk characteristic of apes. In the closeness of the eyes and facial prominence, an orangutan looks a little like a chimpanzee, except that its hair is reddish. Orangs walk with their forelimbs in a fists-sideways or a palms-down position. They are somewhat more arboreal than the African apes. Although sociable by nature, the orangs of upland Borneo spend most of their time alone (except in the case of females with young), as they have to forage over a wide area to obtain sufficient food. By contrast, fruits and insects are sufficiently abundant in the swamps of Sumatra to sustain groups of adults and permit coordinated group travel. Thus, gregariousness is a function of habitat productivity.[8]

Gorillas, found in equatorial Africa, are the largest of the apes; an adult male can weigh over 180 kilograms. The body is covered with a thick coat of glossy black hair, and mature males have a silvery grey upper back. There is a strikingly human look about the face, and, like humans, gorillas focus on things in their field of vision by directing the eyes rather than moving the head. Gorillas are mostly ground dwellers but may sleep in trees in carefully constructed nests. Because of their weight, brachiation is limited to raising and lowering themselves among the tree branches when searching for fruit. They knuckle-walk, using all four limbs with the fingers of the hand flexed, placing the knuckles instead of the palm of the hand on the ground. They will stand erect to reach for fruit, to see something more easily, or to threaten perceived sources of danger with their famous chest-beating displays. Although gorillas are gentle and tolerant, bluffing is an important part of their behavioural repertoire.

Chimpanzees and bonobos are two species of the same genus (*Pan*), bonobos being the least well known and restricted in their distribution to the rain forests of the Democratic Republic of Congo. The common chimpanzee, by contrast, is widely distributed in the forested portions of sub-Saharan Africa. They are probably the best known of the apes and have long been favourites in zoos and circuses. Although chimpanzees are thought of as particularly quick and clever, all four great apes are of equal intelligence, despite some differences in cognitive styles. More arboreal than gorillas,

---

[8] Normile, D. (1998). Habitat seen as playing larger role in shaping behaviour. *Science, 279,* 1454.

but less so than orangs, chimpanzees and bonobos forage on the ground much of the day, knuckle-walking like gorillas. At sunset, they return to the trees, where they build their nests. Chimps' nests are more dispersed than those of bonobos, who prefer to build their nests close to one another.

THE SOCIAL BEHAVIOUR OF PRIMATES

The physical resemblance of human beings to the other catarrhines is striking, but the most startling resemblance of all is in their social behaviour. Because of their highly developed brains, monkeys and apes behave in ways that are far more complex than most other animals except humans. In the 1920s S. Zuckerman studied baboons in the London, England, zoo and reported a high degree of aggression and fighting among them. Primatologists now understand that this was a result of crowding and confinement, and the same response to these conditions can be seen in humans. Only over the past four decades have primatologists made prolonged close-range observations

Gender. The cultural construction of masculinity and femininity as well as third genders and androgynous identities and roles.

GENDER PERSPECTIVES

Gender Bias in Primatology

A popular but controversial view holds that, until female primatologists began to study primates, the importance of female primates was undervalued and misunderstood. The early twentieth century primatologist, S. Zuckerman, who was a male, saw aggression, violence, and a well-defined hierarchy in baboons confined in the London Zoo. To what extent were his interpretations related to who he was as an individual and to his choice of a zoo as his study site? How the role of the observer may affect observations and interpretations is an important question. Male scholars had apparently constructed theories about male dominance hierarchies, as one example, through their filter of masculinity. Biruté Galdikas, Jane Goodall, and Dian Fossey are prominent primatologists in the public eye, reinforcing another view—that women are disproportionately drawn to, and qualified to conduct, primatology. In fact, there are probably as many male primatologists as there are female, many have studied with the same professors, and some of the earliest studies of monkeys by male scholars paid close attention to female roles.[1] The idea that male and female scientists approach issues differently isn't new. Naomi Quinn is a prominent feminist anthropologist who holds that academia in general is a male world and men produce male-biased theory and treat women as inherently inferior. A feminine approach is thought to consider cooperation, empathy, and holism whereas a masculine approach would not. Linda Fedigan, though, raises questions whose answers are not all that clear. What is **gender** and why is it relevant? Why would we want to know if the gender or sex of a researcher affects their research? We need to come to terms with such questions in order to understand if the gender of a researcher affects their research.

Linguists use gender to describe gendered words; psychologists transformed the concept to one related to the sexes but not primarily biological. Today, gender is considered to be the cultural construction of masculinity and femininity as well as third genders and androgynous identities and roles. Shirley Strum, a baboon researcher, believes that being a female has had no impact on her work. Her approach is based on many years of studying baboons. Japanese primatologists, as a group (mainly men), appear to have approaches that fit the stereotype of Western female scholars. There is no agreement on how to evaluate gender and its effects in science, let alone primatology. Some support the idea that men and women do science differently; others do not.

[1] Strum, Shirley C., & Fedigan, Linda. (2000). *Primate encounters: Models of science, gender, and society.* Chicago: University of Chicago Press, 635.

of catarrhines in their natural habitats, and we are discovering much about social organization, learning ability, and communication among our closest relatives in the animal kingdom. In particular, we are finding that a number of behavioural traits that we used to think of as distinctively human are found to one degree or another among other primates, reminding us once again that many of the differences between us and them are differences of degree, rather than kind.

The range of behaviour shown by living primates is great—too great to be adequately surveyed in this book. Instead, we shall look primarily at the behaviour of those species most closely related to humans: bonobos, chimpanzees, and gorillas.

The Group

Primates are social animals, living and travelling in groups that vary in size from species to species. In most species, females and their offspring constitute the core of the social system. This is true of chimpanzees to a degree. In two Tanzanian communities studied, females often leave their natal group for another, although up to 50 percent do not.[9] In both cases, however, females in ovulation may temporarily leave their group to mate with males of another. But whatever the case, their sons, and often their daughters, remain in their mother's group for life. Among bonobos, females always transfer to another group, in which they establish bonds with females already there. Female bonobos are especially skilled at establishing such bonds with one another, so they are far more sociable than are their chimpanzee counterparts. Among the latter, the stronger bonds are between males, as young ones reaching maturity spend more and more time with the adult males of their group. In the case of gorillas, either sex may or may not leave its natal group for another.

Among chimps, the largest organizational unit is the community, composed of 50 or more individuals. Rarely, however, are all these animals together at a single time. Instead, they are usually found ranging singly or in small subgroups consisting of adult males together, females with their young, or males and females together with their young. In the course of their travels, subgroups may join forces and forage together, but sooner or later these will break up again into smaller units. When they do, members are often exchanged, so that new subunits are different in their composition from the ones that initially came together.

Although relationships among individuals within the community are relatively harmonious, dominance hierarchies exist. Generally, males outrank females, although high-ranking females may dominate low-ranking males. Physical strength and size help determine an animal's rank, but so too does the rank of its mother, its skill at building coalitions with other individuals, and, in the case of the male, its motivation to achieve high status. Highly motivated males, even though they may not be the biggest in their group, may bring considerable intelligence and ingenuity to bear in their quest for high rank. For example, in the community studied by Jane Goodall, a pioneer in the study of primate behaviour, one chimp hit upon the idea of incorporating noisy kerosene cans into his charging displays, thereby intimidating all the other males.[10] As a result, he rose from relatively low status to the number one (alpha) position.

On the whole, bonobo females form stronger bonds with one another than do their chimpanzee counterparts. Moreover, the strength of the bond between mother and son is such as to interfere with that between males. Thus, instead of the male dominance characteristic of chimps, one sees female dominance. Not only do bonobo males defer to females in feeding, but alpha females have been observed chasing high-ranking males. Alpha males even yield to low-ranking females, and groups of females form alliances in which they may cooperatively attack males, to the point of inflicting blood-drawing injuries.[11]

The gorilla group is a "family" of 5 to 20 individuals led by a mature, silver-backed male and including younger, black-backed males, females, the young, and sometimes other silverbacks. Subordinate males, however, are usually prevented by the dominant male from mating with the group's females, although he may occasionally allow access to lower-ranking ones. Thus, young silverbacks often leave their natal family to start their own families by winning outside females. If the dominant male is weakening with age, however, one of

---

[9] Moore, J. (1998). Comment. *Current Anthropology, 39*, 412.

[10] Goodall, J. (1986). *The chimpanzees of Gombe: Patterns of behaviour* (p. 424). Cambridge, MA: Belknap Press.

[11] de Waal, F., Kano, T., & Parish, A.R. (1998). Comment. *Current Anthropology, 39*, 408, 410, 413.

BIOGRAPHY

Linda Fedigan and Biruté Galdikas

One of the foremost primatologists in Canadian anthropology is Linda Fedigan. During her 30-year career, she has played a pivotal role in putting primatology on the academic map. Fedigan has focused on three international projects: the Arashiyama Texas-Japan project; the Santa Rosa primate project in Costa Rica; and a gender and science study.

One of Fedigan's most significant contributions to the science of primatology is bringing female primates into the limelight. She examines the biological and social nature of primates from the female's perspective, and asks questions such as, How and why do male and female primates (including humans) live together year-round? What makes some females more reproductively successful than others? Using primates as biological models, Fedigan and colleagues have explored the puzzling question of how and why menopause evolved in humans. Reproductive aging in mammals is quite variable and not well known. Comparative studies will help to understand how the human reproductive aging pattern developed.

Fedigan has documented the life histories of primates, in particular the Arashiyama Japanese macaques and Costa Rican capuchins, howlers, and spider monkeys. Her book *Primate Paradigms: Sex Roles and Social Bonds* (1982) has been influential in the study of female primates, and a compilation of primate life histories, *The Monkeys of Arashiyama. Thirty-Five Years of Research in Japan and the West* (1991) is considered the best data set in primatology.

Fedigan has directed her conservation efforts to the recovery of primate habitats, and has conducted biennial censuses of monkeys in the Santa Rosa National Park in Costa Rica. Unlike many conservation studies that focus on the loss of plant and animal species, Fedigan has concentrated on the natural return of animals to regenerating tropical forests. Fedigan believes that if primatologists can determine how female reproductive and life history variables (e.g., age at first and last birth) are affected by ecological variables and demographic trends, then scientists

can recommend the types of environments humans must maintain or restore to save primate populations. Fedigan's conservation efforts in Costa Rica have been highlighted in the 1998 film *Champions of the Wild*.

Fedigan has also studied the role of gender in anthropology, primatology, and biological sciences. She has collaborated with other scientists to analyze the role of theory, method, and gender in the scientific community's changing ideas about sociality, and how the gender of a scientist affects research on sex differences. Among her many research contributions, Fedigan has addressed questions such as what determines how often females produce infants, and what factors enable females to live longer.

In 1974, Fedigan began teaching at the University of Alberta; in 2001 she assumed the Canada Research Chair at the University of Calgary. Organizations such as National Geographic, Nature, and Survival Anglia regularly consult Fedigan regarding the accuracy of their scripts for films on primates. Ultimately, Fedigan is endeavouring to understand the social and biological nature of primates and, thus, our human place in nature.

Known as one of "Leakey's Angels," (Dian Fossey and Jane Goodall being the other two), **Biruté Galdikas** is considered the world's foremost authority on wild orangutans (Lessem 1995). Galdikas received her master's degree in primatology from UCLA in 1969, followed by a doctorate in anthropology in 1978. Since 1971, she has lived and worked in the rain forests of Borneo (Kalimantan), at the Orangutan Research and Conservation Centre in the Tanjung Puting National Park. At the park, Galdikas studies orangutans in their natural habitat, also developing conservation programs and caring for orangutan infants that have been orphaned by poachers. She hopes that studying orangutan subsistence, sociality, reproduction, cognitive potential, communication, and tool use will shed some light on the development of early hominins. Galdikas says, "I've always wanted to study the one primate who never left the Garden of Eden. I want to know what we left behind"

(Continued)

(GCS Research Society 1996). She strongly believes we must reach back to our evolutionary roots, to a more stable lifestyle, for the sake of humankind's social, environmental, and mental well-being.

When Galdikas began her research, she developed close mothering relationships with the orphaned orangutans, even raising her oldest son, Binti, with the orangutans. Today, she maintains a degree of distance between her private life and the orangutans. Nonetheless, Galdikas continues to act as an advocate for the conservation and protection of the rain forest ecosystem and orangutans who live there by establishing a nonprofit organization, the Orangutan Foundation International. She actively campaigns for the creation of a large wildlife preserve in Borneo and was instrumental in the Taiwan government banning the import of primates.

Galdikas has received numerous awards that recognize her contributions to primate studies: Indonesia's "Hero for the Earth," the Tyler Prize for Environmental Achievement, the Mini-Nobel Science Award, and the United Nations Global 500 Environmental Award, to name a few (Orangutan Foundation International 1999). In 1995 Galdikas received the Order of Canada for her work with endangered orangutans in the rain forests of Borneo. Earlier that year, her much anticipated autobiography, *Reflections of Eden: My Years with the Orangutans in Borneo*, was released. Galdikas currently teaches human origins and primate behaviour at Simon Fraser University in British Columbia for several months of the year. The rest of the time, she lives with her husband and two children at Camp Leakey, Borneo.

his sons may remain with the group to succeed to his father's position. Alternatively, an outside male may take over the group. Unlike chimpanzees, gorillas rarely fight over food, territory, or sex, but will fight fiercely to keep outsiders out.

Individual Interaction

One of the most notable primate activities is grooming, the ritual cleaning of another animal's coat to remove parasites, shreds of grass, or other matter. The grooming animal deftly parts the hair of the one being groomed and removes any foreign object, often eating it. Interestingly, different chimp communities have different styles of grooming. In one East African group, for example, the two animals groom each other face to face, with one hand, while the other clasps the partner's free hand. In another group 145 kilometres distant, the hand clasp is unknown. In East Africa, all communities incorporate leaves in their grooming, but in West Africa they do not. However hygienic it may be, it is as well an important gesture of friendliness, submission, appeasement, or closeness. Embracing, touching, and jumping up and down are forms of greeting behaviour among chimpanzees. Touching is also a form of reassurance.

Gorillas, though gentle and tolerant, are also aloof and independent, and individual interaction among adults tends to be quite restrained. Friendship or closeness between adults and infants is more evident. Among

bonobos, chimpanzees, and gorillas, as among most other primates, the mother–infant bond is the strongest and most long lasting in the group. It may endure for many years—commonly for the lifetime of the mother. Gorilla infants share their mothers' nests and have been seen sharing nests with mature, childless females. Bonobo, chimpanzee, and gorilla males are attentive

Grooming is an important activity among all catarrhine primates, as shown here. Such activity is important for strengthening bonds between individual members of the group. ANITA DE LAGUNA HAVILAND

Female bonobos frequently engage in genital rubbing, as here. Males also engage in similar sexual activities. Such sexual activity is an important means of reducing tension. **AMY PARISH/ ANTHRO-PHOTO**

to juveniles and may share in parental responsibilities. Bonobo males seem most involved with their young and even carry infants on occasion, including those from different groups. Moreover, a male's interest in a youngster does not elicit the nervous reaction from the mother that it does among chimps. This latter relates to the regular, if infrequent, practice of infanticide on the part of chimpanzee males, a practice never observed among bonobos.

Sexual Behaviour

Among the three foregoing species, as with humans, there is no fixed breeding season. Sexual activity between the sexes, however—initiated by either the male or the female—occurs frequently during the period when the female is receptive to impregnation. This is signalled, in the case of chimps, by vivid swelling of the skin around their genitals. Because this swelling continues even after conception up until youngsters are weaned (at about age four), females continue to attract attention of males. Bonobo females, by contrast, are constantly swollen, concealing their time of ovulation by looking (and behaving) as if they are fertile at all times. Gorillas differ in that they show little interest in sex after conception. To a degree, chimps are promiscuous in their sexual behaviour, and 12 to 14 males have been observed to have as many as 50 copulations in one day

with a single female. Mostly, females mate with males of their own group and rarely with outsiders. Generally, dominant males try to monopolize females in full estrus, although cooperation from the female is usually required for this to succeed. By making herself scarce, she is able to exercise some choice, showing preference for a male who has previously shared food and groomed her. In the chimpanzee community studied by Jane Goodall, about half the infants were sired by low- or mid-level males. An alpha male, however, is able to monopolize the females to some extent, and some alphas have been seen to monopolize several estrous females at the same time.

Although mating behaviour among bonobos resembles that of chimps, there are differences. For one thing, bonobo females are constantly swollen, making them constantly attractive to males. For another, forced copulation has never been observed among bonobos.[12] But their sexuality goes far beyond male–female mating, and approximately three-quarters of their sexual activity has nothing to do with reproduction. Bonobos have been observed having sex in virtually all combinations of ages and sex.[13] The variety is remarkable, including sporadic oral sex, tongue-kissing, and massage of another's genitals. Male bonobos may mount each other or, standing

---

[12] de Waal, F. (1998). Comment. *Current Anthropology, 39,* 407.

[13] de Waal, F. (2001). *The ape and the sushi master* (pp. 131–132). New York: Basic Books.

back to back, one will rub his scrotum against another's. Bonobo males have also been observed "penis fencing," as two males hang from a branch facing each other while rubbing their erect penises together as if crossing swords. Among females genital rubbing is particularly common. The function of most of this sex, both heterosexual and homosexual, is to reduce tension. Whereas chimps often settle disputes by aggressive behaviour, bonobos often do so through sex.

In gorilla families, the dominant silverback has exclusive breeding rights with the females, although he may allow a young silverback occasional access to a low-ranking female. In one group studied in Rwanda, in which there was more than one adult male, all but 1 of 10 juveniles were fathered by a single male.[14] So it is that a young silverback must leave "home" in order to have much of a sex life, usually by luring away partners from other established groups.

Although the vast majority of primate species are not "monogamous" in their mating habits, many smaller species of New World monkeys, a few island-dwelling populations of leaf-eating Old World monkeys, and all of the smaller apes (gibbons and siamangs) usually mate for life with a single individual of the opposite sex. None of these species is closely related to human beings, nor do "monogamous" species ever display the degree of **sexual dimorphism**—anatomical differences between males and females—that is characteristic of our closest primate relatives, or that was characteristic of our own ancient ancestors.

Play

Frequent play activity among primate infants and juveniles is a means of learning about the environment, testing strength (rank in dominance hierarchies is based partially—but only partially—on size and strength), and generally learning how to behave as adults. Chimpanzee infants mimic the food-getting activities of their mothers, "attack" dozing adults, and "harass" adolescents.

Observers have watched young gorillas do somersaults, wrestle, and play tug-of-war, follow the leader, and king of the mountain. One juvenile, becoming annoyed at repeated harassment by an infant, picked it up, climbed a tree, and deposited it on a branch from which it was unable to get down on its own. Its mother had to retrieve it.

Communication

Primates, like many animals, vocalize. They have a great range of calls that are often used together with movements of the face or body to convey a message. Observers have not yet established the meaning of all the sounds, but a good number have been distinguished, such as warning calls, threat calls, defence calls, and gathering calls; the behavioural reactions of other animals hearing the call have also been studied. Among bonobos, chimpanzees, and gorillas, vocalizations are mainly emotional rather than propositional. Much of these species' communication takes place through specific gestures and postures. Indeed, a number of these, such as kissing and embracing, are in virtually universal use today among humans, as well as apes.

Primatologists have classified numerous kinds of chimpanzee vocalization and visual communication (Figure 4.5, p. 124). Together, these facilitate group protection, coordination of group efforts, and social interaction in general. Research by Anne Zeller of the University of Waterloo on three species of macaques indicates that their communication shares eight key properties with human language: generalization, interchangeability, duality of patterning, cultural transmission, specialization, creativity, prevarication (deception), and arbitrariness.[15] Their communication is a combination of vocalization and facial signatures, as it is in other monkeys and apes. Macaques use facial expressions to add information such as their sex, age, and kin group. Zeller has learned a great deal from a careful frame-by-frame examination of film she took of macaques.[16] For example, basic message content is expressed by the non-mouth region of the face; details on age, sex, and

---

[14] Gibbons, A. (2001). Studying humans—and their cousins and parasites. *Science, 292,* 627.

[15] Zeller, A. (1994). Evidence of structure in macaque communication. In R.A. Gardner et al. (Eds.), *The ethological roots of culture,* (pp. 15–39). Netherlands: Kluwer Academic Publishers.

[16] Zeller, A. (1996). The inter-play of kinship organisation and facial communication in the macaques. In J.E. Fa & D.G. Lindberg (Eds.), *Evolution and ecology of macaque societies,* (pp. 527–550). Cambridge, UK: Cambridge University Press.

Sexual dimorphism. Within a single species, the presence of marked anatomical differences between males and females.

possibly kin group membership of the message sender are expressed by the mouth region. Underlying this communicative ability is the need to function within a variety of social relationships in rich foraging habitats. Zeller's work also shows how self-aware monkeys are, and that they are capable of pretence for a variety of reasons, including redirecting attention and concealing resources.[17]

Experiments with captive apes, carried out over several decades, reveal that their communicative abilities exceed what they make use of in the wild. In some of these experiments, bonobos and chimpanzees have been taught to communicate using symbols, as in the case of Kanzi, a bonobo who uses a keyboard. Other chimpanzees, gorillas, and orangutans have been taught American Sign Language. Although this research provoked extreme controversy, it has become evident that all four apes are capable of understanding language quite well and are able to use a primitive grammar. They are able to generate original utterances, distinguish naming something from asking for it, ask questions, develop original ways to tell lies, coordinate their actions, and even spontaneously teach language to others. It is now clear that all of the great ape species can develop language skills to the level of a two- to three-year-old child.[18] From such knowledge, we may learn something about the origin of human language.

Home Ranges

Primates usually move about within circumscribed areas, or **home ranges,** which are of varying sizes, depending on the size of the group and on ecological factors such as availability of food. Ranges are often moved seasonally. The distance travelled by a group in a day varies but may include many kilometres. Some areas of a range, known as *core areas,* are used more often than others; they may contain water, food sources, resting places, and sleeping trees. The ranges of different groups may overlap, as among bonobos, where 65 percent of one territory may overlap with another.[19] By contrast, chimpanzee territories, at least in some regions, are exclusively occupied.

Gorillas do not defend their home ranges against incursions of others of their kind, and in the lowlands of Central Africa, it is not uncommon to find several families feeding in close proximity to one another,[20] although they

certainly will defend their group if it is in any way threatened. In encounters with other communities, bonobos will defend their immediate space through vocalizations and displays, but rarely through fighting. Usually, they settle down and feed side by side, not infrequently grooming, playing, and engaging in sexual activity between groups as well. Chimpanzees, by contrast, have been observed patrolling their territories to ward off potential trespassers. Moreover, Goodall has recorded the destruction of one chimpanzee community by another that invaded the first one's turf. This sort of lethal intercommunity interaction has never been observed among bonobos. Some have interpreted this apparent territorial behaviour as an expression of the supposedly violent nature of chimpanzees, but another interpretation is possible.[21] In Africa today, human encroachment is squeezing chimps into ever smaller pockets of forest. This places considerable stress on animals whose level of violence tends to increase in the absence of sufficient space. Perhaps the violence that Goodall witnessed was a response to crowding as a consequence of human encroachment. Another factor may be frustration engendered by artificial feeding. Among primates in general, the clearest territoriality appears in arboreal species, rather than in those that are more terrestrial in their habits.

Learning

Observation of monkeys and apes has shown that their learning abilities are remarkably humanlike. Numerous examples of inventive behaviour have been observed among Japanese macaques, as well as among apes. One

---

[17] Zeller, A. (2001). Pretending in monkeys. In R.W. Mitchell (Ed.), *Pretence in animals and children* (pp. 183–195). Cambridge, UK: Cambridge University Press.

[18] Lestel, D. (1998). How chimpanzees have domesticated humans. *Anthropology Today, 14* (3); Miles, H.L.W. (1993). Language and the orangutan: The "old person" of the forest. In P. Cavalieri & P. Singer (Eds.), *The great ape project* (pp. 45–50). New York: St. Martin's Press.

[19] Parish, A.R. (1998). Comment. *Current Anthropology, 39,* 414.

[20] Parnell, R. (1999). Gorilla exposé. *Natural History, 108* (8), 43.

[21] Power, M.G. (1995). Gombe revisited: Are chimpanzees violent and hierarchical in the "free" state? *General Anthropology, 2* (1), 5–9.

Home range. The area within which a group of primates usually moves.

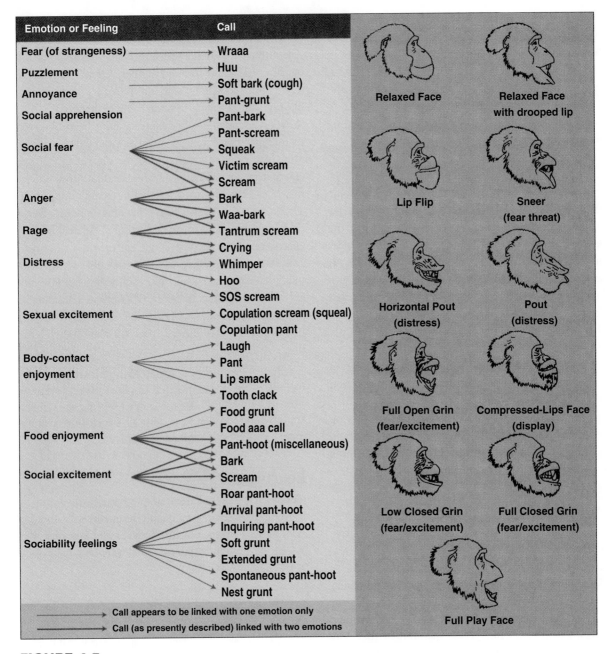

FIGURE 4.5

Chimpanzee communication combines a number of distinctive calls with different facial expressions.

newly discovered example is a technique of food manipulation on the part of captive chimpanzees in the Madrid zoo. It began when a five-year-old female rubbed apples against a sharp corner of a concrete wall in order to lick the mashed pieces and juice left on the wall. From this youngster, the practice of "smearing" spread to her

ANTHROPOLOGY APPLIED

Primate Conservation

Most primate species are in imminent danger of extinction. The quest to understand our closest relatives has taken on a matter of urgency in recent years; we need to get to know them before they disappear. Loss of habitat, being hunted for food and for trophies, or captured for medical experimentation, product testing, and the exotic pet trade have all had a devastating impact on world primate populations.

Ever-increasing human populations and the accompanying urbanization and deforestation have encroached on primate habitats, placing tremendous stress on nonhuman primate populations; simply put, there is not enough room. The impact of deforestation on primates is manifold, as illustrated by the chimpanzees of the Gombe National Park (Morbeck 1999; Goodall 1986). The Gombe National Park is a 32-square-kilometre area on the eastern shore of Lake Tanganyika, Tanzania. People living near the park have cut down trees for various uses, including clearing the land for crops. This deforestation has had a significant impact on the chimpanzees of the park. Diminished forest means less habitat and compressed ranging territory, reducing the quantity and variety of foods available. Smaller ranging territory has limited the chimpanzees' social interactions with other groups and with each other, and has resulted in more conflicts as they compete for food and territory. Natural predators of chimpanzees have all but disappeared because of human activities, resulting in abnormally large chimpanzee populations for the region. Although increasing primate populations is usually a goal of conservationists, in such a small area this is not advantageous. Large populations of chimpanzees, crammed into small pockets of forest, have resulted in a corresponding increase in infectious diseases (e.g., respiratory infections), parasites (e.g., intestinal worms), and an overall diminishing of their general health. Fragmented forests, such as those in Gombe, have altered chimpanzees' behaviour patterns in particular, reducing reproductive opportunities and encouraging inbreeding. Recent DNA studies at Gombe have shown that female chimpanzees are closely related, perhaps because the females, who usually leave their natal group at reproductive maturity, are not doing so because of reduced habitat. This has resulted in mating with closer relatives.

Relying on primates as a primary source of food, along with the commercialization of this enterprise in developing countries, has further depleted primate populations in some areas. In some regions, primate body parts are harvested for trophies, for example, in the mountainous areas of Rwanda, where gorilla hands and heads are sold to collectors (Montgomery 1991). Although not in the same league as the first two causalities, capturing primates for pets, medical experimentation (e.g., prescription medications, medical procedures), product testing (e.g., cosmetics, shampoos), and zoos has also reduced numbers.

Using animals for medical and product research has created significant controversy. Animal welfare organizations and animal rights activists have fought long and hard to end this practice, citing scientific evidence that primates are intelligent, socially complex, and communicative animals. Yet the benefits to humans from medical research are unquestionable. Many people have personally benefited from new medications and new medical procedures developed through animal testing, and medical authorities such as the U.S. National Institute of Health still insist on all new medications being tested on primates before humans can use them.

Primate conservation has become a top priority for primatologists and others seeking ways for human and nonhuman primates to coexist. Conservation efforts range from censuses of populations and surveying habitats to monitoring population decline and habitat destruction (Strum & Fedigan 1999). Three well-known Canadian primatologists—Biruté Galdikas, Linda M. Fedigan, and Anne Zeller—have worked tirelessly to not only to study primates but also develop conservation programs to save the few species still living free.

Nut cracking is an important activity among West African chimpanzees. Requiring the use of two objects as tools and complex eye–hand coordination, the task takes years for young chimps to learn from their elders. BROMHALL/ANIMALS, ANIMALS/MAXXIMAGES.COM

peers, and within five years, most group members were performing the operation frequently and consistently. The innovation has become standardized and durable, having transcended two generations in the group.[22]

Another dramatic example of learning is afforded by the way chimpanzees in West Africa crack open oil-palm nuts. For this they use tools: an anvil stone with a level surface on which to place the nut and a good-sized hammer stone to crack it. Not any stone will do; it must be of the right shape and weight, and the anvil may require levelling by placing smaller stones beneath one or more edges. Nor does random banging do the job; the nut has to be hit at the right speed and the right trajectory, or else the nut simply flies off into the forest. Last but not least, the apes must avoid mashing their fingers, rather than the nut. According to fieldworkers, the expertise of the chimps far exceeds that of any human who tries cracking these hardest nuts in the world.

Youngsters learn this process by hanging around adults who are nut cracking, where their mothers share some of the food. This teaches them about the edibility of the nuts, but not how to get at what's edible. This they learn by observing and by "aping" (copying) the adults. At first they play with a nut or stone alone; later they begin to randomly combine objects. They soon learn, however, that placing nuts on anvils and hitting them with a hand or foot gets them nowhere. Only after three years of futile efforts do they begin to coordinate all of the multiple actions and objects, but even then it is only after a great deal of practice, by the age of six or seven years, that they become proficient.

In short, after at least three years of failure, with no reward to reinforce their effort, they persevere. They do this for over 1000 days without slacking off. Evidently, it is *social* motivation that keeps them going. At first, they are motivated by a desire to act like the mother; only later does the desire to feed on the tasty nut-meat take over.[23]

[22] Fernandez-Carriba, S., & Loeches, A. (2001). Fruit smearing by captive chimpanzees: A newly observed food-processing behaviour. *Current Anthropology, 42,* 143–147.

[23] de Waal, F. (2001). *The ape and the sushi master* (pp. 227–229). New York: Basic Books.

Use of Objects as Tools

The nut cracking just discussed is the most complex tool-use task known from the field, involving, as it does, both hands, two tools, and exact coordination. It is not, however, the only case of tool use among apes in the wild. For our purposes, a **tool** may be defined simply as an object used to facilitate some task or activity. Here, a distinction must be made between simple tool use, as when one pounds something with a convenient stone when a hammer is not available, and toolmaking, which involves deliberate modification of some material for its intended use. Thus, otters that use unmodified stones to crack open clams may be tool users, but they are not toolmakers. Chimpanzees not only modify objects to make them suitable for particular purposes, but also to some extent modify them to regular and set patterns. Chimpanzees also pick up, and even prepare, objects for future use at some other location, and they can use objects as tools to solve new and novel problems. Thus, chimps have been observed using stalks of grass, twigs that they have stripped of leaves, and even sticks up to a metre long that they have smoothed down to "fish" for termites. They insert the modified stick into a termite nest, wait a few minutes, pull the stick out, and eat the insects clinging to it, all of which requires considerable dexterity. Chimpanzees are equally deliberate in their nest building. They test the vines and branches to make sure they are usable. If they are not, the animal moves to another site.

Other examples of chimpanzee use of objects as tools involve leaves, used as wipes or as sponges, to get water out of a hollow to drink. Large sticks may serve as clubs or as missiles (as may stones) in aggressive or defensive displays. Twigs are used as toothpicks to clean teeth as well as to extract loose baby teeth. They use these dental tools not just on themselves but on other individuals as well.[24]

Interestingly, tool use to fish for termites or to crack open nuts is most often exhibited by females, whereas aimed throwing of rocks and sticks is most often exhibited by males. Such tool-using behaviour, which (like nut cracking) young animals learn from their mothers and other adults in their group, may reflect one of the preliminary adaptations that, in the past, led to human cultural behaviour.

In the wild, bonobos have not been observed making and using tools to the extent that chimpanzees do. However, the use of large leaves as trail markers may be considered a form of tool use. That these animals do have further capabilities is exemplified by a captive bonobo who has figured out how to make tools of stone that are remarkably like the earliest such tools made by our own ancestors.

Another interesting practice observed among chimps is the use of *Aspilia* leaves for medicinal purposes. When feeling a bit under the weather, they seek out these leaves, hold them in their mouths for a while, then swallow them whole, which removes parasites from their digestive tract.

Until recently, tool use among great apes has been linked to food getting. Curiously, until recently gorillas have never been observed to use tools in the wild to collect or process food so they were thought to be the exception to great ape tool users. In 2004 observations were made of two different western gorillas—one using a walking stick for support while crossing a swamp and another using a stick for support while reaching for food at the bottom of a swamp.[25] In the second case, the gorilla then used the stick as a bridge over the swampy ground. These observations show that tool use among great apes now includes other functional demands that reflect environmental adaptations.

Hunting

The hunting, killing, and eating of small to medium-sized mammals, something that is seen only in a few primates, has been observed among bonobos and chimps, but not among gorillas. Although chimpanzee females sometimes hunt, males do so far more frequently. When on the hunt, they may spend up to two hours watching,

---

[24] McGrew, W.C. (2000). Dental care in chimps. *Science, 288,* 1747.

[25] Breuer T., Ndoundou-Hockemba, M., & Fishlock, V. (2005). First observation of tool use in wild gorillas. *PLoS Biology, 3,* e380.

> **Tool.** An object used to facilitate some task or activity. Although toolmaking involves intentional modification of the material of which it is made, tool use may involve objects either modified for some particular purpose or completely unmodified.

following, and chasing intended prey. Moreover, in contrast to the usual primate practice of each animal finding food for itself, hunting frequently involves teamwork to trap and kill prey. The most sophisticated examples of this occur when hunting baboons; once a potential victim has been partially isolated from its troop, three or more adults will carefully position themselves so as to block off escape routes while another climbs toward the prey for the kill. Once a kill has been made, it is common for most of those present to get a share of the meat, either by grabbing a piece as the chance affords, or by sitting and begging for a piece. Whatever the nutritional value of meat, hunting is not done purely for dietary purposes, but for political and sociosexual reasons as well. The giving of meat helps cement alliances among males, and its sharing may be used also to entice a swollen female to have sex. In fact, males are more apt to hunt if a swollen female is present, and females in estrus are more successful at begging for meat.

Bonobos, too, hunt, but in their case it is usually the females that do so—duikers (a kind of small antelope) being the most frequent prey. The huntresses regularly share the carcasses with other females, but less often with males. Even when the most dominant male throws a tantrum nearby, he may still be denied a share.[26] Females not only control the spoils of the hunt, but also are unusual also in the degree to which they will share fruit. Otherwise, it is interesting to note that, in primates, as among many carnivores, increased cooperation seems to go hand in hand with predation and meat eating.

THE QUESTION OF CULTURE

The more we learn of the behaviour of our nearest primate relatives, the more we become aware of the importance to chimps of learned, socially shared practices and knowledge. This raises the question: Do chimpanzees (and perhaps other apes) have culture? This question is now receiving a good deal of attention, as the following Original Study attests.

Primate Behaviour and Human Evolution

Although not true of all humanity, in many societies there is an unfortunate tendency to erect what palaeontologist Stephen Jay Gould refers to as "golden barriers" that set us apart from the rest of the animal kingdom.[27] The practice is unfortunate, for it blinds us to the fact that there are many continuities between "us" and "them" (animals). We have already seen that the physical differences between humans and apes are largely differences of degree, rather than kind. It now appears that the same is true with respect to behaviour. As primatologist Richard Wrangham once put it, "Like humans, [chimpanzees] laugh, make up after a quarrel, support each other in times of trouble, medicate themselves with chemical and physical remedies, stop each other from eating poisonous foods, collaborate in the hunt, help each other over physical obstacles, raid neighboring groups, lose their tempers, get excited by dramatic weather, invent ways to show off, have family traditions and group traditions, make tools, devise plans, deceive, play tricks, grieve, and are cruel and are kind."[28]

This is not to say that we are "just" another ape; obviously, "degree" does make a difference. Nevertheless, the continuities between us and our primate kin are a reflection of a common evolutionary heritage; it is just that our later evolution has taken us in a somewhat different direction. But by looking at the range of practices displayed by contemporary apes and other catarrhines, we may find clues to the practices and capabilities possessed by our own ancestors as their evolutionary path diverged from those of the other hominins.

[26] Ingmanson, E.J. (1998). Comment. *Current Anthropology, 39,* 409.

[27] de Waal, F. (2001). *The ape and the sushi master* (p. 235). New York: Basic Books.

[28] Quoted in Mydens, S. (2001, August 12). He's not hairy, he's my brother. *New York Times*, sec. 4, p. 5.

ORIGINAL STUDY

The Culture of Chimpanzees

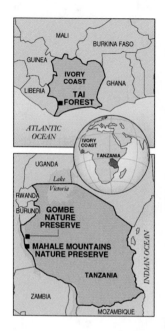

Homo sapiens and *Pan troglodytes* have coexisted for hundreds of millennia and share more than 98 percent of their genetic material, yet only 40 years ago we still knew next to nothing about chimpanzee behaviour in the wild. That began to change in the 1960s, when Toshisada Nishida of Kyoto University in Japan and Jane Goodall began their studies of wild chimpanzees at two field sites in Tanzania. (Goodall's research station at Gombe—the first of its kind—is more famous, but Nishida's site at Mahale is the second-oldest chimpanzee research site in the world.)

In these initial studies, as the chimpanzees became accustomed to close observation, remarkable discoveries began. Researchers witnessed a range of unexpected behaviours, including fashioning and using tools, hunting, meat eating, food sharing, and lethal fights between members of neighbouring communities. In the years that followed, other primatologists set up camp elsewhere, and, despite all the financial, political, and logistical problems that can beset African fieldwork, several of these outposts became truly long-term projects. As a result, we live in an unprecedented time, when an intimate and comprehensive scientific record of chimpanzees' lives at last exists not just for one but for several communities spread across Africa.

As early as 1973, Goodall recorded 13 forms of tool use as well as eight social activities that appeared to differ between the Gombe chimpanzees and chimpanzee populations elsewhere. She ventured that some variations had what she termed a "cultural origin." But what exactly did Goodall mean by "culture"? According to the *Oxford Encyclopedic English Dictionary*, culture is defined as "the customs ... and achievements of a particular time or people." The diversity of human cultures extends from technological variations to marriage rituals, from culinary habits to myths and legends. Animals do not have myths and legends, of course. But they do have the capacity to pass on behavioural traits from generation to generation—not through their genes but by learning. For biologists, this is the fundamental criterion for a cultural trait: It must be something that can be learned by observing the established skills of others and thus passed on to future generations.

By the 1990s the discovery of new behavioural differences among chimpanzees made it feasible to begin assembling comprehensive charts of cultural variations for these animals. William C. McGrew, in his 1992 book *Chimpanzee Material Cultures,* was able to list 19 different kinds of tool use in distinct communities. One of the authors of this book (Boesch), along with colleague Michael Tomasello of the Max Planck Institute for Evolutionary Anthropology in Leipzig, Germany, identified 25 distinct activities as potential cultural traits in wild chimpanzee populations.

The most recent catalogue of cultural variations results from a unique collaboration of nine chimpanzee experts (including the two authors) who pooled extensive field observations that, taken together, amounted to a total of 151 years of chimp watching. The list cites 39 patterns of chimpanzee behaviour that we believe to have a cultural origin, including such activities as using sticks to "fish" for ants, making dry seats from leaves, and a range of social grooming habits. At present, these 39 variants put chimpanzees in a class of their own, with far more elaborate customs than any other animal studied to date. Of course, chimpanzees also remain distinct from humans, for whom cultural variations are simply beyond count. (We must point out, however, that scientists are only beginning to uncover

(Continued)

the behavioural complexity that exists among chimpanzees—and so the number 39 no doubt represents a minimum of cultural traits.)

Multicultural Chimpanzees

When describing human customs, anthropologists and sociologists often refer to "Italian culture" or "Chinese culture"; these terms encompass a wide spectrum of activities—language, forms of dress, eating habits, marriage rituals, and so on. Among animals, however, culture has typically been established for a single behaviour, such as song dialects among birds. Ornithologists haven't identified variation in courtship patterns or feeding practices, for example, to go alongside the differences in dialect.

Chimpanzees, though, do more than display singular cultural traits: Each community exhibits an entire set of behaviours that differentiates it from other groups. As a result, we can talk about "Gombe culture" or "Taï culture." Indeed, once we observe how a chimpanzee behaves, we can identify where the animal lives. For instance, an individual that cracks nuts, leaf-clips during drumming displays, fishes for ants with one hand using short sticks, and knuckle-knocks to attract females clearly comes from the Taï Forest. A chimp that leaf-grooms and hand-

Grooming is an activity seen in all chimpanzee communities, but styles differ between communities. Shown here is the hand- clasping style characteristic of one East African community. **DAVID BYGOTT/KIBUYU PARTNERS**

clasps during grooming can come from the Kibale Forest or the Mahale Mountains, but if you notice that he also ant-fishes, there is no doubt anymore: he comes from Mahale.

In addition, chimpanzee cultures go beyond the mere presence or absence of a particular behaviour. For example, all chimpanzees dispatch parasites found during grooming a companion. But at Taï they will mash the parasites against their forearms with a finger, at Gombe they squash them onto leaves, and at Budongo they put them on a leaf to inspect before eating or discarding them. Each community has developed a unique approach for accomplishing the same goal. Alternatively, behaviours may look similar yet be used in different contexts: at Mahale, males "clip" leaves noisily with their teeth as a courtship gesture, whereas at Taï chimpanzees incorporate leaf-clipping into drumming displays.

The implications of this new picture of chimpanzee culture are many. The information offers insight into our distinctiveness as a species. When we first published this work in the journal *Nature,* we found some people quite disturbed to realize that the characteristic that had appeared to separate us so starkly from the animal world—our capacity for cultural development—is not such an absolute difference after all.

But this seems a rather misdirected response. The differences between human customs and traditions, enriched and mediated by language as they are, are vast in contrast with what we see in the chimpanzee. The story of chimpanzee cultures sharpens our understanding of our uniqueness, rather than threatening it in any way that need worry us.

Human achievements have made enormous cumulative progress over the generations, a phenomenon Boesch and Tomasello have dubbed the "ratchet effect." The idea of a hammer—once simply a crude stone cobble—has been modified and improved on countless times until now we have electronically controlled robot hammers in our factories. Chimpanzees may show the beginnings of the ratchet effect—some that use stone anvils, for example, have gone a step further, as at Bossou, where they wedge a stone beneath their anvil when it needs levelling on bumpy ground—but such behaviour has not become customary and is rudimentary indeed beside human advancements.

The cultural capacity we share with chimpanzees also suggests an ancient ancestry for the mentality that must underlie it. Our cultural nature did not emerge out of the blue but evolved from simpler beginnings. Social learning similar to that of chimpanzees would appear capable of sustaining the earliest stone-tool cultures of human ancestors living 2 million years ago.

CHAPTER SUMMARY

The modern primates, like most mammals, are intelligent animals that bear their young live and then nourish them with milk from their mothers. Like other mammals, they maintain constant body temperature, and have respiratory and circulatory systems that will sustain high activity. Their skeleton and teeth also resemble those of other mammals, although there are differences of detail.

Modern primates are divided into two suborders. The strepsirhines include lemurs and lorises, which resemble small rodents in body outline. The haplorhines include tarsiers, New and Old World monkeys, apes, and humans. To a greater degree among the haplorhines, and a lesser degree among the strepsirhines, primates show a number of characteristics that developed as adaptations to insect predation in the trees. These adaptive characteristics include a generalized set of teeth, suited to eating not only insects but also a variety of fruits and leaves. These teeth are fewer in number and set in a smaller jaw than in most mammals. Other evolutionary adaptations in the primate line include binocular stereoscopic vision, or depth perception, and an intensified sense of touch. This combination of developments had an effect upon the primate brain, resulting in larger size and greater complexity in later appearing species. There were also changes in the primate skeleton; in particular, a reduction of the snout, an enlargement of the brain case, and numerous adaptations for upright posture and flexibility of limb movement. In addition, changes in reproduction resulted in fewer offspring born to each female and a longer period of infant dependency than among most mammals.

The apes are humans' closest relatives. Apes include gibbons, siamangs, orangutans, gorillas, bonobos, and chimpanzees. In their outward appearance, the great apes seem to resemble each other more than they do humans, but their genetic structure and biochemistry reveal that bonobos, chimpanzees, and gorillas are closer to humans than to orangs and thus must share a more recent common ancestry.

The social life of primates is complex. Primates are social animals, and most species live and travel in groups. Among bonobos and chimpanzees, it is females that may transfer from one group to another, though not all do so; their sons and often their daughters remain with their mothers for life. Among gorillas, either males or females may transfer. In all three species, both males and females are organized into dominance hierarchies. In the case of females, the better food and reduced harassment that are a consequence of high rank enhance their ability to successfully raise offspring.

A characteristic primate activity is grooming, which is a sign of closeness between individuals. Among bonobos, gorillas, and chimpanzees, sexual interaction between adults of opposite sex generally takes place only when a female is in estrus. In bonobos, however, constant swelling of the female's genitals suggests constant estrus, whether or not she is actually fertile. Although dominant males try to monopolize females while they are in estrus, the cooperation of the females is usually required for this to succeed. Among bonobos, sex between both opposite and same-sex individuals serves as a means of reducing tensions, as in the genital rubbing that frequently takes place between females. Primates have elaborate systems of communication based on vocalizations and gestures. In addition, bonobos employ trail signs to communicate their whereabouts to others. Usually primates move about within home ranges, rather than defended territories.

The diet of most primates comprises a variety of fruits, leaves, and insects, but bonobos and chimpanzees sometimes hunt, kill, and eat animals as well. Among chimps, most hunting is done by males and may require considerable teamwork. By contrast, it is usually bonobo females that hunt. Once a kill is made, the meat is generally shared with other animals.

Among chimpanzees and other apes, learned behaviour is especially important. From adults, juveniles learn to use a variety of tools and substances for various purposes. Innovations made by one individual may be adopted by other animals, standardized, and passed on to succeeding generations. Because practices are learned, socially shared, and often differ from one group to another, we may speak of chimpanzee culture.

QUESTIONS FOR CRITICAL THOUGHT

1. What do long-term language studies among monkeys and apes tell us about our understanding of what makes humans distinct?

2. How does nonhuman primate research help us understand the evolution of humans?

3. Maintaining nonhuman primate habitats has become an urgent problem. What options exist for saving these habitats and the animals living in them?

INTERNET RESOURCES

Biruté Galdikas's Orangutans

www.science.ca/scientists/scientistprofile.php?ID=7
A brief look at Biruté Galdikas's world and the orangutans.

Cebidae Family

http://animaldiversity.ummz.umich.edu/site/accounts/information/Cebidae.html
A discussion of New World monkeys.

Chimpanzee Toolmaking

www.units.muohio.edu/dragonfly/tools/chimptools.shtml
An interesting website dedicated to teaching people about the toolmaking capabilities of chimps. Features Wolfgang Kohler's studies of chimpanzees in the wild.

Koko's World

www.koko.org/world
A site dedicated to the Gorilla Foundation that informs students about the work with gorillas and sign language.

Primate Conservation

www.primate.org
shttp://coombs.anu.edu.au/~vern/iebr.html
Contains information on work being done in Vietnam to protect primates.

http://bushmeat.net
Explains the action of a conservation group working to protect the endangered primate species being slaughtered for meat and medicine. The project mission states that "the Bushmeat Project has been established to develop and support community-based partnerships that will help the people of equatorial Africa to develop alternatives to unsustainable bushmeat. The programme is a long-term effort to provide economic and social incentive to protect great apes and other endangered wildlife."

www.eurekalert.org/pub_releases/2006-07/ns-wdt070506.php
Describes how bushmeat is finding its way into North American and European cuisine.

www.ucalgary.ca/~fedigan/fedigan.htm
Linda Fedigan's website describes her research as well as that of her students.

Primates

http://pin.primate.wisc.edu
A comprehensive site with links to many fact sheets. This site provides information on many topics, including anatomy, behaviour, ecology, evolution, and taxonomy.

www.primates.com
This photo site offers an excellent pictorial essay of primates, enabling students to become familiar with various primates, from lemuriformes to the great apes.

www.indiana.edu/~primates.html
A pictorial and auditory site that offers opportunities for students to see and hear primates.

www.emory.edu/living_links
See and hear living primates through this site that features a host of information about primate behaviour, biology, and conservation. See classic videos from primate field research such as "Chimpanzee Conflict" and "Chimpanzee Food Sharing."

http://news.nationalgeographic.com/news/2001/12/1204_hominin_id.html
An article by Lee Berger that explains the use of two terms, "homind" and "hominin" to refer to humans and their closest fossil representatives.

SUGGESTED READINGS

For a list of suggested readings, visit the textbook's website at www.humanevolution2.nelson.com.

CHAPTER

5

THE EARLY PRIMATES

Meeting the challenge of understanding human origins requires us to trace the evolutionary history of the entire primate order. A comprehensive view of primate evolution brings us also to a consideration of how palaeoanthropologists use fragmentary fossil and geologic data to reconstruct extinct groups. This model of a member of the extinct ape genus *Gigantopithecus,* for example, is based on evidence from jaw bones and teeth found in China combined with the anatomy of living species such as the gorilla. The model was created by Hollywood monster maker Bill Munn and anthropologist Russell Ciochon.

RUSSELL L. CIOCHON

CHAPTER PREVIEW

1. When Did the First Primates Appear, and What Were They Like?

The earliest primates had developed by 60 million years ago and became widespread in Africa, Eurasia, and North America. The initial adaptation of these small, arboreal fruit and insect eaters to life in the trees set the stage for the subsequent appearance of other primate models.

2. When Did the First Monkeys and Apes Appear, and What Were They Like?

By the late Eocene epoch, about 37 million years ago, small primates ancestral to monkeys and apes were living in Africa and Asia. By about 20 million years ago, they had proliferated and were common in many parts of the Old World. Some forms remained relatively small, while others became quite large, some even larger than present-day gorillas. Small versions of these apelike primates seem to have had the right kind of anatomy, and at least some were exposed to the right kind of selective pressures to transform them into primitive hominines (subfamily Homininae).

CHAPTER OUTLINE

Almost a century and a half ago, Charles Darwin shattered the surface calm of the Victorian world with his startling theory that humans are cousins of the living apes and monkeys and are descended from the same prehistoric ancestors. What would have been the public reaction, one wonders, if they had known, as we do, that even earlier ancestors were mouse-sized and smaller creatures that subsisted chiefly on insects and worms? Such primitive creatures date back about 60 million years. These ancient forebears of ours evolved over time into different species as mutations produced variation, which was acted upon by natural selection and genetic drift.

Although many of the primates discussed in this chapter no longer exist, their descendants, which were reviewed in Chapter 4, are to be found living throughout the world. The successful adaptation of the primates is believed to be due largely to their intelligence, a characteristic that provides for adaptive flexibility. Other physical traits, such as stereoscopic vision and a grasping hand, have also been instrumental in the success of the primates.

What is the justification for studying a form of life whose history is, at best, fragmentary, and that existed millions of years ago? The study of these prehistoric primates tells us something we can use to interpret the evolution of the entire primate line, including ourselves. It gives us a better understanding of the physical forces that caused these early creatures to evolve into today's primates. Ultimately, the study of these ancient ancestors gives us a fuller knowledge of the processes through which an insect-eating, small-brained animal evolved into a toolmaker and thinker that is recognizably human.

Linear Evolution

Another consequence of natural selection may be what appears to be a linear progression from one form to another without any evident branching. Although this may seem like a case of evolution heading in a particular direction, it is not. Rather, it is nothing more than variational change as discussed in the Original Study in Chapter 3. The example given there was of elephants becoming progressively hairier over time in response to climatic cooling. As generation succeeded generation, those elephants best adapted to cold enjoyed the highest reproductive success. The end result was the woolly mammoth. If, as such change proceeds, populations do not become isolated, then the species as a whole appears to evolve in a particular direction. **Linear evolution** may be defined, then, as a sustained directional change in a population's average characteristics.

As linear evolution proceeds, according the Darwinian model, more recent populations may appear sufficiently changed from ancestral populations to be called different species. The gradualist, Darwinian model of speciation discussed in Chapter 3 predicts the accumulation of gradual changes that ultimately lead to new species arising. The non-Darwinian, punctuate equilibrium model of species origin predicts that such gradations would represent variations within the same species; a new species would have traits representing something more than a gradation of change. Differences among fossils are thus open to considerable interpretation and trying to assign a fossil to one species or the other can be an exercise in frustration.

FIGURE 5.1

Separation of the earth's continents resulted from massive shifting in the platelike segments of the crust as illustrated by the position of continents at the end of the Cretaceous period some 65 million years ago, the time of the dinosaur's extinction. The seas, opened up by continental separation, constituted isolating barriers between major land masses.

Linear evolution. A sustained directional shift in a population's average characteristics.

Although linear evolution produces change, it generally does not transform a population into something radically different. Ultimately, stabilizing selection is likely to take over, as available alleles reach their most adaptive frequencies in a species' gene pool. There will be little change thereafter, as long as the adaptation remains viable. Ironically, a species may become extinct if it becomes too specifically adapted or specialized. If the environment changes for some reason, those organisms most highly adapted to the old environment will have the greatest difficulty surviving in a new one. Such changes took place a number of times during the course of vertebrate evolution; one of the most dramatic examples was the sudden extinction of the dinosaurs. In such cases, it is usually the more generalized organisms that survive; later they may give rise to new lines of specialists.

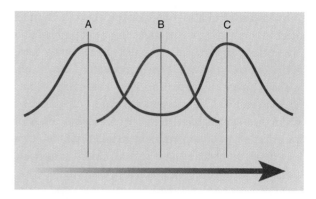

FIGURE 5.2

Linear evolution is a process of variational change that occurs as relatively small changes that (by chance) are advantageous accumulate in a species' gene pool through gene flow, drift, and selection. Over time, this may produce sufficient change to transform an old species into a new one.

The Nondirectedness of Evolution

In the popular mind, evolution is often seen as leading in a predictable and determined way from one-celled organisms, through various multicelled forms, to humans, who occupy the top rung of a ladder of progress. To be sure, one-celled organisms appeared long before multicellular forms, but the latter could hardly emerge before the basic structure of the cell existed. Furthermore, single-celled organisms were not replaced by multicellular descendants, but remain today, as in the past, the dominant forms of life. They exist in greater numbers and diversity than all forms of multicellular life and live in all habitats accessible to *any* form of life.[1]

As for humans, we are indeed recent arrivals in the world (though not as recent as some new strains of bacteria), but our appearance—like that of any kind of organism—was made possible only as a consequence of a whole string of historical accidents. To cite but one example, about 65 million years ago, some sort of extraterrestrial body slammed into earth where the Yucatan Peninsula now exists, disrupting the world's climate to such an extent as to cause the extinction of the dinosaurs (and numerous other species as well). For 100 million years, dinosaurs had ruled most terrestrial environments available for vertebrate animals and would probably have continued to do so were it not for this event. Although mammals appeared at about the same time as reptiles, they existed as small, inconspicuous creatures

that an observer from outer space would probably have dismissed as insignificant. But with the demise of the dinosaurs, all sorts of opportunities became available, and mammals began their great expansion into new niches, including the one in which our own ancestors evolved. So it is that an essentially random event—the collision with a comet or asteroid—made possible our own existence. Had it not happened, or had it happened at some other time (before the existence of mammals), we would not be here, and there might not be any consciously intelligent life on earth.[2]

The history of any species is an outcome of many such contingencies. At any point in the chain of events, had any one element been different, the final result would be markedly different. As Stephen Jay Gould puts it, "All evolutionary sequences include … a fortuitous series of accidents with respect to future evolutionary success. Human brains and bodies did not evolve along a direct and inevitable ladder, but by a circuitous and tortuous route carved by adaptations evolved for different reasons, and fortunately suited to later needs."[3]

---

[1] Gould, S.J. (1996). *Full house: The spread of excellence from Plato to Darwin* (pp. 176–195). New York: Harmony Books.

[2] Gould, S.J. (1985). *The flamingo's smile: Reflections in natural history* (p. 409). New York: Norton.

[3] Ibid., p. 410.

The history of life is not one of progressive advancement in complexity; if anything, it is one of proliferation of enormously varied designs that subsequently have been restricted to a few highly successful forms. Even at that, imperfections remain. As Gould so aptly puts it, "Our world is not an optimal place, fine-tuned by omnipotent forces of selection. It is a quirky mass of imperfections, working well enough (often admirably); a jury-rigged set of adaptations built of curious parts made available by past histories in different contexts.[4]

EARLY MAMMALS

By 190 million years ago—the end of what geologists call the Triassic period—true mammals were on the scene. We know these and the mammals from the succeeding Jurassic (190–135 million years ago) and Cretaceous (135–65 million years ago) periods from hundreds of finds of mostly teeth and jaw parts. Because these structures are the most durable, they often outlast other parts of an animal's skeleton. Fortunately, investigators often are able to infer a good deal about the total animal on the basis of only a few teeth found lying in the earth. For example, knowledge of the way the teeth fit together indicates much about the operation of the jaws, suggesting the types of muscles needed. This in turn indicates how the skull must have been shaped to provide accommodation for the musculature. The shape of the jaws and details of the teeth also suggest the type of food that they were suited to deal with, indicating the probable diet of the specimen. Thus, a mere jawbone reveals a great deal about the animal from which it came.

An interesting fact about the evolution of the mammals is that the diverse forms with which we are familiar today, including the primates, are the products of an **adaptive radiation**, the rapid increase in number of related species following a change in their environment. This did not begin until after mammals had been present on the earth for over 100 million years. Actually, the story of mammalian evolution starts as early as 280 to 230 million years ago (Figure 5.3). From deposits of this period, which geologists call the Permian, we have the remains of reptiles with features pointing in a distinctly mammalian direction. These mammal-like reptiles were slimmer than most other reptiles and were flesh eaters. In a series of graded fossils, we can see in them a reduction of bones to a more mammalian number, the shifting

of limbs underneath the body, development of a separation between the mouth and nasal cavity, differentiation of the teeth, and so forth.

All of these early mammals were small eaters of flesh—such things as insects, worms, and eggs. They seem to have been nocturnal in their habits, which is probably why the senses of smell and hearing became so developed in mammals. Although things cannot be seen as well in the dark as they can in the light, they can be heard and smelled just as well. Both sound and smell are more complex than sight. If something can be seen it is right there in the animal's line of vision. By contrast, it is possible to smell and hear things around corners and in other hidden places, and in addition to figuring out what it is that is smelled or heard and how far away it is, the animal must also figure out where it is. A further complication is the fact that smells linger, and so the animal must figure out if the cause of an odour is still there or, if not, how old the odour is.

Many mammals such as rabbits, cats, and dogs see poorly or not at all in colour. As these mammals' senses of hearing and smell became keener, they lost the ability (possessed by reptiles) to see in colour. But the new, keener senses and the importance of outwitting both prey and predators served to improve their information-processing capacities and enlarge the part of the brain that handles these—the cerebral cortex—beyond that of reptiles. And to the extent that they became "brainier," they became more flexible in their behaviour.

Because mammals were developing as such bright, active creatures, it may seem puzzling that reptiles continued to be the dominant land animals for more than 100 million years. After all, **warm-blooded** mammals, with their constant body temperature, can be active at any time, whereas **cold-blooded** reptiles, who take their body temperature from the surrounding environment, become

---

[4] Ibid., p. 54.

> **Adaptive radiation.** Rapid diversification of an evolving population as it adapts to a variety of available niches.
>
> **Warm-blooded.** Animals that maintain a relatively constant body temperature.
>
> **Cold-blooded.** Animals whose body temperature rises or falls according to the temperature of the surrounding environment.

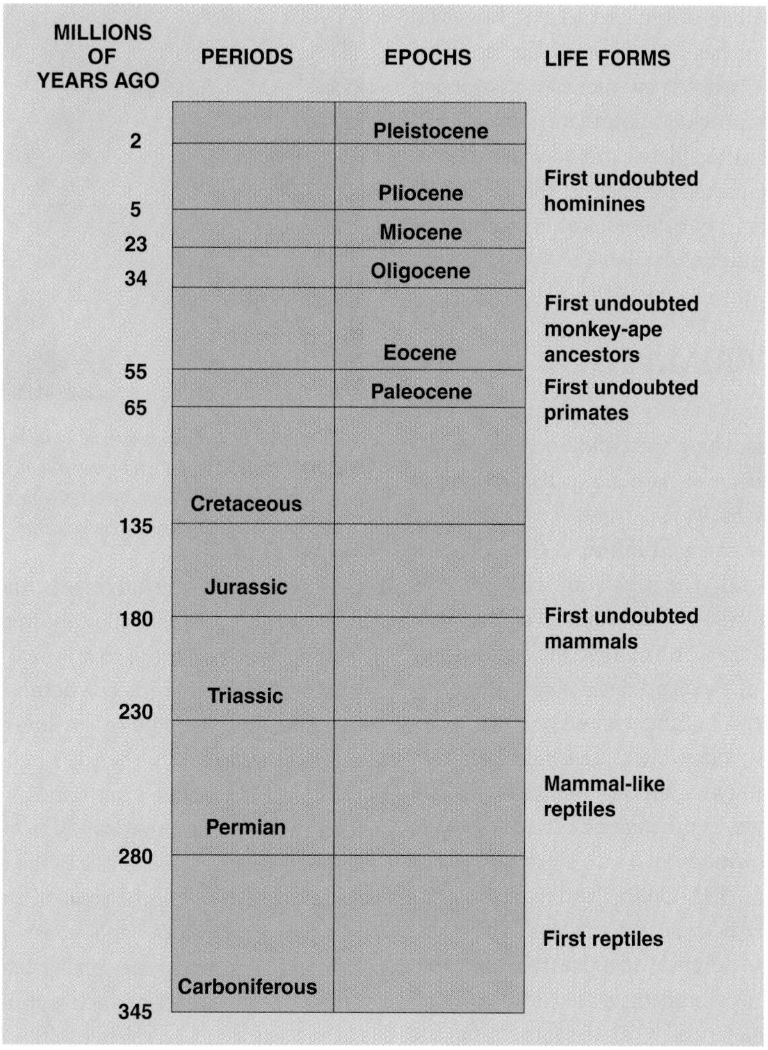

MILLIONS OF YEARS AGO	PERIODS	EPOCHS	LIFE FORMS
2		Pleistocene	
5		Pliocene	First undoubted hominines
23		Miocene	
34		Oligocene	
55		Eocene	First undoubted monkey-ape ancestors
65		Paleocene	First undoubted primates
135	Cretaceous		
180	Jurassic		First undoubted mammals
230	Triassic		
280	Permian		Mammal-like reptiles
345	Carboniferous		First reptiles

FIGURE 5.3

This timeline highlights some major milestones in the evolution of those mammals from which humans are descended.

more sluggish as the surrounding temperature drops. Furthermore, mammals provide care for their young, whereas most reptiles leave theirs to fend for themselves. But the mammals faced two limitations. For one, their high activity demanded more nutrition than did the less constant activity of reptiles. Such high-quality nutrition is provided by the fruits, nuts, and seeds of flowering plants, but these plants did not become common until late in the Cretaceous period. High-quality nutrition is also provided by the flesh of other animals, but the mammals were small and therefore dependent particularly on small prey such as insects and worms. These were limited in numbers until flowers and fruits provided them with a host of new **ecological niches**, or functional positions in their habitats, to exploit.

The second limitation that affected mammals was the slight head start enjoyed by reptiles; this allowed them to preempt most available niches, which therefore were not available to mammals. With the mass extinction

Ecological niche. A species' way of life considered in the context of its environment, including other species found in that environment.

of many reptiles at the end of the Cretaceous, however, a number of existing niches became available to mammals; at the same time, whole new niches were opened up as the new grasses provided abundant food in arid places, and other flowering plants provided abundant, high-quality food elsewhere. By chance, the mammals had what it took in the way of biological equipment to exploit the new opportunities available to them.

RISE OF THE PRIMATES

Considering that primates have tended through the ages to live in environments where the conditions for fossilization are generally poor, we have a surprising number of fossils with which to work. These fossils indicate that the early primates emerged during a time of great change all over the world. The separation of continents was under way as the result of movement of the great platelike segments of the earth's crust on which they rest. The distribution of fossil primates across the earth makes sense only when one understands that the positions of the continents today differ tremendously from what was found in the past. Although Europe was still joined to North America, South America and India were isolated, while a narrow body of water separated Africa from Eurasia (see Figure 5.1). On the land itself the great dinosaurs had recently become extinct, and the mammals were undergoing the great adaptive radiation that ultimately led to the development of the diverse forms with which we are familiar today. At the same time, the newly evolved grasses, ivies, shrubs, and other flowering plants were undergoing an enormous proliferation. This diversification, along with a milder climate, favoured the spread of dense, lush tropical and subtropical forests over much of the earth, including North and South America and much of Eurasia and Africa. With the spread of these huge belts of forest, the stage was set for the movement of some mammals from niches on the ground into the trees. Forests would provide our early ancestors with the ecological niches in which they would flourish.

The move to an arboreal existence brought to early primates a combination of the problems of earthbound existence with those of flight. In their move into the air, birds developed highly stereotyped behaviour; primates, on the other hand, brought with them to the trees the flexible decision-making behaviour characteristic of the mammals. The initial forays into the trees must have

The appearance of angiosperm plants provided not only highly nutritious fruits, seeds, and flowers but also a host of habitats for numerous edible insects and worms—just the sorts of foods required by mammals with their high metabolism. **GARY CRAWFORD**

produced many misjudgments and errors of coordination, leading to falls that injured or killed the individuals poorly adapted to arboreal life. Natural selection favoured those that judged depth correctly and gripped the branches strongly. It is quite likely that the early primates that took to the trees had not only behavioural flexibility but better vision and more dexterous fingers than their contemporaries.

The relatively small size of the early primates allowed them to make use of the smaller branches of trees; larger, heavier competitors, and most predators, could not follow. The move to the smaller branches also gave them access to an abundant food supply; the primates were able to gather insects, leaves, flowers, and fruits directly rather than waiting for them to fall to the ground. The details of how early primates evolved these characteristics are only now coming to light. Anthropologists are testing a number of hypotheses to explain primate specialization: that grasping-leaping came first and led to successful arboreal locomotion, that good depth perception facilitated successful predation, or that primates adapted to terminal branch fruit or nectar foraging.[5]

The strong selection to a new environment led to an acceleration in the rate of change of primate characteristics. Paradoxically, these changes eventually made possible a return to the ground on the part of some primates, including the ancestors of the genus *Homo*.

---

[5] Bloch J.I., & Boyer, D.M. (2002). Grasping primate origins. *Science, 298*, 1606–1610.

Palaeocene Primates

Both genetics and anatomy suggest that the ancestry of primates lies with the insectivores, a diverse group of small mammals represented today by tree shrews, moles, and hedgehogs. Thus, we would expect to have difficulty distinguishing the earliest primate fossils from ancient insectivores. In fact, the earliest surely known primate fossils, 10 teeth from a site in Morocco, are about 60 million years old. These cheek teeth (molars and premolars) are very similar to the corresponding teeth of the modern mouse lemur, a tiny strepsirhine primate weighing a mere 56 grams. These teeth are sufficient to show that the primates were going their separate evolutionary way by 60 million years ago, having arisen as part of the great Palaeocene adaptive radiation of mammals. Whether they originated in Africa or came from somewhere else is not known; certainly mammals that differed little from early primates were widespread at the time throughout what is now North America and Europe.

About 4 million years after the Moroccan primate, at least one primate had characteristics that are helping sort out the various hypotheses relating to the initial success of primates. In 2002, anthropologists investigating fossil deposits in Wyoming uncovered a 56-million-year-old skeleton that represents the best example of a Palaeocene primate so far discovered (Figure 5.4).[6] *Carpolestes*

simpsoni lacks both orbital convergence and adaptations for leaping. That is, it would not have had had good depth perception and would not have been jumping after food in trees. However it had a nail on its big toe and claws on its other digits, indicating it was developing the ability to grasp. Its blunt teeth are suited for fruit eating. *Carpolites* also has long arms suitably adapted to tree life. It seems safe to conclude that the ability for grasping came before the ability to leap for food in trees. Among the several hypotheses explaining the initial success of primates, the foraging for fruit at the ends of small, terminal branches is the best at the moment.

Eocene Primates

The Eocene lasted from about 55 to 34 million years ago and began with an abrupt warming trend. With this, many older forms of mammals became extinct, to be replaced by recognizable progenitors of many of today's forms. Among the latter were numerous forms of lemur-like and tarsierlike primates, of which over 50 genera are known. Fossils of these creatures have been found in Africa, North America, Europe, and Asia, where the warm, wet conditions of the Eocene sustained extensive rain forests.

---

[6] Ibid.

The abilities to judge depth correctly and grasp branches strongly are of obvious importance to animals as active in the trees as most primates. **MARTIN HARVEY**

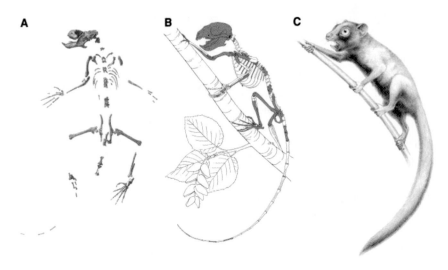

FIGURE 5.4

Skeleton (A) and reconstructions (B and C) of *Carpolestes simpsoni*. Bones shaded in grey were recovered.   REPRINTED WITH PERMISSION FROM BLOCH AND BOYER, SCIENCE 298, FIG 2, P. 1606-1610 (22 NOVEMBER 2002)

Most Eocene primates are classified into two families. One family consisted of mostly diurnal (active during daylight) creatures that generally ate fruit and leaves. Although for the most part small, some of these creatures were a bit larger than the smallest of today's monkeys. In many ways they were remarkably similar to modern lemurs and lorises, which likely are their descendants. Smaller in size were members of the other family, which were nocturnal eaters of fruits and insects. Tarsierlike in their anatomy, they are closely related to today's tarsier.

What the members of these early primate families have in common are somewhat enlarged brain cases, slightly reduced snouts, and a somewhat forward position of the eye orbits, which, though not completely walled in, are surrounded by a complete bony ring (Figure 5.5). Their dentition, however, was primitive and unlike that of modern forms in the total number of teeth. In their limb skeleton, they were well adapted to grasping, leaping, and perching. Moreover, nails like those possessed by modern primates, rather than claws, may be seen on some digits.

Other Eocene primates, represented by fossils from China and Egypt's Fayum depression, show unique mixes of lemurlike, tarsierlike, and platyrrhine-catarrhinelike characteristics and probably played a role in the ancestry of later monkeys and apes (Figure 5.6). The Chinese fossils, which are roughly 45 million years old, represent several species of tiny, insect-eating animals whose locomotion was by a combination of quadrupedalism and leaping. They include the smallest primates ever documented.[7] The Fayum fossils, not as old at 37 million years, are of a small leaf- or insect-eater. Although this creature's front teeth resemble those of the Eocene lemurlike primates, it has the catarrhinelike dental formula of two incisors, a canine, two premolars, and three molars on each side of the jaw, and the eye orbit has a complete wall, the latter being a feature of both catarrhine and platyrrhine primates. The foramen magnum has a somewhat forward position beneath the skull, and the brain was about 3.1 cubic centimetres in size.[8]

Although there is still much to be learned about these Eocene primates, it is clear that they were abundant, diverse, and widespread. Among them were ancestors of today's lemurs, as well as tarsiers and other haplorhines. The tarsierlike forms, with their large eyes, seem to have reverted to nocturnal habits, whereas the

---

[7] Gebo, D.L., Dagosto, D., Beard, K.C., & Tao, Q. (2001). Middle Eocene primate tarsals from China: Implications for haplorhine evolution. *American Journal of Physical Anthropology, 116*, 83–107.

[8] Simons, E. (1995). Skulls and anterior teeth of *Catopithecus* (Primates: Anthropoidea) from the Eocene and anthropoid origins. *Science, 268*, 1885–1888.

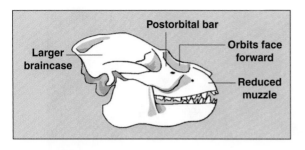

FIGURE 5.5

The Eocene genus *Adapis* is a lemurlike form. Like modern lemurs, it has a postorbital bar, a bony ring around the eye orbit. Note that the orbit is open behind the ring.

ancestors of platyrrhines and catarrhines did not. They shifted to a more herbivorous diet, with greater emphasis on arboreal quadrupedalism, in contrast to the emphasis on leaping seen in lemurlike and in tarsierlike forms.[9]

With the end of the Eocene, substantial changes took place among the primates, as among other mammals. In North America, now well isolated from Europe, primates became extinct, and elsewhere their range seems to have been reduced considerably. A driving force in all this was probably climatic change. Already, through the late Eocene, climates were becoming somewhat cooler and drier, but at the end temperatures took a sudden dive, sufficient to trigger formation of a substantial ice cap over previously forested Antarctica. The result was a marked reduction of the environments to which early

primates were adapted. At the same time, some early primate niches may have been more effectively utilized by newly evolved rodent forms. Finally, the precursors of monkeys and apes, up to then overshadowed by lemurlike and tarsierlike forms, may have been able to take over some other niches they formerly occupied.

Oligocene Monkeys and Apes

The Oligocene epoch began about 34 million and ended about 23 million years ago. Primate fossils that have thus far been discovered and definitely placed in the Oligocene are not common, but enough exist to prove that haplorhines were becoming quite prominent and diverse by this time. The scarcity of Oligocene primate fossils stems from the reduced habitat available to them and from the arboreal nature of primates then living, which restricted them to damp forest environments where conditions are exceedingly poor for fossil formation.

Fortunately, Egypt's Fayum depression has yielded sufficient fossils (more than 1000) to reveal that by 33 million years ago, haplorhine primates existed in considerable diversity. Moreover, the cast of characters is growing, as new fossils continue to be found in the

---

[9] Kay, R.F., Ross, C., & Williams, B.A. (1997). Anthropoid origins. *Science, 275,* 803–804.

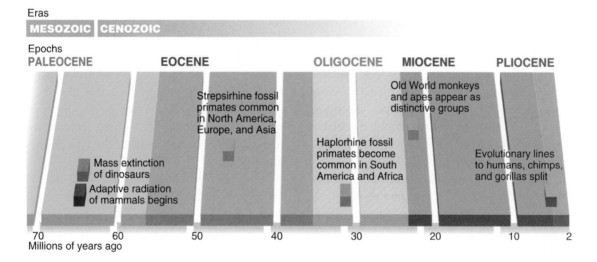

FIGURE 5.6

Timeline for the evolution of the major primate groups from the earliest mammals.

Egypt's Fayum depression in the desert west of Cairo. Here, winds and flash floods have uncovered sediments more than 22 million years old, exposing the remains of a tropical rain forest that was home to a variety of primates that combine monkeylike and apelike features. **E.L.SIMONS/DUKE PRIMATE CENTER**

Fayum, as well as in newly discovered localities in Algeria and Oman. At present, we have evidence of at least 60 genera included in two families. All show a combination of monkeylike and apelike features, and their origins probably lie in the group of Eocene primates in which traits of platyrrhines and catarrhines are first evident. But in the Oligocene the tables have been turned; now lemurlike and tarsierlike forms have become far less prominent than forms that combine monkeylike and apelike features. Only on the island of Madagascar (off the coast of East Africa), which was devoid of haplorhines until humans arrived, did lemurs thrive. In their isolation, they underwent a further adaptive radiation.

Included among the smaller Oligocene haplorhine species may be the ancestors of true monkeys. In their dental formula and limb bones, these primates (about the size of a modern squirrel monkey) resemble platyrrhine monkeys. Some of them could easily have gotten to South America, which at the time was not attached to any other land mass, by means of floating masses of vegetation of the sort that originate even today in the

great rivers of West and Central Africa. In the Oligocene, the distance between the two continents was far less than it is today; favourable winds and currents could easily have carried "floating islands" of vegetation across within the 13 days that platyrrhine ancestors could have survived, given an existing adaptation to seasonal variation in availability of fresh water.[10]

The earliest surely known true catarrhine monkey fossil comes from the Miocene epoch, but its ancestry may lie among the same primates that gave rise to the platyrrhines. This fossil's molars look as if they evolved from a similar form, and loss of one premolar on each side of the jaw would result in the typical catarrhine formula.

Given our obsession with our own ancestry, one particular genus of Oligocene catarrhine is worth a closer look. This is *Aegyptopithecus* ("Egyptian ape"). It is one of a number of genera with a specifically apelike

---

[10] Houle, A. (1999). The origin of platyrrhines: An evaluation of the Antarctic scenario and the floating island model. *American Journal of Physical Anthropology, 109,* 554–556.

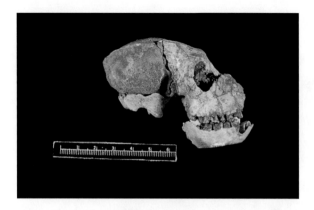

This Aegyptopithecus *skull dates to the Oligocene epoch. The enclosed eye sockets and dentition mark it as a catarrhine primate, probably ancestral to* Proconsul. **OLLIE ELLISON/DUKE PRIMATE CENTER**

dentition: Its lower molars have the five cusps of an ape, and the upper canine and lower first premolar exhibit the sort of shearing mechanism found in monkeys and apes. Its skull possesses eye sockets that are in a forward position and completely protected by a bony wall, as is typical of modern monkeys and apes. Evidently *Aegyptopithecus,* and probably its Fayum contemporaries as well, possessed vision superior to the lemurlike and tarsierlike primates of the Eocene. In fact, the inside of the skull of *Aegyptopithecus* reveals that its brain had a larger visual cortex and smaller olfactory lobes than do modern lemurs or tarsiers. Although the brain of *Aegyptopithecus* was smaller relative to body size than that of more recent catarrhines, this primate seems to have had a larger brain than any lemur or tarsier, past or present.

Aegyptopithecus, besides being the best-known Oligocene primate, is also of interest to us because its teeth suggest that it belongs in the ancestry of those Miocene forms that gave rise to both humans and today's African apes. Although no bigger than a modern house cat, *Aegyptopithecus* was nonetheless one of the larger Oligocene primates. Possessed of a monkeylike skull and body, with limb proportions not unlike those seen in some modern platyrrhine monkeys, and fingers and toes capable of powerful grasping, it evidently moved about in a quadrupedal monkeylike manner.[11] Differences between males and females include larger body size, more formidable canine teeth, and deeper mandibles (lower jaws) in the males. In modern catarrhines, species with these traits generally live in groups that include several adult females with one or more adult males.

Miocene Apes

The beginning of the Miocene epoch, which succeeded the Oligocene about 23 million years ago, saw a proliferation of apes in the forests that covered many parts of the Old World. Thus began a kind of golden age of apelike forms. East Africa is an area particularly rich in the fossils of apes from the early through the middle part of the Miocene. One of the earliest of these apes, *Proconsul* (Consul was the name of a chimpanzee prominent on the London vaudeville circuit), is one of the best known, owing to preservation of almost all elements of its skeleton. Four recognized species of *Proconsul* varied considerably in size, the smallest being no larger than a modern female baboon and the largest the size of a female gorilla. That they were apes is clearly shown by their dentition, particularly the five-cusped lower molars. Moreover, their skull, compared to that of Oligocene proto-apes like *Aegyptopithecus,* shows a reduced snout and a fuller, more rounded brain case. Cranial capacity for one species is estimated at about 167 cubic centimetres, about 1.5 times larger than that typical of a mammal of comparable body size and relatively larger than in modern monkeys. Still, some features are reminiscent of monkeys, particularly the forward thrust and narrowness of the face.

Although its overall configuration is not quite like any living monkey or ape, the elbow, hip, knee, and foot anatomy of *Proconsul* is similar to what one sees in living apes, and like them, it had no tail (Figure 5.7). The wrist and pelvis, however, are monkeylike, and the lumbar vertebrae and leg bones show features that are intermediate between those of a gibbon and a monkey. Overall, the vertebral column was longer and more flexible and the torso narrower than in apes, but the hind limb was less monkeylike, being more mobile as are ape hind limbs. The consensus is that *Proconsul* represents an unspecialized tree-dwelling, fruit-eating **hominoid** (the catarrhine superfamily to which modern apes and humans belong).

Some of *Proconsul's* contemporaries were even more apelike. At least one species had a shoulder joint allowing suspension of the body when hanging by the arms. Its leg bones suggest strong climbing ability, and vertebrae are

---

[11] Ankel-Simons, F., Fleagle, J.G., & Chatrath, P.S. (1998). Femoral anatomy of *Aegyptopithecus zeuxis,* an early Oligocene anthropoid. *American Journal of Physical Anthropology, 106,* 421–422.

> **Hominoid.** A catarrhine primate superfamily that includes apes and humans.

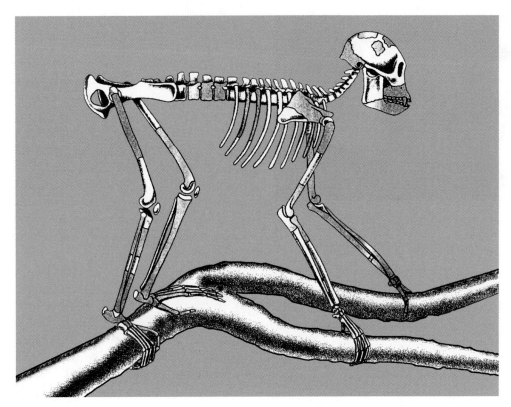

FIGURE 5.7

Reconstructed skeleton of *Proconsul*. Note apelike absence of tail, but monkeylike limb and body proportions. *Proconsul,* however, was capable of greater rotation of forelimbs than monkeys.

indicative of a stiff, apelike body. Otherwise, details of the teeth, face, and body are comparable to *Proconsul.*[12] Like *Proconsul,* this species is easily derivable from an animal like *Aegyptopithecus* and was almost certainly ancestral to hominoids of the middle Miocene. Like their probable ancestor as well as their descendants, *Proconsul* and other early Miocene apes were sexually dimorphic, the males being the larger sex with more formidable canine teeth.

Hominoids of the middle and late Miocene (from roughly 16 million to 5 million years ago) were a varied lot that ranged over a remarkably wide geographical area: Their fossils have been found in Europe, Asia, and Africa (by this time, Africa had collided with the Eurasian land mass, allowing faunal interchange). Such abundance and wide distribution indicates that these primates were very successful animals. With teeth and jaws very much like those of *Proconsul,* they seem to have been somewhat more apelike than monkeylike in their overall appearance; like some of *Proconsul*'s contemporaries, they had relatively

rigid bodies as well as limb bones well adapted for suspension and climbing. Some species surely were ancestral to later large-bodied apes, including the homininae—the primate family in which the African apes and humans are placed (Table 4.1). According to David Pilbeam, who has made the study of Miocene hominoids his life-work, "Any ... would make excellent ancestors for the living hominoids: human bipeds, chimpanzee and gorilla knucklewalkers, Orangutan contortionists."[13] Figure 5.8 shows some important similarities and differences among hominoids. Over the years, these forms have been known by a confusing assortment of generic and specific names, not all of which have turned out to be justified, as the following Original Study explains.

---

[12] Gebo, D.L., MacLatchy, L., Kityo, R., Deino, A., Kingston, J., & Pilbeam, D. (1997). A hominoid genus from the early Miocene of Uganda. *Science, 276,* 401–404.

[13] Pilbeam, D. (1986). *Human origins* (p. 6). David Skamp Distinguished Lecture in Anthropology, Indiana University.

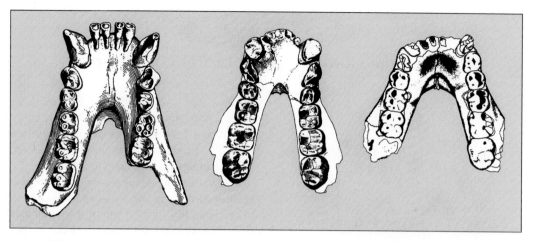

FIGURE 5.8

The lower jaws of two Miocene apes (A) and (B) and early *Australopithecus* (C), a hominine who lived 4 million years ago. Relative to the cheek teeth, all have comparatively small teeth at the front of the jaw. There is general similarity between A and B, as well as between B and C. The major difference between B and C is that the rows of cheek teeth are farther apart in the hominine.

For many years, potential hominin ancestors were known exclusively from the remains of teeth and jaws. Relative to the size of the cheek teeth (premolars and molars), their incisor teeth are comparable in size to those of other large hominoids of the time, although they are placed a bit more vertically in the mouth. The canines are substantially larger in males than in females, but even in males they are significantly smaller relative to the cheek teeth than the canines of the other hominoids. Still, they do project beyond adjacent teeth so that, when closed, the jaws interlock. Furthermore, the shearing function of the upper canine with the first lower premolar is retained. The molars, which show the same five-cusp pattern as the other hominoids, have noticeably thicker enamel and low, rounded cusps. The tooth row tends to be slightly V-shaped, whereas that of the other hominoids is more like a U, with the rows of cheek teeth parallel to one another (see Figure 5.8). The palate, or roof of the mouth, is high and arched. Finally, the lower facial region is narrow, short, and deep. Overall, the dental apparatus was built for powerful chewing, especially on the back teeth.

In the past three decades, our dependence on teeth and jaws for our knowledge of these hominoids has lessened as a number of their skull and limb bone fragments have been found in China, Greece, Hungary, Pakistan, and Turkey. In the best-known genus (*Sivapithecus*),

the face is remarkably orangutanlike in its profile and a number of other details. The mandible, however, is only broadly rather than specifically similar to that of an orang, nor are the upper arm bones quite the same. *Dryopithecus*, on the other hand, with its downward-tilting face resembles African apes and early hominines (see profile on page 152).

MIOCENE APES AND HUMAN ORIGINS

As long as several late-Miocene apes were known only from fossils of teeth and jaws, it was easy to postulate some sort of relationship between them and ourselves. This was because a number of features—the position of the incisors, the reduced canines, the thick enamel of the molars, and the shape of the tooth row—are linked to human ancestry. Some fossils (notably one from East Africa called *Kenyapithecus*) even show a shallow concavity above the position of the canine tooth, a feature not found in any recent ape but often found in humans. Indeed, some anthropologists went so far as to see such creatures as the earliest representatives of a human, as opposed to any ape lineage. This view was challenged when molecular evidence indicated a more recent split between apes and humans. The discovery

ORIGINAL STUDY

Will the Real Human Ancestor Please Stand Up?

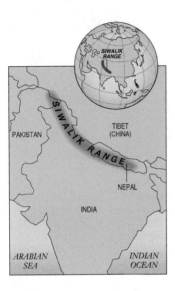

Today, humans are the only "ape" to have a global distribution. We inhabit every continent, including areas as inhospitable as the icy Antarctic or the scorching Sahara. Our closest living relatives, the other members of the superfamily *Hominoidea*, don't come close to occupying as much real estate. Instead these apes live in very circumscribed areas of the Old World tropical rain forest. Chimps, bonobos, and gorillas can be found only in portions of Central Africa. Orangutans are limited to the treetops on the islands of Sumatra and Borneo. Gibbons and siamangs swing through the branches only of the Southeast Asian forests.

This was not always the case. In the distant past, long before any human ancestor walked upon two legs, apes could be found throughout much of the Old World. True apes first appeared in the fossil record during the Miocene epoch, 5 to 23 million years ago. It was also during this time period that the African and Eurasian land masses made direct contact. For most of the preceding 100 million years, the Tethys Sea was a continuous body of water that more or less joined what are now the Mediterranean and Black Seas to the Indian Ocean. The Tethys Sea was a formidable barrier to migration. Once Africa and Eurasia were joined together through what is now the Middle East, Old World primate species that

got their start in Africa could expand their ranges into Eurasia. Miocene ape fossil remains have been found everywhere from the caves of China, to the forests of France, to eastern Africa where the earliest fossil remains of bipeds have been found.

So varied and ubiquitous were the fossil apes of this period that the Miocene has even been labelled by some as the "golden age of the hominoids." The word *hominoid* comes from the Latin roots *Homo* and *Homin* (meaning "human being") and the suffix *oïdes* ("resembling"). As a group, the hominoids get their name from their resemblance to humans. The likeness between humans and the other apes bespeaks an important evolutionary relationship. One of the Miocene apes is the direct ancestor of the human lineage. Exactly which one is a question still to be resolved.

The first Miocene ape fossil remains were found in Africa in the 1930s and 1940s by A.T. Hopwood and the renowned palaeoanthropologist Louis Leakey. These fossils turned up on one of the many islands in Lake Victoria, the 70 000-square-kilometre lake that separates Kenya, Tanzania, and Uganda. Impressed with the chimplike appearance of these fossil remains, Hopwood suggested that the new species be named *Proconsul* after a chimpanzee who was performing on the London stage at the time. *Pro* is the Latin root for "before" and Consul was the stage name of the acting chimp. Dated to the early Miocene 17 to 21 million years ago, *Proconsul* has some of the classic hominoid features, namely no tail and the characteristic pattern of Y5 grooves in the lower molar teeth. However, the adaptations of the upper body seen in later apes (including humans) for hanging suspended below tree branches in search of ripe fruits were absent. In other words, *Proconsul* has some apelike features as well as some features of more generalized four-footed Old World monkeys. This mixture of ape and monkey features makes *Proconsul* a contender for a "missing link" between monkeys and apes but not as a connection between Miocene apes and bipeds. We know that the ape that stood was fully apelike in all the ways that humans are apes. Our broad shoulders and mobile upper limb joints are fully adapted for hanging from branches. A dentist would recognize the cusp pattern of human molars in the mouth of any hominoid.

At least seven groups besides *Proconsul* have been found in East Africa in the early to middle Miocene. But between 14 and 5 million years ago this fossil record thins out. It is not that all the apes suddenly moved from Africa to Eurasia, but rather that the geologic conditions for preservation of bones as fossils made it less likely that any of the African remains would survive. Tropical forests inhabited by chimps and gorillas today are just about the worst conditions for the preservation of bones. In order to become a fossil, bones must be quickly incorporated into the earth before any rotting or decomposition occurs. In tropical forests the heat, humidity, and the general abundance of life make this unlikely. The bones' organic matrix is consumed by other creatures before it can be fossilized.

Nevertheless, the scarcity of African fossil evidence for this time period fits well with prevailing notions about human origins. Two factors were at work to take the focus away from Africa. First, at this time no investigators thought that humans were any more closely related to the African apes than they were to the other intelligent great ape—the Asian orangutan. Chimps, bonobos, gorillas, and orangutans were thought to be more closely related to each other than any of them were to humans. Moreover, the construction of evolutionary relationships still relied upon visual similarities between species much as it did when Linnaeus developed the taxonomic scheme that grouped humans with other primates. Chimps, bonobos, gorillas, and orangutans all possess the same basic body plan adapted to hanging by their arms from branches or knuckle-walking on the ground. Humans and their ancestors had an altogether different form of locomotion: walking upright on two legs. On an anatomical basis, it seemed as though the first Miocene ape to stand up and become a hominine could have come from any part of the vast Old World range of the Miocene apes.

The second factor at work to pull attention away from African origins was more subtle and embedded not in the bones from the earth but in the subconscious of the scientists of the day. It was hard for these scientists to imagine that humans originated entirely in Africa. Indeed, it took many years for the first bipedal

hominine fossils discovered in South Africa in the 1920s to be accepted by the scientific community as a key part of the human line (see Chapter 6). Instead, human origins were imagined to involve a close link between those who invented the first tools and the people responsible for Western civilization. In this regard, a contender for a Miocene ape ancestor from southern Asia, near the ruins of the great Indus Valley civilization, may have been more palatable to anthropologists in the middle of the 20th century.

During the 1960s, it appeared as though this Miocene human ancestor lived in the Siwalkis, the foothills of the majestic Himalayan mountain range along the northern borders of India and Pakistan. The Himalayas are some of the youngest mountains of the world. They began forming during the Miocene when the Indian subcontinent collided with the rest of Eurasia and have been growing taller ever since.

In honour of the Hindu religion practised in the region where the fossils were found, the contender was given the name *Ramapithecus,* after the Indian deity Rama and the Greek word for ape, *pithekos.* Rama is the avatar, or incarnation, of the Hindu god Vishnu, the preserver. He is meant to portray what a perfect human can be. He is benevolent, protects the weak, and embodies all noble human characteristics. Features like the relative delicacy and curvature of the jaw and palate as well as thick tooth enamel led palaeoanthropologists David Pilbeam and Elwyn Simons to suggest that this was the first hominoid to become a hominine. They suggested that *Ramapithecus* was a bipedal tool user—the earliest human ancestor. With these qualities, *Ramapithecus* was perfectly named.

Other Miocene apes were also present in the foothills of the Himalayas. *Sivapithecus* was named after the Hindu deity Siva, the god of destruction and regeneration. In the Hindu religion Siva is depicted as an asocial hermit who, when provoked, reduces his enemies to smouldering ashes in fits of rage. Though never an aspiring human ancestor, *Sivapithecus* also has the humanlike characteristic of thick molar tooth enamel (unlike the African apes). *Sivapithecus* also had large projecting canine teeth more suitable to a destroyer than to a human ancestor. The *Sivapithecus* and *Ramapithecus* fossils were dated to between 7 and 12 million years ago.

(Continued)

Fossils are not the only discoveries that have changed our understanding of human evolutionary history. By the 1970s, biochemical and genetic evidence was beginning to be used to establish evolutionary relationships. A Berkeley biochemist named Vince Sarich brought molecular techniques to evolutionary studies and developed the revolutionary concept of a "molecular clock." Such clocks help detect when the branching of related species from a common ancestor took place in the distant past.

Sarich used a molecular technique that had been around since the beginning of the 20th century: comparison of the blood proteins of living groups. He worked on serum albumin, a protein from the fluid portion of the blood that (like the albumin that forms egg whites) can be precipitated out of solution. One of the forces that will cause such precipitation is contact of this protein with antibodies directed against it, as in the immune response of the body when fighting an infection. The technique relies on the notion that the stronger the biochemical reaction between the protein and the antibody, the closer the evolutionary relationship, because the antibodies and proteins of closely related species will resemble one another more than the antibodies and proteins of distant species.

Sarich made immunological comparisons between a variety of species and suggested that he could establish a molecular clock by calculating a rate of change over time. By assuming a constant rate of change in the protein structure of each species over time, Sarich used these results to predict times of divergence between related groups. Each molecular clock needs to be set, or calibrated, by a known event such as the divergence between strepsirhine and haplorhine primates or Old World monkeys and apes. These dates are established directly by well-dated fossil specimens.

Using this technique, Sarich proposed a sequence of divergence for the living hominoids that showed that human, chimp, and gorilla lines split roughly 5 million years ago. He boldly stated that it was impossible to have a direct human ancestor before 7 million years ago "no matter what it looked like." In other words, anything that old would also have to be ancestral to chimps and gorillas. Because *Ramapithecus*, even with its humanlike jaws, was dated to between 7 and 12 million years ago, it could no longer be considered a human ancestor.

In the meantime, David Pilbeam and Elwyn Simons continued fossil hunting in the Himalayan foothills. Further specimens began to show that *Ramapithecus* was actually a smaller, perhaps female version of *Sivapithecus*. Eventually all the specimens referred to as *Ramapithecus* were "sunk" or absorbed into the *Sivapithecus* group so that today *Ramapithecus* no longer exists as a valid name for a Miocene ape. Instead of two distinct groups, one of which went on to evolve into humans, they are considered males and females of the sexually dimorphic species *Sivapithecus*. A spectacularly complete specimen found in the Potwar Plateau by David Pilbeam showed that *Sivapithecus* was undoubtedly the ancestor of living orangutans. This conclusion matched well with the molecular evidence that the separate line to orangutans originated 10 to 12 million years ago.

As the human lineage developed since the Miocene, our closest living relatives—the chimpanzees and gorillas—followed their own separate evolutionary trajectories. Today they inhabit the tropical forested pockets of Central Africa leaving little trace of their evolutionary history behind. Hominines took a different course and have left behind a rich fossil record in Eastern and Southern Africa beginning about 5 million years ago. Several million years after the ability to walk on two feet appeared, hominines began to spread throughout the Old World. Today, humans inhabit every continent. The details of our evolutionary history will continue to be redrawn in light of new evidence that appears from the bones, the molecules, or some area yet to be discovered. Though we have not found the fossil remains of the common ancestor of chimps, gorillas, and hominines, we know from the molecules that Africa is the place where the first ape stood up.

Source: Adapted from Walrath, D.E. (2001). *Will the real human ancestor please stand up?* © by author, College of Medicine, University of Vermont.

of the orangutanlike skulls and apelike limb bones of *Sivapithecus* added fuel to the fire, leading many anthropologists to conclude that this and similar forms could have nothing to do with human origins. Rather, orangutans were seen as the sole modern survivors of an ancient group from which the line leading to the hominins (African apes and humans) had branched off, as molecular evidence suggested, some 18 to 12 million years ago.

Eventually, opinion shifted back to a middle position. Although a link between Miocene *Sivapithecus* and modern orangutans seems undeniable (Figure 5.10), this does not rule out the possibility of a link between other related late-Miocene hominoids on the one hand and hominins on the other.[14] For example, some late Miocene species from Africa seem closer in dental proportions and other features of their teeth to early **hominines** than do related Asian fossils.

---

[14] Ciochon, R.L., & Fleagle, J.G. (1987). *Ramapithecus* and human origins. In R.L. Ciochon & J.G. Fleagle (Eds.), *Primate evolution and human origins* (p. 208). Hawthorne, NY: Aldine de Gruyter.

Palaeoanthropologist Alan Walker displays bones of Proconsul, *an unspecialized tree-dwelling, fruit-eating hominoid of the early Miocene.*
DAVID L. BRILL

Hominine. Member of the *Homininae*, the subfamily of hominins to which humans belong.

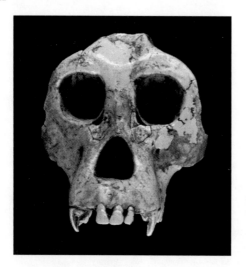

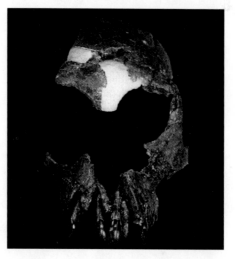

Stellar specimens of Dryopithecus, *one of the earliest great apes, have come from sites in Spain (left) and Hungary (right).* REPRINTED BY PERMISSION OF SCIENTIFIC AMERICAN (C) FROM "PLANET OF THE APES" BY DAVID BEGUN, AUGUST 2003.

BIOGRAPHY

David R. Begun

David Begun is a palaeoanthropologist and professor of anthropology at the University of Toronto. His Ph.D. is in biological anthropology from the University of Pennsylvania. He and his students are investigating great ape evolution and its implications for human origins. In collaboration with colleagues in Europe and Western Asia, Begun and his students have been examining the spread and diversification of great apes across Eurasia. He is also studying endocasts of fossils to understand the evolution of intelligence in apes and humans. His fieldwork has taken him to Turkey lately, where there is a rich record of several lineages of fossil great apes. He has also done fieldwork in Spain, Hungary, and Kenya. In 1998 he described a Miocene ape called *Ankarapithecus* and concluded that *Sivapithecus* and the gorilla are closely related[1] and that *Ankarapithecus* is probably a common ancestor to both. The relationships of *Ankarapithecus* to *Sivapithecus* and the gorilla, as well as the evidence that it lived in Turkey, point to a migration of a *Sivapithecus* ancestor back to Western Asia from the East. Anatolia appears to have been a migration route of early hominoids between South Asia and Africa. Since this discovery, Begun has come to the view that the birthplace of the common human and ape ancestor is Eurasia, not Africa as has been the prevailing view.

The ancestors of great apes did spread out of Africa to what is now Europe and Asia as far east as China between 17 and 16.5 million years ago, some 5 million years after the first appearance of apes.[2] Miocene apes were extraordinarily diverse compared with today's. Begun and his colleagues estimate that there were about 40 genera compared with eight now. The apes that migrated from Africa were eventually isolated by rising sea levels until about 15 million years ago when sea levels dropped. By 13 million years ago, the first great apes were recognized in Eurasia, but not in Africa. Drastic environmental changes in Europe wiped out all but two of the early great apes, *Sivapithecus* and *Dryopithecus*, at the end of the Miocene. They managed to survive by migrating to Africa and Southeast Asia where suitable habitats existed. *Sivapithecus* is the ancestor of the orang-utan while *Dryopithecus* is ancestral to African great apes. Begun's analysis of a *Dryopithecus* specimen from Hungary places it squarely in the evolutionary line to African apes and humans. The specimen is the first nearly complete *Dryopithecus* cranium and has a long, low brain case and an enlarged face that tilts downward. These characteristics are common to early hominines.

[1] Begun, D.R., & Güleç, E. (1998). Restoration of the type and palate of Ankarapithecus meteai: Taxonomic, phylogenetic, and functional implications. *American Journal of Physical Anthropology, 105*, 279–314.

[2] Begun, D.R. (2003). Planet of the apes. *Scientific American, 289* (2), 74–83.

  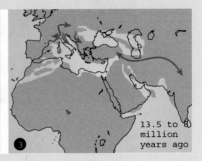

FIGURE 5.9

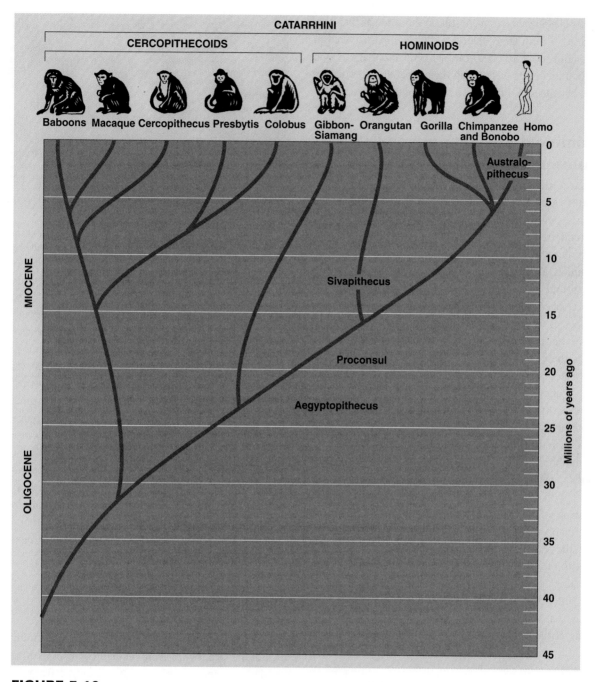

FIGURE 5.10

Although debate continues over details, this chart represents a reasonable reconstruction of evolutionary relationships among the catarrhine primates. (Not shown are extinct evolutionary lines.)

That the ancestry of humans may ultimately be among late-Miocene apes of Africa that show some resemblance to *Sivapithecus*, then, is consistent with dental evidence. It is consistent as well with estimates, based on molecular similarities and differences among humans, bonobos, chimpanzees, and gorillas, that they could not have separated from a common ancestral stock more than 8 million years ago. We know from the fossils that forms like *Sivapithecus* were still on the scene at that time (indeed, a form larger than a modern gorilla survived in Asia until about 300 000 years ago) and also that our own human ancestors were going their separate evolutionary way by at least 4.4 million, if not 6 million, years ago.

Hominoid Adaptations and Late Miocene Climatic Change

Molar teeth like those of some late Miocene apes, which feature low crown relief, thick enamel, and surfaces poorly developed for cutting, are found in a number of modern primates.[15] Some of these species are terrestrial and some are arboreal, but all have one thing in common: They eat very hard nuts, fruits with very tough rinds, and some seeds. This provides them with a rich source of easily digested nutrients that are not accessible to species with thin molar enamel incapable of standing up to the stresses of tough rind removal or nut cracking. Thus these Miocene apes probably ate food similar to that eaten by these latter-day nut crackers.

Analysis of other materials from deposits in which these fossils have been found suggests utilization of a broad range of habitats, ranging from tropical rain forests to drier bush country. Of particular interest to us, from the standpoint of human origins, are those populations that lived in mosaic environments, where there was forested as well as some open country, where food could be obtained through foraging on the ground as well as in the trees of the forests. As it happened, a climatic shift was under way, associated with the geological events involved in the formation of East Africa's rift valleys. This caused a gradual but persistent breaking up of forested areas, with a consequent expansion of open grassland.[16] Under such circumstances, it seems likely that those populations of late Miocene hominoids living at the edge of forests were obliged to supplement food from the trees more and more with other foods readily available on the ground in more open country. Consistent with this theory, late Miocene ape fossils are typically found in association with greater numbers of the remains of animals adapted to grasslands than are earlier ape fossils.

Those Miocene apes that already had large, thickly enamelled molars were capable of dealing with the tough and abrasive foods available on the ground when necessary. What they lacked, however, were canine teeth of sufficient size to have served as effective weapons of defence. By contrast, most modern monkeys and apes that spend much

Although not identical, the modern ape most like Sivapithecus *is the orangutan. Chimpanzees and gorillas, like humans, have come to differ more from the ancestral condition than have these Asian apes.* **GARY CRAWFORD**

time on the ground rely heavily for defence on the massive, fanglike canines possessed by the males. Because catlike predators were even more numerous on the ground than now, these Miocene apes, especially the smaller ones (which probably weighed no more than about 18 kilograms[17]), would seem to have been especially vulnerable primates. Probably the forest fringe was more than just a source of foods different from those on the ground; its trees would have provided refuge when danger threatened. Yet, with continued expansion of open country, trees for refuge would have become fewer and farther between. Slowly, however, physical and behavioural changes must have improved these primates' chances for survival out in the open on the ground. For reasons discussed in the next chapter, bipedal locomotion was a key element in this new adaptation.

EARLY APES AND HUMAN EVOLUTION

Although some late Miocene apes display a number of features from which hominine characteristics may be derived, and some may occasionally have walked bipedally, they were much too apelike to be considered

[15] Kay, R.F. (1981). The nut-crackers—A new theory of the adaptations of the Ramapithecinae. *American Journal of Physical Anthropology, 55*, 141–151.

[16] Conroy, G.C. (1997). *Reconstructing human origins: A modern synthesis* (pp. 84–86). New York: Norton.

[17] Pilbeam, D.R. (1987). Rethinking human origins. In Ciochon & Fleagle, p. 217.

hominines. No matter how often some of them may have resorted to bipedalism, they had not yet developed the anatomical specializations for this mode of locomotion that are seen in the earliest known hominines. They were optional rather than obligatory bipeds. Nevertheless, existing anatomical and molecular evidence allows the hypothesis that apes and humans separated from a common evolutionary line sometime near the end of the Miocene, and some fossils, particularly the smaller hominoids, do possess traits seen in humans. Moreover, the Miocene apes possessed a limb structure less specialized for brachiation than modern apes; this structure could well have provided the basis for the development of human as well as ape limb types.

Clearly not all late Miocene apes evolved into hominines. Those that did might, in a sense, be regarded as losers, in that they were squeezed out of the most favourable forested habitat. It was just their good luck that their physical characteristics enabled them to make a go of it under changed conditions. Most contemporary hominoids, by contrast, remained in the forests and woodlands where they continued to develop as arboreal apes, although ultimately some of them, too, took up a more terrestrial life. These are the bonobos, chimpanzees, and gorillas, which have changed far more from the ancestral hominoid condition than have the still arboreal orangutans.

EARLY PRIMATE EVOLUTION: AN OVERVIEW

Looking back over the first several million years of primate evolution, we see an initial diversification of strepsirhine and some haplorhine forms as they adapt

Ground-dwelling primates, like this male baboon, depend heavily on their massive canine teeth for protection from other animals. Some Miocene apes, by contrast, lacked such massive weapons of defence.

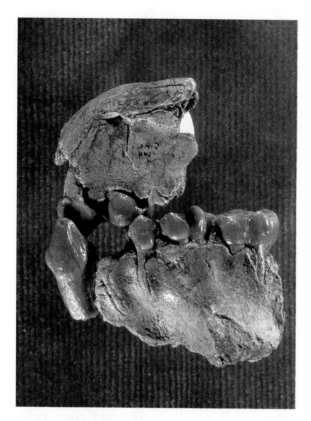

Kenyapithecus *from East Africa is a Miocene ape that has relatively small canine teeth and a facial profile suitable for an ancestor of African apes and humans.* NATIONAL MUSEUMS OF KENYA

to life in the trees. Despite their initial success, however, the strepsirhines tended to lose out to competition from rodents and the haplorhines. The exceptions were those forms that made it to Madagascar, or that adapted to nocturnal niches. Meanwhile, haplorhines diversified into a large variety of monkeylike apes, from which developed true monkeys, true apes, and (later) humans. Like the strepsirhines before them, the apes did well at first but eventually took a back seat in the forests to monkeys. This happened at least in part because monkeys, with shorter reproductive cycles, can out-reproduce apes. At the same time, forests continued to shrink, with some apes eventually adopting more terrestrial lifestyles. But unfortunately for them, by the time they did this, ground-dwelling niches for primates were already occupied by baboons and humans.

CHAPTER SUMMARY

The primates arose as part of a great adaptive radiation, a branching of mammalian forms that began more than 100 million years after the appearance of the first mammals. The reason for this late diversification was that most ecological niches that mammals have since occupied were either preempted by the reptiles or were nonexistent until the flowering plants became widespread beginning about 65 million years ago.

The first primates were arboreal insect eaters, and the characteristics of all primates developed as adaptations to this initial way of life. Although some primates no longer inhabit the trees, it is certain that those adaptations that evolved in response to life in the trees were (by chance) preadaptive to the niche now occupied by the hominines.

The earliest primates had developed by 60 million years ago in the Palaeocene epoch and were small arboreal creatures. A diversity of lemurlike and tarsier-like forms were common in the Eocene across what is now North America and Eurasia. By the late Eocene, perhaps 45 million years ago, small primates combining lemurlike and tarsierlike features with those seen in monkeys and apes were on the scene. In the Miocene epoch, apes proliferated and spread over many parts of the Old World. Among them were apparent ancestors of the large apes and humans. These appeared by 16 million years ago and were widespread even as recently as 8 million years ago. Details of dentition suggest that hominines, as well as the African apes, arose from these earlier apes. At least some populations of these primates lived in parts of Africa where the right kind of selective pressures existed to transform a creature just like it into a primitive hominine. Other populations remained in the forests, developing into today's bonobo, chimpanzee, and gorilla.

QUESTIONS FOR CRITICAL THOUGHT

1. S.J. Gould, with reference to evolution, said that the world of living organisms "is a quirky mass of imperfections." Discuss how humans are imperfect adaptations to the world and how our evolutionary history among early mammals and primates made us this way.

2. What lines of evidence are helping us understand early human evolution? What techniques would you like to see develop in order to resolve issues that are currently difficult or seemingly impossible to solve?

3. Discuss the range of selective pressures that appear to have influenced the early evolution of the primate order and the earliest human ancestors.

INTERNET RESOURCES

Continental Drift and Plate Tectonics

http://kids.earth.nasa.gov/archive/pangaea
Find out about plate tectonics and continental drift from this NASA site. Use interactive maps to understand how these phenomena shape our world and beyond.

Geologic Time Scale

www.zoomdinosaurs.com/subjects/Geologictime.html
Provides a detailed, interactive geologic time scale, highlighting pivotal events in each period and epoch.
www.geocities.com/CapeCanaveral/Lab/8932/cenozoic.htm

A time scale of the Cenozoic, with links to associated hominins, hominoids, and proto-hominoids, including plesiadapiformes, omomyidae, adapidae, *Aegyptopithecus*, *Dryopithecus*, *Sivapithecus*, *Kenyapithecus*, and so on.

Primate Fossils

www.carnegiemnh.org/research/eosimias/
An article on two new discoveries, one of a 45-million-old shrew-sized primate and another of the smallest primate known.

www.washingtonpost.com/wp-stv/national/daily/aug99/skeleton27.htm
An article on the partial skeleton of an apelike creature that roamed Kenya 15 million years ago.

www.niu.edu/pubaffairs/RELEASES/2000/ MAR/primate/Nature.htm
A news release about newly discovered fossils from China that shed light on the common ancestry of anthropoids.

http://homepages.about.com/darwin1963/ evolution.html
A layperson's discussion of DNA and human evolution.

www.mc.maricopa.edu/dept/d10/asb/anthro2003/origins/primates/evolution.html
An examination of the visual predation theory for the origins of primates. Links to general trends in primate evolution. Extensive links to extant primate sites.

http://pin.primate.wisc.edu
A trip to this Wisconsin Regional Primate Research Center's Primate Info Net opens the door to information about living and fossil primates as well as the people who study them. The site's search engine is a tremendous resource.

SUGGESTED READINGS

For a list of suggested readings, visit the textbook's website at www.humanevolution2.nelson.com.

THE FIRST BIPEDS

The fossilized remains of the earliest bipeds from Eastern, Southern, and Central Africa help us meet the challenge of understanding human origins. Clear evidence of bipedalism is preserved in various aspects of the skeleton. Fossilized footprints have even been preserved in volcanic ash at the 3.6 million-year-old Tanzanian site of Laetoli. As shown here, the foot of a living human fits right inside these ancient footprints, which show the characteristic pattern of bipedal walking.

ANTHRO-PHOTO

CHAPTER PREVIEW

1. What Is the Anatomy of Bipedalism and How Is It Preserved in the Fossil Record?

Bipedalism is the shared derived characteristic used to establish whether a fossilized hominoid is part of the evolutionary line that produced humans. Evidence of for bipedalism is preserved literally from head to toe. Bipedalism can be inferred from the forward position of the large opening in the base of the skull, a series of curves in the spinal column, the basin-shaped structure of the pelvis, the angle of the lower limbs from the hip joint to the knees, and the shape of the foot bones. Thus even fragmentary evidence can prove the "right" fragment is preserved. Several groups from between 4 and 7 million years ago have been proposed as the earliest bipeds.

2. Who Were the Australopithecines and What Were They Like?

The fossil record indicates that some time during the early Pliocene, beginning 5 million years ago, the genus *Australopithecus* appeared in Africa. Several candidates for its ancestor date back to between 7 and 6 million years ago. *Australopithecus,* remarkably human from the waist down, had become fully adapted for moving about on the ground on its hind legs in the distinctive human manner. But from the waist up, *Australopithecus* was still essentially apelike, with a brain suggesting intellectual abilities roughly comparable to those of a modern-day African ape. The earliest forms of *Australopithecus* preserve a number of features indicative of a more apelike ancestor. By 2.5 million years ago, this form gave rise to one whose chewing apparatus had become larger and more massive while its brain size remained relatively stable. For a while, this late form coexisted with a less radically altered version of the earlier form. One of the small australopithecine species, though it is not clear which one, appears to be a direct ancestor of the genus *Homo*.

3. Why Did *Australopithecus* Become a Bipedal Walker?

Early hominins (tribe Hominini) venturing out in the open on the ground would have been vulnerable in two ways: to damaging buildup of heat in the brain from direct exposure to the sun and to the many predators that prowled on the ground. Bipedal locomotion solves the heat problem by reducing the exposure of the body to direct solar radiation and positioning the body for most effective heat loss through convection. It also enabled *Australopithecus* to scan the savanna for danger, carry food to places where it could be consumed in safety, transport offspring, and grab hold of objects with which to threaten predators.

CHAPTER OUTLINE

Australopithecus	Environment, Diet, and Australopithecine
Australopithecine Predecessors	Origins

Though genetic evidence established that the human line diverged from those leading to chimpanzees and gorillas between 5 and 8 million years ago, for a long time, the fossil evidence of the early stages of human evolution was both sparse and tenuous. Today, however, several interesting specimens from Africa fill in this important period. Inclusion of any fossil specimen in the human evolutionary line depends upon evidence for bipedalism (also called bipedality), the initial defining characteristic of the hominin group. The next hominin characteristic to appear in the fossil record is increased brain size. The archaeological record for

tool use also plays an important role in identifying the appearance of hominins, particularly when archaeological sites have no fossil remains. Whether hominins were the only tool users in the past is still an open question. The possible human ancestors from Africa, dated 6 to 7 million years ago, were described in the last chapter. In this chapter, we will pick up our story with a diverse array of fossil bipeds less than 5 million years old.

Most of the early bipeds are members of the genus *Australopithecus*, a name coined for this group of fossils back in 1924 when the first important fossil from Africa proposed to be a human ancestor came to light. This unusual fossil, consisting of a partial skull and natural brain cast of a young individual, was brought to the attention of Professor Raymond Dart of the University of Witwatersrand in Johannesburg, South Africa. The "Taung child," named for the limestone quarry in which it was found, was unlike any creature Dart had ever seen before. Recognizing an intriguing mixture of ape and human characteristics in this unusual fossil, anatomist Dart proposed a new taxonomic category for his discovery—*Australopithecus africanus,* or southern ape of Africa—suggesting that this specimen represented an extinct form that was ancestral to humans.

Although the anatomy of the base of the skull indicated that the Taung child was probably a biped, the scientific community was not ready to accept the notion of a small-brained African ancestor to humans.

These footprints from Laetoli, Tanzania, confirm that Australopithecus *walked bipedally. They were made by three individuals, one of whom was careful to walk directly in the footsteps of one in front.* **TIM WHITE/DAVID L. BRILL, ATLANTA**

The Anatomy of Bipedalism

Because comparative anatomy is a key to palaeoanthropologists' work, understanding the anatomy of bipedalism—the shared derived characteristic distinguishing humans and their ancestors (hominines) from the other African apes—is important. Bipedalism is associated

Australopithecus The first well-known hominin; lived between 4.2 and 1 million years ago. Characterized by bipedal locomotion when on the ground, but with an apelike brain; includes at least five species: *afarensis, africanus, anamensis, boisei,* and *robustus.*

with anatomical changes literally from head to toe (Figures 6.1 and 6.2). As noted in the Taung child, evidence of bipedalism can even be preserved in the skull. In order for the head to be balanced above the spinal column in an upright posture, the position of the skull is relatively centred above the spinal column. The spinal cord leaves the skull at its base through an opening called the foramen magnum. In a knuckle-walker like a chimp, the foramen magnum is more toward the back of the skull; in a biped it is in a more forward position.

Working down from the skull of a biped, the spinal column makes a series of convex and concave curves that together maintain the body in an upright posture by positioning the body's centre of gravity above the legs rather than forward. The curves correspond to the neck (cervical), chest (thoracic), lower back (lumbar), and pelvic (sacral) regions of the spine, respectively. In a chimp, the shape of the spine follows a single arching curve.

The shape of the pelvis also differs considerably between bipeds and other apes. Rather than an elongated shape following the arch of the spine as seen in chimps, the shape of the pelvis is wider and foreshortened so that it can provide structural support for the upright body. With a wide bipedal pelvis, the lower limbs would be oriented away from the body's center of gravity if the thigh bones

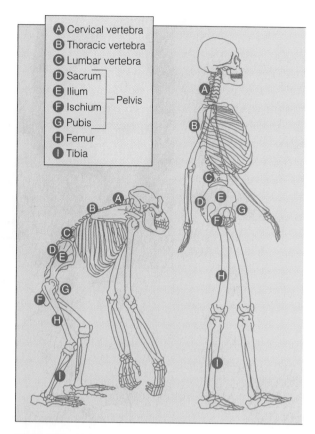

FIGURE 6.2

(femora) didn't angle in toward each other from the hip to the knee, a phenomenon described as "kneeing-in." This angling does not continue in shin bones (tibia), wluch are vertically oriented toward the ground. The resulting knee joint is not symmetrical, allowing the thigh and shin bones to meet despite their different orientations (Figure 6.3). Another characteristic of bipeds is their stable arched feet and the absent opposable big toe. In general, humans and their ancestors possess shorter toes than the other apes.

These anatomical features allow palaeoanthropologists to "diagnose" bipedal locomotion even in fragmentary remains such as the top of the shin bone or the base of a skull. In addition, bipedal locomotion can also be established through fossilized footprints, preserving not so much the shape of foot bones but the characteristic stride used by humans and their ancestors. Bipedal locomotion is really a process of alternation between supporting the

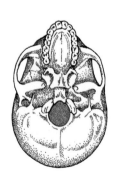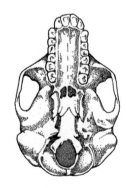

FIGURE 6.1

Bipedalism can be inferred from the position of the foramen magnum, the large opening at the base of the skull. Note its relatively forward position on the human skull (left) compared to the chimp skull.

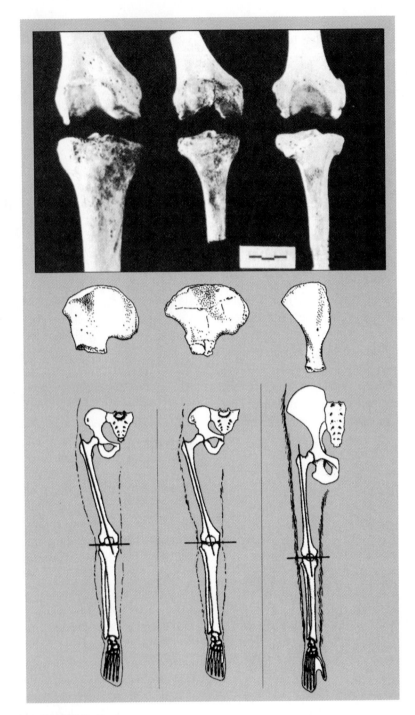

FIGURE 6.3

Examination of the upper hip bones and lower limbs of (from left) *H. sapiens, Australopithecus*, and an ape can be used to determine means of locomotion. The similarities of the human and Australopithecine bones are striking and are indicative of bipedal locomotion. (The reconstruction of the Australopithecine limb is based on the knee joint shown in the photograph.) ORIGINAL PUBLICATION: FROM "LUCY: THE BEGINNINGS OF HUMANKIND" ILLUSTRATION CREDIT: ©1981 LUBA DMYTRYK GUDZ \ BRILL ATLANTA

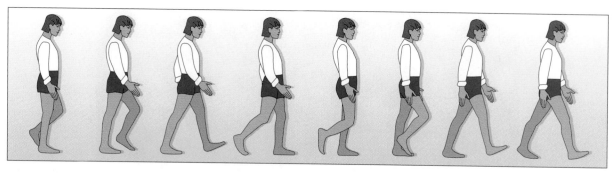

FIGURE 6.4

The bipedal gait in some regards is really "serial monopedalism" or locomotion one foot at a time. Note how the body's weight shifts from one foot to the other as an individual moves through the swing phase to heel strike and toe off.

body's weight on either foot. While the body is supported in a one-legged stance, a biped takes a stride by swinging the other leg forward. The heel of the foot is the first part of the swinging leg to hit the ground. Then as the biped continues to move forward, he or she rolls from the heel toward the toe, pushing or 'toeing off' into the next swing phase of the stride. While one leg is moving from heel strike to toe off of the stance phase, the other leg is moving forward through the swing phase of walking (Figure 6.4).

The most dramatic confirmation of Australopithecine's walking ability comes from Laetoli, Tanzania, where, 3.6 million years ago, three individuals walked across newly fallen volcanic ash. Because it was damp, the ash took the impressions of their feet, and these were sealed beneath subsequent ash falls until discovered by chemist Paul Abell in 1978. The shape of the footprints, the linear distance between the heel strikes and toe off, are all quite human.

The exploration of the fossil record of human evolution throughout this and the next several chapters will entail making anatomical comparisons among various fossil and living groups. Once bipedalism is established in a fossil specimen, palaeoanthropologists turn to other features such as the skull or teeth to establish relationships among the various hominins.

AUSTRALOPITHECUS

Since Dart's original find, hundreds of other fossils of *Australopithecus* have been found, first in South Africa and later in Tanzania, Malawi, Kenya, Ethiopia, and Chad (Figure 6.5). As they were discovered, many were given a number of different specific and generic names, but now usually all are considered to belong to the single genus *Australopithecus*. Most anthropologists recognize at least four species of the genus, if not as many as seven (Table 6.1 and Figure 6.6). For our purposes, we may discuss them in terms of two broad categories: **gracile** and **robust Australopithecus**. The latter are notable for having jaws that are massive (robust) relative to the size of the brain case. The gracile forms are slightly smaller on average and lack such robust jaws.

Gracile Australopithecines

Included in this group are numerous fossils found beginning in the 1930s at Sterkfontein and Makapansgat in South Africa, in addition to Dart's original find from Taung (Figure 6.5). One unusually complete skeleton discovered in 1994 has been dated by palaeomagnetism to about 3.5 million years ago. The other South African remains are difficult to date but seem to fit between 3 and 2.3 million years ago. Specimens from Ethiopia's

Gracile Australopithecines. Smaller, more lightly built members of the genus *Australopithecus*.

Robust Australopithecines. Slightly larger and more robust than gracile members of genus *Australopithecus*, with larger, more powerful jaws.

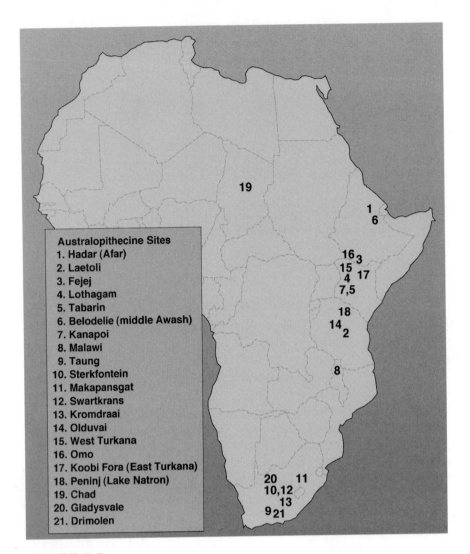

FIGURE 6.5

Australopithecine fossils have been found in South Africa, Malawi, Tanzania, Kenya, Ethiopia, and Chad.

Afar region, first discovered in 1970, are securely dated by potassium argon to between 3.9 and 2.9 million years ago. These include the famous "Lucy," represented by bones from almost all parts of a single skeleton, and "the First Family," a collection of bones from at least 13 individuals of both sexes, ranging in age from infancy to adulthood, who died together as a result of some single calamity. Recently, a discovery in Ethiopia at the 3.3-million-year-old Dikika site represents the most complete skeleton of a gracile *Australopithecus* as well as the most complete skeleton of an ancient juvenile hominin.[1] It is estimated to have been about three years old at death. Also securely dated is material, close

to 4 million years old, from Laetoli, in Tanzania, that is usually assigned to the same species as the Afar fossils. Thus, although there is overlap, the East African fossils seem for the most part to be earlier than those of South Africa.

Other pieces of gracile Australopithecines have been found at other East African sites that generally are 2 million or more years old. The oldest so far found are some jaw and limb bones from Kenya that

---

[1] Alemseged Z., Spoor, F., Kimbel, W.H., Bobe, R., Geraads, D., Reed, D., & Wynn, J.G. (2006). A juvenile early hominin skeleton from Dikika, Ethiopia. *Nature, 443,* 296–301.

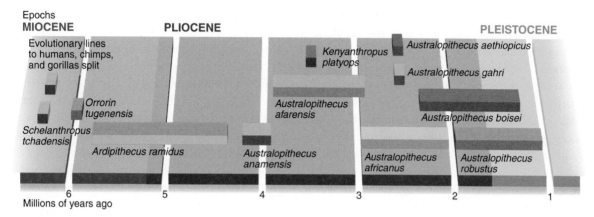

FIGURE 6.6

The earliest hominin fossils and the scientific names by which they have been known, arranged according to when they lived. *A. aethiopicus, A. boisei,* and *A. robustus* are all robust Australopithecines; *A. afarensis, A. africanus,* and *A. anamensis* are gracile Australopithecines. Recently, *Sahelanthropus tchadensis* was added to the record (7.0 to 6.5 million years ago). Whether all the different species names are warranted is hotly debated.

TABLE 6.1   Species of *Australopithecus**

GRACILE SPECIES	LOCATION
A. afarensis	Ethiopia and Tanzania
A. africanus	South Africa
A. anamensis	Kenya
ROBUST SPECIES	
A. aethiopicus	Kenya
A. boisei	Kenya
A. gahri	Ethiopia
A. robustus	South Africa

*Not all palaeoanthropologists recognize as many as seven species; *A. aethiopicus*, for example, could be an early variety of *A. boisei*.

date to between 4.2 and 3.9 million years ago (see *A. anamensis* in Table 6.1 and Figure 6.6). All gracile species were sexually dimorphic, bipedal hominins. Their stature ranged between 1 and 1.5 metres, and they are estimated to have weighed between 29 and 45 kilograms.[2] Their physical appearance was unusual by our standards: They may be described as looking like an

<hr/>

[2] McHenry, H.M. (1992). Body size and proportions in early hominids. *American Journal of Physical Anthropology, 87,* 407.

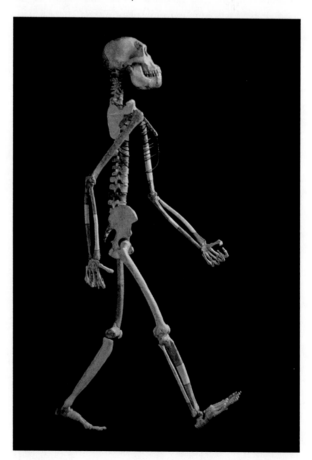

Sufficient parts of the skeleton of "Lucy," an Australopithecine that lived between 3.3 and 2.6 million years ago, survived to permit this reconstruction. Her hip and leg bones reveal that she walked about in a distinctly human manner. DAVID L. BRILL BY PERMISSION OF OWEN LOVEJOY

ape from the waist up and like a human from the waist down (Figure 6.7). The cranium was relatively low, the forehead sloped backward, and the brow ridge that helps give apes such massive-looking foreheads was also present. The lower half of the face was chinless and accented by jaws that were quite large, relative to the size of the skull.

Much has been written about Australopithecine teeth. Speaking generally, the gracile forms possessed small incisors, short canines in line with adjacent teeth, and a rounded dental arch. The molars and premolars are larger in size but similar in form to modern human teeth (Figure 6.8). The molars are unevenly worn; the upper cheek teeth are worn from the inside, and the lower cheek teeth are worn from the outside. This indicates that both species chewed food in a hominin fashion, even though they were probably capable of two to four times the crushing force of modern human beings. Heavy wear indicates that the food chewed was high in tough plant fibres. There is usually no gap between the canines and the teeth next to them on the upper jaw, as there would be in apes. Further, the large mandible is very similar to that of the later hominin, *H. erectus* (Chapter 8).

As one might expect, there are differences between the later South African fossils and the earlier ones from East Africa. The teeth of the Ethiopian specimens, but especially those from Laetoli, show numerous features reminiscent of some late Miocene apes that the later ones do not (see Figure 5.8). Generally, the incisors and canines are a bit larger in the earlier ones, there is sometimes a gap between upper lateral incisors and canines, the canines tend to project noticeably, the first lower premolars are less like molars and show more shearing wear, and the dental arch is less rounded. One jaw from Laetoli even shows a partial interlock of upper canines with lower canines and premolars. The oldest jaws of all, from Kenya (*A. anamensis*), are even more apelike, with a shallow palate, large canines, and nearly parallel rows of cheek teeth.

In addition to differences between earlier and later gracile Australopithecines, there were also differences between the sexes. For one thing, males were about one and a half times the size of females. In this respect, they were somewhat like the Miocene apes, with sexual dimorphism greater than one sees in a modern chimpanzee but less than one sees in gorillas and orangutans. Male canines, too, are significantly larger than those of females (Figure 6.9). There is as well a clear evolutionary trend for the first lower premolar of males to become more

molarlike, through development of a second cusp. Those of females, by contrast, do not. By analogy with modern orangutans, such differences might be expected if male and female foraging patterns were not quite the same—for example, if females got more of their food from the trees, while males consumed large amounts of lower-quality food to be found on or near the ground. Consistent with this pattern, some features of the skeleton are somewhat better suited to climbing in females than in males.[3]

Although the brain is small and apelike and the general conformation of the skull seems nonhuman (even the semicircular canal, a part of the ear crucial to maintenance of balance, is apelike), the foramen magnum of these Australopithecines is placed forward and is downward looking, as it is in later bipedal hominins of the **genus *Homo***. Cranial capacity, commonly used as an index of brain size, varied from 310 to 485 cubic centimetres in East African and 428 to 510 cubic centimeters in South African representatives,[4] roughly the size of a large chimpanzee brain. Although three times larger than the brain of any Miocene ape, it was only about one-third the size of a modern human brain. Intelligence, however, is not indicated by absolute brain size alone but is roughly indicated by the ratio of brain to body size. Unfortunately, with such a wide range of adult weights it is not clear whether brain-size was larger than a modern ape's relative to body size. Although some researchers think they see evidence for some expansion of the brain, others vigorously disagree. Moreover, the outside appearance of the brain, as revealed by casts of the insides of skulls, is more apelike than human, suggesting that cerebral reorganization toward a human condition had not yet occurred.[5] Consistent is the fact that the system for drainage of the blood from the cranium of the earlier Australopithecines

---

[3] Simons, E.L. (1989). Human origins. *Science, 245*, 1346.

[4] Grine, F.E. (1993). Australopithecine taxonomy and phylogeny: Historical background and recent interpretation. In R.L. Ciochon & J.G. Fleagle (Eds.), *The human evolution source book* (pp. 201–202). Englewood Cliffs, NJ: Prentice-Hall.

[5] Falk, D. (1989). Apelike endocast of "ape-man" Taung. *American Journal of Physical Anthropology, 80*, 339.

Genus *Homo*. Hominin genus characterized by expansion of brain, reduction of jaws, and reliance on cultural adaptation.

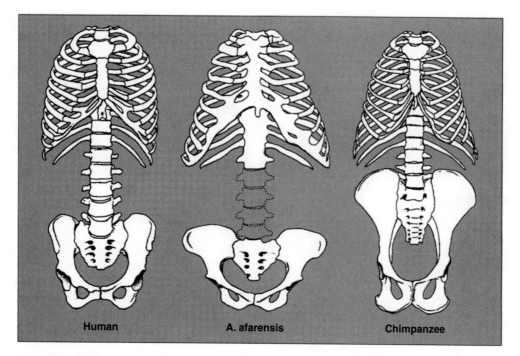

FIGURE 6.7

Trunk skeletons of modern human, gracile *Australopithecus,* and chimpanzee, compared. In its pelvis, the Australopithecine resembles the modern human, but its rib cage shows the pyramidal configuration of the ape.

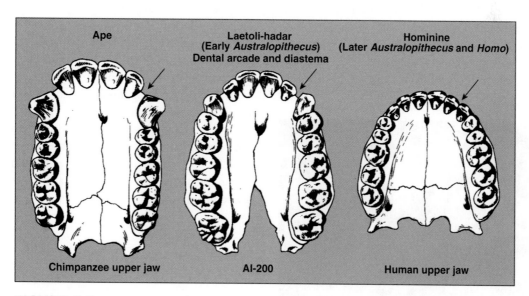

FIGURE 6.8

The upper jaws of an ape, *Australopithecus,* and modern human show important differences in the dental arch and the spacing between the canines and adjoining teeth. Only in the earliest Australopithecines can a diastema (a large gap between the teeth) be seen.

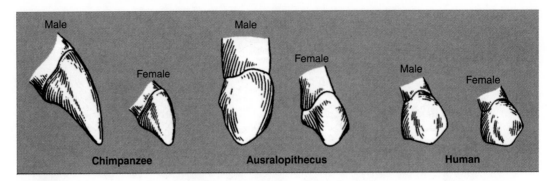

FIGURE 6.9

Sexual dimorphism in canine teeth.

is significantly different from that of the genus *Homo*. At the moment, the weight of the evidence favours mental capabilities for all gracile Australopithecines as being comparable to those of modern great apes.

The fossil remains of gracile *Australopithecus* have provided anthropology with two indisputable facts. First, as early as 4 million years ago, this hominin was bipedal, walking erect. This is indicated first of all by the curvature of the spine, which is like that of humans rather than of apes. This served to place the centre of gravity over, rather than in front of, the hip joint. The Dikika juvenile's scapula, however, is more similar to that of a gorilla's than to a modern human's. This raises the possibility that Australopithecines retained some form of adaptation to arboreal life. A forearm bone from "Lucy," which is shorter than that of an ape, suggests that the upper limb was lighter and the centre of gravity lower in the body than in apes. Still, the arms

of Lucy and her kind are long compared to their relatively short legs. While these make for a shorter stride length than in *Homo,* they were well suited to vertical climbing. Moreover, the somewhat elevated position of the shoulder joint was more adapted to arboreal performance; fingers and toes show more curvature; and a partial foot skeleton between 3.5 and 3 million years old from Sterkfontein, South Africa (Figure 6.10), shows a long, flexible toe still useful for grabbing onto tree limbs.[6] The combination of traits indicate that the tree-climbing abilities of the gracile Australopithecines exceeded those of more recent hominins and that they spent time in trees as well as on the ground.

The second indisputable fact provided by gracile *Australopithecus* is that hominins acquired their erect bipedal position long before they acquired their highly enlarged brain. Not only is the latter more apelike than human in its size and structure, but also it is probable that *Australopithecus* did not have prolonged maturation as do modern humans; instead they grew up rapidly as do apes.[7] Thus, no matter how important bipedal locomotion may have been in setting the stage for the later expansion and elaboration of the human brain, it cannot by itself account for those developments.

Shown here is the skull of a gracile Australopithecine from Ethiopia.
WILLIAM H. KIMBEL, PH.D., INSTITUTE OF HUMAN ORIGINS

[6] Oliwenstein, L. (1995). New footsteps into walking debate. *Science, 269,* 476.

[7] Tardieu, C. (1998). Short adolescence in early hominids: Infantile and adolescent growth of the human femur. *American Journal of Physical Anthropology, 107,* 173–174.

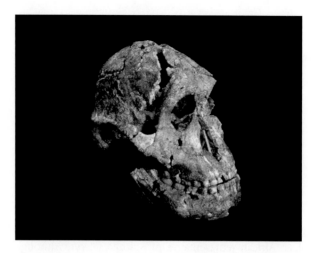

Sexual dimorphism was marked in the robust Australopithecines from South Africa. Although male skulls show a sagittal crest, female skulls like the one shown here do not. LEE R. BURGER, PURE, UNIVERSITY OF WITWATERSTAND

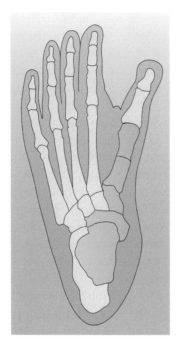

FIGURE 6.10

Drawing of the foot bones of a 3- to 3.5-million-year-old *Australopithecus* from Sterkfontein, South Africa, as they would have been in the complete foot. Note how long and flexible the first toe (at right) is.

Robust Australopithecines

The remains of robust Australopithecines were first found at Kromdraai and Swartkrans in South Africa by Robert Broom and John Robinson in 1948 in deposits that, unfortunately, cannot be securely dated. Current thinking puts them anywhere from 1.8 to 1.0 million years ago. Usually referred to as the species *A. robustus* (see Table 6.1 and Figure 6.2), it shared practically all of the traits listed for the species of gracile *Australopithecus* just discussed, especially the South African ones. A few scientists prefer to classify the robust forms as a separate genus: *Paranthropus*. They probably are distinctive enough to merit such a classification, but naming a new genus is still an arbitrary process. The robust forms have been called *Australopithecus* for nearly half a century, and it would complicate the taxonomy needlessly to change it now. Although of similar size, the bones of *robustus*'s body were thick for their size, with prominent markings where their muscles attached. The skull of the robust form was thicker and larger than that of the graciles, with a slightly larger cranial capacity (around 530 cubic centimetres). Its skull also possessed a simianlike **sagittal crest** (more

evident in males than in females) running from front to back along the top. This feature provides sufficient area on a relatively small braincase for attachment of the huge temporal muscles required to operate powerful jaws, such as robust *Australopithecus* possessed and gorillas have today; hence what we have here is an example of convergent evolution in gorillas and hominins.

The first robust Australopithecine to be found in East Africa was discovered by Mary Leakey in the summer of 1959, the centennial year of the publication of Darwin's *On the Origin of Species*. She found it

Sagittal crest. A crest running from front to back on the top of the skull in the midline.

Olduvai Gorge, Tanzania. DES BARTLETT/NGS IMAGE COLLECTION

in Olduvai Gorge, a fossil-rich area near Ngorongoro Crater, on the Serengeti Plain of Tanzania, East Africa. Olduvai is a huge gash in the earth, about 40 kilometres long and 90 metres deep, which cuts through Pleistocene and recent geological strata revealing close to 2 million years of the earth's history.

Mary Leakey's discovery was reconstructed by her husband, Louis, who gave it the name "*Zinjanthropus boisei.*" At first, he thought this hominin seemed more humanlike than *Australopithecus* and extremely close to modern humans in evolutionary development. Further study, however, revealed that *Zinjanthropus*, the remains of which consisted of a skull and a few limb bones, was an East African representative of *Australopithecus.* Although similar in many ways to *A. robustus*, most commonly it is referred to as *A. boisei* (see Table 6.1 and Figure 6.6). Potassium-argon dating places this early hominin at about 1.75 million years old. Since the time of Mary Leakey's original find, numerous other fossils of this robust species have been found at Olduvai, as well as north and east of Lake Turkana in Ethiopia and Kenya. Although one (often referred to as the "Black Skull," sometimes as *A. aethiopicus*) is known to be as much as 2.5 million years old, some date to as recently as 1.3 million years ago.

The size of the teeth and certain cranial features of these East African fossils are reminiscent of the robust Australopithecines from South Africa. Molars and premolars are enormous, as are the mandible and palate. Even so, the anterior teeth (canines and incisors) are often crowded, owing to the room needed for the cheek teeth. The heavy skull, more massive even than its robust South African relative's, has a sagittal crest and prominent brow ridges; cranial capacity ranges from about 500 to 530 cubic centimetres. Body size, too, is somewhat larger; whereas the robust South Africans are estimated to have weighed between 32 and 40 kilograms, the East Africans probably weighed from 34 to 49 kilograms.

Because the earliest robust skull from East Africa (2.5 million years), the so-called Black Skull from Kenya (*A. aethiopicus* in Table 6.1 and Figure 6.6), retains a number of primitive features shared with East African graciles, it is probable that it evolved from gracile ancestors, giving rise to the later robust East Africans. Whether the South African robusts represent a southern offshoot of the East African lineage or convergent evolution from a South African ancestor is so far not settled; arguments can be presented for both interpretations. In either case, the later Australopithecines

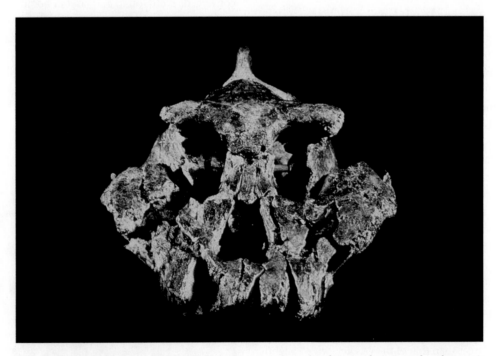

The so-called Black Skull, found at West Turkana, Kenya, is the earliest known robust Australopithecus. *At 2.5 million years old, it appears ancestral to later robust Australopithecines from East Africa.* **NATIONAL MUSEUMS OF KENYA**

170

BIOGRAPHY

Louis S.B. Leakey (1903–72)
Mary Leakey (1913–96)

Few figures in the history of palaeoanthropology discovered so many key fossils, received so much public acclaim, or stirred up as much controversy as Louis Leakey and his second wife, Mary Leakey. Born in Kenya of missionary parents, Louis received his early education from an English governess and subsequently was sent to England for a university education. He returned to Kenya in the 1920s to begin his career there.

MELVILLE BELL GROSVENOR/NGS IMAGE COLLECTION

It was in 1931 that Louis and his research assistant from England, Mary Nicol (whom he married in 1936), began working in their spare time at Olduvai Gorge in Tanzania, searching patiently and persistently for remains of early hominins. It seemed a good place to look, for there were numerous animal fossils, as well as crude stone tools lying scattered on the ground and eroding out of the walls of the gorge. Their patience and persistence were not rewarded until 1959, when Mary found the first hominin fossil. A year later, another skull was found, and Olduvai was on its way to being recognized as one of the most important sources of hominin fossils in all of Africa. While Louis reconstructed, described, and interpreted the fossil material, Mary made the definitive study of the Oldowan tools.

The Leakeys' important discoveries were not limited to those at Olduvai. In the early 1930s, they found the first fossils of Miocene apes in Africa at Rusinga Island in Lake Victoria. Also in the 1930s, Louis found a number of skulls at Kanjera, Kenya, that show a mixture of modern and more primitive features. In 1961, at Fort Ternan, Kenya, the Leakeys found the remains of a late Miocene ape with features that seemed appropriate for a hominin ancestor. After Louis's death, a member of an expedition led by Mary Leakey found the first footprints of *Australopithecus* at Laetoli, Tanzania.

In addition to their own work, Louis Leakey promoted a good deal of important work on the part of others. He made it possible for Jane Goodall to begin her landmark field studies of chimpanzees; later on, he was instrumental in setting up similar studies among gorillas (by Dian Fossey) and orangutans (by Biruté Galdikas). Last but not least, the Leakey tradition has been continued by son Richard and his wife, Maeve.

Louis Leakey had a flamboyant personality and a way of making interpretations of fossil materials that frequently did not stand up to careful scrutiny, but this did not stop him from publicly presenting his views as if they were the gospel truth. It was this aspect of the Leakeys' work that generated controversy. Nonetheless, the Leakeys accomplished and promoted more work that resulted in the accumulation of knowledge about human origins than anyone before them. Anthropology clearly owes them a great deal.

developed molars and premolars that are larger than those of earlier gracile ones (though some tendency in this direction can be seen in the South African graciles). Larger teeth require more bone to support them, hence the prominent jaws of the robust Australopithecines. Finally, the larger jaws and the chewing of more food require more jaw musculature that attaches to the skull. The marked crests seen on skulls of the late

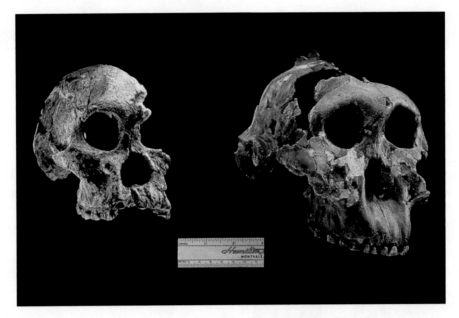

This photo contrasts gracile (left) and robust (right) Australopithecine skulls. Both were probably male; the gracile skull is from South Africa, the robust from East Africa. **DAVID L. BRILL**

These teeth and jaw fragment are from Ardipithecus, *a hominin that lived between 5.8 and 4.4 million years ago in Ethiopia.*
1994, TIM O. WHITE/DAVID L. BRILL, ATLANTA

Australopithecines provide for the attachment of such a musculature on a skull that has increased very little in size. In effect, robust Australopithecines had evolved into highly efficient chewing machines. Clearly, their immense cheek teeth and powerful chewing muscles bespeak the kind of heavy chewing a diet restricted to uncooked plant foods requires. Many anthropologists believe that, by becoming a specialized consumer of plant foods, the late Australopithecines avoided competing for the same niche with early *Homo*, with which they were contemporaries. In the course of evolution, the **law of competitive exclusion** dictates that when two closely related species compete for the same niche, one will outcompete the other, bringing about the loser's extinction. That early *Homo* and late *Australopithecus* did not compete for the same niche is suggested by their coexistence for something like 1.5 million years.

Law of competitive exclusion. When two closely related species compete for the same niche, one will outcompete the other, bringing about the latter's extinction.

AUSTRALOPITHECINE PREDECESSORS

Although the Australopithecines are now fairly well known, the same cannot be said about their immediate predecessors. As already noted, the earliest fossils of *Australopithecus* displayed a number of traits suggestive of an ancestry among the late Miocene apes. In addition to the features of the teeth, hands, and feet already noted, the earliest *Australopithecus* skulls are thick-boned and have a forward thrust to the face, large flaring cheekbones, and heavy cresting. But what about fossils that date between late Miocene apes on the one hand and early *Australopithecus* on the other?

Until the 1990s, fossils from the crucial period of about 7 to 4 million years ago were so few and fragmentary that they provided scant information. The oldest potential relatives of *Australopithecus* have come to light only in the last few years. One is ***Sahelanthropus tchadensis***, represented by the substantial part of a cranium discovered at Locality TM 266 in the Djurab Desert, northern Chad, far to the west of any known find

> ***Sahelanthropus tchadensis.*** Probable hominin ancestor to Ardipithecus; lived 7 to 6 million years ago.

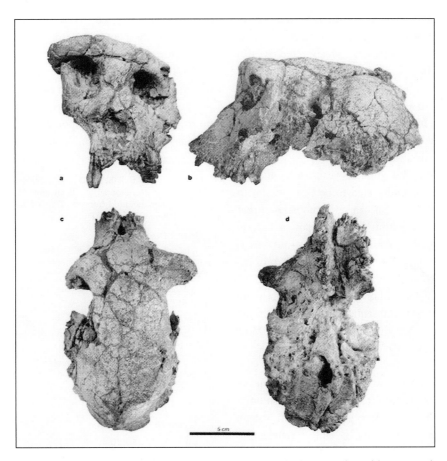

This 6- to 7-million-year-old cranium of Sahelanthropus tchadensis *is claimed by its French discoverers to be the oldest known hominin.* NATURE, VOL. 418, P. 147, (C) 2002 NATURE PUBLISHING GROUP

like it.[8] Its location makes it clear that humans did not have an exclusively East African origin. The skull has a small brain case like an ape, but its canines are small and the face is humanlike, suggesting to its discoverers that it is close to the common ancestor of the chimpanzee and humans. The fossil dates between 7 and 6 million years ago. A recent 3D digital reconstruction of the cranium corrects for distortion caused by fracturing and deformation over time and confirms that it is more closely related to the hominin line rather than the great apes and that it was probably bipedal. For now, it is the only known candidate that could be ancestral to all hominins.

Another potential ancestor is the 6-million-year-old "Millennium Man," so called because its discovery was announced at the turn of the millennium (Figure 6.2). Its discoverers have dubbed it **Orrorin tugenensis** (*orrorin* means "original man" in the local dialect). Found in Chad,[9] the remains include 13 pieces of lower jaw, teeth, and broken thighbones. Because the head of the thighbone is relatively large (though not as large as in modern humans), *Orrorin* may have walked bipedally, though this is by no means certain (the crucial knee joint, which would give this away, is missing). The molars, like those of *Australopithecus*, are thickly enamelled but much smaller. At the moment, specialists are unsure what to make of this creature; some see it as the earliest human ancestor, whereas others doubt that it was even a hominin. It could even be on the line to chimps, or to an extinct side branch.

Between 6 and 4.4 million years ago, another genus, *Ardipithecus*, is interpreted to be the ancestor to the *Australopithecus* line. If it can be demonstrated that *Ardipeithecus* descended from *Sahelanthropos* or *Orrorin* then one (or both) is ancestral to humans—but this is still hotly debated. In 1994, Tim White and two of his students, Gen Suwa and Berhane Asfaw, discovered 17 fossil fragments in 4.4 million-year-old deposits along Ethiopia's Awash River. Subsequent finds in the same region date between 5.8 and 5.2 million years.[10] Most are thought to represent *Ardipithecus kadabba* and date to 5.8 to 5.6 million years ago.[11] The younger fossils (5.6 to 5.2 million years ago) are classified as **Ardipithecus ramidus** (the name is fitting for an ultimate human ancestor as, in the local Afar language, *Ardi* means "floor" and *ramid* means "root"). Unfortunately, the task of freeing the actual fossils from their matrix has proved time consuming and is not yet complete; hence a full description of this important material is not yet

available. This evidence indicates that the human and chimpanzee lineages diverged between 8 and 6 million years ago.[12]

Preliminary indications are that *Ardipithecus*, which was about the size of a modern chimpanzee, was more apelike than any Australopithecine. Although the large canines and lower first premolar resemble those of apes, chewing did not sharpen the upper canines as happens in apes. The thin-enamelled molars are larger than in apes, and the diet included a greater variety of fibrous foods than typical of chimpanzees. Although the relative proportions of *Ardipithecus*'s arms and legs appear chimplike, the foramen magnum is in the forward position consistent with bipedal locomotion. Consistent, too, is an upper arm bone that is not built to sustain the weight of a quadruped. Moreover, a toe bone is more like that of a human than an ape; unfortunately, it was not found in association with the other material. Still, it is likely that *Ardipithecus* walked bipedally when on the ground. But because it lived in a more forested environment than later hominins, it undoubtedly spent significant time in the trees.

To further complicate matters, Maeve Leakey, daughter-in-law of Louis and Mary Leakey, announced the discovery in 1998 and 1999 of an almost complete cranium, parts of two upper jaws, and assorted teeth from a site in northern Kenya.[13] Contemporary with early East African *Australopithecus* (Figure 6.2), she sees this as a different

---

[8] Brunet M., Guy, F., Pilbeam, D., Mackaye, H.T., Likius, A., Ahounta, D., Beauvilain, A., Blondel, C., Bocherens, H., Boisserie, J.-R. et al. (2002). A new hominid from the Upper Miocene of Chad, Central Africa. *Nature, 418*, 145–151.

[9] Ibid.

[10] White, T., Suwa, G., & Asfaw, B. (1994). *Australopithecus ramidus*, a new species of early hominid from Aramis, Ethiopia. *Nature, 371*, 306–312.

[11] Haile-Selassie, Y., Suwa, G., & White, T. (2004). Late Miocene teeth from Middle Awash, Ethiopia and early hominid dental evolution. *Science, 303*, 1503–1505.

[12] Begun, D. (2004). The earliest hominids—is less more? *Science, 303*, 1478–1480.

[13] Balter, M. (2001). Fossil tangles roots of human family tree. *Science, 291*, 2289–2291.

Orrorin tugenensis. Possible hominin; lived 6 million years ago.

Ardipithecus ramidus. Probable early hominin; lived about 6 to 4.4 million years ago.

species named **Kenyanthropus platyops** ("flat-faced man of Kenya"). Unlike contemporary *Australopithecus*, *Kenyanthropus* is said to have a small braincase and small molars set in a large, flat face. But again, there is controversy; Leakey sees her fossil as ancestral to the genus *Homo*, whereas others are not convinced it falls outside the range of variation for early gracile *Australopithecus*.

So what are we to make of these fossils? Until we have better samples, we will not know for sure. What seems likely on present evidence is that hominins evolved from late Miocene apes, becoming distinct by 5 million years ago. This move into a new primate niche probably saw the emergence of more than one bipedal model, but just how many is not known. Whether *Ardipithecus* or any other candidates for "human ancestor" discussed here really were ancestral to later humans, or side branches that went extinct, remains to be seen. The thin enamel of *Ardipithecus's* molars might suggest the latter. But out of this early hominin branching emerged *Australopithecus*.

Undoubtedly this evolution took place in fits and starts, rather than at a steady pace. For example, fragments of an *Australopithecus* skull 3.9 million years old are virtually identical to the corresponding parts of one 3 million years old. Evidently, once a viable bipedal adaptation was achieved, stabilizing selection took over, and there was little change for at least a million years. But 2.5 million years ago, change was again in the works, resulting in the branching out of new forms, including one or two robust species. But again, from about 2.3 million years until it became extinct around 1 million years ago, the East African robust species, at least, shows relatively little change.[14] Evidently, the pattern in early hominin evolution has been relatively short periods of marked change with diversification, separated by prolonged periods of relative stasis of surviving species.

ENVIRONMENT, DIET, AND AUSTRALOPITHECINE ORIGINS

Having described the fossil material, we may now consider *how* evolution transformed an early ape into *Australopithecus*. Because a major driving force in evolution is climatic change, we must take into account the effects of such changes in the late Miocene epoch that were profound enough to cause the temporary drying up of the Mediterranean Sea. On the land, tropical forests underwent reduction or, more commonly, broke up into

This 3- to 4-million-year-old skull could be an Australopithecine or a separate species its discoverer calls K.enyanthropus platyops.
DR. FRED SPOOR/NATIONAL MUSEUMS OF KENYA

mosaics where patches of forest were interspersed with savanna or other types of open country. The forebears of the hominin line lived in places where there was access to both trees and open country. With the breaking up of forests, these early ancestors of ours found themselves spending more and more time on the ground and had to adapt to this new, more open, environment.

The most obvious problem facing these hominin ancestors in their new situation, other than getting from one patch of trees to another, was food getting. As the forest thinned or shrank, the traditional ape-type foods found in trees became less available, especially in seasons of reduced rainfall. Therefore, it became more and more necessary to forage on the ground for foods such as seeds, grasses, and roots. Associated with this change in diet is a change in their dentition; male canines (used by other primates as defensive weapons), not large to begin with, became as small as those of females, leaving both

---

[14] Wood, B., Wood, C., & Konigsberg, L. (1994). *Paranthropus boisei*: An example of evolutionary stasis? *American Journal of Physical Anthropology, 95,* 134.

Kenyanthropus platyops. Hominin contemporary with early Australopithecines; not certainly a separate species.

BIOGRAPHY

Dr. Becky Sigmon

Dr. Becky Sigmon has dedicated her career to the study of human evolution, in particular the origin of erect bipedal posture and locomotion in hominins. Sigmon approaches this research by examining human and nonhuman primate anatomy and comparative morphology of the lower limb. She has studied fossil hominins, from Australopithecines to *H. erectus* and *H. sapiens neanderthalensis*, again to understand the development of their locomotion, and variations in morphological patterns.

Among Sigmon's many contributions, she has assembled an impressive collection of nonhuman primate skeletal material, including great apes, New and Old World monkeys, and prosimians, now located at the University of Toronto where she is a professor. She organized the first Special Symposium for biological anthropologists in Prague in September 1989.

Although Sigmon has mainly studied human evolution and the processes that led to the development of the human condition, she has also branched into other areas. She has expanded her research interests to examine the effects of mating and reproductive patterns on posture and locomotion, and recently she has focused her research on the role of cognition and narrative and its effects on "humanizing" early *H. sapiens* populations. Sigmon's undergraduate and graduate students have worked with her as she examined the link between cognition, language, and verbal and pictorial narrative. This research culminated in a paper entitled "Language without Words: A Monumental Early Human Adaptation," which was presented at the Australasian Society for Human Biology in 2000.

sexes relatively defenceless when down on the ground and easy targets for numerous carnivorous predators (Figure 6.11). That predators were a problem is revealed by the South African fossils, most of which are from individuals that were dropped into rock fissures by leopards or, in the case of Dart's original find, by an eagle.

Many investigators have argued that the hands of early hominins took over the weapon functions of the reduced canines, enabling them to threaten predators by using wooden objects as clubs and throwing stones. This set the stage for the much later manufacture of more efficient weapons from bone, wood, and stone. Although the hands of the later Australopithecines were suitable for toolmaking, there is no evidence that any of them actually made stone tools. Captive bonobos have shown that they are capable of making crude chipped stone tools, and chimpanzees from West Africa use stone tools for nut cracking. In 2007 a research team that included scholars from the Universities of Calgary, Saskatchewan, and Alberta reported evidence that chimpanzee stone tool manufacture and use in West Africa spans 200 generations and dates at least to 4300 years ago.[15] The team is still trying to learn if this chimpanzee stone tool use is inherited from a common ancestor to humans and chimpanzees, was an imitation of human behaviour thousands of years ago, or was independently developed. Nevertheless, this evidence makes it quite plausible that Australopithicines also used stone tools. At the moment, the earliest known stone tools are at least 1.5 million years younger than the oldest undoubted fossils of *Australopithecus*, and no one has been able to establish a clear association between stone tools and later *Australopithecus* (as opposed to *Homo*). Considering the number of sites and fossils known (several hundred), this appears to be significant. However, *Australopithecus* certainly had no less intelligence and dexterity than do modern great apes, all of whom make use of tools when necessary. Orangutans, bonobos, chimpanzees, and gorillas have all been observed in the wild making and using simple

---

[15] Mercader J., Barton, H., Gillespie, J., Harris, J., Kuhn, S., Tyler, R., & Boesch, C. (2007). 4,300-Year-old chimpanzee sites and the origins of percussive stone technology. *PNAS, 104*, 3043–3048.

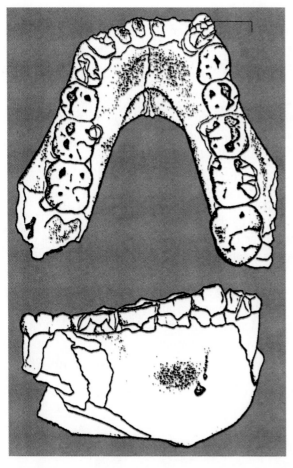

FIGURE 6.11

This lower jaw from Laetoli, Tanzania, is between 3.6 and 3.8 million years old and belonged to *Australopithecus*. Although its canine tooth projects a bit beyond the other teeth, it is a far cry from the projection seen in most other primates.

This bonobo figured out by himself how to make stone tools similar to those made by our ancestors 2.5 million years ago. DR. ROSE SEVCIK, COURTESY OF THE LANGUAGE RESEARCH CENTER, GEORGIA STATE UNIVERSITY

tools such those described in Chapter 4. Most likely, the ability to make and use simple tools is something that goes back to the last common ancestor of the Asian and African apes, before the appearance of hominins.

It is reasonable to suppose, then, that Australopithecines were tool users, though not tool-makers. Unfortunately, few tools that they used are likely to have survived for a million and more years, and any that did would be hard to recognize as such. Although we cannot be certain about this, in addition to clubs and missiles for defence, stout sticks may have been used to dig edible roots, and convenient stones may have been used (as some chimpanzees do) to crack open nuts. In fact, some animal bones from Australopithecine sites in South Africa show microscopic wear patterns, suggesting their use to dig edible roots from the ground. We may also allow the possibility that, like chimpanzees, females may more often have used tools to get and process food than males, but the latter may more often have used tools as "weapons."[16]

Humans Stand on Their Own Two Feet

From an apelike carriage, the early hominins developed a fully erect posture; they became bipedal. Their late Miocene forebears seem to have been primates that combined quadrupedal climbing with at least some

16 Goodall, J. (1986). *The chimpanzees of Gombe: Patterns of behaviour* (pp. 552, 564). Cambridge, MA: Belknap Press.

brachiation and, on the ground, were capable of assuming an upright stance, at least on occasion (optional, versus obligatory, bipedalism). On the basis of the few scrappy fossils that we have for the period of 2 or so million years between the last known African apes of the late Miocene and the first known *Australopithecus*, we may assume that those hominin ancestors that did exist during the period were evolving into fully erect bipeds.

We cannot understand the emergence of bipedalism as a means of locomotion without realizing its very serious drawbacks. For example, it makes an animal more visible to predators, exposes its soft underbelly, or gut, and interferes with the ability to change direction instantly while running. Nor does it make for particularly fast running; quadrupedal chimpanzees and baboons, for example, are 30 to 34 percent faster than we bipeds. For 100-metre distances, our best athletes today may attain speeds of 34 to 37 kilometres per hour, but the larger African carnivores can attain speeds up to 60 to 70 kilometres per hour. Other drawbacks include the frequent lower back problems, hernias, hemorrhoids, and other circulatory problems to which humans are prone by virtue of their bipedal specialization. Nor can we overlook the

consequences of a serious leg or foot injury; a quadruped can do amazingly well on three legs, but a biped with only one functional leg is seriously hindered—an easy meal for some carnivore. Each of these drawbacks would have placed our early hominin ancestors at risk from predators. And so, we must ask, what made bipedal locomotion worth paying such a high price? It is hard to imagine bipedalism becoming a viable adaptation in the absence of strong selective pressure in its favour.

One once-popular suggestion is that bipedal locomotion allowed males to gather food on the savanna and transport it back to females, who were restricted from doing so by the dependence of their offspring.[17] This explanation is unlikely, however, because female apes, not to mention women among food-foraging peoples, routinely combine infant care with foraging for food. Indeed, among food foragers, it is the women who commonly supply the bulk of the food eaten by both sexes. Moreover, the pair bonding (one male attached to one female) presumed by this model is not characteristic of terrestrial primates, nor of those displaying the

[17] Lovejoy, C.O. (1981). The origin of man. *Science, 211,* 341–350.

Just as chimpanzees use wooden probes to fish for termites, so do orangutans use probes to extract termites, ants, or honey. Such tool use likely goes back to a time preceding the split between Asian and African hominoids, long before the appearance of hominins. **JOHN GIUSTINA PHOTOGRAPHY, WWW.TAZAMA.COM**

ORIGINAL STUDY

The Naked and the Bipedal

Human beings are a peculiar species. Among other things, we're the only mostly hairless, consistently bipedal primate. Ever since Darwin, evolutionary biologists have wondered how we acquired these unique traits. Not long ago most would have argued that our upright stance evolved as part of a feedback loop that helped free our hands to use tools. But by the early 1980s a series of discoveries in Africa—including fossilized footprints and early hominin bones—made it clear that bipedalism preceded tool use by at least 2 million years. Lately a new theory has been gaining ground: It holds that our forebears reared up on two legs to escape the heat of the African savanna.

"The African savanna is one of the most thermally stressing habitats on the planet as far as large mammals are concerned," says Pete Wheeler, a physiologist at Liverpool John Moores University in England. For several years now Wheeler has been studying just how stressful such an environment would have been for the first primates to venture out of the shade of the forest. Among the apes, our ancestors are the only ones that managed the switch; no other ape today lives on the savanna full-time.

Most savanna animals, says Wheeler, cope with the heat by simply letting their body temperature rise during the day, rather than waste scarce water by sweating. (Some antelope allow their body temperature to climb above 43°C.) These animals have evolved elaborate ways of protecting the brain's delicate neural circuitry from overheating. Antelope, for instance, allow venous blood to cool in their large muzzles (the cooling results from water evaporation in the mucous lining), then run that cool blood by the arteries that supply the brain, thereby cooling it, too.

"But the interesting thing about humans and other primates," says Wheeler, "is that we lack the mechanisms other savanna animals have. The only way an ape wanting to colonize the savanna could protect its brain is by actually keeping the whole body cool. We can't uncouple brain temperature from the rest of the body, the way an antelope does, so we've got to prevent any damaging elevations in body temperature. And of course the problem is even more acute for an ape, because in general, the larger and more complex the brain, the more easily it is damaged. So there were incredible selective pressures on early hominins favouring adaptations that would reduce thermal stress—pressures that may have favoured bipedalism."

Just how would bipedalism have protected the brain from heat? And why did our ancestors become bipedal rather than evolve some other way to keep cool? Before moving out onto the savanna, says Wheeler, our forebears were preadapted to evolve into bipeds. Swinging from branch to branch in the trees, they had already evolved a body plan that could, under the right environmental pressures, be altered to accommodate an upright stance. Such a posture, says Wheeler, greatly reduces the amount of the body's surface area that is directly exposed to the intense midday sun. It thereby reduces the amount of heat the body absorbs.

Although this observation is not new, Wheeler has done the first careful measurements and calculations of the advantages such a stance would have offered the early hominins. His measurements were rather simple. He took a 30-centimetre-tall scale model of a hominin similar to Lucy—the 3-million-year-old, chimpsize Australopithecine that is known from the structure of her pelvis and legs to have been at least a part-time biped. Wheeler mounted a camera on an overhead track and moved it in a semicircular arc above the model, mimicking the daily path of the sun. Every five degrees along that path—the equivalent of 20 minutes on a summer day—Wheeler stopped the camera and snapped a photograph of the model. He repeated this process with the model in a variety of postures, both quadrupedal and bipedal. To determine how much of the hominin's surface area would have been exposed to the sun's rays, Wheeler simply measured how much of the model's surface area was visible in the sun's-eye-view photos. He found that a quadrupedal stance would have exposed the hominin to about 60 percent more solar radiation than a bipedal one.

A biped not only exposes less of its body to the sun, but also exposes more of its body to the cooler breezes a few feet above ground. The bottom

(Continued)

line, says Wheeler, is that "on a typical savanna day, a knuckle-walking chimp-size hominin would require something in the regi on of five pints of water a day. Whereas simply by standing upright you cut that to something like three pints. In addition to that, you can also remain out in the open away from shade for longer, and at higher temperatures. So for an animal that was foraging for scattered resources in these habitats, bipedalism is really an excellent mode of locomotion."

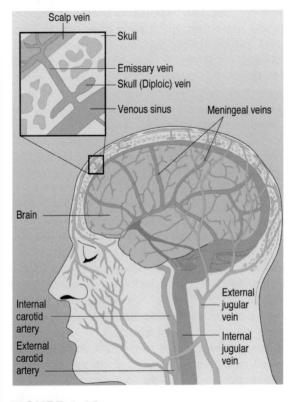

FIGURE 6.12

How the brain is cooled in modern humans: Blood from the face and scalp, instead of returning directly to the heart, may be shunted instead into the braincase, and then to the heart. Already cooled at the surface of the skin, it is able to carry away heat from the brain.

Wheeler suspects that bipedalism also made possible two other uniquely human traits: our naked skin and large brains. "Our work suggests that you can't get a naked skin until you've become bipedal," he says.

"The problem has always been explaining why we don't see naked antelope or cheetahs. The answer appears to be that in those conditions in which animals are exposed to high radiation loads, the body hair acts as a shield. We always think of body hair as keeping heat in, but it also keeps heat out. If you take the fleece off a sheep and stand the animal out in the desert in the outback of Australia, the sheep will end up gaining more heat than you're helping it to dissipate. However, if you do that to a bipedal ape, because the exposure to solar radiation is so much less, it helps the ape lose more heat. Bipedalism, by reducing exposure to the sun, is tipping the balance and turning hair loss, which in quadrupeds would be a disadvantage, into an asset."

We bipeds maximize our heat loss, says Wheeler, by retaining a heat shield only on our most exposed surface—the top of our skull—and by exposing the rest of our body to cooling breezes. And bipedalism and naked skin together, he says, probably allowed us to evolve our oversize brains.

"The brain is one of the most metabolically active tissues in the body," he explains. "In the case of humans it accounts for something like 20 percent of total energy consumption. So you've got an organ producing a lot of heat that you've got to dump. Once we'd become bipedal and naked and achieved this ability to dump heat, that may have allowed the expansion of the brain that took place later in human evolution. It didn't cause it, but you can't have a large brain unless you can cool it."

Source: Adapted from Folger, T. (1993). The naked and the bipedal. *Discover, 14* (11), 34–35.

degree of sexual dimorphism that was characteristic of *Australopithecus*. Nor is it really characteristic of *Homo sapiens*; in a substantial majority of recent human societies, including those in which people forage for their food, some form of polygamy—marriage to two or more people at the same time—is not only permitted, but preferred. And even in supposedly monogamous North America, it is relatively common for an individual to marry two or more others (the only requirement is that he or she not be married to them at the same time).

Another suggestion, that bipedal locomotion arose as an adaptation for nonterritorial scavenging of meat,[18] is also unlikely. Although it is true that a biped is able to travel long distances without tiring, and that a daily supply of dead animal carcasses would have been available to hominins only if they were capable of ranging over vast areas, there is no evidence that hominins did much in the way of scavenging prior to about 2.5 million years ago. Furthermore, the heavy wear seen on Australopithecine teeth is indicative of a diet high in tough, fibrous plant foods. Thus, scavenging was likely an unforeseen byproduct of bipedal locomotion, rather than a cause of it.

Yet more recent is the suggestion (see Original Study) that our ancestors stood up as a way to cope with heat stress out in the open.

An objection to the above scenario might be that when bipedalism developed, savanna was not as extensive in Africa as it is today (Figure 6.12). In both East and South Africa, environments included both closed and open bush and woodlands. Moreover, fossil flora and fauna found with *Ardipithecus* are typical of a moist, closed, wooded habitat. Yet this may not tell us much, as we cannot rule out the possibility that *Ardipithecus* represents a side branch of hominin evolution that moved back into the forest from more open country. Alternatively, even today, similar floral and faunal elements can be found in the otherwise rather desolate region where *Ardipithecus* once lived,[19] and between 5 and 4 million years ago, the environments of Eastern and Southern Africa can best be described as a mosaic of both open and closed country. Although climbing ability would still have been useful to hominin ancestors, inevitably they would have had to spend significant amounts of time out in the open, away from trees.

Another advantage to bipedalism is that it is far more economical than quadrupedal locomotion at walking speed.[20] Successful exploitation of dispersed food sources in the habitats where human ancestors lived, patchy woodlands and grassland, meant covering roughly 10 kilometres every day (Figure 6.13). Chimpanzees and gorillas, in contrast, travel less than 2 kilometres daily in the dense forests where they live. Selection favoured early human ancestors with the most to gain, those who could move longer distances with greater efficiency. The fact

---

[18] Lewin, R. (1987). Four legs good, two legs bad. *Science, 235*, 969–971.

[19] Conroy, G.C. (1997). *Reconstructing human origins: A modern synthesis* (p. 152). New York: Norton.

[20] Leonard, W.R. (2003). Food for thought. *Scientific American, 13* (2), 62–71.

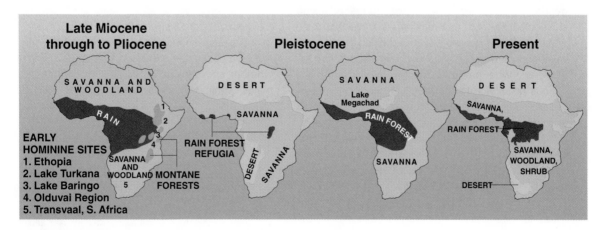

FIGURE 6.13

Since the late Miocene, the vegetation zones of Africa have changed considerably.

is that the causes of bipedalism are likely to have been multiple. Although we may reject as culture-bound the idea of male "breadwinners" provisioning "stay-at-home moms," it is true that bipedal locomotion does make transport of bulky foods possible. A fully erect biped on the ground—whether male or female—has the ability to gather such foods for transport back to a tree or other place of safety for consumption; the animal does not have to remain out in the open, exposed and vulnerable, to do all of its eating. But food may not have been the only thing transported. As we saw in Chapter 4, primate infants must be able to cling to their mothers in order to be transported; because the mother is using her forelimbs in locomotion, to either walk or swing by, she can't very well carry her infant. Chimpanzee infants, for example, must cling for themselves to their mother, and even at the age of four, they make long journeys on their mothers'

backs. Injuries caused by falling from the mother are a significant cause of infant mortality. Thus, mothers able to carry their infants would have made a significant contribution to the survivorship of their offspring, and the ancestors of *Australopithecus* would have been capable of doing just this.

Besides making food transport possible, bipedalism could have facilitated the food quest in other ways. With their hands free and body upright, the animals could reach otherwise unobtainable food on thorn trees too flimsy and too spiny to climb. Furthermore, with both hands free, they could gather other small foods twice as quickly. And in times of scarcity, their ability to travel far without tiring would help get them between widely distributed sources of food. Because the head is positioned higher than in a quadrupedal stance, sources of food and water are easier to spot from afar, thereby facilitating locating them.

GENDER PERSPECTIVES

When Did Gender Evolve?

If we define gender as a cultural construct, then how do we determine gender differentiation in very early hominin species? Did Australopithecines have culture? Did "Lucy" understand a role she filled?

These are interesting questions that underscore the difficulties anthropologists and archaeologists face when attempting to recognize and study gender in the distant past. As discussed in several of the gender perspectives in this text, forward-thinking archaeologists and anthropologists have seriously questioned the stereotypical reduction of gender to dominant male hunters and subordinate female gatherers who produce offspring. An even more serious disservice to the study of gender has been the tendency to reconstruct the gender of the past in accordance with current gender relations and thereby justify the present order: If Lucy gathered, bore children, and submitted to a superior male 4 million years ago, then this must be the way of the world. Hence, the birth of a human-origin myth.

Returning to the concept of culture, at present most archaeologists and anthropologists view culture as a continuum of behaviours, gradually

becoming more complex in nature. Thus, the culture of Australopithecines would more closely resemble that of living nonhuman primates. One interpretation of this question of culture suggests that not until the time of late *H. erectus*, when hominins ventured into new ecozones, and yet did not speciate, did hominins rely on culture rather than biological adaptation to adapt. According to this interpretation, any examination of gender, which is a cultural construct, before 1 million years ago is futile.

Did Lucy know she was female? Likely, within her own conceptual framework. A larger question is whether she considered herself subordinate to the males within her group. Such attitudes likely came much later.

Source: Adapted from Whelan, M.K. (1991). Gender and archaeology: Mortuary studies and the search for the origins of gender differentiation. In D. Walde & N.D. Willows (Eds.), *The archaeology gender* (pp. 358–365). Proceedings of the 22nd Annual Chacmool Conference. Calgary: Archaeological Association of the University of Calgary.

Still other advantages of bipedalism would have enhanced survivability. With their heads well up above the ground, bipeds are more likely to spot predators before they get too close for safety. Finally, if hominins did get caught away from a safe place of refuge by a predator, manipulative and dexterous hands freed from locomotion provided them with a means of protecting themselves by brandishing and throwing objects at their attackers. But, as the fate of the South African specimens attests, even this strategy was not foolproof.

CHAPTER SUMMARY

The course of hominin evolution, revealed by fossil finds, has not been a simple, steady advance in the direction of modern humans. One early hominin that appeared by 4 million years ago was *Australopithecus*, a genus that anthropologists divide into at least four and as many as seven species. All walked erect and chewed food like humans, but their general appearance was that of an apelike human. The size and outward appearance of their brain suggest a degree of intelligence probably not greatly different from that of a modern bonobo, chimpanzee, or gorilla. Like most great apes, gracile Australopithecines may have made some use of objects as tools.

Robust Australopithecines shared practically all of the traits listed for the gracile species but were more highly specialized for the consumption of plant foods. The earliest Australopithecines exhibit traits reminiscent of some of the late Miocene apes of Africa. Fossils that fit time-wise between these apes and *Australopithecus* suggest the latter arose as part of an early diversification of bipeds.

During the late Miocene and Pliocene, the climate became markedly cooler and drier; many areas that had once been heavily forested became a mosaic of woodland and more open country. The ancestors of hominins likely found themselves spending more and more time on the ground; they had to adapt to this altered, more open environment, and food getting became a problem. As their diet changed, so did their dentition. On the whole, teeth became smaller, and many of the defensive functions once performed by the teeth seem to have been taken over by the hands.

Some of the Miocene apes are believed to have been part-time brachiators who may at times have walked erect. *Australopithecus* was a fully bipedal hominin with erect posture, and its immediate predecessors, such as *Ardipithecus*, may have also been. Some disadvantages of bipedalism as a means of locomotion, besides anatomical and circulatory weaknesses, are that it makes an animal more visible to predators, exposes its "soft underbelly," slows the animal, interferes with its ability to change direction instantly while walking or running, and leaves nothing to fall back on if one leg is injured. Its advantages are that it provides hominins with a means of keeping their brains from overheating, of protecting themselves and holding objects while running, of travelling long distances without tiring, and of seeing farther.

QUESTIONS FOR CRITICAL THOUGHT

1. Suggest an alternative evolutionary model for the appearance and development of the Australopithecines that takes into account the fossils discussed in this chapter.

2. How might some or all of the fossil specimens discussed in this chapter be reclassified?

3. Do you think the Australopithecines are more human or closer to chimpanzees and gorillas? Why?

INTERNET RESOURCES

Australopithecines
www.d.umn.edu/cla/faculty/troufs/anth1602/pcaustr.html
A large site with many links to information on Australopithecines and Miocene hominoids.

Bipedalism
www.archaeology.org/online/news/biped.html
A brief article on bipedalism based on new fossil discoveries.

Human Origins

www.gpc.edu/~pgore/students/f97/glenda/australopithecus.htm

Introduces students to Raymond Dart's discovery of Australopithecines.

http://hannover.park.org/Canada/Museum/man/evnman3.html

A brief site with links to other sites describing *Australopithecus* and *Homo*.

www.geocities.com/SoHo/Atrium/1381/index.html

A comprehensive site on hominin evolution, with links to other hominin websites.

www.jqjacobs.net/anthro

A comprehensive site featuring links to timely feature articles on hominins, genetics, and evolution.

www.howcomyoucom.com

A large site offering links to a variety of topics related to the origins of the universe, earth, and humans. Read these articles from a critical perspective.

www.talkorigins.org/faqs/homs

A site presenting evidence of human evolution. Provides new information on fossil discoveries.

www.pbs.org/wgbh/aso/tryit/evolution/#

Visit this site to use the interactive tree and determine the relationships among the ancestral hominin groups.

www.asu.edu/clas/iho

Visit the Institute of Human Origins website and discover more about Lucy and other fossil hominins, as well as the people who discovered them. Also visit the institute's educational site (www.becominghuman.org).

Lee Berger

www.nationalgeographic.com/research/index.html

A trip to National Geographic's Committee for Research and Exploration site follows the trail of palaeoanthropologist Lee Berger as he searches for human origins in Botswana.

Louis Leakey

www.utexas.edu/courses/wilson/ant304/biography/arybios97/weimanbio.html

An extensive biography of Louis Leakey.

www.leakeyfoundation.org

An interactive site advertising the Leakey foundation and its goals, events, and research projects.

Piltdown Man

www.talkorigins.org/faqs/piltdown.html

Learn about the most famous hoax in the history of science through a trip to this site about Piltdown man. Learn who was thought to be behind this hoax and how it interfered with the acceptance of Australopithecines as human ancestors when they were discovered.

SUGGESTED READINGS

For a list of suggested readings, visit the textbook's website at www.humanevolution2.nelson.com.

Homo Habilis and Cultural Origins

Integrated biological and cultural capabilities allowed the earliest members of the genus *Homo* to face the challenges of existence. In turn, palaeoanthropologists like Sileshi Semaw are faced with the challenge of establishing the relationship between biological change and cultural change throughout human evolutionary history. Semaw, who is from Ethiopia himself, discovered the oldest known human artifacts—stone tools dated to between 2.5 and 2.6 million years ago in Gona, Ethiopia.

© 1999 DAVID L. BRILL

CHAPTER PREVIEW

1. When, Where, and How Did Human Culture Develop?

Human culture appears to have developed in Africa, beyond what one sees in modern apes, as some populations of early hominins began making stone tools with which they could butcher animals for their meat. Actually, the earliest stone tools and evidence of significant meat eating date to about 2.6 million years ago, just prior to the appearance of the genus *Homo*.

2. When Did Reorganization and Expansion of the Human Brain Begin?

Reorganization and expansion of the human brain did not begin until at least 1.5 million years after the development of bipedal locomotion. It began in conjunction with scavenging and the making of stone tools. This marks the appearance of the genus *Homo*, an evolutionary offshoot of *Australopithecus*. The two forms coexisted for a million years or so, during the course of which *Australopithecus* relied on a vegetarian diet while developing a massive chewing apparatus. In contrast, *Homo* ate more meat and became brainier.

3. Why Did the Eating of More Meat Lead to Improved Brains?

The making of stone tools—needed to skin, butcher, and crack open the bones of animals for marrow—put a premium on improved eye-hand coordination and precision grip, both of which selected for more complex brains. Increased meat eating, too, led to changes in the subsistence activities of both females and males. These changes required both sexes to do more in the way of thinking and planning, which again selected for larger, more complex brains.

CHAPTER OUTLINE

Early Representatives of the Genus *Homo*

Lower Palaeolithic Tools

The Earliest Signs of Culture: Tools

Cooperation and Sharing

Language Origins

In 1931 when Louis and Mary Leakey began work at Olduvai Gorge, they did so because of the presence of stone tools in deposits dating back to very early in the Pleistocene epoch, which began almost 2 million years ago. When they found the bones of the robust *Australopithecus boisei* in 1959, in association with some of these tools, they thought they had found the remains of one of the toolmakers. They later changed their minds, however, and suggested that these tools were not produced by *A. boisei,* nor were the bones of the birds, reptiles, antelopes, and pigs found with the remains of *A. boisei* the remains of the latter's dinner. Instead, *A. boisei* may have been a victim of a rather different contemporary who created the tools, ate the animals, and possibly had the unfortunate *A. boisei* for dessert. That contemporary was called by the Leakeys **Homo habilis** ("handy man").

Of course, we don't really know that the Leakey's *boisei* met its end in this way, but we do know that cut marks from a stone tool are present on a 2.4-million-year-old hominin from South Africa.[1] This was done, presumably, to remove the mandible, but for what purpose we do not know. Although it might have involved cannibalism, other possibilities include curation or just plain mutilation. In any event, it does lend credibility to the idea of *boisei* on occasion being dismembered by *H. habilis.*

EARLY REPRESENTATIVES OF THE GENUS HOMO

The Leakeys discovered the remains of this second hominin in 1960, only a few months after their earlier discovery, just a couple of metres below it. The remains, which were those of more than one individual, consisted of a few cranial bones, a lower jaw, a clavicle, some finger bones (Figure 7.1), and the nearly complete left foot of an adult (Figure 7.2). These fossils date from about 1.8 million years ago and represent a hominin with a cranial capacity in the 650 to 690 cubic centimetre range, a skull that lacks noticeable bony crests, and almost modern-looking hands and feet. Subsequent work at Olduvai has unearthed not only more skull fragments but also other parts of the skeleton of *H. habilis.* These indicated that, aside from their more modern-looking heads, hands, and feet, the skeleton of this hominin from the neck down does not differ greatly from that of the gracile Australopithecines. Overall size was about

the same, as was the degree of sexual dimorphism (Figure 7.3, p. 191), and they were equally adept at climbing trees.[2] Moreover, dental evidence suggests that, as with *A. afarensis* and *africanus,* the period of infancy and childhood in *H. habilis* was not prolonged, as it is in modern humans, but was more in line with apes.[3]

Since the late 1960s, fossils of the genus *Homo* that are essentially contemporaneous with those from Olduvai have been found elsewhere in Africa—in South Africa, in Kenya near Lake Baringo as well as east of Lake Turkana at Koobi Fora, and in Ethiopia just north of Lake Turkana. One of the best of these, known as KNM ER 1470, was discovered by the Leakeys' son Richard. (The letters *KNM* stand for Kenya National Museum; the *ER,* for East Rudolf, the former name for Lake Turkana.) The deposits in which it was found are about 1.9 million years old; these deposits, like those at Olduvai, also contain stone tools. The KNM ER 1470 skull is more modern in appearance than any *Australopithecus* skull and has a cranial capacity of 752 cubic centimetres. Furthermore, the inside of the skull shows a pattern in the left cerebral hemisphere that, in living people, is associated with a speech area.[4] This shape is in keeping with indications of brain asymmetry more like that of humans than apes, as is evident from wear patterns on tools used by early *Homo* that reveal that these hominins were predominately right-handed. In humans, the speech organs and the right hand are controlled by adjacent areas in the left cerebral hemisphere. Although this doesn't prove that early *Homo* had a spoken language, it does show that its brain was not only larger than that of *Australopithecus* but also reorganized along more human lines.

---

[1] White, T.D., & Toth, N. (2000). Cutmarks on a Plio-Pleistocene hominid from Sterkfontein, South Africa. *American Journal of Physical Anthropology, 111,* 579–584.

[2] Wood, B., & Collard, M. (1999). The human genus. *Science, 284,* 68.

[3] Ibid., p. 69.

[4] Ambrose, S.H. (2001). Paleolithic technology and human evolution. *Science, 291,* 1750.

Homo habilis   Earliest representative of the genus *Homo;* lived between 2.4 and 1.6 million years ago. Characterized by expansion and reorganization of the brain, compared to *Australopithecus.*

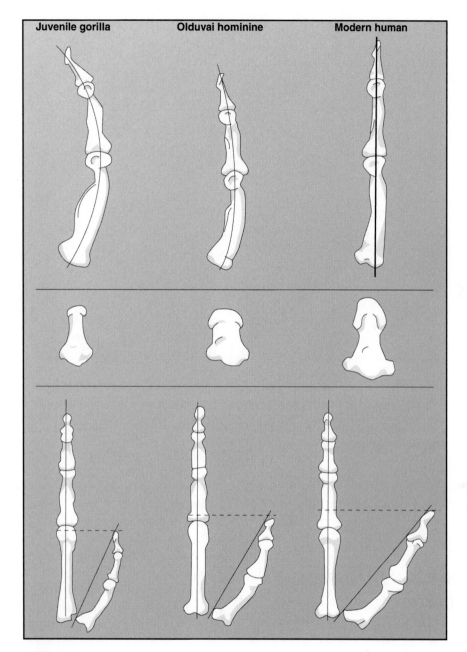

Juvenile gorilla **Olduvai hominine** **Modern human**

FIGURE 7.1

A comparison of hand bones of a juvenile gorilla, *H. habilis* from Olduvai, and a modern human highlights important differences in the structure of fingers and thumbs. In the top row are fingers and in the second row are terminal thumb bones. Although terminal finger bones are more human, the *H. habilis's* lower finger bones are more curved and powerful. The bottom row compares thumb length and angle relative to the index finger.

Although the 1470 skull and other early *Homo* fossils from localities other than Olduvai are frequently assigned to the same species, *H. habilis,* there are those who argue that a second distinct species (*H. Rudolfensis*) may be present. A rigorous evaluation of the arguments in favour of the two-species hypothesis, however, by an independent investigator, failed to sustain them. The conclusion, then, is that "the data, at this point, are

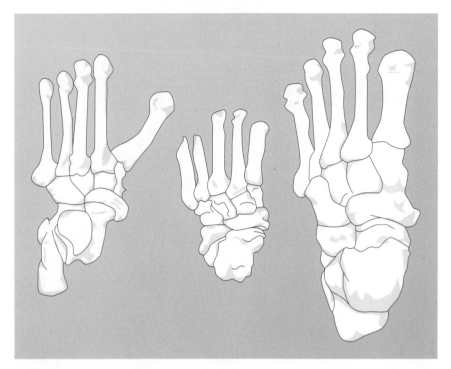

FIGURE 7.2

A partial foot skeleton of *H. habilis* (centre) is compared with the same bones of a chimpanzee (left) and modern human (right). Note how *habilis*'s bone at the base of the great toe is in line with the others, as in modern humans, making for effective walking but poor grasping.

actually quite consistent in showing that the *H. habilis* sample is neither too great in degree nor too different in pattern of variation to warrant rejection of the single species hypothesis."[5]

Relations between *H. habilis* and *Australopithecus*

Homo is the genus to which modern humans belong and the attribution means that species of the genus *Homo* have much more in common with each other than they do with hominins belonging to other genera such as *Australopithecus*. There is no agreement on what characteristics distinguish *Australopithecus* from *Homo*. Mark Collard of the University of British Columbia and his co-author, Bernard Wood of George Washington University, have criticized the use of absolute brain size being greater than 600 cubic centimetres, the use of language and tools, and a precision grip to distinguish *Homo* from other genera.[6] Instead, they prefer to assign fossils to the genus *Homo* if there is evidence that they were adapted

to the same habitats. Members of Australopithicines have a relatively low body mass, a body shape suited to a relatively closed environment such as a forest, a diet that was apelike, an apelike development pattern (relatively fast), and locomotion that combines bipedalism and climbing. *Homo*, on the other hand, has a larger body mass, a body shape like ours that is better suited to open habitats, a diet more like ours, and a humanlike development pattern (slow). In this text we review many of the characteristics that have been used to determine whether a fossil belongs to *Homo*. Until there is universal acceptance of the criteria, there will still be debates about some fossils, particularly the earliest representatives of the genus *Homo*.

H. habilis has all the characteristics of an Australopithicene but its brain size is about 100 cubic centimetres larger than that of the *A. africanus*. To some

---

[5] Miller, J.M.A. (2000). Craniofacial variation in *Homo habilis*: An analysis of the evidence for multiple species. *American Journal of Physical Anthropology, 112*, 122.

[6] Wood B., & Collard, M. (1999). The human genus. *Science, 284*, 65–71.

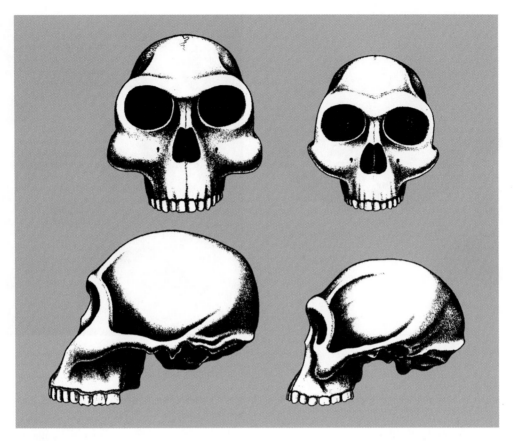

FIGURE 7.3

As these two skulls from Koobi Fora, Kenya, demonstrate, that of female *H. habilis* (right) was markedly smaller than that of the male (left).

anthropologists this means that there was a marked increase in information-processing capacity over that of the Australopithecines. Because larger brains generate more heat, it is not surprising to find that *habilis*'s brain was provided with a heat exchanger of a sort not seen in *Australopithecus,* save to a very rudimentary degree in the late gracile forms.[7] This heat-exchange system consists of small openings in the braincase through which veins pass, allowing cooled blood from the face and scalp to be shunted to the brain, from which the blood can then carry off excess heat (see Figure 6.12). In this way, damage to the brain from excessive heat is prevented.

Although these hominins had teeth that are large by modern standards—or even by those of a half-million years ago—they are smaller in relation to the size of the skull than those of any Australopithecine. Because major brain-size increase and tooth-size reduction are important trends in the evolution of the genus *Homo,* but not

of *Australopithecus,* it looks as if KNM ER 1470 and similar hominins were becoming somewhat more human. Consistent with this are the indications that the brain of KNM ER 1470 was less apelike and more human in structure. It is probably no accident that the earliest fossils to exhibit these features appear by 2.4 million years ago (the age of the Baringo fossil), soon after the earliest evidence (to be discussed shortly) for stone toolmaking and increased consumption of meat.

As noted earlier, the Australopithecine diet seems to have consisted largely of plant foods, although the gracile species may have consumed limited amounts of animal protein as well. The later robust Australopithecines from East and South Africa evolved into more specialized "grinding machines" as their molars, and therefore their jaws, became markedly larger (Figure 7.4), while their

---

[7] Falk, D. (1993). A good brain is hard to cool. *Natural History, 102* (8), 65.

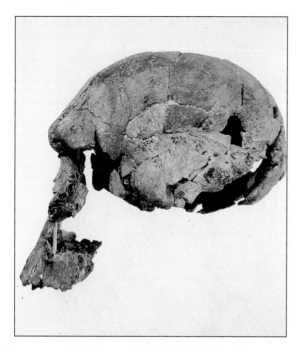
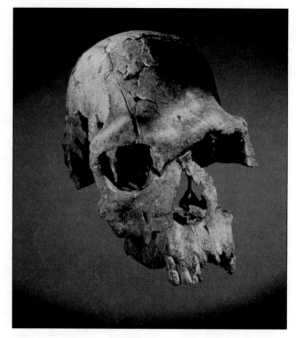

The KNM ER 1470 skull (left): One of the most complete skulls of H. habilis *is close to 2 million years old and is probably a male; it contrasts with the KNM ER 1813 skull (right), probably a female.* **NATIONAL MUSEUMS OF KENYA**

brain size did not. Nor is there firm evidence that they made stone tools. Thus, in the period between 2.5 and 1 million years ago, two kinds of hominins were headed in very different evolutionary directions.

If none of the robust species of *Australopithecus* belong in the direct line of human ancestry, what of earlier species of *Australopithecus*? From the standpoint of anatomy alone, it has long been recognized that the gracile species constitutes suitable ancestors for the genus *Homo,* and it now seems clear that the body of *Homo habilis* had changed little from them. Precisely which of the gracile species gave rise to *H. habilis* is vigorously debated. The arguments have become more complex with the discovery of *Kenyanthropus* (Chapter 6), which Maeve Leakey argues excludes all Australopithecines from the ancestry of *Homo*. At the moment, hers is a minority view. Most see the early East African graciles as sufficiently generalized to have given rise to both *Homo* and the robust *Australopithecus,* noting that the earliest skull to show the latter, the so-called Black Skull, nonetheless shows some holdovers from the earlier East Africans. This skull's age, 2.5 million years, is too old for any but the very earliest South African gracile to have figured in its ancestry. Because the earliest *Homo habilis* skull is nearly as old, the same must be true for it. Evidently, at least a three-way split was under way

by 2.5 million years ago, with the third line represented by late South African gracile *Australopithecus* (Figures 7.5 and 7.6). This persisted until about 2 million years ago (or later, if South African robusts are descended independently from graciles, rather than from East African robusts), by which time the other two lineages had become widespread in nonforested parts of Africa.

LOWER PALAEOLITHIC TOOLS

The earliest tools known to have been made by hominins have been found in the vicinity of Lake Turkana in Kenya and southern Ethiopia, Olduvai Gorge in Tanzania, and Hadar in Ethiopia. Their appearance marks the beginning of the **Lower Palaeolithic**, the first part of the Old Stone Age.

The makers of these early tools were highly skilled, consistently producing many well-formed flakes with few misdirected blows.[8] The object was to obtain large,

---

[8] Ambrose, p. 1749.

> **Lower Palaeolithic.** The first part of the Old Stone Age; its beginning is marked by the appearance 2.6 million years ago of Oldowan tools.

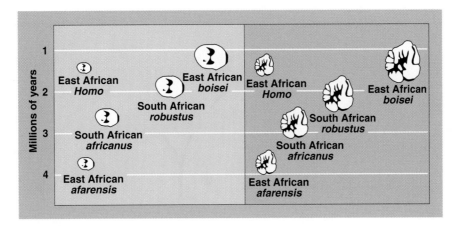

FIGURE 7.4

Premolars (left) and molars (right) of *Australopithecus* and *H. habilis* compared. Though there is little difference in absolute size between the teeth of early *Australopithecus* (*afarensis*) and those of *habilis,* those of *afarensis* are larger relative to the size of the skull. Moreover, the teeth become even larger in later species of *Australopithecus.*

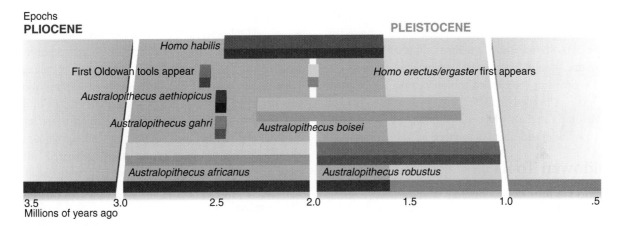

FIGURE 7.5

H. habilis and other early hominins.

sharp-edged flakes from available raw materials with the least effort. At Olduvai and Lake Turkana, these tools are close to 2 million years old; the Ethiopian tools are older at 2.6 million years.

Olduvai Gorge

What is now Olduvai Gorge was once a lake. Almost 2 million years ago, its shores were inhabited not only by numerous wild animals but also groups of hominins, including robust Australopithecines and *H. habilis* as well as the later *H. erectus* (Chapter 8). The gorge, therefore, is a rich source of Palaeolithic remains as well as a key

site providing evidence of human evolutionary change. Among the finds are assemblages of stone tools that are about 2 million years old. These were found little disturbed from when they were left, together with the bones of now-extinct animals that provided food. At one spot, in the lowest level of the gorge, the bones of an elephant lay in close association with more than 200 stone tools. Apparently, the animal was butchered here; there are no indications of any other activity. At another spot, on an occupation surface 1.8 million years old, basalt stones were found grouped in small heaps forming a circle. The interior of the circle was practically empty, while

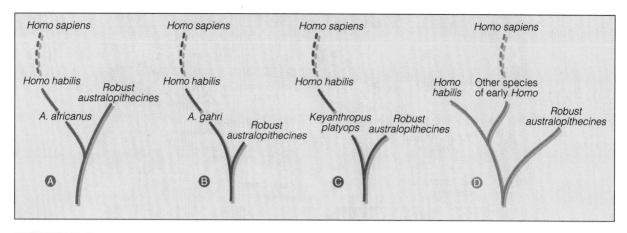

FIGURE 7.6

These diagrams present alternate views of early human evolution. Though the nature of the transition to the genus *Homo* is hotly debated, palaeoanthropologists agree that the robust Australopithecines represent an evolutionary dead end.

numerous tools and food debris littered the ground outside, right up to the edge of the circle. This was once interpreted as evidence for some sort of shelter, seeing the stone piles as supports for the framework of a protective fence of thorn branches, or perhaps a hut with a covering of animal skins or grass. Subsequent analysis suggests that the stones were "stockpiled" ahead of time, to be made into tools as needed, or to be hurled as missiles to hold off carnivorous animals while the hominins extracted meat, marrow, hide, and sinew from pieces of animal carcass.

Oldowan Tools

The oldest tools found at Olduvai Gorge belong to the **Oldowan tool tradition**, which is characterized by flakes struck from a stone (often a large, water-worn pebble) by either using another stone as a hammer (a hammerstone) or striking the pebble against a large rock (anvil) to remove the flakes. This system of manufacture is called the **direct percussion method** (Figure 7.7). The finished flakes are characterized by specific features, including two sharp edges, effective for cutting and scraping (Figure 7.8). Microscopic wear patterns show that these flakes were used for cutting meat, reeds, sedges, and grasses, and for cutting and scraping wood. The leftover cores, from which the flakes were struck, were also useful for bashing open bones for marrow and perhaps also defending the user.

Oldowan tools mark an important technological advance for early hominins; previously, they depended on found objects requiring little or no modification, such as bones, sticks, or conveniently shaped stones. Oldowan tools made possible new additions to the diet, because,

without such tools, hominins could eat few animals (only those that could be skinned by tooth or nail); therefore, their diet was limited in terms of animal proteins. The advent of Oldowan tools meant more than merely saving labour and time: They made possible the addition of meat to the diet on a frequent, rather than occasional, basis. Much popular literature has been written about this penchant for meat, often with numerous colourful references to "killer apes." Such references are misleading, not only because hominins are not apes but also because killing has been greatly overemphasized. Meat can be obtained, after all, by scavenging or by stealing it from other predators. What is significant is that a dentition such as that possessed by *Australopithecus* and *H. habilis* was poorly suited for meat eating. If substantial amounts of meat are to be eaten, without teeth like those possessed by carnivorous animals (or chimpanzees), sharp tools for butchering are required.

Tradition. In archaeology, a distinctive tool kit or technology that lasts a long time at one or more localities

Oldowan tool tradition. The earliest identifiable stone tools.

Direct percussion method. A technique of stone tool manufacture performed by striking the raw material with a hammerstone or by striking raw material against a stone anvil to remove flakes.

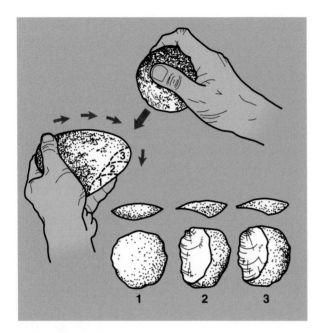

FIGURE 7.7

By 2.6 million years ago, hominins in Africa had invented the direct percussion method of stone tool manufacture. This drawing illustrates how Oldowan toolmakers detached flakes from a core using this technique. A technological breakthrough, the production of stone tools by direct percussion made possible the butchering of meat from scavenged carcasses.

The initial use of tools was probably the result of adaptation to an environment that we know was changing between 3 and 2 million years ago from forests

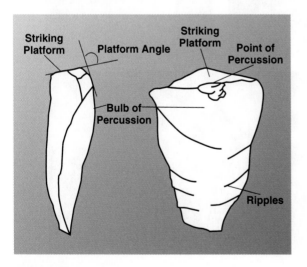

FIGURE 7.8

Diagram of a flake (right is ventral view and left is lateral view) produced by the direct percussion technique.

to grasslands (see Figure 6.13). The physical changes that adapted hominins for spending increasing amounts of time on the new grassy terrain encouraged tool-making. It has been observed that monkeys and apes, for example, often use objects, such as sticks and stones, in their threat displays. The change to a nearly upright bipedal posture, coupled with existing flexibility at the shoulder, arms, and hands, allowed hominins to do so as well, helping them to compete successfully with the large predatory carnivores that shared their environment.

What else do these assemblages of Oldowan tools and broken animal bones tell us about the life of early *Homo*? First, they indicate that both *H. habilis* and large carnivorous animals were active at these locations, for in addition to marks on the bones made by slicing, scraping, and chopping with stone tools, there are tooth marks from gnawing. Some of the gnawing marks overlie the butcher marks, indicating that enough flesh remained on the bones after the hominins were done with them to attract the other carnivores. In other cases, though, the butcher marks overlie the tooth marks of carnivores, indicating that the animals got there first. This is what we would expect if *H. habilis* were scavenging the kills of other animals, rather than doing its own killing. Consistent with this picture is that whole carcasses are not represented; evidently, only parts were transported away from the original location where they were obtained, again what we would expect if they were "stolen" from the kill of some other animal. The stone tools, too, were made of raw material procured at distances of up to 10 kilometres from where they were used to process the parts of carcasses. Finally, the incredible density of bones at some of the sites and patterns of weathering indicate that, although *H. habilis* didn't linger longer than necessary at any one time (and for good reason—the carnivores attracted by the meat could have made short work of *habilis* as well), the sites were repeatedly used over periods guessed to be on the order of 5 to 15 years.

All of this is quite unlike the behaviour of historically known food-foraging peoples who bring whole carcasses back to camp where they are completely processed. Neither meat nor marrow is left (as they were at Oldowan sites), and the bones themselves are broken up not only to get at the marrow (as at Oldowan sites) but also to fabricate tools and other objects of bone (unlike at Oldowan sites). Nor do historically known food foragers normally camp in the midst of so much garbage. The picture that emerges of our Oldowan forebears, then, is of scavengers, getting their meat from the Lower Palaeolithic equivalent of modern-day roadkills, taking the spoils of their scavenging to particular places where tools, and the raw materials for making them (often procured from faraway sources), had been stockpiled in advance for the purpose of butchering. At these sites, the remains were quickly processed, so that those doing the butchering could clear out before their lives were endangered by carnivores attracted by the meat. Thus, the Oldowan sites were not campsites or "home bases" at all. Quite likely, *H. habilis* continued to sleep in trees or rocky cliffs, as do other small-bodied terrestrial or semi-terrestrial primates, in order to be safe from predators. However, the advanced preparation for meat processing implied by the caching of stone tools, and the raw materials for making tools, attests to considerable foresight and ability to plan ahead.

Tools, Meat, and Brains

As we have seen, by 1.5 million years or so after early hominins became fully bipedal, the size and structure of the brain were beginning to change. Until about 2.5 million years ago, early hominins lived on foods that could be picked or gathered: plants, fruits, invertebrate animals such as ants and termites, and perhaps even an occasional piece of meat scavenged from kills made by other animals. After 2.5 million years ago, meat became more important in their diet, and they began to scavenge for it on a more regular basis.

Because early hominins lacked size and strength to drive off predators, or to compete directly with other scavengers attracted to kills, they must have had to rely on their wit and cunning for success. One may imagine them lurking in the vicinity of a kill, sizing up the situation as

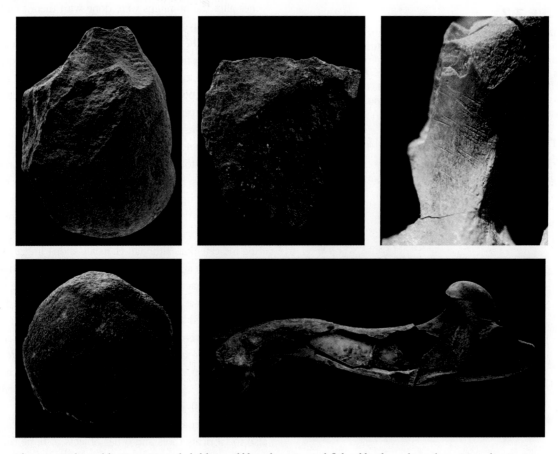

The stone tools used by H. habilis *included lava cobbles, choppers, and flakes like those shown here. Most choppers were probably the result of flakes being struck from one cobble by another. These flakes were used to remove meat from bones, leaving cut marks (upper right). The cobbles and choppers were used to break open bones (lower right) to get at the marrow.* DAVID L. BRILL/THE NATIONAL GEOGRAPHIC

the predator ate its fill while hyenas and other scavengers gathered, and devising strategies to outwit them all so as to seize a piece of the carcass. A hominin depending on stereotyped instinctual behaviour in such a situation would have been at a competitive disadvantage. One that could anticipate problems, devise distractions, bluff competitors into temporary retreat, and recognize, the instant it came, its opportunity to rush in and grab what it could of the carcass stood a much better chance of surviving, reproducing, and proliferating.

One means by which early hominins gained access to a reasonably steady supply of carcasses while at the same time minimizing the risks involved is suggested by recent field studies of leopards. How this could have worked and the arguments in favour of it are the subject of the following Original Study.

Palaeoanthropological depictions of early *Homo* from the 1960s and 1970s focused on "man the hunter," wielding tools in a savannah teeming with meat, while females stayed at home tending their young. These

ORIGINAL STUDY

Cat in the Human Cradle

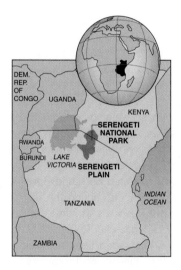

Recent evidence, such as marks on some of the Olduvai bones, indicates that animals the size of wildebeests or larger were killed, eaten, and abandoned by large predators such as lions, hyenas, and sabre-toothed cats; hominins may have merely scavenged the leftovers. Several specialists now agree that early hominins obtained at least marrow mainly in this way. The picture with regard to the remains of smaller animals, such as gazelle-sized antelopes, is less certain. Palaeoanthropologists Henry Bunn and Ellen Kroll believe that the cut-marked upper limb bones of small, medium-sized, and large animals found at Olduvai Gorge demonstrate that hominins were butchering the meaty limbs with cutting tools. Since modern-day lions and hyenas rapidly and completely consume

small prey, leaving little or nothing for potential scavengers, Bunn and Kroll conclude that hominins must have acquired the smaller animals by hunting. But another scholar, Kay Behrensmeyer, suggests that a small group of hominins could have obtained these bones, not by hunting, but by driving off timid predators, such as cheetahs or jackals, from their kills.

Since carnivores play a key role in all these scenarios, three years ago I began thinking about studying their behaviour and ecology. About the same time, a colleague directed me to a paper on the tree-climbing abilities of early hominins. The authors (anatomists Randall L. Susman, Jack T. Stern, and William L. Jungers) analyzed the limb bones of *H. habilis* specimens from Olduvai Gorge, as well as those of the early hominin *A. afarensis* (better known as Lucy). They concluded that early hominins were probably not as efficient as we are at walking on two feet, but they were better than we are at climbing trees and suspending themselves from branches. At the very least, given their apparent lack of fire, early hominins must have used trees as refuges from large predators and as sleeping sites.

One evening, as I watched a documentary film by Hugh Miles about a female leopard and her cubs in Kenya's Masai Mara Reserve, carnivore behaviour and early hominin tree climbing suddenly connected for me. In the film, a pack of hyenas attempt to scavenge an antelope that the mother leopard has killed. At the sight of the hyenas, the leopard grabs the prey in her jaws and carries it up a small tree. This

(Continued)

striking behaviour sparked my curiosity and sent me to the library the next morning to find out more about leopards.

I learned that the leopard differs from other large African carnivores in a variety of ways. Although it occasionally kills large animals, such as adult wildebeests and topi or young giraffes, the leopard preys primarily on smaller antelopes, such as Thomson's gazelles, impala, and Grant's gazelles, and on the young of both large and small species. Unable to defend its kills on the ground from scavenging by lions and spotted hyenas, both of which often forage in groups, the usually solitary leopard stores each kill in a tree, returning to feed but otherwise frequently abandoning it for varying lengths of time.

Although the leopard may not consume its entire prey immediately, the tree-stored kills are relatively safe from theft. (Even lions, which can climb trees, usually take little notice of this resource.) As a result, a kill can persist in a tree for several days. Also, leopard kills appear to be more predictably located than those of lions and hyenas because leopards tend to maintain a small territorial range for several years and occasionally reuse feeding trees. Finally, leopard kills are usually found in the woodlands near lakes and rivers, the habitat apparently preferred by early hominins. Such circumstances, I reasoned, might have once provided an ideal feeding opportunity for tree-climbing hominins, particularly *H. habilis*. By scavenging from the leopard's temporarily abandoned larder, early hominins could have obtained the fleshy and marrow-rich bones of small- to medium-sized prey animals in relative safety.

This leopard has carried part of a Thomson's gazelle up into a tree to prevent other scavengers from consuming what is left. Such tree-stored carcasses may have been the principal source of meat for H. habilis. **E.R. DEGGINGER/COLOR-PIC, INC.**

Fossil evidence shows that ancestors of present-day leopards were contemporaneous with early hominins and shared the same habitats. The antiquity of tree-caching behaviour is harder to prove, but it is supported by palaeoanthropologist C.K. Brain's excavations of ancient caves in southern Africa's Sterkfontein Valley. In the vertical, shaftlike caves, Brain found the fossil remains of hominins, baboons, and antelopes, and of leopards and other large carnivores. The size of the prey animals and the selection of body parts, as well as puncture marks on some of the cranial bones of hominins and baboons, suggested that many of these fossils were the remains of leopard meals. Brain guessed that they had fallen into the caves from leopard feeding trees growing out of the mouths of the caves.

Given its similarities to the ancient environments represented at the early archaeological sites—extensive grasslands with wooded lakes, rivers, and streams—the Serengeti National Park in northern Tanzania seemed an ideal living laboratory in which to test my hypothesis. I travelled there in July 1987, accompanied by Robert J. Blumenschine, who had conducted an earlier study there on scavenging opportunities provided by lions and hyenas. Along the Wandamu River, a tributary of the Seronera, we were fortunate to find an adult female leopard and her 13-month-old (nearly full-grown) male cub that tolerated our Land Rover. We spent a total of about 50 hours, during the day and at night, observing these leopards at three fresh, tree-stored kills of Thomson's gazelles. The leopards frequently left the carcasses unguarded between feedings. On one occasion, a complete young Thomson's gazelle, killed the previous evening, was abandoned for nine daylight hours (we found the leopards resting approximately 3 kilometres away). Without directly confronting these predators, therefore, a creature able to climb trees could have easily carried off the same amount of flesh and marrow as it could obtain from hunting.

While Brain's work in South Africa implicates leopards as predators of early hominins, including the genus *Homo*, some hominins may have also benefited from living near these carnivores. Tree-stored leopard kills could have provided an important resource to early scavenging hominins, and the sharp, broken limb bones from the partly eaten prey could have been used to peel back the hide, expose the flesh of the carcasses, and remove large muscle bundles. This activity may even have given early hominins the initial impetus to make and use tools in the extraction of animal nutrients.

Some palaeoanthropologists have argued that scavenging was an unlikely subsistence strategy for early hominins, since large predators require expansive home ranges, and kills by these carnivores are rare in any particular area. They also contend that very little is left over from such kills after the predator is finished and that hominin competition with large carnivores for these leftovers would be a dangerous activity. My 1988 observations suggest something quite different. During approximately two months in the dry season, I documented 16 kills of small and medium antelopes made by my adult male and female leopards within an approximately 6.5-by-12.5-kilometre area. The majority of these kills, still retaining abundant flesh and marrow, were temporarily abandoned by the leopard for three to eight and a half hours during a single day.

The tree-stored leopard kills consisted mainly of adult and juvenile Thomson's gazelles. Compared with kills of similar-sized prey made on the ground by Serengeti lions and hyenas, as recorded by Blumenschine, the tree-stored leopard kills lasted longer, offering large quantities of fl esh and marrow for two or more days. In part this was because they were not subject to many scavengers. The leopard kills were also more predictably located on the landscape than those of lions in the same area. In modern leopard populations, a male maintains a relatively large territory that overlaps with the usually smaller territories of several females. This pattern often means that several tree-stored kills are available simultaneously during a given period of time within a relatively small area.

Like modern baboons and chimpanzees, early hominins may have killed some small animals, such as newborn antelopes. But they could have acquired all sizes of animal carcasses without hunting if the prey killed by leopards is taken into account. The wide assortment of animal bones at sites like Olduvai Gorge, which have been attributed to ground-based hunting and scavenging, could instead be attributed to scavenging only, both in trees and on the ground. Leopard kills would then have provided much of the flesh consumed by early hominins, while carcasses abandoned on the ground by other large predators would have yielded primarily bone marrow. Additional flesh may have come from the remains of large kills made by sabre-toothed cats or from the carcasses of animals that drowned when herds migrated across ancient lakes.

Although chimpanzees in western Tanzania are the occasional prey of leopards, there is a report that one day some chimpanzees scavenged what was apparently a tree-stored leopard kill. On a more dramatic occasion, also during the day, a group of chimpanzees was observed noisily surrounding a leopard lair from which an adult leopard was heard growling. A male chimpanzee entered the lair and emerged with a leopard cub, which it and the others killed without reprisal from the adult leopard. This type of shifting day-night, predatory-parasitic relationship may once have existed between leopards and our early hominin ancestors.

Source: Adapted from Cavallo, J.A. (1990). Cat in the human cradle. *Natural History*, 54–56, 58–60.

---

depictions of our ancestors mirrored the cultural norms of middle-class North Americans and Europeans as well as the scientists who discovered and interpreted the fossil specimens in the 1960s. The best hypothesis-testing traditions of science allowed for reworking of the "man the hunter" hypothesis with each new scientific discovery. The first modification of the "man the hunter" model began with the documentation of the vital role of "woman the gatherer" in provisioning the social group.

In this model, the development of some cooperation in the procurement of foods and a division of labour by sex are seen as prime factors in the success of early *Homo*. Because these evolutionary speculation relate to proposed behavioural differences between males and females in the *distant* past, they are generally attributed to biologically determined sex differences rather than the socially defined category of gender. However, the gender roles internalized by the working palaeoanthropologist from his or her own culture may be inadvertently applied to the fossil specimens in these behavioural reconstructions. Palaeoanthropologists literally have only fragmentary evidence with which to reconstruct behaviour.

Palaeoanthropologists' behavioural reconstructions from fragments of bone and stone have relied heavily on observations of living primates, including both human and nonhuman living primates. For example, the

H. habilis filled the same niche on the ground that these vultures fill in the air: a nonterritorial scavenger. **WILLIAM A. HAVILAND**

observation that food sharing and a division of labour by gender characterize many modern food foragers has been used to support depictions of our male and female ancestors as "hunter" and "gatherer," respectively. However, the division of labour among contemporary food foragers, like all gender relations, reflects both cultural and biological factors. Division of labour by food-foraging societies does not conform to fixed boundaries defined through biologically based sex differences. Instead, it is influenced by cultural and environmental factors. It appears likely that the same principle applied to our human ancestors.

Evidence from chimpanzees and bonobos casts further doubt on the notion of a strict, sex-based division of labour in human evolutionary history. As described in Chapter 4, among chimpanzees, females have been observed to participate in male hunting expeditions. Meat gained from the successful hunt of a smaller mammal is shared within the group whether provided by a male or a female chimpanzee. Among bonobos, females hunt regularly and share meat and plant foods with one another. In other words, patterns of food sharing and hunting behaviours in these apes are variable, lending credit to the notion that culture plays a role in establishing these behaviours. Similarly, in our evolutionary history it is likely that culture—the shared learned behaviours of each H. habilis group—played a role in their food-sharing behaviours rather than strict biological differences between the sexes.

Though increased consumption of scavenged meat on the part of H. habilis may have promoted more food sharing among adults, this remains a hypothesis, as does the notion that a division of labour characterized early Homo. The fossil and archaeological records provide evidence only of cut marks on bones, the stone tools that made these marks, along with information about our ancestors' bodies and brains. No evidence exists to establish definitively how procured foods may have been shared. When the evidence is fragmentary, as it is in all palaeoanthropological reconstructions of behaviour, gaps are all too easily filled in with behaviours that seem "natural" and familiar such as contemporary gender roles. In reconstructing the behaviour of our ancestors from the distant past, current palaeoanthropologists today pay careful attention to the ways in which contemporary gender norms and other cultural factors inform their models. A return to the evidence with an awareness of its limits will define which inferences can be legitimately made about behaviours in human evolutionary history.

Evolving hominins' increased interest in meat is a point of major importance. The most readily accessible plant sources would have been the proteins available in leaves and legumes (nitrogen-fixing plants, familiar modern examples being beans and peas), but these are hard for primates like us to digest unless they are cooked. The problem is that leaves and legumes contain substances that cause the proteins to pass right through the gut without being absorbed.[9]

Chimpanzees have a similar problem when out on the savanna. In such a setting, they spend about 37 percent of their time on a yearly basis going after insects like ants and termites, while at the same time increasing their predation of eggs and vertebrate animals. Such animal foods not only are easily digestible, but also provide high-quality proteins that contain all the essential amino acids in just the right percentages.

No one plant food does this by itself; only if the right combination is consumed can plants provide what meat does by itself in the way of amino acids. Moreover, there is abundant meat to be had on the savanna. All things considered, then, we should not be surprised if our own ancestors solved their protein problem in somewhat the same way that chimps on the savanna do today.

---

[9] Stahl, A.B. (1984) Hominid dietary selection before fire. *Current Anthropology, 25*, 151–168.

BIOGRAPHY

Adrienne Zihlman (b. 1940)

Until the 1970s, the study of human evolution, from its very beginnings, was permeated by a deep-seated bias reflecting the privileged status enjoyed by men in Western society. Beyond the obvious labelling of fossils as particular types of "men," irrespective of the sex of the individual represented, it took the form of portraying males as the active players in human evolution. Thus, it was males who were seen as providers and innovators, using their wits to become ever more effective providers of food and protection for passive females. The latter were seen as spending their time getting pregnant and caring for offspring, while the men were getting ahead by becoming ever smarter. Central to such thinking was the idea of "man the hunter," constantly honing his wits through the pursuit and killing of animals. Thus, hunting by men was seen as the pivotal humanizing activity in evolution.

PHOTO BY ANDY FREEBERG

We now know, of course, that such ideas are culture-bound, reflecting the hopes and expectations of late-19th- and early-20th-century European and European American culture. This recognition came in the 1970s and was a direct consequence of the entry of a number of highly capable women into the profession of palaeoanthropology. Up until the 1960s, there were few women in any field of biological anthropology, but with the expansion of graduate programs and changing attitudes toward the role of women in society, increasing numbers of them went on to earn a Ph.D. One of these was Adrienne Zihlman, who earned her doctorate at the University of California at Berkeley in 1967. Subsequently, she authored a number of important papers critical of "man the hunter" scenarios. She was not the first to do so; as early as 1971, Sally Linton had published a preliminary paper on "Woman the Gatherer," but it was Zihlman from 1976 on who especially elaborated on the importance of female activities for human evolution. Others have joined in the effort, including Zihlman's companion in graduate school and later colleague, Nancy Tanner, who collaborated with Zihlman on some of her papers and has produced important works of her own.

The work of Zihlman and her coworkers was crucial in forcing a reexamination of existing "man the hunter" scenarios, out of which came recognition of the importance of scavenging in early human evolution as well as the importance of female gathering and other activities. Although there is still plenty to learn about human evolution, thanks to these women we now know that it wasn't a case of women being "uplifted" as a consequence of their association with progressively evolving men. Rather, the two sexes evolved together with each making its own important contribution to the process.

Meat-eating animals, like these lions, do not have to spend as much time eating as do those that rely on plant foods alone. Consequently, they have more time available for play and exploration. **ANITA DE LAGUNA HAVILAND**

Increased meat consumption on the part of early hominins did more than merely ensure an adequate intake of essential amino acids, important though this was. Animals that live on plant foods must eat large quantities of vegetation, and obtaining such foods consumes much of their time. Meat eaters, by contrast, have no need to eat so much, or so often. Consequently, meat-eating hominins may have had more leisure time available to explore and manipulate their environment; like lions and leopards, they would have had time to spend lying around and playing. Such activity, coupled with the other factors already mentioned, may have been a stimulus to hominin brain development.

The importance of increased consumption of meat for early hominin brain development is suggested by the size of their brains: The cranial capacity of the largely plant-eating *Australopithecus* ranged from 310 to 530 cubic centimetres; that of the most primitive known meat eater, *H. habilis* from East Africa, ranged from 580 to 752 cubic centimetres; and *H. erectus*, who eventually hunted as well as scavenged for meat, possessed a cranial capacity of 775 to 1225 cubic centimetres. The

energy needs of the larger brain are not trivial. The large human brain consumes 20 to 25 percent of an adult's energy while at rest, more than twice that of nonhuman primates. *H. erectus*'s brain probably required about 17 percent of its resting energy. Meat is much more energy-dense than plant food and would have been important for the maintenance of the evolving brain.[10]

THE EARLIEST SIGNS OF CULTURE: TOOLS

The use of specially made tools of stone appears to have arisen out of a need for implements to butcher and prepare meat, because hominin teeth were inadequate for the task. Even chimpanzees, whose canine teeth are far larger and sharper, frequently have trouble tearing through the skin of other animals.[11] Besides overcoming this problem, the

---

[10] Leonard, W.R. (2003). Food for thought. *Scientific American, 13* (20), 62–71.

[11] Goodall, J. (1986). The chimpanzees of Gombe: Patterns of behavior (p. 372). Cambridge, MA: Belknap Press.

A power grip (left) utilizes more of the hand, whereas the precision grip (right) relies on the fingers for control. **MARY ANN FITTIPALDI**

manufacture of stone tools must have played a role in the evolution of the human brain, first by putting a premium on manual dexterity and fine manipulation over mere power in the use of the hands. This in turn put a premium on improved organization of the nervous system. Second, the transformation of a lump of stone into a "chopper," "knife," or "scraper" is a far cry from what a chimpanzee does when it transforms a stick into a termite probe. Although the probe is not unlike the stick, the stone tool is (with the exception of hammerstones) quite unlike the lump of stone. Thus, the toolmaker must have an abstract idea of the tool to be made, as well as a specific set of steps that will accomplish the transformation from raw material to finished product. Furthermore, only certain kinds of stone have the flaking properties that will allow the transformation to take place. The toolmaker must know about these, as well as where such stone can be found.

LANGUAGE ORIGINS

The evident importance of cooperation, planning, and foresight in the life of *H. habilis* raises the issue of this species' ability to communicate. Modern apes communicate through a combination of calls and gestures, and humans, though we rely on spoken language, also use this gesture-call system. Like the apes, we have inherited this from ancient ancestors that predate the evolutionary split between humans and non-human apes. After three decades of experiments by several different researchers with captive apes, there is a growing consensus that all great apes share an ability to develop language skills at least to the level of a two- to three-year-old.[12] Of course, they do not do so in the wild, even though the potential is there (just as bonobos do not make chipped stone tools in the wild, even though experiments show they are capable of it). Nor do they display these language skills through speech, but rather through use of gestures. Again, because this linguistic potential is shared, it must be one that the earliest hominins possessed as well. In view of these considerations, the previously noted features of the brain of *H. habilis* that in modern humans are associated with language take on added interest.

Moreover, the speech area is adjacent to and probably derived from that involved in precise hand control. This brings us back to the fact that the manufacture of

---

[12] Miles, H.L.W. (1993). Language and the orangutan: The old person of the forest. In P. Singer (Ed.), The great ape project (p. 46). New York: St. Martin's.

Oldowan tools requires manual skills that go beyond those of chimpanzees, or even Kanzi the bonobo.[13] And, as previously noted, the Oldowan toolmakers, like modern humans, were overwhelmingly right-handed; in making tools, they gripped the core in the left hand, striking flakes off with the right. Chimpanzees, by contrast, show no overall preference for right-handedness at the population level.[14] Handedness (whether right or left) is associated with lateralization of brain functions, that is, the two hemispheres specialize for different functions rather than duplicating each other. Lateralization, in turn, is associated with language. Thus, toolmaking may have set the stage for language development. Putting this all together, we must at least allow the possibility that *H. habilis* had developed gestural language, though it may have been rudimentary. With the hands freed from locomotion to do other things, they were certainly more available for communication than are the hands of apes.

[13] Ambrose, p. 1749.

[14] Ibid., p. 1750.

CHAPTER SUMMARY

Since 1960 a number of fossils have been found in East Africa at Olduvai Gorge, Lake Baringo, and east of Lake Turkana, and in South Africa at Sterkfontein and Swartkrans, which have been attributed to *H. habilis*, the earliest representative of this genus. Among them is the well-known KNM ER 1470 skull, which is more modern in appearance than any *Australopithecus* skull. From the neck down, however, the skeleton of *H. habilis* differs little from that of *Australopithecus*. Because it does show a significant increase in brain size and some reorganization of its structure, *H. habilis*'s mental abilities must have exceeded those of *Australopithecus*. By 2.4 million years ago, the evolution of *Homo* was proceeding in a direction different from that of *Australopithecus*.

The same geological strata that have produced *H. habilis* have also produced the earliest known stone tools. These Lower Palaeolithic artifacts from Olduvai Gorge, Lake Turkana, and sites in Ethiopia are simple in form but required considerable skill and knowledge for their manufacture.

Finds made at Olduvai Gorge have provided important evidence of human evolutionary development. The oldest Lower Palaeolithic tools found at Olduvai are in the Oldowan tool tradition, which is characterized by all-purpose generalized flakes and chopping tools. The direct percussion method of manufacture was used to make them. The simple but effective Oldowan choppers and flakes made possible the addition of meat to the diet on a regular basis because one could now butcher meat, skin any animal, and break open bones for marrow. Many Oldowan archaeological sites appear to be temporary places where meat was processed, rather than campsites.

Some changes in the brain structure of *H. habilis* seem to have been associated with the changed diet. Increased consumption of meat, beginning about 2.5 million years ago, made new demands on their coordination and behaviour. Successful procurement of meat through scavenging depended on *H. habilis*'s ability to outthink far more powerful predators and scavengers. Obtaining animal food presented problems that very often had to be solved on the spot; a small scavenger depending on stereotyped instinctual behaviour alone would have been at a competitive disadvantage in such a situation. Eaters of high-protein foods, such as meats, do not have to eat as often as vegetarians do. Consequently, meat-eating hominins may have had more leisure time available to explore and experiment with their environment.

Toolmaking and use also favoured the development of a more complex brain. To make stone tools, one must have at the beginning a clear vision of the tool to be made, know the precise set of steps necessary to transform the raw material into the tool, and be able to recognize the kind of stone that can be successfully worked. Complex eye-hand coordination is also required.

A prime factor in the success of early hominins may have been the development of some cooperation in the procurement of foods. Although the males probably supplied much of the meat, the females continued to gather the sorts of food eaten by other primates; however, instead of consuming what they gathered as they gathered it, they shared a portion with the males in exchange for meat. This required foresight and planning on the part of females, which played as important a role as male scavenging in favouring the development of larger, more complex brains. Food sharing with a sexual division of labour is characteristic of modern food foragers, and some hint of it can be seen among chimpanzees and bonobos, among whom meat is frequently shared.

The cooperation, planning, and foresight inferred for *H. habilis* suggest the existence of some sort of rudimentary language, as do some features of this species' brain. Experiments with captive apes favour some sort of gestural language.

QUESTIONS FOR CRITICAL THOUGHT

1. What are the difficulties (methodology, gaps in the record, scholarly points of view, etc.) determining when humans appear in the archaeological and fossil record?

2. How does the study of other (nonprimate) mammals help us understand the behaviour of our early ancestors?

3. If you had the opportunity and all the money you needed to investigate the period from 6 million years ago to 1 million years ago for early human sites, where would you look and what methods would you use in your investigation? What more would you hope to learn about our early behaviour and evolution?

INTERNET RESOURCES

The Human Family Tree

www.mnh.si.edu/anthro/humanorigins
Sponsored by the Smithsonian Institution, offers detailed information on human evolution, with links to all known species of hominins, as well as links to primate sites, and an interesting discussion on the debate about *H. habilis*'s place in hominin evolution.

http://anthro.palomar.edu/homo/homo_1.htm
An examination of early hominins, including *H. habilis*. Unique to this site are sound bits that offer pronunciation guides for anthropological terms. Several links to other related sites.

Homo habilis

www.wsu.edu/gened/learn-modules/top_longfor/timeline/habilis/habilis-a.html
An interesting site, offering descriptive information concerning *H. habilis*, including photos of fossils.

http://users.hol.gr/~dilos/prehis.htm
An extremely worthwhile site, providing information on numerous topics concerning hominin evolution, and excellent photos of Lucy, Venus figurines, and the cave paintings at Lascaux. This site is particularly relevant because it introduces readers to topics discussed throughout the rest of the text.

Human Evolution

www.talkorigins.org/origins/faqs-qa.html
Provides a comprehensive source of information about human evolutionary history and takes the evolution–creationism controversy head on. Search the site for excellent descriptions of each of the fossil hominin species discovered.

www.leakeyfoundation.org
The Leakey Foundation website is true to its mission to increase scientific knowledge and public understanding of human origins and evolution. The site provides an interactive timeline of key discoveries in palaeoanthropology and documents the groundbreaking research conducted by the Leakey family and the investigators they have supported for over three decades.

www.archaeologyinfo.com
Packed with information about human evolution, including each new discovery, a comprehensive glossary, and a perspective feature where new voices and ideas in the field can be heard.

Oldowan Tool Tradition

www.handprint.com/LS/ANC/stones.html
Describes Oldowan tools and provides links to a detailed (and controversial) chart of human evolution, as well as a tour of the human fossil records, the hominin brain, and hominin fossil sites.

Olduvai Gorge

http://archserve.id.ucsb.edu/Anth3/Courseware/OlduvaiForm/5_Map_Oludvai_Gorge.html
Provides a map of Olduvai Gorge, highlighting important localities for early hominins, as well as information on the hominin fossils found at Olduvai.

SUGGESTED READINGS

For a list of suggested readings, visit the textbook's website at www.humanevolution2.nelson.com.

CHAPTER

8

Homo Erectus and the Emergence of Hunting and Gathering

More clearly human than *Homo habilis,* though less so than *Homo sapiens,* a new species known either as *Homo erectus* or *H. ergaster* emerged about 1.8 million years ago, by which time the genus *Homo* was spreading to parts of Asia. Shown here is one of the most famous *H. erectus* sites at Zhoukoudian, China. Discovered in the 1920s, it is now included on UNESCO's World Heritage List.

CHEN SHEN

CHAPTER PREVIEW

1. Who Was *Homo erectus/ergaster*?

H. erectus/ergaster was probably the direct descendant of early members of the genus *Homo*. Populations of *H. erectus* were widespread between about 1.8 million and 400 000 years ago, from Africa and Europe in the West, to Southeast Asia and China in the East. Geographic variation among the fossils suggest that *H. erectus* is strictly an East Asian species while the African fossils are a different species, *H. ergaster*.

2. What Were the Cultural Capabilities of *H. erectus/ergaster*?

Having a larger brain than its ancestors, *H. erectus* became increasingly able to adapt to different situations through the medium of culture. This is reflected by better-made tools, a greater variety of tool types, regional diversification of tool kits, use of fire, and improved organizational skills.

3. What Were the Consequences of *H. erectus/ergaster*'s Improved Abilities to Adapt through Culture?

As culture became more important as the vehicle through which this species secured its survival, life became somewhat more secure than it had been. The result was increased reproductive success, allowing populations to grow, with "spillover" into previously uninhabited regions. This expansion in turn contributed to the further evolution of culture, as populations of *H. erectus/ergaster* had to find solutions to new problems of existence in newly inhabited regions.

CHAPTER OUTLINE

H. erectus/ergaster Fossils	Other Aspects of *H. erectus*'s Culture
The Culture of *H. erectus/ergaster*	The Question of Language

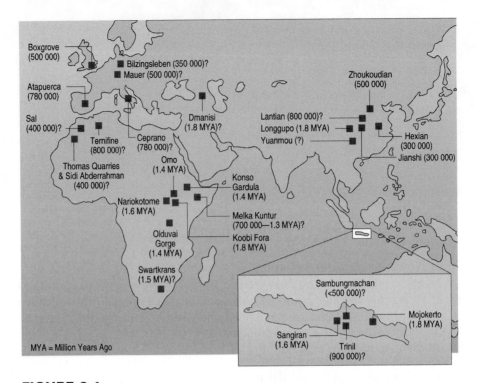

FIGURE 8.1

Sites, with dates, at which *H. erectus/ergaster* remains have been found.

In 1891, Dutch army surgeon Eugene Dubois, intent upon finding the fossils of a "missing link" between humans and apes, set out for Indonesia (then the Dutch East Indies), which he considered to have provided a suitable environment for such a creature. At Trinil, on the island of Java, Dubois found what he was searching for: the fossil remains of a primitive kind of hominin, consisting of a skull cap, a few teeth, and a thighbone. Its features seemed to Dubois part ape, part human. Indeed, Dubois at first thought the remains did not even belong to the same individual. The flat skull, for example, with its low forehead and enormous brow ridges, appeared to be like that of an ape; but it possessed a cranial capacity much larger than an ape's, even though small by modern human standards. The femur, or thighbone, was clearly human in shape and proportions, and indicated the creature was a biped. Although Dubois called his find *Pithecanthropus erectus,* or "erect ape man," it has since been assigned to the species *H. erectus.*

HOMO ERECTUS/ERGASTER FOSSILS

Until 1.9 to 1.8 million years ago, hominins lived only in Africa. It was on this continent that hominins, and later the genus *Homo,* originated. It was also in Africa that the first stone tools were invented. But by 1 million to 500 000 years ago hominins had spread far beyond the confines of their original homeland. Fossils of this species are now known from a number of localities in not only Africa, but China, Europe, the Republic of Georgia, and India, as well as Java (Figure 8.1). Although remains of this species have been found in many different places in three continents, "lumpers" emphasize that they are unified by a number of shared characteristics. However, evidence suggest that populations of *Homo* immediately post-dating 1.9 million years ago in different regions of Africa, Asia, and Europe show some differences from one another. Although some anthropologists assign all

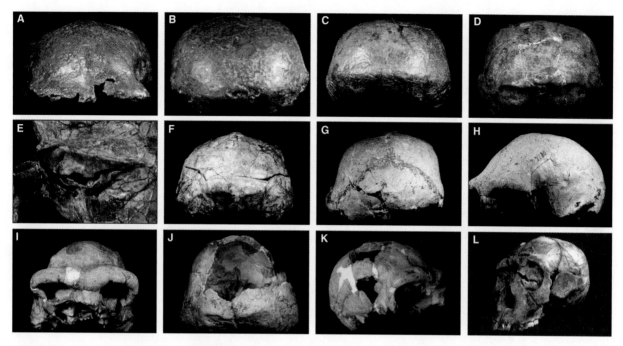

FIGURE 8.2

All of these fossils have been attributed to the same species, *H. erectus,* and show considerable variation. (**A** and **B**) Trinil skull cap (front and rear views). (**C**) Sangiran 2 (rear view). (**D**) Sangiran 12 (rear view). (**E**) Sangiran 4 (internal view of right petrosal bone that is on the side the cranium, rear toward right; note number of grooves behind and across the bone, rather than a single, well-defined sigmoid sinus coursing behind). (**F**) Sangiran 4 (rear view). (**G**) Dmanisi D2282 (rear view). (**H**) Dmanisi D2280. (**I** and **J**) OH 9 (front and rear views). (**K**) Ceprano (three-quarter view). (**L**) KNM-WT 15000 (three-quarter view). Images not to scale.

the *Homo* fossils dating immediately after *H. habilis* to the species *H. erectus,* others view the variation to be significant enough to warrant assigning the fossils to at least two species: *H. erectus* and *H. ergaster* (Fig. 8.2). Recently *H. georgicus* and *H. antecessor* have been suggested as other species. In this chapter this complex of fossils is referred to generally as *H. erectus/ergaster.* Where specialists refer to the fossils in their research area as one species or the other, that species name is used. In particular, the African fossils are called *H. ergaster* and the Chinese fossils are *H. erectus.* Rather than assuming gene flow from Africa to Asia that eliminated species boundaries, the conservative interpretation of isolated populations is assumed. Nevertheless, there are great

adaptive similarities, both biological and behavioural, that permit a discussion of this hominin complex as a meaningful group.

There are doubts concerning *H. habilis* being the earliest representative of the genus *H.* but the subsequent hominins are undoubtedly members of the genus. The specific features characteristic of the Asian *H. erectus* are best known from the skull. Interestingly many of the *H. erectus/ergaster* fossils consist of isolated skull caps as in Dubois's original discovery; cranial capacity in *H. erectus/ergaster* ranges from 600 to 1225 cubic centimetres (average about 1000 cubic centimetres). Thus cranial capacity overlaps with the nearly 2-million-year-old KNM ER 1470 skull from East Africa (752 cubic centimetres) and the 1000 to 2000 cc range (average 1300 cubic centimetres) for modern human skulls (Figure 8.3). The cranium itself has a low vault (height of the dome of the skull top), and the head is long and narrow. When viewed from behind, its width is greater than its height, with its greatest width at the base. The skulls of modern humans when similarly viewed are higher than they are wide, with the widest dimension in the region above the ears. The shape of the inside of *H. erectus* braincase shows near-modern development of the brain, especially in the speech area.[1] Although some anthropologists argue that the vocal apparatus was not adequate for speech, others argue that asymmetries of the brain suggest the same

pattern of right-handedness with left cerebral dominance that, in modern peoples, is correlated with the capacity for language.

H. erectus/ergaster possessed massive brow ridges (Figure 8.4). When viewed from above, a marked constriction or "pinching in" of the skull can be seen just behind the massive brow ridges. *H. erectus/ergaster* also possessed a sloping forehead and a receding chin. Powerful jaws with large teeth, a protruding mouth, and huge neck muscles added to *H. erectus/ergaster's*

---

[1] Holloway, R.L. (1981). The Indonesian *Homo erectus* brain endocasts revisited. *American Journal of Physical Anthropology, 55,* 521.

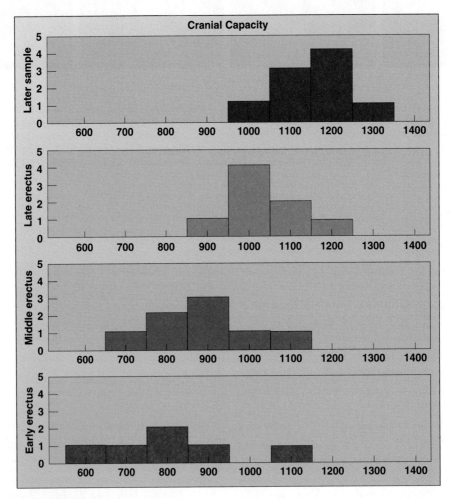

FIGURE 8.3

Cranial capacity in *H. erectus/ergaster* increased over time, as illustrated by these bar graphs, shown in cubic centimetres. The cranial capacity of late *H. erectus/ergaster* overlaps with the range seen in living humans.

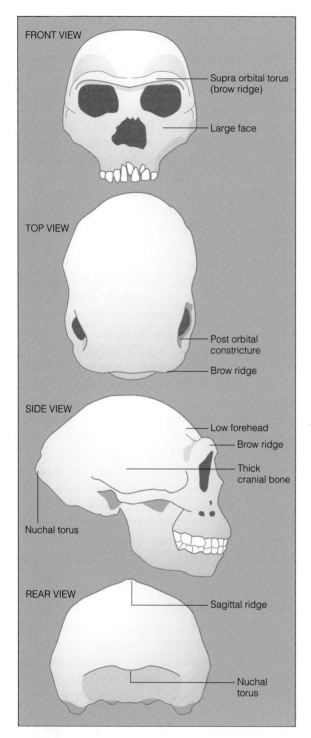

FRONT VIEW

Supra orbital torus (brow ridge)

Large face

TOP VIEW

Post orbital constricture

Brow ridge

SIDE VIEW

Low forehead

Brow ridge

Thick cranial bone

Nuchal torus

REAR VIEW

Sagittal ridge

Nuchal torus

FIGURE 8.4

To understand the evolution of any species, the full range of variation must be considered, not merely typical representatives. The fact that fossils seemingly attributed to *H. habilis* and *H. erectus/ergaster* coexisted between 1.8 and 1.6 million years ago (mya) need not mean coexistence of two separate species. If one evolved from the other, we would expect that at some point the full range of variation included some individuals who still resembled *H. habilis*, whereas others were increasingly taking on the appearance of *H. erectus/ergaster*.

generally rugged appearance. Nevertheless, the face, teeth, and jaws of this hominin are smaller than those of *H. habilis*.

Apart from its skull, the skeleton of *H. erectus/ergaster* differs only subtly from that of modern humans and as we saw in Chapter 7, the post-cranial skeleton is significantly different from that of the Australopithecines. The skeleton is known mainly from the African *H. ergaster*. Although its bodily proportions are like ours rather than the Australopithecines, it was more heavily muscled than ours. Stature seems to have increased from the smaller size typical of the Australopithecines and the earliest members of the genus *Homo*. The best evidence for this comes from a remarkably well-preserved skeleton of an adolescent male from Lake Turkana in Kenya. Sexual dimorphism in body size also appears to have decreased in *H. erectus/ergaster* compared to earlier hominins. A reduction in sexual dimorphism may be due to the increase in female size as an adaptation to childbirth.

H. erectus from Java

For a long time, the scientific community was reluctant to accept Dubois's claim that his Javanese fossils were of human lineage. It was not until the 1930s, particularly when other fossils of *H. erectus* were discovered by G.H.R. von Königswald at Sangiran, Java, in the Early Pleistocene Djetis beds, that scientists almost without exception agreed that both discoveries were the remains of an entirely new kind of early hominin. Von Königswald found a small skull that fluorine analysis and (later) potassium-argon dating indicated to be older than Dubois's approximately 500 000- to 700 000-year-old Trinil specimen. Since 1960, additional fossils have been found in Java, and we now have remains of approximately 40 individuals. A long continuity of *H. erectus* populations in Southeast Asia is indicated, from perhaps as many as 1.8 million to about 500 000 years ago. Interestingly, the teeth and jaws of some of the earliest Javanese fossils are in many ways quite similar to those of *H. habilis*.[2]

[2] Tobias, P.V., & von Königswald, G.H.R. (1964). A comparison between the Olduvi hominines and those of Java and some implications for hominid phylogeny. *Nature, 204*, 515–518.

H. erectus from China

The dismissal of the Javanese finds did not discourage scientists from looking for an ancient human ancestor elsewhere. Research in China broke the 35-year drought in significant discoveries. In 1927 Davidson Black, a Canadian professor of anthropology and neurology at Peking Union Medical College, published his assessment of a lower permanent molar excavated from the Zhoukoudian site near Beijing. He concluded that it was from a hominin, but it was sufficiently different from that of a humans to propose that it represented a seperate genus, *Sinanthropus* or "Chinese man."[3] Two years later, the site field supervisor, Pei Wenchung, discovered part of a cranium as he was preparing to close the site because the monsoon season was approaching. The next day he had the fossil in Black's laboratory, where he made a cast of the discovery. The discovery

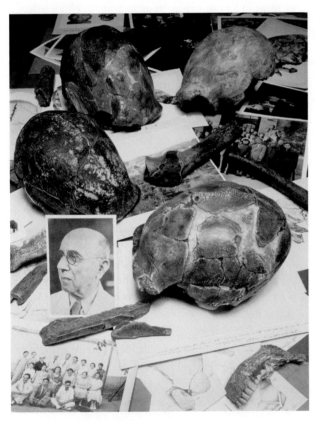

The original *Sinanthropus* (H. erectus/ergaster) *fossils from Zhoukoudian had been packed and shipped to the United States for safe keeping during World War II, but they mysteriously disappeared. Fortunately, excellent casts of the specimens and detailed anatomical descriptions (by Weidenreich) were made before the fossils were lost during the war.* **RUSSELL CIOCHON, UNIVERSITY OF IOWA**

erased any doubt about an early hominin having lived near Beijing and revitalized interest in the Javenese research. Pei and Black laboured together almost continuously on the Zhoukoudian project until Black's death in 1934. Franz Weidenreich was selected to replace Black, and by the beginning of World War II an estimated 45 *Sinanthropus* individuals, more than half of them women and children, were eventually recovered from Zhoukoudian. The fossils document the best collection of 600 000- to 300 000-year-old hominins ever found. Most were represented by teeth, jawbones, and skull fragments. World War II brought a halt to the digging, and the original Zhoukoudian specimens were lost in 1941 during the Japanese occupation of China. The fossils had been carefully packed by Weidenreich and his team and apparently placed with the U.S. marines, but the precious fossils disappeared. In 2005 a Chinese search committee was established to investigate every possible angle in hopes of recovering the fossils. Some witnesses say the marines buried the fossils or hid the boxes containing the fossils in a basement. Attempts have been made to find them but few clues have been left. Fortunately Weidenreich's technician, probably trained by Black, made superb casts of most of the fossils. The casts are now in various institutions where they can still be studied.

After the war, other specimens were discovered in China, at Zhoukoudian and at a number of other localities (Figure 8.2). The oldest skull is about 700 000 to 800 000 years old and comes from Lantian in Shensi Province. Even older is a fragment of a lower jaw from a cave in south-central China (Lunggupo) that is as old as the oldest Javanese fossils. Like some of their Javanese contemporaries, this Chinese hominin is reminiscent of African *H. habilis.* By contrast with these ancient remains, the original Zhoukoudian fossils appear to date between 600 000 and 300 000 years ago (Figure 8.4).

Although the two populations overlap in time, the Chinese fossils are, on the whole, not quite as old as those from Java. Not surprisingly, Chinese *H. erectus* is a bit less "primitive" looking. Its average cranial capacity is about 1000 cubic centimetres, compared to 900 cubic centimetres for Javanese *H. erectus* (see Figure 8.5). The smaller teeth, short jaw, and lack of

---

[3] Black, D. (1928). Discovery of further hominid remains of lower Quaternary age from the Chou Kou Tien deposit. *Science, 67,* 136–137.

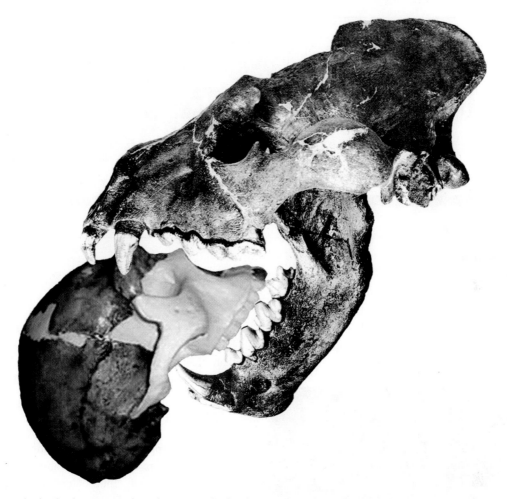

The fossils of H. erectus *from the cave at Zhoukoudian are the remains of individuals who were consumed in the cave by the now-extinct giant hyena. This composite shows how the giant hyena attacked the face.*
RUSSELL CIOCHON, UNIVERSITY OF IOWA

diastema in the lower dentition—a gap in the teeth to accommodate a large upper canine when the jaws are closed—of the Chinese fossils are further evidence of their more modern status.

The African Fossils

Several important specimens of *H. ergaster* have been found in Africa. Fossils from this stage of human evolution in Africa are less well represented than they are outside Africa so it is understandable that the African situation is not particularly clear. This is odd because archaeological sites from the same period as *H. erectus/ergaster* (Middle Pleistocene) are quite common in Africa. Three partial jaws were discovered in Algeria over 50 years ago, but the better-known finds have been

made since 1960, at Olduvai and at Lake Turkana. The most complete H. skeleton found from this period is that of a boy who died 1.6 million years ago at about the age of 12. Another partial skeleton, that of an adult, had diseased bones, possibly the result of a massive overdose of vitamin A. This excess could have come from eating the livers of carnivorous animals, for they accumulate vitamin A in their livers at levels that are poisonous to human beings. Another possibility might have been heavy consumption of bee brood and other immature insects, producing the same result.

The variation between the Asian and African/European fossils may lie beyond that expected in a single species. Only in the last few years have *H. ergaster* fossils been found at the well-studied Acheulean site of Olorgesailie in Kenya.[4] They are slightly younger than

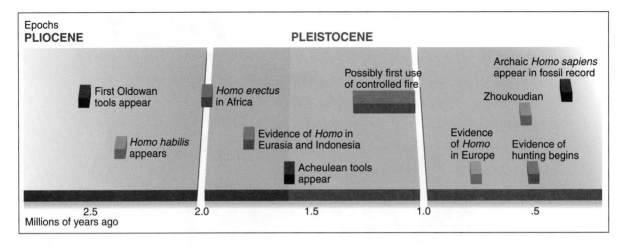

FIGURE 8.5

H. and cultural evolution.

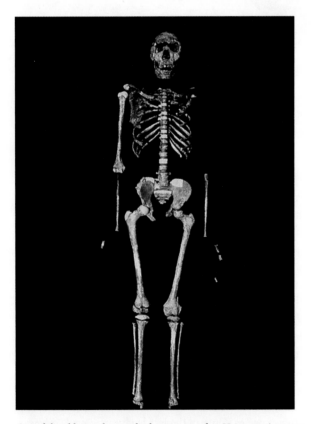

One of the oldest and certainly the most complete H. erectus/ergaster *fossil is the Strapping Youth from Lake Turkana. The remains are those of a boy who died in his early teens.* **NATIONAL MUSEUMS OF CANADA**

1 million years old. The cranium from Olorgesailie is the smallest of any from this period. The brow ridge is double-arched and more strongly developed than in the Asian *H. erectus.* The brow ridge of the Olduvai skull is similar and muscle scars on the temporal bones are prominent. Other specimens such as those from Koobi Fora have thinner crania and more primitive mandibles than their Asian counterparts.[5] These characteristics support its classification as *H. ergaster* rather than the closely related *H. erectus* although the issue is still somewhat controversial.[6,7]

As in Asia, the most recent African fossils are less primitive in appearance, and the oldest fossils (up to 1.9 million years old) display features reminiscent of the earlier *H. habilis.* Indeed, one of the problems is distinguishing early *H. erectus* or *H. ergaster* from late *H. habilis*—precisely what one would expect if one evolved from the other.

Earliest *Homo* from Europe

The Dmanisi site in the republic of Georgia dating to about 1.7 million years ago is perhaps the best collection of early *Homo* fossils ever found from any single site.[8]

[4] Potts, R., Behrensmeyer, A.K., Deino, A., Ditchfield, P., & Clark, J. (2004). Small Mid-Pleistocene hominin associated with East African Acheulean technology. *Science, 305,* 75–78.

[5] Wood, B. (1991). *Koobi Fora research project.* Oxford; New York: Clarendon Press. v. 4.

[6] Schwartz, J.H. (2004). Anthropology: Getting to know *Homo erectus. Science, 305,* 53–54.

[7] Rightmire, G.P. (1998). Evidence from facial morphology for similarity of Asian and African representatives of *Homo erectus. American Journal of Physical Anthropology, 106,* 61.

[8] Vekus, A., Lordkipanidze, D., Rightmire, G.P., Agusti, J., Ferring, R., Maisuradze, G., Mouskhelishvili, A., Nioradze, M., Ponce de Leon, M., Tappen, M., Valchrelidze, M., & Zollikofer, C. (2002). A new skull of early *Homo* from Dmanisi, Georgia. *Science, 297,* 85–89.

BIOGRAPHY

Davidson Black (1884–1934)

Davidson Black, a graduate of the University of Toronto, was one of the most prominent researchers in the early days of human origins research. In an all-too-familiar story to many Canadians, Black was first recognized outside Canada as among the most respected palaeoanthropologists in the world. His impact on our thinking about early hominin fossils and how to study them ranks among the most influential of his day. In some ways, his upbringing was typically Canadian. As a young man he was captivated by the Kawartha Lakes in Ontario, and he became an accomplished outdoorsman who was fascinated with natural history.[1] This fascination influenced a critical life choice. He studied medicine at the University of Toronto (U of T), but practising medicine didn't interest him. Through the influence of colleagues and summer work opportunities it was clear that there were other things that excited Black, so he went back to U of T and completed a B.A. degree in 1911. He apparently wasn't interested in human evolution until a fateful trip to Europe. In 1914 he took a research leave from Case Western Reserve University in Ohio (where he was teaching) and travelled to Europe to broaden his experience in neuroanatomy with a prominent Dutch specialist, Ariens Kappers, and an English specialist, Grafton Elliot Smith. Smith encouraged Black to explore the evolution of the human brain.[2] A pivotal event occurred when the Piltdown controversy erupted while Black was working with Smith who took on the task of studying the endocranial cast of the Piltdown skull. Black obviously developed an interest in this aspect of Smith's research and went on to learn cast making in Manchester.

One final piece to the puzzle that explains why Black found himself in China in 1919 is the influence of William D. Matthew, a Canadian palaeontologist whose writings[3] convinced Black that China was the place to look for human ancestors. First Black needed to get to China, so when he was offered a job teaching at Peking Union Medical College, soon to become the best medical school in the world at the time, he jumped at the chance. Black used his spare time to look for fossils. He collaborated with J.G. Andersson, a Swedish engineer working in China as a mining consultant[4] but who also was interested in Chinese prehistory. The two men worked together on Neolithic sites, and Black published the first physical anthropological study of Neolithic skeletal remains in China. Coincidentally, excavations were under way at the Zhoukoudian site by a Swedish team including Andersson. Plenty of animal bones were recovered but the team was unable to find any obvious evidence for early humans and gave up in 1923. The team had, however, found two teeth that Black confirmed (back in Beijing) were hominin. This was all team members needed to propose continuing the Zhoukoudian excavations. Black took up where the Swedish team left off after he persuaded the Rockefeller Foundation to support the continued research. His assistant, Birger Bohlin, discovered a tooth during the 1927 field season and brought it to Black in Beijing. Black took a leave from Peking Union Medical College in 1928 and made his way to Europe, touring with the tooth and visiting as many archaeologists as he could in order to be prepared for his work in China. Skepticism greeted Black's interpretations that the tooth was not from the genus Homo but from *Sinanthropus*, a closely related genus (his sample was quite small). However, by 1929 Black was proven correct when two crania of what we now know to be *H. erectus* were recovered from Zhoukoudian. Eugene Dubois had discovered a similar fossil in Java in 1891, but most scientists had not considered the evidence from Java sufficient to demonstrate the existence of a new type of early human. The Javanese material was all but forgotten for decades. The evidence from China confirmed that an early human relative existed in the fossil record and had lived at Zhoukoudian. In 1932, Black was elected a Fellow of The Royal Society in recognition of his research. Unfortunately, Davidson Black died in 1934 when he was 49, the same age as his father and from the same congenital heart problem, so he did not live to see the full implications of his research realized. Black's contributions have left an indelible imprint on the field of human origins research. Black

(Continued)

did not directly supervise the development of students who would eventually come to teach human origins, but his publications and impact on palaeoanthropology research in China are, to this day, a credit to this young Canadian scholar.

[1] Hood, D. (1964). *Davidson Black: A biography.* Toronto: University of Toronto Press.

[2] Shapiro, H.L. (1981). Davidson Black, an appreciation, In B.A. Sigmon & J.S. Cybulski (Eds.), *Homo erectus: Papers in honor of Davidson Black* (pp. 21–26). Toronto: University of Toronto Press.

[3] Matthew, W.D. (1915). Climate and evolution. *Annals of the New York Academy of Sciences, 24,* 171–318.

[4] Cormack, J.L. (2003). Davidson Black and his role in Chinese palaeoanthropology. In C. Shen & S.G. Keates (Eds.), *Current research in Chinese Pleistocene archaeology* (pp. 9–19). British Archaeological Reports 11.

The age places them as a likely ancestor to the Asian *H. erectus*. The fossils are difficult to assign to a particular species because they share characteristics with both earlier and later fossils. They may be *H. habilis*, primitive *H. erectus/ergaster* or a new species, *H. georgicus*. The cranium is small and rounded with a face similar to that of early African *H. erectus/ergaster*. The Dmanisi mandible is unique. However they are classified, their brain size is small, within the range of *H. habilis*. The tools at the site are Oldowan. So they did not yet have the hallmarks of the larger-brained and more culturally developed *H. erectus/ergaster* who lived in Europe after 1 million years ago. An even more astounding discovery is that one of the individuals lost most of their teeth long before death.[9] This individual would have eaten soft foods such as bone marrow or brain tissue, or soft plant foods. The individual would also appear to have needed more group care than we see among other primates. Dmanisi is challenging established views of early *Homo*.

A robust shinbone from Boxgrove, England, and a large lower jaw from Mauer, Germany, are close to half a million years old. The jaw certainly came from a skull wide at the base, as is that of *H. erectus/ergaster*. Older yet and dating to between 860 000 and 780 000 years ago are at least six individuals from the Gran Dolina Cave site in the Sierra de Atapuerca of north-central Spain. Many traits of the fossil crania are primitive, but the face is distinctly modern, with a double-arched brow ridge and bone surface below the eyes that slopes down and slightly backward.[10] These Western European representatives of *Homo* are the oldest human ancestors with a relatively modern face, and because these are derived traits not present in *H. erectus/ergaster*, the excavators assigned these fossils to a separate species, *H. antecessor*. From 500 000 years ago, the proposed descendant of *H. antecessor* is *H. heidelbergensis*, whose teeth shape and

size are identical to those of the later Neandertals. This finding, and the fact that the earliest evidence of hominins in Europe comes from Spain and Italy, suggests that they arrived there by crossing from North Africa.[11] At the time, a mere 6 or 7 kilometres separated Gibraltar from Morocco (compared to 13 kilometres today), and islands dotted the straits from Tunisia to Sicily. Still there was no land connection, requiring that open water be crossed, but evidence from Indonesia (discussed later in this chapter) demonstrates that *H. erectus/ergaster* was capable of doing this by 800 000 years ago. All of this evidence, in turn, undermines arguments made by some European researchers that the early Europeans represent a separate species from *H. erectus/ergaster* (Table 8.1). Such speciation would require isolation of Europeans from other populations, but if ancient humans could cross between North Africa and southern Europe at least once, they could do it any number of times and thus maintain at least a modicum of gene flow between populations.

Other European fossils are not as old as the Mauer and Boxgrove remains and display a mosaic of features characteristic of both *H. erectus/ergaster* and subsequent archaic *H. sapiens*. Here, as in Africa and Asia, a distinction between late *H. erectus* and early *H. sapiens* is difficult to make.

[9] Lordkipanidze, D., Vekus, A., Ferring, R., Rightmire, G.P., Agusti, J., Kiladze, G., Mouskhelishvili, A., Nioradze, M., Ponce de León, M.S., Tappen, M., and Zollikofer, C.P.E. (2005). The earliest toothless hominin skull. *Nature, 434,* 717–718.

[10] Bermudez de Castro, J.M., Arsuaga, E., Carbonell, E., Rosas, A., Martinez, I., & Mosquera, M. (1997). A hominid from the Lower Pleistocene of Atapuerca, Spain: Possible ancestor to Neandertals and modern humans. *Science, 276,* 1392–1395.

[11] Balter, M. (2001). In search of the first Europeans. *Science, 291,* 1724.

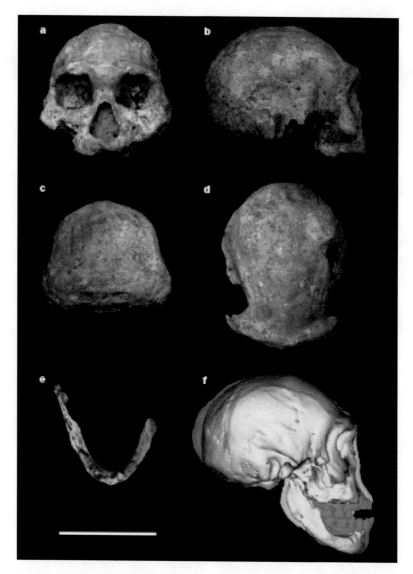

Skull of a toothless Homo (classified as either H. habilis, H. erectus, *or* H. georgicus*) from Dmanisi, republic of Georgia. Bottom row, right are comparative computer-tomography-based lateral views of skull D3444/D3900 (coloured), the juvenile skull D2700/D2735 (light grey), and cranium D2282 with articulated mandible D211 (dark grey) (for details of D2700 and D2282). Scale bar, 10 cm.* FIGURE 1 FROM LORDKIPANIDZE D., VEKUA A., FERRING R., RIGHTMIRE G.P., AGUSTI J., KILADZE G., MOUSKHELISHVILI A., NIORADZE M., PONCE DE LEÓN M.S., TAPPEN M., & ZOLLIKOFER C.P.E. (2005). THE EARLIEST TOOTHLESS HOMININ SKULL. NATURE, 434, 717–718.

Relationship between *H. erectus/ergaster* and *H. habilis*

The smaller teeth and larger brains of *H. erectus/ergaster* seem to mark continuation of a trend first seen in *H. habilis*. What is new is the increased body size, reduced sexual dimorphism, and more "human" body form of *H. erectus*. Nonetheless, there is some resemblance to *habilis*, for example, in the conical shape of the rib cage, the long neck and low neck angle of the thighbone, the long low vault and marked constriction of the skull behind the eyes, and smaller brain size in the earliest *H. erectus* fossils. Indeed, as already noted, it is very difficult to distinguish between the earliest

TABLE 8.1 **Names Used for the Earliest and Latest Fossils in Europe also referred to as *Homo erectus***

NAME	EXPLANATION
Homo antecessor	Coined for the earliest fossils from Spain; antecessor is Latin for "explorer" or "pioneer."
H. heidelbergensis	Originally coined for the Mauer jaw (Mauer is not far from Heidelberg), this name is now used by some as a designation for all European fossils from about 500 000 years ago until the appearance of the Neandertals (Chapter 9).

H. erectus/ergaster and the latest *H. habilis* fossils (Figure 8.6). Presumably the one form evolved from the other, evidently fairly abruptly, in the period between 1.9 and 1.6 million years ago.

THE CULTURE OF *HOMO ERECTUS/ERGASTER*

As one might expect given its larger brain, *H. erectus/ergaster* outstripped its predecessors in cultural ability. In Africa, Europe, and Asia, there was refinement of the stone tool-making technology begun by the makers of earlier flake and chopper tools. At some point, fire began

to be used for protection, warmth, and cooking, though precisely when is still a matter for debate. Finally, there is indirect evidence that the organizational and planning abilities of *H. erectus/ergaster,* or at least the later ones, were improved over those of their predecessors.

The Acheulean Tool Tradition

Associated with the remains of *H. erectus/ergaster* in Africa, Europe, and Southwest Asia are tools of the **Acheulean tradition**. The signature piece of this tradition is the handaxe: a teardrop-shaped tool pointed at one end with a sharp cutting edge all around. In East Africa, the earliest handaxes are about 1.6 million years old; those found in Europe are no older than about 500 000 years. At the same time that handaxes appeared, archaeological sites in Europe became dramatically more common than earlier ones, suggesting an influx of people bringing with them Acheulean technology (and implying continued gene flow into Europe). Since the spread of the genus *Homo* from Africa took place before the invention of the handaxe, it is not surprising to find that different forms of tools were developed in East Asia.

That the Acheulean grew out of the Oldowan tradition is indicated by an examination of the evidence discovered at Olduvai. In Bed I, the lowest level, chopper tools were found along with remains of *H. habilis.* In lower Bed II, the first crude handaxes were found intermingled with chopper tools. Acheulean handaxes having a more finished look appear in middle Bed II, together with *H. ergaster* remains.

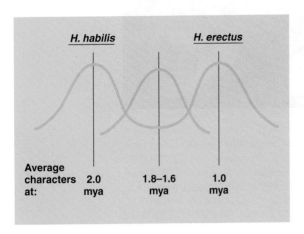

H. habilis   H. erectus

| Average characters at: | 2.0 mya | 1.8–1.6 mya | 1.0 mya |

FIGURE 8.6

To understand the evolution of any species, the full range of variation must be considered, not merely typical representatives. The fact that fossils seemingly attributed to *H. habilis* and *H. erectus/ergaster* coexisted between 1.8 and 1.6 million years ago need not mean coexistence of two separate species. If one evolved from the other, we would expect that, at some point, the full range of variation included some individuals that still resembled *habilis*, whereas others were increasingly taking on the appearance of *H. erectus/ergaster.*

Acheulean tradition. The toolmaking tradition of *H. erectus/ergaster* in Africa, Europe, and Southwest Asia in which handaxes were developed from the earlier Oldowan chopper.

Acheulean handaxes like this one show that the ability to transform large pieces of stone into tools by controlled flaking techniques became widespread not long after 1.5 million years ago. **GARY CRAWFORD**

Early Acheulean tools represent a significant step beyond the generalized cutting, chopping, and scraping tools of the Oldowan tradition. The shapes of Oldowan tools were largely controlled by the original form, size, and mechanical properties of raw materials. The shapes of handaxes and some other Acheulean tools, by contrast, are more standardized, apparently reflecting arbitrary preconceived designs imposed upon a diverse range of primary forms.[12] Overall, sharper points and more regular cutting edges were produced, and more cutting edge was available from the same amount of stone.

During this part of the **Palaeolithic**, or Old Stone Age, tool kits began to diversify (Figure 8.7). Besides handaxes, *H. erectus/ergaster* used tools that functioned as cleavers (these were handaxes with a straight, sharp edge where the point would otherwise be), picks and knives (variants of the handaxe form), and flake tools (generally smaller tools made by hitting a flint core with a hammerstone, thus knocking off flakes with sharp edges). Many flake tools were byproducts of handaxe

---

[12] Ambrose, S. H. (2001). Paleolithic technology and human evolution. *Science, 291,* 1750.

Palaeolithic. The Old Stone Age, characterized by manufacture and use of chipped stone tools.

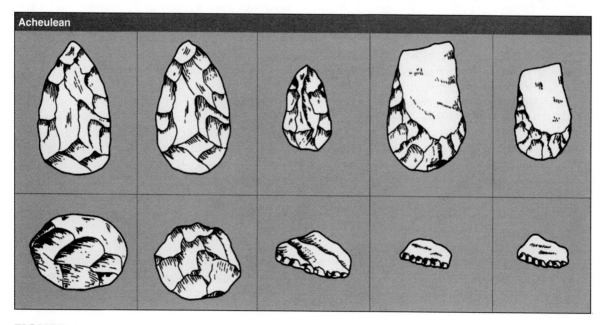

Acheulean

FIGURE 8.7

Ten percent of the shaped tools in a typical Acheulean assemblage are the forms drawn here.

ORIGINAL STUDY

H. erectus/ergaster and the Use of Bamboo

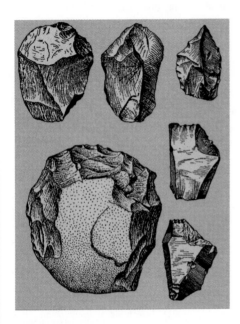

FIGURE 8.8

Choppers and flakes like these were used by *H. erectus/ergaster* at Zhoukoudian, China. Adapted from Pope, G.C., (1989). Bamboo and human evolution. *Natural History, 10,* 50–54. Copyright © American Museum of Natural History.

Bamboo provides, I believe, the solution to a puzzle first raised in 1943, when the late archaeologist Hallam Movius of Harvard began to publish his observations on Palaeolithic (Old Stone Age) cultures of the Far East. In 1937 and 1938 Movius had investigated a number of archaeological localities in India, Southeast Asia, and China. Although most of the archaeological "cultures" that he recognized are no longer accepted by modern workers, he made another, more lasting contribution. This was the identification of the "Movius line" (which his colleague Carleton Coon named in his honour): a geographical boundary, extending through northern India, that separates two long-lasting Palaeolithic cultures. West of the line are found collections of tools with a high percentage of symmetrical and consistently proportioned handaxes (these are called Acheulean tools, after the French site of Saint Acheul). More or less

similar tool kits also occur in Mongolia and Siberia, but with few exceptions (which are generally relatively late in time), not in Eastern China or Southeast Asia, where more tools known as choppers and chopping tools prevail [Figure 8.8].

My own research on the Movius line and related questions evolved almost by accident. During the course of my work in Southeast Asia, I excavated many sites, studied a variety of fossil faunal collections, and reviewed the scientific literature dealing with Asia. As part of this research I compared fossil mammals from Asia with those recovered from other parts of the world. In the beginning, my purpose was biostratigraphic—to use the animals to estimate the most likely dates of various sites used by early hominins. On the basis of the associated fauna, for example, I estimate that Kao Pah Nam [a site in Thailand] may be as old as 700 000 years. After years of looking at fossil collections and faunal lists, I realized that something was very strange about the collections from Southeast Asia: There were no fossil horses of Pleistocene age or for a considerable time before that. The only exceptions were a few horse fossils from one place in southern China, the Yuanmou Basin, which was and is a special small grassland habitat in a low, dry valley within the Shan-Yunnan Massif.

To mammalian biostratigraphers this is unusual, since members of the horse family are so common in both the Old and New World that they are a primary means of dating various fossil localities. Fossil horses have been reported from Western Burma, but the last one probably lived there some 20 million years ago. Not a single fossil horse turns up later than that in Southeast Asia, although they are known from India to the west and China to the north and every other part of Europe and Asia.

I then began to wonder what other normally common animals might be missing. The answer soon became apparent: camels—even though they too were once widespread throughout the world—and members and relatives of the giraffe family. Pleistocene Southeast Asia was shaping up as a kind of "black hole" for certain fossil mammals! These animals—horses, camels, and giraffids—all dwell in open country. Their absence on the Southeast Asian mainland and islands (all once connected, along with the now inundated Sunda Shelf) is indicative of a forested environment. The mammals that are present—orangutans, tapirs, and gibbons—confirm this conclusion.

The significance of this is that most reconstructions of our evolutionary past have emphasized the influence of savanna grassland habitats, so important in Africa, the cradle of hominin evolution. Many anthropologists theorize that shrinking forests and spreading grasslands encouraged our primarily tree-dwelling ancestors to adapt to ground-dwelling conditions, giving rise to the unique bipedal gait that is the hallmark of hominins. Bipedalism, in turn, freed the hands for tool use and ultimately led to the evolution of a large-brained, cultural animal. Tropical Asia, instead, apparently was where early hominins had to readapt to tropical forest.

In studying the record, I noticed that the forested zone—the zone that lacked open-dwelling mammals—coincided generally with the distribution of the chopper-chopping tools. The latter appeared to be the products of a forest adaptation that, for one reason or another, de-emphasized the utilization of standardized stone tools. At least this held for Southeast Asia; what at first I could not explain was the existence of similar tools in northern China, where fossil horses, camels, and giraffids were present. Finally, I came upon the arresting fact that the distribution of naturally occurring bamboo coincided almost directly with the distribution of chopper-chopping tools. The only exceptions that may possibly be of real antiquity—certain handaxe collections from Kehe and Dingcun, in China, and Chonggok-Ni, in Korea—fall on the northernmost periphery of the distribution of bamboo and probably can be attributed to fluctuation of the boundary.

Today there are, by various estimates, some 1000 to 1200 species of bamboo. This giant grass is distributed worldwide, but more than 60 percent of the species are from Asia. Only 16 percent occur in Africa, and those on the Indian subcontinent—to an unknown extent the product of human importation and cultivation—are discontinuous in distribution and low in diversity. By far, the greatest diversity occurs in East and Southeast Asia.

Based on these observations, I hypothesized that the early Asians relied on bamboo for much of their technology. At first I envisioned bamboo simply as a kind of icon representing all nonlithic technology. I now think bamboo specifically must have been an extremely important resource. This was not, in my opinion, because appropriate rock was scarce but because bamboo tools would have been efficient, durable, and highly portable.

There are few useful tools that cannot be constructed from bamboo. Cooking and storage containers, knives, spears, heavy and light projectile points, elaborate traps, rope, fasteners, clothing, and even entire villages can be manufactured from bamboo. In addition to the stalks, which are a source of raw material for the manufacture of a variety of artifacts, the seeds and shoots of many species can be eaten. In historical times, bamboo has been to Asian civilization what the olive tree was to the Greeks. In the great cities of the Far East, bamboo is still the preferred choice for the scaffolding used in the construction of skyscrapers. This incomparable resource is also highly renewable. One can actually hear some varieties growing, at more than 30 centimetres per day.

Some may question how bamboo tools would have been sufficient for killing and processing large and medium-size animals. Lethal projectile and stabbing implements can in fact be fashioned from bamboo, but their importance may be exaggerated. Large game accounts for a relatively small proportion of the diet of many modern hunters and gatherers. Furthermore, animals are frequently trapped, collected, killed, and then thrown on a fire and cooked whole prior to using bare hands to dismember the roasted carcass. There are many ethnographic examples among forest peoples of this practice.

The only implements that cannot be manufactured from bamboo are axes or choppers suitable for the working of hard woods. More than a few archaeologists have suggested that the stone choppers and resultant "waste" flakes of Asia were created with the objective of using them to manufacture and maintain nonlithic tools. Bamboo can be easily worked with stone flakes resulting from the manufacture of choppers (many choppers may have been a throwaway component in the manufacture of flakes).

Source: Adapted from Pope, G.C. (1989). Bamboo and human evolution. *Natural History, 10,* 50–54.

and cleaver manufacture. Their sharp edges made them useful as is, but many were retouched to make points, scrapers, borers, and other sorts of tools. Diversification of tool kits is also indicated by the smaller numbers of handaxes in Northern and Eastern Europe, where people relied more on simple flaked choppers, a wide variety of unstandardized flakes, and supplementary tools of bone, antler, and wood. In Eastern Asia, by contrast, people developed a variety of choppers, scrapers, points, and **burins** (chisellike tools) different from those in the West. Besides direct percussion, anvil (striking the raw material against a stationary stone) and bipolar percussion (holding the raw material against an anvil, but striking it at the same time with a hammerstone) were used to make them. Although tens of thousands of stone tools have been found with *H. erectus* remains at Zhoukoudian, stone implements are not at all common at Southeast Asian sites of this age. Here, favoured materials likely were bamboo and other local woods, from which excellent knives, scrapers, and so on can be made.

The greater variety and sophistication of tools found in the Acheulean and contemporary traditions is indicative of *H. erectus/ergaster*'s increased ability to deal with the environment. The greater the range of tools used, the greater the range of natural resources capable of being exploited in less time, with less effort, and with a higher degree of efficiency. For example, handaxes may have been used to kill game and dig up roots; cleavers to butcher; scrapers to process hides for bedding and clothes; and flake tools to cut meat and shape wooden objects. As argued in the Original Study, the differences between tool kits from the Far East and West are likely indicative of adaptation to specific regions. The same

Burins. Stone tools with chisel-like edges used for working bone and antler.

Large cutting tools, like these from Qingling Mountains that divide North and South China, were made and used in substantial numbers for only a brief period. They are a comparable technology to Acheulean toolmaking, although not identical. The tools have all been collected from the modern surface so are difficult to date. Similar tools from the Baise Basin are associated with an unusual geological event that occurred around 800 000 years ago. At the time, a large meteorite struck the region, igniting fires that caused widespread deforestation. The tools appear to be an adaptation to this event; once the vegetation recovered, early humans may have reverted to the use of bamboo for tools. **COURTESY OF CHEN SHEN**

may be indicated by the differences between the tool kits of Northern and Eastern Europe on the one hand, and Southern and Western Europe on the other. One suggested explanation for this is that certain resources were scarcer in the latter region, which was more heavily forested than the former, and that this scarcity was a spur to increasing the efficiency of technology.[13]

The improved technological efficiency of *H. erectus/ergaster* is also evident in the selection of raw materials. Although Oldowan toolmakers frequently used coarse-grained stone such as basalt, their Acheulean counterparts generally used such stone only for their heavier implements, preferring flint or other stones with a high silica content for the smaller ones. During later Acheulean times, two techniques were developed that produced thinner, more elegant axes with straighter edges and more regular forms. The **baton method** of direct percussion manufacture involved using a bone or antler punch to strike the edge of the flint core. This method produced shallow flake scars, rather than the crushed edge that the hammerstone method produced on the earlier Acheulean handaxes. In later Acheulean times, the striking- platform method was also used to create sharper, thinner axes; the toolmakers would often strike off flakes to create a flat surface near the edge. These flat surfaces, or striking platforms, were set up along the edge of the tool perpendicular to its sides, so that the toolmaker could remove long, thin flakes stretching from the edge across each side of the tool.

Use of Fire

Another sign of *H. erectus/ergaster*'s developing technology is evidence of fires and cooking. Compelling evidence comes from the 700 000-year-old Kao Poh Nam rock shelter in Thailand, where a roughly circular arrangement of fire-cracked basalt cobbles was found in association with artifacts and animal bones. Because such rocks are not native to the rock shelter and are quite heavy, they probably had to have been carried in by hominins. The reason more readily available limestone rocks were not used for hearths is that, when burned, they produce a quicklime, which causes itchy and burning skin rashes.[14] The bones associated with

---

[13] Gamble, C. (1986). *The paleolithic settlement of Europe* (p. 310). Cambridge, U.K.: Cambridge University Press.

[14] Pope, G.C. (1989). Bamboo and human evolution. *Natural History, 10,* 48–57.

> **Baton method.** The technique of stone tool manufacture performed by striking the raw material with a bone or antler "baton" to remove flakes.

Experimentation on an elephant that died of natural causes demonstrates the effectiveness of Acheulean tools. Simple flint flakes easily slice through the thick hide, while handaxes sever large muscles. With such tools, two men working together can each butcher 45 kilograms of meat in an hour. **1985 DAVID L. BRILL**

the hearth (which was located near the rock shelter entrance, away from the deeper recesses favoured by denning animals) show clear evidence of cut marks from butchering, as well as burning.

H. erectus/ergaster may have been using fire even earlier, based on evidence from Swartkrans, in South Africa. Here, in deposits estimated to date between 1.3 and 1 million years ago, bones have been found that had been heated to temperatures far in excess of what one would expect as the result of natural fires. Natural grass fires in the region will not heat bones above 100°C, whereas coals in campfires reach temperatures from 482° to 648°C. Consequently, bones thrown into such fires reach temperatures higher than 100°C. Furthermore, the burned bones do not occur in deeper deposits, even though natural grass fires would have been no less common. South African palaeoanthropologists Andrew Sillen and C.K. Brain suggest that the purpose of the Swartkrans fires was protection from predators, as the bones were heated to such high temperatures that any meat on them would have been inedible.[15] Thus, fire may not have been "tamed" initially for cooking or to keep people warm; such uses may have come later.

Whatever the reason for *H. erectus/ergaster*'s original use of fire, it proved invaluable to populations that spread out of the tropics into regions with cooler climates. It not only provided warmth, but also may have assisted in the quest for food. In places like Europe and China, food would have been hard to come by in the long, cold winters, as edible plants were unavailable and the large herds of animals, whose mobility exceeded the potential of humans to maintain contact, dispersed and migrated. One solution could have been to search out the frozen carcasses of animals that had died naturally in the late fall and winter, using long wooden probes to locate them beneath the snow, wooden scoops to dig them out, and fire to thaw them so that they could be butchered and eaten.[16] Furthermore, such fire-assisted scavenging would have made available meat and hides of woolly mammoths, woolly rhinoceroses, and bison, which were probably beyond the ability of *H. erectus/ergaster* to kill, at least until late in the species' career.

Perhaps it was the use of fire to thaw carcasses that led to the idea of cooking food, thereby altering the forces of natural selection, which previously favoured individuals with heavy jaws and large, sharp teeth (food is tougher and needs more chewing when it is uncooked), thus favouring further reduction in tooth size along with supportive facial architecture. And it is a fact that, between early and late *H. erectus/ergaster*, chewing-related structures underwent reduction at a rate markedly above the fossil vertebrate average.[17] Cooking did more than soften food, though. Cooking detoxifies a number of otherwise poisonous plants; alters digestion-inhibiting substances so that important vitamins, minerals, and proteins can be absorbed while in the gut, rather than just passing through it unused; and makes complex carbohydrates like starch (high-energy foods) digestible. With cooking, the nutritional resources available to humans were substantially increased and made more secure. The partial predigestion of food by cooking also may have caused a reduction in the size of the digestive tract. Despite its overall similarity of form to those of apes, the digestive tract of modern humans is substantially smaller. The advantage of this gut reduction is that it draws less energy to operate, thereby competing less with the high energy requirements of a larger brain. (Although a mere 2 percent of body weight, the brain accounts for about 20 to 25 percent of energy consumed at resting metabolism in modern human adults.[18])

Like tools, then, fire gave people more control over their environment. Possibly, *H. erectus/ergaster* in Southeast Asia used fire, as have more recent populations living there, to keep areas in the forest clear for foot traffic. Certainly, the resistance to burning characteristic of many hardwood trees in this forest today indicates that fire has for a long time been important in their evolution. Fire may also have been used by *H. erectus/ergaster,* as it was by subsequent hominins, not only for protection from animals out in the open but also to frighten away cave-dwelling predators so that the fire users might live in the caves themselves; fire could then be used to provide warmth and light in these otherwise cold and dark habitations. Even more, it modified the natural succession of day and night, perhaps encouraging *H. erectus/ergaster* to stay up

---

[15] Sillen, A., & Brain, C.K. (1990). Old flame. *Natural History, 4,* 10.

[16] Gamble, p. 387.

[17] Wolpoff, M.H. (1993). Evolution in *Homo erectus*: The question of stasis. In R.L. Ciochon & J.G. Fleagle (Eds.), *The human evolution source book* (p. 396). Englewood Cliffs, NJ: Prentice-Hall.

[18] Leigh, S.R., & Park, P.B. (1998). Evolution of human growth prolongation. *American Journal of Physical Anthropology, 107,* 347.

GENDER PERSPECTIVES

Genderlithics?[1]

Until recently, archaeologists have generally failed to consider gender when analyzing lithic technology. Instead, most stone tool production studies have assumed that males exclusively made and used flaked stone tools. Sexual division of labour on decisions made by flintknappers has not been routinely considered. In response to this limited perspective, Margaret Conkey suggests that those who used tools were likely the ones who originally made them: "These females would be making their own scrapers for hide-working, their own needles, and their own harpoons for fishing. This implies that they had to work at least some blanks of antler and flint or quartzite for such implements."[2] For now, archaeologists do not have a clear technological means to assess who made or used stone tools, but the assumptions about stone tool manufacture and use need to be examined.

To assist in interpreting lithic technology from an engendered point of view, archaeologists have used contemporary assumptions about labour divisions, in particular, comparing and contrasting male and female activities. Critics of the "man-the-toolmaker" scenario point out that the term "stone tool" is usually restricted to standardized forms such as projectile points and knives. The majority of stone from a site is in the form of flakes, many of which show evidence in the form of scars and polishes that they were used. Thus, they are tools, but archaeologists tend to call such tools "utilized flakes," and this puts them outside the discussion of tools. Ethnographic evidence indicates females made significant use of such flakes. Archaeologists need to learn how tools actually functioned. Because an artifact looks like a knife does not mean that it was a knife. Evidence that it was used for cutting should be found on its edge. Without such knowledge, the roles of people at a site cannot be adequately understood. A study by Joan Gero on artifacts from Huaricoto, Peru, documents the transition of a site from a ceremonial centre to a village settlement. A corresponding change in the stone tool assemblage may be attributed to a shift in gender roles as the function of the site shifted, reflecting increased participation in the production and use of tools by women through time. Engendered archaeologists take into account the interdependence of male and female tool-using activities, in order to explain variation in the archaeological record that cannot be fully explained through tool function, choice of raw materials, or group mobility.

Researchers do not need to develop new excavation techniques, nor are new analytical techniques required; they merely need to become more sensitive to gender issues, and learn to ask questions from a gendered point of view. As such, this new direction uses lithic technology to find variation in gender relations and roles, and to explain processes of culture change and continuity.

---

[1] Gero, J.M. (1991). Genderlithics: Women's roles in stone tool production. In J.M. Gero & M.W. Conkey (Eds.), *Engendering archaeology: Women and prehistory* (pp. 163–193). Oxford: Basil Blackwell.

[2] Conkey, M.W. (1991). Contexts of action, contexts for power: Material culture and gender in the Magdalenian. In J.M. Gero & M.W. Conkey (Eds.), *Engendering archaeology: Women and prehistory* (p. 78). Oxford: Basil Blackwell.

Sources: Conkey, M.W. (1991). Contexts of action, contexts for power: Material culture and gender in the Magdalenian. In J.M. Gero & M.W. Conkey (Eds.), *Engendering archaeology: Women and prehistory* (pp. 57–92). Oxford: Basil Blackwell.

Sassaman, K.E. (1998). Lithic technology and the hunter-gatherer sexual division of labor. In K. Hays-Gilpin & D.S. Whitley (Eds.), *Reader in gender archaeology.* (pp. 159–172). New York: Routledge.

Sørensen, M.L.S. (2000). *Gender archaeology.* Malden, MA: Blackwell Publishers.

---

after dark to review the day's events and plan the next day's activities. That *H. erectus/ergaster* was capable of at least some planning is implied by the existence of populations in temperate climates, where the ability to anticipate the needs of the winter season by preparing in advance to protect against the cold would have been crucial to survival.[19]

---

[19] Goodenough, W.H. (1990). Evolution of the human capacity for beliefs. *American Anthropologist, 92,* 601.

At some point, H. erectus/ergaster *ceased relying on scavenging as a source of meat, in favour of hunting live animals. One of those animals was the elephant hunted at Ambrona, Spain, where the tusk remains.* **1985 DAVID L. BRILL**

OTHER ASPECTS OF *HOMO ERECTUS/ERGASTER'S* CULTURE

Presumably, control of fire was a key element in permitting *H. erectus/ergaster* to move into cooler regions like Europe and China. In cold winters, however, a fire is of little use without adequate shelter, and *H. erectus/ergaster's* increased sophistication in the construction of shelters is suggested by three circular foundations of bone and stone 2.74 to 3.96 metres across at a 350 000-year-old site in Bilzingsleben, Germany. These could mark the bases of shelters of poles and grass similar to those used in recent times by people like the Ju/'hoansi of Southern Africa. In the middle of one foundation was a long elephant tusk, possibly used as a centre post. Adjacent to these possible huts were hearths.

Keeping warm by the hearth is one thing, but keeping warm away from the hearth when procuring food or other necessities is another. Studies of modern humans indicate that they can remain reasonably comfortable down to 10°C with a minimum of clothing as long as they are active; below that temperature, the extremities cool to the point of pain;[20] thus the dispersal of early humans into regions where winter temperatures regularly went below 10°C, as they must have in China and Europe, was probably not possible without more in the way of clothing than hominins had hitherto worn. Unfortunately, clothing, like many other aspects

of behaviour, does not fossilize, so we have no direct evidence as to the kind of clothing worn by *H. erectus/ergaster*. We know only that it must have been more sophisticated than before.

That *H. erectus/ergaster* developed the ability to organize in order to hunt live animals is suggested by remains such as those from the 400 000-year-old sites of Ambrona and Torralba, in Spain. At the latter site, in what was an ancient swamp, were found the remains of several elephants, horses, red deer, wild oxen, and rhinoceroses. Their skeletons were dismembered, rather than in proper anatomical order, a fact that cannot be explained as a result of any natural geological process. Therefore, it is clear that these animals did not accidentally get mired in a swamp where they simply died and decayed.[21] In fact, the bones are closely associated with a variety of stone tools—a few thousand of them. Furthermore, there is very little evidence of carnivore activity, and none at all for the really big carnivores. Clearly, hominins were involved—not just in butchering the animals but evidently in killing them as well. It appears that the animals were actually driven into the

[20] Whiting, J.W.M., Sodergem, J.A., & Stigler, S.M. (1982). Winter temperature as a constraint to the migration of pre-industrial peoples. *American Anthropologist, 84,* 289.

[21] Freeman, L.G. (1992). *Ambrona and Torralba: New evidence and interpretation.* Paper presented at the 91st Annual Meeting, American Anthropological Association, San Francisco.

swamp so that they could be easily dispatched. The remains of charcoal and carbon, widely but thinly scattered in the vicinity, raises the possibility that grass fires were used to drive the animals into the swamp. In any event, this provides evidence of more than opportunistic scavenging; this implies that *H. erectus/ergaster* was not only able to hunt, but also possessed considerable organizational and communicative skills.

Additional evidence for hunting 400 000 years ago was discovered accidentally in 1995 in the course of strip mining at Schöningen in northern Germany. Here were found five well-made and finely balanced spears made entirely of wood, the longest one measuring more than 2 metres in length. These are sophisticated weapons made by hunters who clearly knew what they were doing. The effectiveness of their weapons is attested to by the butchered bones of more than a dozen horses nearby.

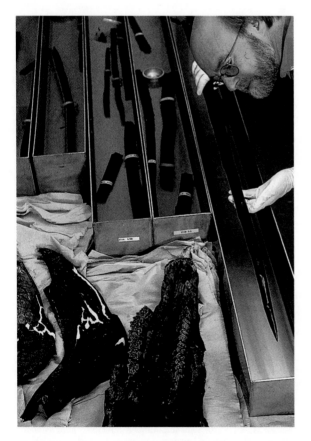

Shown here are wooden spears made by H. erectus/ergaster *400 000 years ago. Found in a bog in northern Germany, they are anything but crude, testifying to the sophisticated toolmaking and hunting skills developed by then.* **KENNETH GARRETT/NGS IMAGE COLLECTION**

At Bilzingsleben, Germany, archaeologists have uncovered an arrangement of stones and bones suggesting pavement of an area, perhaps for group rituals. **KENNETH GARRETT/NGS IMAGE COLLECTION**

There is no reason to suppose that *H. erectus/ergaster* became an accomplished hunter all at once. Presumably, the most ancient members of this species, like *H. habilis* before them, got the bulk of their meat through scavenging. As their cultural capabilities increased, however, they could have devised ways of doing their own killing, rather than waiting for animals to die or be killed by other predators. As they became more proficient predators over time, they would have been able to count on a more reliable supply of meat.

Yet other evidence of *H. erectus/ergaster*'s capabilities comes from the island of Flores, in Indonesia. This island lies east of a deepwater strait that has acted as a barrier to the passage of animals to and from Southeast Asia. To get to Flores, even at times of lowered sea levels, required crossing open water: at minimum 25 kilometres from Bali to Sumbawa, with a further 19 kilometres to Flores. That early humans did just this is indicated by the presence of

This 300 000-year-old ox rib from a site in France is one of several from the Lower Palaeolithic that exhibit engraved designs. **ALEXANDER MARSHACK**

800 000-year-old stone tools.[22] Precisely how they navigated across the deep, fast-moving water is not known, but at the least it required some sort of substantial raft.

Evidence for a developing symbolic life is suggested by the increased standardization and refinement of Acheulean handaxes over time. Moreover, at several sites in Europe deliberately marked objects of stone, bone, and ivory have been found in Acheulean contexts (see p. 229). These include several objects from Bilzingsleben, Germany; among them an elephant bone with a series of regular lines that appear to have been deliberately engraved. Though a far cry from the later Palaeolithic cave art of France and Spain, these are among the earliest Palaeolithic artifacts that have no obvious utility or model in the natural world. Such apparently symbolic artifacts became more common in later phases of the Palaeolithic, as more modern forms of the genus *Homo* appeared on the scene. Similarly, the world's oldest known rock carvings are associated with Acheulean tools in a cave in India.[23] Alexander Marshack argues that the use of such symbolic images requires some sort of spoken language, not only to assign meaning to the images but also to maintain the tradition they seem to represent.[24] That such a symbolic tradition did exist is suggested by similar motifs on later Palaeolithic artifacts. It is also in late Acheulean contexts on three continents that we have our earliest evidence for the use of red ochre, a pigment that more modern forms of *Homo* employed to colour symbolic as well as utilitarian artifacts, to stain the bodies

of the dead, to paint the bodies of the living, and (ultimately) to make notations and paint pictures.

THE QUESTION OF LANGUAGE

We do not, of course, know anything definitive about *H. erectus/ergaster*'s linguistic abilities, but the evidence for a developing symbolic life, as well as the need to plan for seasonal changes and to coordinate hunting activities (and even to cross bodies of open water as many scholars believe happened), implies improving linguistic competence. In fact, the vocal tract and brain of *H. erectus/ergaster* are intermediate between those of *H. sapiens* on the one hand and earlier *Australopithecus* on the other. Another clue is the size of the **hypoglossal canal**, the opening in the skull through which the nerve that controls tongue movements, so important for spoken language, passes from the skull. In modern humans this is twice the size that it is in any ape. It is in the skulls of late *H. erectus/ergaster*, about

[22] Gibbons, A. (1998). Ancient island tools suggest *Homo erectus* was a seafarer. *Science, 279,* 1635.

[23] Bednarik, R.G. (1995). Concept-mediated marking in the lower Paleolithic. *Current Anthropology, 36,* 610–611.

[24] Marshack, A. (1976). Some implications of the paleolithic symbolic evidence for the origin of language. *Current Anthropology, 17,* 280.

Hypoglossal canal. The opening in the skull through which the tongue-controlling hypoglossal nerve passes.

500 000 years ago, that we first see this characteristic in fossil remains.[25] Possibly, a changeover from gestural to spoken language was a driving force in these evolutionary changes. It also may have played a role in reduction of tooth and jaw size, thereby facilitating the ability to articulate speech sounds.

Certainly, the advantages of a spoken language over a gestural one seem to be obvious; not only does one *not* have to stop whatever one is doing with one's hands to "talk" (useful to a species increasingly dependent on tool use), but also it is possible to talk in the dark, past opaque objects, or among people whose gaze is concentrated on something else (potential prey, for example).

With *H. erectus/ergaster,* then, we find a clearer manifestation of the interplay among cultural, physical, and environmental factors than ever before. However slowly, social organization, technology, and communication developed in tandem with an increase in brain size and complexity. In fact, the cranial capacity of late *H. erectus/ergaster* is 31 percent greater than the mean for early *H. erectus/ergaster,* a rate of increase more rapid than the average fossil vertebrate rate.[26] As a consequence of increased brain size and complexity, *H. erectus/ergaster's* resource base was enlarged significantly; the supply of meat could be increased by hunting as well as by scavenging, and the supply of plant foods was increased as cooking allowed the consumption of vegetables that otherwise are toxic or indigestible. This, along with an increased ability to modify the environment in advantageous ways—for example, by using fire to provide warmth—undoubtedly contributed to a population increase and territorial expansion. In humans, as in other mammals, any kind of adaptation that enhances reproductive success causes population growth. This growth causes fringe populations to spill over into neighbouring regions previously uninhabited by the species.

Out of Africa: More Questions than Answers

The foregoing discussion is the basis for the well-accepted view that *H. erectus/ergaster* was able to move into areas that had never been inhabited by hominins before; first into the warm, southern regions of Asia, and ultimately into the cooler regions of China and Europe. This was possible because grasslands dominated Asia and grasslands provided at least a narrow range of plant food for early humans. Meat, however, would have been readily available.

The new commitment to a carnivorous diet would have provided the means to survive outside Africa.[27] In turn, the larger brains that were being fed by this diet also enabled the success of cultural innovations such as fire making, clothing, and even language that would help early humans succeed at more northern latitudes such as in Europe and northern Asia. However, the earliest *Homo* fossils outside Africa contradict this long-standing view. The Dmanisi *Homo* of 1.7 million years ago is evidence that a human ancestor with a considerably smaller brain than that of *H. erectus/ergaster* and with inconclusive links to *H. erectus/ergaster* was living successfully outside Africa. The Dmansi fossils are associated with the primitive Oldowan Tradition rather than the more developed Acheulean.

Hominin fossils are rare because their population was relatively low. Their stone tools, however, are far more common. Without hominin fossils from early stone tool sites in China for example, the assumption tends to be that they were made by *H. erectus*. Robin Dennell and Wil Roebroeks wonder why, if small-brained hominins whose ancestry is somewhat problematic were outside Africa by 1.7 million years ago, why not by 2.6 million years ago or even earlier?[28] Dennell and Roebroeks also remind us that *H. habilis* could easily be classified as *Australopithecus habilis* and that *Australopithecus* was already adapted to grasslands in Africa, so available habitat did not have to limit its range. The discovery of a stone tool assemblage dating between 1.9 and 2 million years ago in Pakistan suggests that hominins were in South Asia before *H. erectus/ergaster.*[29] Furthermore, an assemblage of stone tools including cores and two flakes that could be refitted has been recovered from the Goudi site in the Nihewan Basin in central China by a team that includes an archaeologist from the Royal Ontario Museum. The assemblage is from layers dated to 1.66 million years ago.[30] Considerable research still needs to be done before we have a good understanding of the evolution and spread of our early ancestors.

[25] Cartmill, M. (1998). The gift of gab. *Discover, 19* (11), 64.

[26] Wolpoff, pp. 392, 396.

[27] Dennell, R., and Roebroeks, W. (2005). An Asian perspective on early human dispersal from Africa. *Nature,* 438, 1099–1104.

[28] Dennell, R., Rendell, H., & Hallwood, E. (1988). Early toolmaking in Asia: Two-million-year-old artefacts in Pakistan. *Antiquity,* 62, 98–106.

[29] Ibid.

[30] Gao, X., Qi, W., Shen, C., & Keates, S. (2005). New light on the earliest hominid occupation on East Asia. *Current Anthropology,* 46, Supplement, S115–S120.

CHAPTER SUMMARY

The remains of *H. erectus/ergaster* have been found at several sites in Africa, Europe, China, and Java. Some anthropologists prefer to reserve the *H. erectus* name for the East Asian fossils and call the African specimens *H. ergaster*. The earliest *H. erectus* is 1.9 million years old. By 200 000 years ago human fossils exhibit a mosaic of features characteristic of both *H. erectus/ergaster* and *H. sapiens*. *H. erectus/ergaster* appears to have evolved, rather abruptly, from *H. habilis*. From the neck down, the body of *H. erectus/ergaster* was essentially modern in appearance, and much larger than in earlier hominins. The brain, although small by modern standards, was larger than that of *H. habilis*. The skull was generally low, with maximum breadth near its base, and massive brow ridges. Powerful teeth and jaws added to a generally rugged appearance.

With *H. erectus/ergaster* we find a greater interaction among cultural, physical, and environmental factors than ever before. Social organization and improved technology developed along with an increase in brain size. The Oldowan chopper evolved into the Acheulean handaxe. These tools, the earliest of which are about 1.6 million years old, are teardrop-shaped, with a pointed end and sharp cutting edges. They were remarkably standardized in form over large areas. During Acheulean times, tool cultures began to diversify. Along with handaxes, tool kits included cleavers, picks, scrapers, and flakes. Further signs of *H. erectus/ergaster*'s developing technology were the selection of different stone for different tools and the use of fires for protection, warmth, and light; thawing frozen carcasses; and cooking. Cooking is a significant adaptation, in this case a cultural one, that accommodated the reduction of certain physical adaptations such as large, heavy jaws and teeth, because cooked food is easier to chew. Because it detoxifies various substances in plants, cooking also increased the food resources available and allowed reduction in the size of the digestive tract. Reduced jaw and tooth size may also correlate with a change from a gestural to spoken language. The complex tongue movements associated with speech are also indicated by features of the skull, and aspects of *H. erectus/ergaster*'s behaviour imply improved communicative skills.

During later Acheulean times, *H. erectus/ergaster* used the baton and striking-platform methods to make thinner axes with straighter, sharper cutting edges. From Germany comes evidence of the building of huts and the making of nonutilitarian artifacts; from Spain comes evidence of cooperative efforts to kill large amounts of game.

H. erectus/ergaster's improved organizational, technological, and communicative abilities led to more effective hunting and a greater ability to modify the environment in advantageous ways. As a result, the populations of these early hominins increased and they expanded into new geographic areas.

QUESTIONS FOR CRITICAL THOUGHT

1. To what extent was *H. erectus/ergaster* like us in appearance and behaviour?

2. Discuss the impact classification of a fossil may have on its interpretation and how expectations of an investigator might impact how a fossil is classified.

3. If the success of a species is signalled by its longevity in the fossil record and its spatial distribution, how successful was *H. erectus* in your view?

INTERNET RESOURCES

Early Homo in Europe and China

www.ucm.es/info/paleo/ata/english/index.htm
Take a trip to the Sierra de Atapuerca and learn about the earliest hominins of Europe. See virtual fossils, and learn about the research team, their excavation techniques, and the place of these recently discovered specimens in human evolutionary history.

www.unesco.org/ext/field/beijing/whc/pkm-site.htm
The Peking Man World Heritage Site at Zhoukoudian presents the history, fossils, and artifacts from this site known by locals as Dragon Bone Hill. Review the evidence for the use of fire and hunting and gathering by *H. erectus*.

H. erectus

http://anthro.palomar.edu/homo/homo_2.htm
An excellent site that examines *H. erectus*'s place in hominin evolution and presents an analysis of *H. erectus*'s anatomy. The site also provides a brief history of the palaeoanthropological search for *H. erectus*.

www.omniology.com/Jackalopian-Homo-Erectus
.html
Features vivid images of *H. erectus* fossils.

www.archaeology.org/9703/newsbriefs/h.erectus
.html
Offers a different perspective on *H. erectus*, suggesting that this hominin lived as recently as 53 000 to 27 000 years ago.

www.mnh.si.edu/anthro/humanorigins/ha/erec.html
A comprehensive site, featuring extensive information and photos of fossil remains, although unfortunately the photos are difficult to distinguish against a black background.

www.chineseprehistory.org
The Center for the Study of Chinese Prehistory discusses the fossil evidence for human evolution in China. Includes several related links.

http://news.bbc.co.uk/2/hi/science/nature/
745080.stm
Introduces the remains of what might be the earliest human ancestors to migrate from Africa into Europe.

Human Evolution

www.factmonster.com/ce6.society. A0824496.html
An introduction to human evolution, with links to many sites that provide basic information. Includes a section on *H. erectus* and an examination of the evolution of culture.

Gender and Tool Use

http://williamcalvin.com/bk2/bk2ch3.htm

www.napa.ufl.edu/2003news/womentoolmakers.htm
These sites add additional perspectives on females and stone tool manufacturing.

SUGGESTED READINGS

For a list of suggested readings, visit the textbook's website at www.humanevolution2.nelson.com.

Homo Heidelbergensis, Neandertals, and the Middle Palaeolithic

A significant challenge for palaeoanthropologists and archaeologists studying the Middle Palaeolithic (200 000 to 40 000 years ago) is to determine the relationship between biological change and cultural change in fossil groups of this time period. Though possessing modern-sized brains, the skulls of Neandertals, and their immediate predecessors, retain a number of the ancestral features as well as some specialized features typically not seen in modern *Homo sapiens.* Do these features in the shape of the skull indicate biological differences in brain structure sufficient to affect the cultural capabilities of these fossil groups?

© GIANNI DAGLI ORTI/CORBIS

CHAPTER PREVIEW

1. Who Were the Descendents of *Homo erectus/ergaster*?

Fossils from the Middle Pleistocene with essentially modern-sized brains in skulls that still retain a number of features similar to those found in *H. erectus/ergaster* and *H. antecessor* are increasingly being classified as *H. heidelbergensis*. *H. heidelbergensis* appears between as much as 800 000 and 130 000 years ago. The Neandertals, who lived in Europe and Western Asia between about 125 000 and 29 000 years ago appear to be descendents of *H. heidelbergensis*. Other populations somewhat like them lived in Africa, China, and Southeast Asia.

2. What Was the Culture of *Homo heidelbergensis* and Neandertals Like?

By 125 000 years ago, the human brain had reached its modern size, and by then human culture everywhere had become rich and varied. People not only made a wide variety of tools for special purposes, but also created objects for purely symbolic purposes, engaged in ceremonial activities, and cared for the old and disabled.

3. What Became of the Neandertals?

Although there is still some debate, the most likely explanation is that modern *H. sapiens* replaced Neandertals who became extinct not long after *H. sapiens* moved into their territory. Anatomically modern *H. sapiens* had evolved in Africa by 190 000 years ago. Experts debate whether modern humans and Neandertals interbred. Whether they became extinct by being outcompeted by modern humans or through some other mechanism such as climate change is not yet known.

CHAPTER OUTLINE

The Appearance of *Homo heidelbergensis* and the Neandertals

The Culture of Neandertal and its Contemporaries

Modern Human Origins

The anthropologist attempting to piece together the innumerable parts of the puzzle of human evolution must be as good a detective as a scholar, for the available evidence is often scant, enigmatic, or full of misleading clues. The quest for the origin of modern humans from more ancient representatives of the genus *Homo* has elements of a detective story, for it contains a number of mysteries concerning the emergence of humanity, none of which has been completely resolved to this day. The mysteries involve the appearance of the first fully sapient humans, the identity of the Neandertals, and the relationship of both to more modern forms.

ARCHAIC *HOMO SAPIENS* OR OTHER SPECIES?

Modern humans belong to the species *H. sapiens*. Our species is not as robust as its predecessors and has specific cranial architecture described in more detail in Chapter 10. During the Middle Pleistocene, (about 800 000 to 120 000 years ago) were hominins that differ from *H. erectus/ergaster* yet did not have all the traits of modern humans. Like *H. erectus/ergaster*, the face and brow ridges were large, and the cranial vault was relatively thick. The brain size was larger, the braincase was rounded, and the back of the cranium was more rounded. Some anthropologists lump these fossils into a group of archaic *H. sapiens* because of their apparent

similarity to modern humans yet with differences that appear to be at the subspecies level. Others, who are increasingly becoming the majority, believe that the variations represent different species. For them, the earlier Middle Pleistocene fossils, particularly those from Europe and Africa, are assigned to *H. heidelbergensis*.[1] This hominin is the best candidate to be the common ancestor to both the Neandertals (*H. neanderthalensis*) and *H. sapiens*. To the archaic *H. sapiens* proponents, the Neandertals are a supspecies of modern human, *H. sapiens neanderthalensis*. Preceding it was a grab bag of variants of *H. sapiens*. In this chapter, because of new genetic information and the view that archaic *H. sapiens* is a category that does not account appropriately for variation among the fossils, we take the perspective that the Middle Pleistocene fossils and the Neandertals are not *H. sapiens*. Nevertheless, the taxonomy is still a work in progress.

At various sites in Europe and Africa, a number of hominin fossils—primarily skulls, jaws, and jaw fragments—have been found that seem to date roughly between 800 000 and 130 000 years ago (Figure 9.1). Most consist of parts of one or a very few individuals, the one exception consisting of a large number of bones and teeth from the Sierra de Atapuerca in northern Spain, not far from the Gran Dolina cave where

---

[1] Rightmire G.P. (1998). Human evolution in the Middle Pleistocene. *Evolutionary Anthropology: Issues, News, and Reviews, 6*, 218–227.

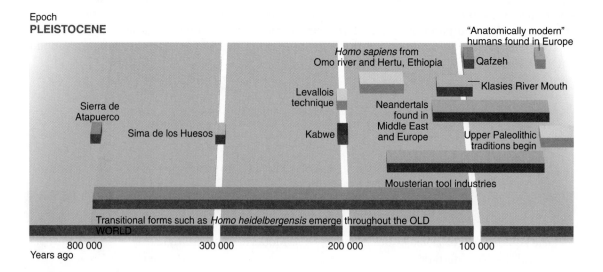

FIGURE 9.1

Emergence of *H. sapiens*.

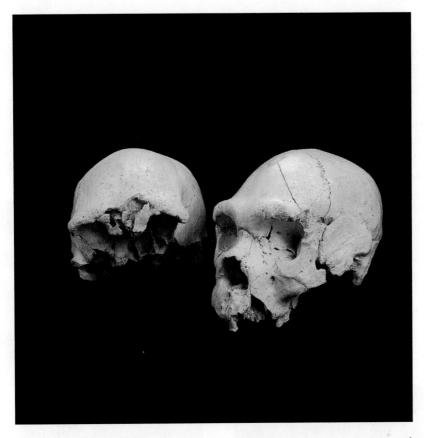

These two skulls are from the 300 000-year-old site of Sima de los Huesos in Spain and represent H. heidelbergenis, *a species representing the transition from* H. erectus/ergaster *to Neandertals in Europe.* **JAVIER TRUEBA/MADRID SCIENTIFIC FILMS**

H. antecessor was found, dating to about 800 000 years ago. In fact, *H. antecessor* may be an extremely early form of *H. heidelbergensis*. Sometime between 325 000 and 205 000 years ago,[2] the remains of at least 32 individuals of both sexes, juveniles as well as adults, were deliberately dumped (after their skulls were defleshed as preparation for burial) by their contemporaries into a deep cave shaft known today as Sima de los Huesos ("Pit of the Bones"). This makes it the best population sample from this time period anywhere in the world. As expected of any population, this one displays a significant degree of variation; cranial capacity ranges, for example, from 1125 to 1390 cubic centimetres, overlapping the upper end of the range for *H. erectus/ergaster* and the lower end of the range for *H. sapiens*. Overall, the bones display a mix of features, some typical of *erectus/ergaster,* others of *sapiens,* including some incipient Neandertal characteristics consistent with *H. heidelbergensis*. Of interest is the fact that, varied as it

is, the sample shows no more sexual dimorphism than displayed by modern humans.[3]

Other remains from Africa and Europe dating between 400 000 and 200 000 years ago have sometimes been classified as *H. sapiens*—for example, skulls from Ndutu in Tanzania, Swanscombe in England, and Steinheim in Germany—and sometimes as *H. erectus/ergaster,* as in the case of skulls from several African sites as well as Arago, France; Bilzingsleben, Germany; and Petralona, Greece. Yet all have cranial capacities that fit within the range exhibited by the Sima de los Huesos skulls, and all display the same

[2] Parés, J.M., Perez-Gonzalez, A., Weil, A.B., & Arsuaga, J.L. (2000). On the age of hominid fossils at the Sima de los Huesos, Sierra de Atapuerca, Spain: Paleomagnetic evidence. *American Journal of Physical Anthropology, 111,* 451–461.

[3] Lorenzo, C., Carretero, J.M., Arsuaga, J.L., Gracia, A., & Martinez, I. (1998). Intrapopulational body size variation and cranial capacity variation in middle Pleistocene humans: The Sima de los Huesos sample (Sierra de Atapuerca, Spain). *American Journal of Physical Anthropology, 106,* 30.

mosaic of features found in *H. heidelbergensis.* Compared to us, for instance, the Swanscombe and Steinheim skulls are large and robust, with their maximum breadth lower on the skull, and they had more prominent brow ridges, larger faces, and bigger teeth. Conversely, a skull from Salé in Morocco, which had a rather small brain for *H. sapiens* (930–960 cubic centimetres), looks surprisingly modern from the back. Finally, various jaws from Morocco and France seem to combine features of *H. erectus/ergaster* with those of the European Neandertals.

A similar situation exists in East Asia, where skulls from Dali and Jinniushan in China exhibit the same mix of characteristics. To call some of these early humans late *H. erectus* or early *H. sapiens* serves no useful purpose and merely obscures their apparently transitional status. Whether they are *H. heidelbergensis* has not been determined but it is a strong possibility. If they are not, then they are an as-yet-unnamed species of hominin. Despite their retention of a number of features of *H. erectus,* their brain size shows a clear increase over that of even late representatives of that species (see Figure 8.3).

This skull from Ethiopia is one of several from Africa indicative of a transition from H. erectus/ergaster *to* H. sapiens.

1985 DAVID L. BRILL

Levalloisian Technique

With the appearance of hominins, particularly *H. heidelbergensis,* transitional between *H. erectus/ergaster* and *H. sapiens,* the pace of culture change began to accelerate. Although handaxes and other Acheulean tools were still made, a new method of flake manufacture was invented. This is the **Levalloisian technique,** and flake tools produced by this technique have been found widely in Africa, Europe, the Middle East, and

The practice of hafting, the fastening of small stone bifaces and flakes to handles of wood, was a major technological advance appearing in the archaeological record at about the same time as the invention of the Levalloisian technique. © PHOTODISC/GETTY IMAGES

Levalloisian technique. Tool-making technique by which three or four long triangular flakes were detached from a specially prepared core. Developed by humans transitional from *H. erectus* to *H. sapiens.*

China. In the latter region, the technique could represent a case of independent invention, because Eastern Asia is somewhat distinct culturally from the West. Or it could represent the spread of ideas from one part of the inhabited world to another. In the Levalloisian technique, the core was shaped by removal of small flakes over its surface, following which a striking platform was set up by a crosswise blow at one end of the core of stone (Figure 9.2). Then the platform was struck, removing three or four long flakes, whose size and shape had been predetermined by the preceding preparation. What was left, besides small waste flakes, was a nodule that looked like a tortoise shell. This method produced a longer edge for the same amount of flint than the previous ones. The edges were sharper and could be produced in less time.

At about the same time, another technological breakthrough occurred. This was the invention of hafting—the affixing of small stone bifaces and flakes in handles of wood—to make improved spears and knives. Unlike the older handheld tools made simply by reduction (flaking of stone or working of wood), these new composite tools involved three components: assembly of a handle or shaft, a stone insert, and binding materials. The acquisition and modification of each component involved planned sequences of actions that could be performed at different times and places.

With this new technology, regional stylistic and technological variants are clearly evident, suggesting emergence of more distinct cultural traditions and culture areas. At the same time, the proportion of raw materials procured from faraway sources increases; whereas sources of stone for Acheulean tools were rarely more than 20 kilometres away, Levalloisian tools are found up to 300 kilometres from the sources of their stone.[4]

Another development, in Africa, was the increasing use of yellow and red pigments of iron oxide, becoming especially common by 130 000 years ago.[5] This may signal a rise in ritual activity, as may the deliberate deposition of the human remains in the Sima de los Heusos, already noted. One possibility is that this involved ritual activity that presaged burial of the dead, a practice that became common 100 000 years ago. Alternatively, the presence of other animal bones in the same pit with humans raises the possibility that all were eaten by the people who then simply dumped the bones.

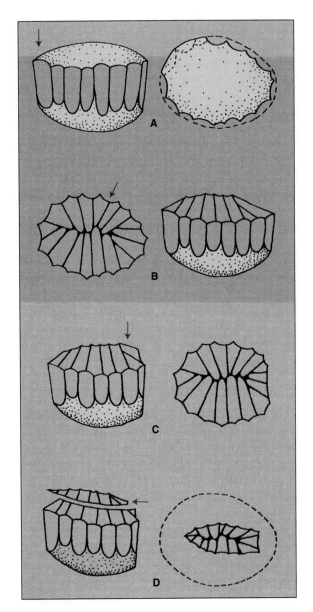

FIGURE 9.2

These drawings show top and side views of the steps in the Levalloisian technique. Drawing A shows the preparatory flaking of the stone core; B, the same of the top surface; C, the striking platform; and D, the final step of detaching a flake of a size and shape predetermined by the preceding steps.

[4] Ambrose, S.H. (2001). Paleolithic technology and human evolution. *Science*, 291, 1752.

[5] Barham, L.S. (1998). Possible early pigment use in south-central Africa. *Current Anthropology*, 39, 703–710.

The Neandertals

Of all the remains of Middle Pleistocene *Homo*, none have received more attention than a group from Europe. These remains, dating from at least 125 000 to 29 000 years ago are so distinctive that they are classified as a separate species, *H. Neanderthalensis*. Because many of the **Neandertal** traits are found in *H. heidelbergensis*, their first appearance is may be as early as 800 000 years ago if we consider that *H. antecessor* may be an early *H. heidelbergensis*. Recent DNA sequencing of Neandertal remains has used a novel technique to analyze a substantial part of this hominin's genome.[6] The recent study confirms earlier, less comprehensive DNA studies that showed that Neandertals are more closely related to one another than to modern humans. These studies relied on the analysis of mitochondrial DNA (mtDNA). Unlike nuclear DNA (in the cell nucleus), mitochondrial DNA is located elsewhere in the cell, in compartments that produce the energy needed to keep cells alive. Because sperm does not contribute mitochondrial DNA to the fertilized egg, it is inherited only from one's mother and is not "rescrambled" with each succeeding generation. Therefore, it should be altered only by mutation. Studies using mitochondrial DNA indicate that maternal DNA from Neandertals is virtually absent in modern humans.

The new study sequenced both Neandertal mtDNA and nuclear DNA from a bone AMS radiocarbon dated to about 38 000 years ago.[7] Although scientists have a long way to go to analyze the complete Neandertal genome, the feat now seems possible and could be completed by late 2008. So far it seems (there are many ways error can creep into DNA analysis) that Neandertals and modern humans began to diverge around 500 000 years ago.

The first publicized discovery of Neandertals came in 1856, three years before publication of Darwin's *On the Origin of Species*. In that year, the skeletal remains of a man were found in the Neander Valley—Neandertal in German—near Dusseldorf, Germany. Although the discovery was of considerable interest, experts were generally at a loss as to what to make of it. Examination of the fossil skull, a few ribs, and some limb bones revealed that the individual was a human being, but it did not look "normal." Some people believed the bones were those of a sickly and deformed contemporary. Others thought the skeleton belonged to a soldier who had succumbed to "water on the brain" during the Napoleonic Wars. One prominent anatomist thought the remains were those of an "idiot" suffering from malnutrition, whose violent temper had gotten him into many scrapes, flattening his forehead and making his brow ridges bumpy.

The idea that Neandertals, as remains like this came to be called, were somehow deformed or aberrant was given impetus by an analysis of a skeleton found in 1908 near La Chapelle-Aux-Saints in France. The analysis mistakenly concluded that the specimen's brain was apelike and that it walked like an ape. Although a team of North American investigators subsequently proved that this French Neandertal specimen was that of an elderly *H. sapiens* who had suffered from malnutrition, severe arthritis, and other deformities, the apelike image has persisted. To many nonanthropologists, Neandertal has become the quintessential "caveman," portrayed by imaginative cartoonists as a slant-headed, stooped, dim-witted individual clad in animal skins and carrying a big club as he plods across the prehistoric landscape, perhaps dragging behind him an unwilling female or a dead leopard. The stereotype has been perpetuated in many a work of fiction, one of the more recent being John Darnton's *Neandertal*, published in 1997. So it is that many people still think of Neandertals as brutish and incapable of spoken language, abstract or innovative thinking, or even thinking ahead.

Despite this popular stereotype, evidence was forthcoming that Neandertals were nowhere near as brutish and apelike as originally portrayed, and some scholars began to see them as no more than "less finished" versions of the anatomically modern populations that held exclusive sway in Europe and the Middle East after 30 000 years ago. For example, C. Loring Brace of the University of Michigan observes that such "classic" Neandertal features as a sloping forehead, a bunlike back of the skull, and a distinctively small, inward-sloping mastoid process (behind the ear) are commonly present in medieval skulls

---

[6] Green, R.E., Krause, J., Ptak, S.E., Briggs, A.W., Ronan, M.T., Simons, J.F., Du, L., Egholm, M., Rothberg, J.M., Paunovic, M., and others. (2006). Analysis of one million base pairs of Neanderthal DNA. *Nature, 444*, 330–336.

[7] Ibid.

Neandertals. Lived in Europe and Western Asia, from about 125 000 years ago to about 29 000 years ago.

from Denmark and Norway.[8] Nevertheless, Neandertals are somewhat distinctive, when compared to more recent populations. Although they held modern-sized brains (average cranial capacity 1400 cubic centimetres, versus 1300 cubic centimetres for modern *H. sapiens*), Neandertal skulls are notable in the projection of their noses and teeth, and the swollen appearance of the midfacial region. This is due at least in part to the large size of their front teeth, which were heavily used for tasks other than chewing. In many individuals, front teeth were worn down to the stubs of their roots by 35 to 40 years of age. The large noses, for their part, probably were necessary to warm frigid air to prevent damage to the lungs and brain, and to moisten and clean the dry, dusty air of the glacial climate. The eye sockets were also positioned well forward, with prominent brow ridges above them.

---

[8] Ferrie, H. (1997). An interview with C. Loring Brace. *Current Anthropology, 38,* 861.

Perceptions about the capabilities of fossil groups are expressed in visual representations of fleshed-out versions of fossil remains. The Neandertal diorama from the 1920s exhibit in the Field Museum of Chicago contains a message about their evolutionary distance from us, while positive cultural attributes are given to "anatomically modern" specimens.

© BETTMANN/CORBIS (LEFT), © THE FIELD MUSEUM, JOHN WEINSTEIN (RIGHT)

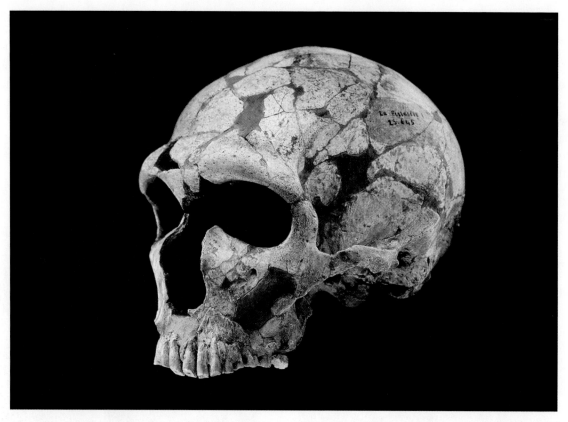

This Neandertal, from a site in France, shows the marked bony ridge above the eyes, receding forehead, and heavy wear on the front teeth that are common in these Europeans. **1985 DAVID L. BRILL**

At the back of the skull, a bunlike bony mass provided for attachment of powerful neck muscles, needed to counteract the weight of a heavy face.

Both sexes were extraordinarily muscular, with extremely robust and dense limb bones. Relative to body mass, the limbs were relatively short (as they are in modern humans native to especially cold climates). Details of the shoulder blades indicate the importance of overarm and downward thrusting movements; their arms were exceptionally powerful, and pronounced attachments on their hand bones attest to a remarkably strong grip. It has been suggested that a healthy Neandertal could lift an average football linebacker over his head and throw him through the goalposts.[9] Their massive foot and leg bones (their shin bones, for example, were twice as strong as those of any recent human population) suggest a high level of endurance; evidently, Neandertals spent long hours walking and scrambling about. Because brain size is related to overall body mass as well as intelligence, the large average size of the Neandertal brain (compared to that of modern humans) is accounted for by their heavy, robust bodies.

The Neandertal pelvis, too, shows differences from that of anatomically modern humans, but these do not support suggestions that obstetric requirements were different for Neandertals than they are for modern humans. Dimensions of the pelvic outlet are fully consistent with those of a modern woman of the same size.[10] Differences in pelvic shape are easily accounted

---

[9] Shreeve, J. (1995). *The Neandertal enigma: Solving the mystery of modern human origins* (p. 5). New York: William Morrow.

[10] Wolpoff, M.H. (1999). Review of Neandertals and modern humans in western Asia. *American Journal of Physical Anthropology, 109,* 418.

As this face-off between palaeoanthropologist Milford Wolpoff and his reconstruction of a Neandertal shows, the latter may not have differed all that much from modern humans of European descent. **PAUL JARONSKI, UM PHOTO SERVICES**

for as a consequence of posture-related biomechanics and deviation in modern humans from a shape characteristic of earlier hominins.

African, Chinese, and Javanese Populations

Other parts of the world were inhabited by variants of archaic *H. sapiens* lacking the extreme mid-facial projection and massive muscle attachments on the back of the skull characteristic of the Neandertals. A number of skulls have been found in Java, Africa, and China that date to roughly the same time period.

Among them are 11 skulls that were found in the 1930s near the Solo river at Ngandong, Java. Though their dating was not precisely known, they were generally considered to be Southeast Asian equivalents of the Neandertals

with modern-sized brains (from 1013 to 1252 cubic centimetres), while on the exterior they retained features of earlier Javanese *H. erectus*. With time, opinion on their dating changed, with scholars regarding them as considerably earlier than the Neandertals. This opinion focused attention on their resemblance to *erectus*, so that when their dating was recently revised (to sometime between 53 000 and 27 000 years ago) some concluded that this proved a late survival of *erectus* in Asia, contemporary with *H. sapiens* elsewhere. But the skulls remain what they always were: representatives of archaic *sapiens*, with modern brains in otherwise ancient-looking skulls.

Fossils from various parts of Africa, the most famous being a 200 000-year-old skull from Kabwe in Zambia, show a similar combination of ancient and modern traits. Finally, equivalent remains have been found at several localities in China.

African and Asian contemporaries of the Neandertals differ from the Neandertals primarily in their lack of mid-facial projection and massive muscle attachments on the back of the skull. Elsewhere, the so-called archaics look like robust versions of the early modern populations that lived in the same regions or, if one looks backward, somewhat less primitive versions of the *H. erectus/ergaster* populations that preceded them. All had fully modern-sized brains in skulls that still retained some older features on the outside.

THE CULTURE OF NEANDERTALS

As the first hominins to possess brains of modern size, Neandertals, their immediate predecessors and contemporaries had, as we would expect, greater cultural capabilities than their near ancestors. Such a brain made possible technological innovations as well as conceptual thought of considerable sophistication and, almost surely, communication by speech. In short, Neandertals and others like them were a fully sapient species of human being, relatively successful in surviving and thriving even in environments that would seem to us impossibly cold and hostile.

Middle Palaeolithic

The improved toolmaking capabilities of archaic *H. sapiens* are represented by various **Middle Palaeolithic** traditions, of which the best known are the Mousterian

and Mousterianlike traditions of Europe, Western Asia, and North Africa. These date between about 166 000 and 40 000 years ago. Comparable traditions are found as far east as China and Japan, where they arose independently from local predecessors. All these traditions represent a technological advance over what had preceded them. For example, the 40 centimetres of working edge that an Acheulean flint worker could get from a 1-kilogram core compares with the 182 centimetres the Mousterian could get from the same core.

The Mousterian Tradition

The **Mousterian tradition** is named after the Neandertal site of Le Moustier, France. The presence of Acheulean handaxes at Mousterian sites is one indication that this culture was ultimately rooted in the older Acheulean tradition. Neandertals and their contemporaries developed Levalloisian techniques to make Mousterian flake tools

Middle Palaeolithic. The middle part of the Old Stone Age characterized by the emergence of archaic *H. sapiens* and the development of the Mousterian tradition of toolmaking.

Mousterian tradition. Toolmaking tradition of the Neandertals and their contemporaries of Europe, Western Asia, and northern Africa, featuring flake tools that are lighter and smaller than earlier Levalloisian flake tools.

 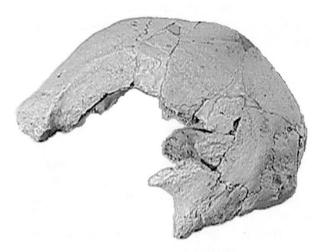

Shown on the left is one of the skulls of archaic H. sapiens *from Ngandong, Java. On the right is an anatomically modern human skull from Lake Mungo in Australia. A similarity between the two is obvious and suggests continuity of populations in Southeast Asia.*
MILFORD H. WOLPOFF

Tools such as these are characteristic of the Mousterian tradition.
© GARY CRAWFORD

that are lighter and smaller than those of the Levalloisian. Whereas Levalloisian toolmakers obtained only two or three flakes from one core, Mousterian toolmakers obtained many smaller flakes, which were then skillfully retouched and sharpened for special purposes.

The Mousterian tool kits contained a much greater variety of tool types than the previous traditions: handaxes, flakes, scrapers, borers, gravers, notched flakes for sawing and shredding wood, and many types of points that could be attached to wooden shafts to form thrusting spears. Many other tools also were hafted in handles of wood or bone, and some populations were experimenting with bitumen as a glue. With this new and varied tool kit, humans intensified their utilization of food resources and increased the availability and quality of clothing and shelter. For the first time, people could cope with the nearly arctic conditions that became prevalent in Europe as the glaciers began to expand about 70 000 years ago.

People likely came to live in cold climates as a result of a slow but steady population increase during the Palaeolithic era. As this caused populations to gradually expand into previously uninhabited colder regions, humans developed a series of cold-climate adaptations that increased their cultural variability. Under near-arctic conditions, vegetable foods are only rarely or seasonally available, and meat is the staff of life. In particular, animal fats, rather than carbohydrates, become the chief source of energy due to their slower rate of metabolism. Abundant animal fat in the diets of cold-climate meat eaters provides them with the extra energy needed for full-time hunting, as well as needed body heat. Insufficient fat in the diet produces lower resistance to disease, lassitude, and a loss of the will to work.

That meat was important to the makers of Mousterian tools is indicated by an abundance of associated animal bones, often clearly showing cut marks. Predators can be opportunistic, taking whatever prey they come across, selectively hunt animals for particular reasons such as for their fur or fat, or focus on a particular species. Neandertals used each of these strategies.[11] Ariane Burke of the Université de Montréal warns against generalizations about Neandertal subsistence.[12] Some sites indicate that a variety of animals were eaten, and probably plants as well while at other sites, the remains

---

[11] Burke, A. (2000). Hunting in the Middle Palaeolithic. *International Journal of Osteoarchaeology, 10*, 281–285.

[12] Burke A. (2004). The ecology of Neanderthals: Preface. *International Journal of Osteoarchaeology, 14*, 155–161.

consist almost entirely of very large game—wild cattle (including bison), wild horses, and even mammoths and woolly rhinoceroses. Particular species in some cases were singled out for the hunt. For example, at one site in the French Pyrenees, well over 90 percent of the faunal assemblage (representing at least 108 animals) consists of large members of the cattle family. These bones accumulated at the foot of a steep riverside escarpment, over which the animals were evidently stampeded. Similar mass hunting techniques are documented at other Mousterian sites: At La Quina in Western France, a dense accumulation of cattle, horse, and reindeer bones (many with clear cut marks from butchering) occurred at the base of a steep cliff; at another site in the Channel Islands, dense deposits of mammoth and woolly rhinoceros bones indicate use of a deep coastal ravine for cliff-fall hunting. Clearly, the Neandertals were not mere unstructured or opportunistic hunters but engaged in a great deal of deliberate hunting of very large and potentially dangerous game.[13] This required careful planning, forethought, and logistical organiza-tion. Although Neandertals were capable of hunting large game animals, they also ate a range of animals that reflected the diversity of the fauna at the time. They also scavenged.

The importance of hunting to Mousterian peoples may also be reflected in their hunting implements, which are more standardized with respect to size and shape than are their domestic and maintenance imple-ments (for maintaining necessary equipment). The complexity of the tool kit needed for survival in a cold climate may have played a role in lessening the mobility of the users of all these possessions. That they were less mobile is suggested by the greater depth of deposits at Mousterian sites compared with those from the ear-lier ("Lower") Palaeolithic. Similarly, evidence for long sequences of production, resharpening and discarding of tools, and large-scale butchering and cooking of game, along with evidence of efforts to improve accommoda-tions in some caves and rock shelters through pebble paving, construction of simple walls, and the digging of postholes and artificial pits, all suggest that Mousterian sites were more than mere stopovers in people's con-stant quest for food. The large number of Mousterian sites uncovered in Europe and Western Asia, as well as clear differences between them, is closely related to

Neandertal's improved hunting techniques, based on superior technology in weapon- and toolmaking, and more efficient social organization than before. These, in turn, were closely related to Neandertal's fully modern brain size.

Neandertal society had developed, evidence shows, even to the point of being able to care for physi-cally disabled members of the group. For the first time, the remains of "oldsters"—individuals well past their prime—are well represented in the fossil record. Furthermore, virtually every elderly Neandertal skeleton that is reasonably complete shows evidence of trauma having been treated, with extensive healing of wounds and little or no infection.[14] Particularly dramatic exam-ples include the remains of a man with a withered arm and an injured eye socket discovered in Shanidar Cave in Iraq, an individual found at Krapina in Croatia whose hand may have been surgically amputated, and a man badly crippled by arthritis unearthed at La Chapelle. The earliest example comes from a 200 000-year-old site in France, where a toothless man was able to survive prob-ably because others in his group processed his food so he could swallow it. Whether or not this evidence indicates true compassion and altruism on the part of these early people is not known; what is certain is that culture had become more than barely adequate to ensure survival.

The Symbolic Life of Neandertals

Burials provide a wealth of insight on what people think about life and death. For the first time in human his-tory there is clear evidence for deliberate burial of the dead. This is one reason for the relative abundance of reasonably complete Neandertal skeletons. To dig a grave large enough to receive an adult body without access to shovels suggests how important a social activity this was. Moreover, intentional positioning of dead hominin bodies by other hominins, whatever the specific reason may have been, nonetheless constitutes evidence of symbolism.[15]

---

13 Mellars, P. (1989). Major issues in the emergence of modern humans. *Current Anthropology, 30*, 356–357.

14 Conroy, G.C. (1997). Reconstructing human origins: *A modern synthesis* (p. 427). New York: Norton.

15 Schepartz, L.A. (1993). Language and modern human origins. *Yearbook of Physical Anthropology, 36*, 113.

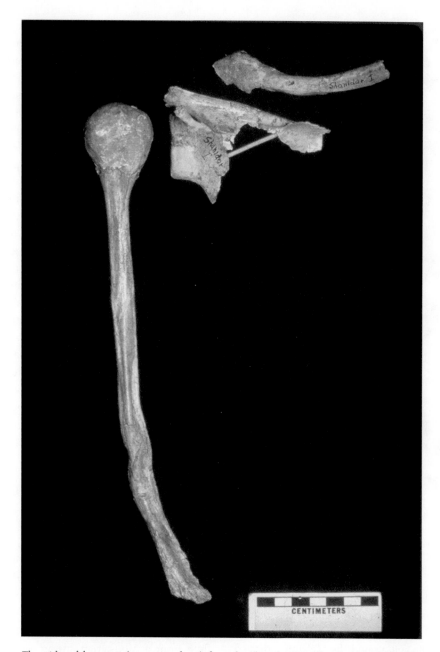

The withered humerus (upper arm bone) from the Shanidar Neandertal indicates that this individual survived for quite a long period of time after losing the lower half of the arm. If the individual had died when the lower arm was lost, the humerus would have a normal appearance. Care of the sick and disabled can be inferred from this specimen. © ERIK TRINKAUS

To date, at least 17 sites in Europe, South Africa, and Southwest Asia include Middle Palaeolithic burials. To cite but two examples, at Kebara Cave in Israel, sometime between 64 000 and 59 000 years ago, a Neandertal male aged between 25 and 35 years was placed in a pit on his back, with his arms folded over his chest and abdomen. Some time later, after complete decay of attaching ligaments, the grave was reopened and the skull removed (a practice that, interestingly, is sometimes seen in burials in the same region roughly 50 000 years later). Another

The position of the body and the careful removal of the skull indicate that the fossil from Kebara Cave in Israel was deliberately buried there about 60 000 years ago. © KENNETH GARRETT/NATIONAL GEOGRAPHIC IMAGE COLLECTION

example is from Shanidar Cave in Iraq, where evidence was found of a burial accompanied by funeral ceremonies. In the back of the cave a Neandertal was buried in a pit. Pollen analysis of the soil around the skeleton indicated that flowers had been placed below the body and in a wreath about the head. Because the key pollen types were from insect-pollinated flowers, few if any of the pollen grains could have found their way into the pit via air currents. The flowers in question consist solely of varieties valued in historic times for their medicinal properties.

Other evidence for symbolic behaviour in Mousterian culture comes from the use of two different naturally occurring pigments: manganese dioxide and red ochre. Finds of these in human trash reveal clear evidence of scraping to produce powder, as well as used crayonlike facets. Thus, Mousterian peoples were clearly using these for applying colour to things. An example is the carved and shaped section of a mammoth tooth, illustrated on page 250, that was worked by Mousterian peoples about 50 000 years ago. One of a number of carved and engraved objects that may have been made for purely symbolic purposes, it is similar to a number of plaques of bone and ivory made by later Palaeolithic peoples, and it is also similar to the *churingas* made of wood by historic Australian aborigines for ritual purposes. The Mousterian object, which was once smeared with red ochre, has a highly polished face as if from long handling. Microscopic examination reveals that it was never provided with a working edge for any utilitarian purpose. As Alexander Marshack observes, "A number of researchers have indicated that the Neandertals did in fact have conceptual models and maps as well as problem-solving capacities comparable to, if not equal to, those found among anatomically modern humans."[16] Thomas Wyn, an anthropologist, and Frederick Coolidge, a psychologist, have tried to analyze the extent to which these cognitive abilities matched those of modern humans.[17] They propose that Neandertals had a long-term working memory similar to that of modern humans. This is what lies behind the technical mastery we see in Neandertal stone tool manufacturing. However, a good memory is not what lies behind innovation. Neandertals were not particularly innovative compared to modern humans. Long-range planning and rapid technological evolution would not be expected among the Neandertals.

Evidence for symbolic activity on the part of Neandertals raises the possibility of the presence and use of musical instruments. One such may be a bone flute from a Mousterian site in Slovenia. The object, discovered by French archaeologist Marcel Otte, consists of a hollow bone with perforations, and it has sparked controversy. Some see it as nothing more than a cave bear bone that was chewed on by carnivores—hence

---

[16] Marshack, A. (1989). Evolution of the human capacity: The symbolic evidence. *Yearbook of Physical Anthropology*, 32, 22.

[17] Wynn T., & Coolidge, F.L. (2004). The expert Neandertal mind: Elsevier Science. 467–487.

GENDER PERSPECTIVES

Evidence of Gender in Neandertal Burials

Palaeoanthropologists have found little archaeological evidence to suggest *H. erectus* possessed a developed gender system, although many physical manifestations of gender relations, such as body painting, tattooing, and hairstyles, are invisible in the archaeological record. Gendered division of labour such as subsistence roles is another aspect of the archaeological record to explore but before modern humans appear, evidence of subsistence roles such as plant food collecting and processing typically filled by women and children has not been found.[1] But with the appearance of Neandertals and other archaic *H. sapiens*, some data begin to show in the archaeological record, particularly in burials. During the Middle and Upper Palaeolithic, hominids appear to identify categories, based on group relationships and material culture. Gender distinctions may be one component of this categorization.

Burial practices are one area where palaeoanthropologists believe they may be able to discern fledgling gender systems. Burials have been used to define the status of individuals, and possible gender roles, based on the grave goods found with each sex. For example, Harrold concludes, "The outstanding tendency noted among Middle Palaeolithic burials was towards differential treatment according to sex. ... Eight of the ten males for whom both variables [sex and age] could be determined were found with grave furnishings but none of the seven females."[2]

There are some difficulties with using mortuary evidence to determine the presence or absence of gender. Considerable controversy has focused on whether the Neandertal burials were intentional or just preserved remains in their natural context. Small sample size (less than 100 individuals have been used in most studies), the lack of complete skeletal material, and the poor state of preservation are also problems in these comparative studies. Unreliable sexing of the fossil material, due to the problems mentioned above, may also skew the data. A further impediment to forming an accurate assessment of gender systems in the Middle Palaeolithic is the geographical diversity among fossil remains: Western burials more often contained grave goods than Near Eastern burials; if samples of females were mainly taken from the Near East (as they were in Harrold's study), then the data would suggest that females were never buried with grave goods, and by association held little status.

In conclusion, until the time of Neandertals, evidence of gender systems remains invisible in the archaeological record. Even in the Middle Palaeolithic, mortuary data is questionable because of problems with sexing fossil remains. However, what little evidence we do have suggests some differentiation of gender status during the Middle Palaeolithic.

---

[1] Kuhn S.L., & Stiner, M.C. (2006). What's a mother to do? *Current Anthropology, 47*, 953–980.

[2] Harrold, F.B. (1980). A comparative analysis of Eurasian palaeolithic burials. *World Archaeology, 12* (2), 199.

Source: Adapted from Whelan, M.K. (1991). Gender and archaeology: Mortuary studies and the search for the origins of gender differentiation. In D. Walde & N.D. Willows (Eds.), *The archaeology gender* (pp. 358–365). Proceedings of the 22nd Annual Chacmool Conference. Calgary: Archaeological Association of the University of Calgary.

---

the perforations. Its discoverer, on the other hand, sees it as a flute. Unfortunately, the object is fragmentary; surviving are five holes, four on one side and one on the opposite side. The regular spacing of the four holes, the fact that they fit perfectly the fingers of a human hand, and the location of the fifth hole at the base of the opposite side, at the natural location of the thumb, all lend credence to the flute hypothesis. Furthermore, signs of gnawing by animals are superimposed on traces of human activity.[18] Thus, the object cannot be rejected as a flute. Were it found in a later Palaeolithic context,

---

[18] Otte, M. (2000). On the suggested bone flute from Slovenia. *Current Anthropology, 41*, 271.

This carved symbolic plaque or churinga *made from a section of a mammoth molar was excavated at the Mousterian site of Tata, Hungary. The edge is rounded and polished from long handling. The plaque has been symbolically smeared with red ochre. The reverse face of the plaque (right) shows the bevelling and shaping of the tooth.* **ALEXANDER MARSHACK, NEW YORK UNIVERSITY**

it would probably be accepted without argument; only because it was clearly made by a Neandertal, whom some are reluctant to accept as fully human, has it been called into question.

Neandertals and Spoken Language

Among modern humans, the sharing of thoughts and ideas, as well as the transmission of culture from one generation to the next, is dependent upon a spoken language. Because the Neandertals had modern-sized brains and a tool kit comparable to that being used in historic times by Australian aborigines, it might be supposed that they had some form of spoken language. And as pointed out by anthropologist Stanley Ambrose, the composite tools of Mousterian and contemporary peoples involved assembly of components in different configurations to produce functionally different tools. He likens this hierarchical assembly of parts into tools to grammatical language, "because hierarchical assemblies of sounds produce meaningful phrases and sentences, and changing word order changes meaning."[19] Furthermore, "a composite tool may be analogous to a sentence, but explaining how to make one is the equivalent of a

recipe or a short story."[20] Talking Neandertals make a good deal of sense, too, in view of the evidence for the manufacture of objects of symbolic significance. Objects such as the mammoth tooth *churinga* already described would seem to have required some form of linguistic explanation.

Despite such considerations, some have argued that the Neandertals lacked the physical features necessary for spoken language. For example, the larynx was asserted to be higher in the throat than it is in modern humans, a reconstruction we now know to be faulty. In the skeleton from the Kebara Cave burial, for instance, the shape and position of the hyoid bone (the "wishbone," associated with the larynx) show that the vocal tract was quite adequate for speech. This is especially noteworthy, for humans pay a high price for the way their vocal tract is positioned. With the lowered position of our larynx, it is far easier for us to choke to death than it is for other mammals. (Before the Heimlich

---

[19] Ambrose, p. 1751.

[20] Ibid.

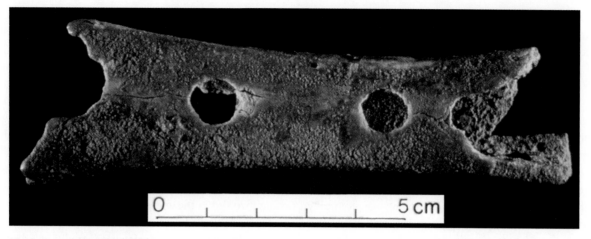

The first musical instrument? There is a strong possibility that this object, found in trash left by Neandertals, is all that remains of a flute made of bone. **UNIVERSITY OF LIEGE**

manoeuvre, for example, choking on food was the sixth leading cause of accidental death in the United States.)[21] The only advantage worth such a price seems to be the ability to speak.

With respect to the brain, palaeoneurologists, working from endocranial casts, are agreed that Neandertals had the neural development necessary for spoken language. Indeed, they argue that the changes associated with speech began even before the appearance of archaic *H. sapiens*.[22] Consistent is the size of the hypoglossal canal, which in Neandertals is like that of modern humans and unlike that of apes.[23] As discussed in the last chapter, this feature is apparent in hominin fossils that are at least 400 000 years old and indicates an ability to make the tongue movements necessary for articulate speech. Consistent, too, is an expanded thoracic vertebral canal (the thorax is the upper part of the body), a feature Neandertals share with modern humans but not early *H. erectus/ergaster* (or any other primate). This feature suggests the increased breath control required for speech.[24] This control enables production of long phrases or single expirations of breath, punctuated with quick inhalations at meaningful linguistic breaks.

Another argument—that a relatively flat base in Neandertal skulls would have prevented speech—has no merit, as some modern adults show as much flattening, yet have no trouble talking. Clearly, when the evidence is considered in its totality, there seems no compelling reason to deny Neandertals the ability to speak.

MODERN HUMAN ORIGINS

For Middle Palaeolithic hominins, their cultural adaptive abilities relate to the fact that brain size was comparable to that of people living today. Archaeological evidence indicates sophisticated technology as well as conceptual thought of considerable complexity, matching the increased cranial capacity. During this same time period, individuals with an anatomically "modern" appearance, a brain of the same size but differently shaped skull, began to appear. The earliest specimens with this skull shape appear first in Africa and later in Asia and Europe. Whether the derived features in the skull, a more vertical forehead, diminished brow ridge, and a chin indicate the appearance of a new species with improved cultural capabilities remains hotly debated.

The transition from the Middle Palaeolithic to the tools of the Upper Palaeolithic may have begun by 70 000 years ago in South Africa and was nearly complete by around 40 000 years ago, long after the appearance of the first anatomically "modern" specimens. The Upper Palaeolithic is known not only for a veritable explosion of tool industries, but also for clear

---

[21] Shreeve, p. 273.

[22] Schepartz, p. 98.

[23] Cartmill, M. (1998). The gift of gab. *Discover, 19* (11), 62.

[24] MacLarnon, A.M. & Hewitt, G.P. (1999). The evolution of human speech: The role of enhanced breathing control. *American Journal of Physical Anthropology, 109*, 341–363.

artistic expression preserved in representative sculptures, paintings, and engravings (see Chapter 10). But the earliest anatomically modern humans used tools of the Middle Palaeolithic traditions like the archaic *H. sapiens*.

The relationship between cultural developments of the Upper Palaeolithic and underlying biological differences between anatomically modern humans and archaic forms remains one of the most contentious debates in palaeoanthropology. The fate of the Neandertals and their cultural abilities are integral to this debate. Whether or not a new kind of human—anatomically modern with correspondingly superior intellectual and creative abilities—is responsible for the cultural explosion of the Upper Palaeolithic is a difficult question to resolve. The biological and cultural evidence preserved in fossil and archaeological records, respectively, do not tell a simple story.

On a biological level, the great debate can be distilled to a question of whether one, some, or all populations of the archaic groups played a role in the evolution of modern *H. sapiens*. Those supporting the **multiregional hypothesis** argue that the fossil evidence suggests a simultaneous local transition from *Homo erectus* to modern *H. sapiens* throughout the parts of the world inhabited by members of the genus *Homo*. By contrast, the **"Out of Africa hypothesis"** of recent African origins uses primarily genetic evidence to argue that all contemporary people are derived from one single population of archaic *H. sapiens* from Africa. This model proposes that the improved cultural capabilities of anatomically modern humans allowed this group to replace other archaic forms as they began to migrate out of Africa some time after 100 000 years ago.

The Multiregional Hypothesis

As several anthropologists have noted, African, Chinese, and Southeast Asian fossils of archaic *H. sapiens* imply local population continuity from *H. erectus,* through archaic, to modern *H. sapiens*,[25] lending strong support to the interpretation that there was genetic continuity in these regions. For example, in China hominin fossils consistently have small forward-facing cheeks and flatter faces than their contemporaries elsewhere, as is

still true today. In Southeast Asia and Australia, by contrast, skulls are consistently robust, with huge cheeks and forward projection of the jaws. In this model, gene flow among populations keeps the human species unified throughout the Pleistocene. No speciation events remove ancestral populations such as *Homo erectus* or Neandertals from the line leading to *H. sapiens*. Although proponents of the multiregional hypothesis accept the idea of continuity from the earliest European fossils through the Neandertals to living people, many other palaeoanthropologists resist the idea that Neandertals were involved in the ancestry of modern Europeans.

No earlier than 36 500 years ago[26] a new technology, known as the **Aurignacian tradition**—named after Aurignac, France, where tools of this sort were first discovered—appeared in Europe (Figure 9.4, p. 255). Though commonly considered to have spread from Southwest Asia, a recent reconsideration of the blade and flake ratios for 23 early Upper Palaeolithic sites failed to sustain this idea, suggesting instead that the Aurignacian is a distinctively European development.[27] The supposed hallmark of the Aurignacian, fully developed blade technology, did not appear suddenly in Europe and is not associated with any particular change in hominin abilities. Skeletal remains are rarely associated with Aurignacian tools, although anatomically modern humans are generally considered the makers of these tools. This is because of the age and complexity of the tools. A notable exception to this

---

[25] Wolpoff, M.H., & Caspari, R. (1997). *Race and human evolution.* New York: Simon & Schuster.

[26] Zilhão, J. (2000). Fate of the Neandertals. *Archaeology, 53* (4), 30.

[27] Clark G.A. (2002). Neandertal archaeology: Implications for our origins. *American Anthropologist, 104,* 50–67.

Multiregional hypothesis. Populations of archaic *H. sapiens* throughout the Old World evolved, at more or less the same time, into modern humans.

"Out of Africa" hypothesis. Modern humans evolved in one geographic region, expanding and replacing other populations.

Aurignacian tradition. Toolmaking tradition in Europe and Western Asia at the beginning of the Upper Palaeolithic.

BIOGRAPHY

Ariane Burke

Anatomically modern humans are frequently associated with the development of a "modern" way of life, including specialized hunting skills, and a seasonal pattern of site occupation and resource use. Ariane Burke's research into the Middle Palaeolithic of the Crimea (Ukraine) poses a challenge to such generalizations. Most of the human skeletal remains associated with Middle Palaeolithic sites in the Crimea are Neandertal. Burke has discovered that these people were more sophisticated in their pattern of land use and their resource exploitation strategies than previously suspected.

Burke is currently co-excavating a site in the Crimean highlands with Ukrainian archaeologists. The site, Karabi Tamchin, is one of only a few stratified, mid-altitude Middle Palaeolithic sites excavated to date in Europe. This site is important because palaeoanthropologists know hardly anything about Neandertal occupations at mid-altitudes. It is hoped Karabi Tamchin will help complete the picture of regional patterns of land use at the close of the Middle Palaeolithic. The broader

implications of this research are important because they have an effect on our understanding of what it means to be truly "modern," as well as helping palaeoanthropologists understand the nature of Neandertal/anatomically modern human interactions at the beginning of the Upper Palaeolithic.

In addition to her Crimean research, Burke maintains a variety of other research interests. She has a continuing interest in bone and tooth growth, focusing on the function of mineralized tissues as recording structures (recording life histories of individual organisms) and their use as a means of estimating an individual's age and season of death. Burke has also conducted collaborative research into the mechanism controlling bone growth during development. Burke recently completed an archaeozoological study of a Late Classical/Byzantine site at Lepitminus, Tunisia, which encouraged her to undertake an ethnozooarchaeological study of *halal* butchery, conducted while in the field in Tunisia. Ariane Burke is an associate professor at the University of Manitoba.

---

notion is the central European site of Vindija Cave, Croatia, where Neandertals are associated with an Aurignacian split-bone point.[28] However, some argue that the **Upper Palaeolithic** technology of the Neandertals was a crude imitation of the true technological advancements practised by anatomically modern humans. In some respects, Neandertals outdid their anatomically modern contemporaries, as in the use of red ocher, a substance less frequently used by Aurignacian peoples than by their late Neandertal neighbours.[29] This cannot be a case of borrowing ideas and techniques from Aurignacians, as these developments clearly predate the Aurignacian.[30] Nevertheless, fossils described as Neandertals are known from sites in Western Europe that date from 35 000 to 33 000 years ago, in which case coexistence between the modern and archaic forms of *sapiens* would seem to be indicated. Given the anatomical differences between the two, some form of population replacement, rather than simple evolution from one to the other, may have occurred.

An alternate explanation is possible, however. If we think in terms of varied populations—as we should[31]—instead of ideal types, we find that features reminiscent of modern humans can be discerned in some of the latest Neandertals. A specimen from Saint Césaire in France, for example, has a higher forehead and chin.

[28] Karavani, I., & Smith, F.H. (2000). More on the Neanderthal problem: The Vindija case. *Current Anthropology*, 41, 839.

[29] Bednarik, R. G. (1995). Concept-mediated marking in the lower Paleolithic. *Current Anthropology*, 36, 606.

[30] Zilhão, p. 40

[31] Gould, S.J. (1996). *Full house: The spread of excellence from Plato to Darwin* (pp. 72–73). New York: Harmony Books.

Upper Palaeolithic. The last part of the Old Stone Age, characterized by the emergence of more modern-looking hominins and an emphasis on the blade technique of toolmaking.

A number of other Neandertals, too, show incipient chin development as well as reduced facial protrusion and thinning of the brow ridges. Conversely, the earliest anatomically modern human skulls from Europe often exhibit features reminiscent of Neandertals (see Chapter 10). Accordingly, we might view the population of this region between 40 000 and 30 000 years ago as a varied one, with some individuals retaining a stronger Neandertal heritage than others, in whom modern characteristics are more prominent (Figure 9.3).

Nothing in the physical or mental makeup of Neandertals would have prevented them from leading a typical Upper Palaeolithic way of life, as in fact the latest Neandertals of Western, Central, and Eastern Europe did.[32] Out of the earlier Mousterian, they created their own Upper Palaeolithic cultures (Figure 9.4).

Another often cited case of coexistence of the two forms is in Southwest Asia. Although Neandertal skeletons are clearly present at sites such as Kebara and Shanidar caves, skeletons from some older sites have been described as anatomically modern. At Qafzeh in Israel, for example, 90 000-year-old skeletons are said to show none of the Neandertal hallmarks; although their faces and bodies are large and heavily built by today's standards, they are nonetheless claimed to be within the range of living peoples. Yet, a statistical study comparing a number of measurements among Qafzeh, Upper Palaeolithic, and Neandertal skulls found those from Qafzeh to fall in between the Aurignacian and Neandertal norms, though slightly closer to the Neandertals.[33] The dentition is not functionally distinguishable when Qafzeh and Neandertal are compared.[34]

At the nearby site of Skuhl, a skeleton similar to those from Qafzeh was part of a population whose continuous range of variation included individuals with markedly Neandertal characteristics. Furthermore, the idea of two distinctly different but coexisting populations receives no support from cultural remains, inasmuch as the people living at Skuhl and Qafzeh were making and using the same Mousterian tools as those at Kebara and Shanidar. Thus, there are no indications of groups with different cultural traditions coexisting in the same region. For that matter, the actual behaviours represented by Middle Palaeolithic and early Upper Palaeolithic cultures were not significantly different. For example, the Upper Palaeolithic people who used Kebara Cave continued to live in exactly the same way as their Neandertal predecessors: They procured the

---

[32] Mellars, p. 378.

[33] Corruccini, R.S. (1992). Metrical reconsideration of the Skhul IV and IX and Border Cave I crania in the context of modern human origins. *American Journal of Physical Anthropology, 87*, 433–445.

[34] Brace, C.L. (2000). *Evolution in an anthropological view* (p. 206). Walnut Creek, CA: Altamira.

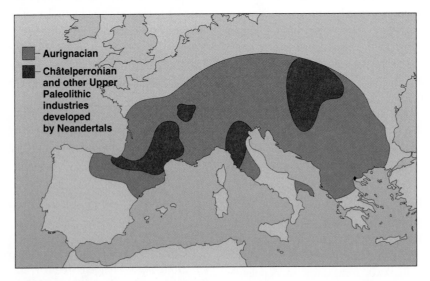

FIGURE 9.3

Between 36 500 and 30 000 years ago, Upper Palaeolithic industries developed from the Mousterian by European Neandertals coexisted with the Aurignacian industry, usually associated with anatomically modern humans.

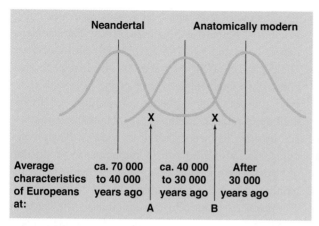

FIGURE 9.4

Graphically portrayed here is a shift in average characteristics of an otherwise varied population over time from Neandertal to more modern features. Between 40 000 and 30 000 years ago, we would expect to find individuals with characteristics such as those of the Saint Césaire "Neandertal" (A) and the almost (but not quite) modern Cro-Magnon (B; this fossil is discussed in Chapter 10).

same foods, processed them in the same way, used similar hearths, and disposed of their trash in the same way. The only evident difference is that the Neandertals did not bank their fires for warmth with small stones or cobbles as did their Upper Palaeolithic successors.[35]

The "Eve" or "Out of Africa" Hypothesis

This alternative to the multiregional hypothesis states that all anatomically modern humans are descended from one specific population of *H. sapiens*, replacing not only the Neandertals, but also other populations of contemporary *Homo* as our ancestors spread out of their original homeland. This idea, although not new, is being supported by studying mitochondrial DNA. By comparing the mitochondrial DNA of living individuals from diverse geographical populations, anthropologists and molecular biologists seek to determine when and where modern *H. sapiens* originated. As widely reported in the popular press (including a cover story in *Newsweek*), preliminary results suggested that the mitochondrial DNA of all living humans could be traced back to a "Mitochondrial Eve" who lived in Africa some 200 000 years ago. If so, all other populations of *Homo*, as well as non-African *H. erectus*, would have to be ruled out of the ancestry of modern humans.

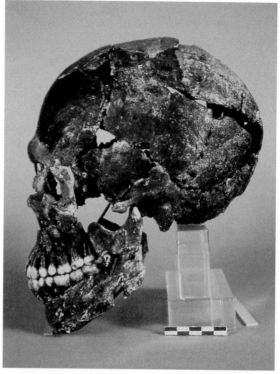

This H. sapiens *skull from Qafzeh, Israel, is 90 000 years old. Though it looks more modern than a Neandertal, measurements taken of the skull fall slightly closer to those of the Neandertals than those of more modern-looking Upper Palaeolithic people.*

QAFZEH ARCHIVES & DR. B. VANDERMEERSCH, COURTESY OF DR. OFER BAR-YOSEF

The analysis of Y chromosome variation supports the conclusions of the mitochondrial DNA studies. Not only is the maternal legacy of humanity discernable but also is the paternal legacy according to a group of researchers from the United States, United Kingdom, Italy, Spain, Pakistan, South Africa and Israel.[36] The ancestry of the paternal lineages is traced to Africa, and it was the descendents of the African group who replaced the archaic paternal lines in Eurasia.

Most scholars today accept that fossils from Africa, scrappy though they are, exhibit the transition from *H. erectus/ergaster* through to anatomically modern *sapiens* on that continent. This by itself, however, offers

---

[35] Corruccini, p. 436.

[36] Underhill, P.A., Shen, P., Lin, A.A., Jin, L., Passarino, G., Yang, W.H., Kauffman, E., Bonne-Tamir, B., Bertranpetit, J., Francalacci, P., and others. (2000). Y chromosome sequence variation and the history of human populations. *Nat Genet*, 26, 358–361.

no confirmation of the "Out of Africa" hypothesis. After all, proponents of the multiregional model also argue that the transition took place here, as in other parts of the Old World. However, anatomically modern fossils significantly older in Africa than elsewhere would support the argument for an African homeland for modern humanity. Such fossils have come to light in the last few years.

In 2003 three near-modern human skulls, two adult males and a six-to-seven-year-old child, were reported from Herto, Ethiopia.[37] Dating from 160 000 to 154 000 years ago, *H. sapiens idaltu*, as the fossils have been classified, provides the first good evidence for African near-modern humans being significantly older than the Neandertals. They are so similar to modern humans that there is no mistaking their identity. The face is broad, the forehead is moderately domed and the brow ridge is halved over a flat mid-face, and the nasal bones are tall and narrow, all modern traits. The protruding brows and flexed bone at the rear of the skull are primitive traits, so considered near-modern. The characteristics of these fossils are unlike those of Neandertals. The child's skull is polished, normally evidence of long-term handling noted on skulls used in rituals in New Guinea. The stone tools associated with the fossils also have older (Acheulean) and more modern (Middle Stone Age) characteristics. Even older anatomically modern humans (AMH) appear to come from the lower Omo river, also in Ethiopia.[38] Here, the volcanic tuff in which two AMH fossils were found in the 1960s has only recently been dated to about 190 000 years ago.

The oldest substantial behavioural evidence linked to modern humans is also from Africa. The people of Klasies River and Blombos Cave, South Africa, between 70 000 and 80 000 years ago, are the first people we know of to augment resources of the land with those from the sea; their gathering of shellfish led to the buildup of middens (refuse heaps) comparable to those left by later Upper Palaeolithic peoples. Their technology was also advanced in the common production of blades—long parallel-sided flakes of a sort not commonly made in Europe until some 36 500 years ago. The people at Klasies River were blunting the backs of blades, much as later Europeans did, for hafting in composite tools. Some take these signs of cultural advancement as indicative of anatomically modern status. Bone tools and evidence of their production, a regular feature of AMH after 40 000 years ago, are a significant part of the assemblage in the 70 000-year-old deposits at Blombos Cave.

The "Out of Africa" hypothesis still has problems though. For one thing, we would expect an early replacement of archaic *sapiens* in Southwest Asia as more anatomically modern humans moved up out of Africa

---

[37] White, T.D., Asfwah, B., DeGusta, D., Gilbert, H., Richards, G.D., Suwa, G., & Howell, F.C. (2003). Pleistocene *Homo sapiens* from Middle Awash, Ethiopia. *Nature, 423,* 742–747.

[38] McDougall I., Brown, F.H., & Fleagle, J.G. (2005). Stratigraphic placement and age of modern humans from Kibish, Ethiopia. *Nature, 433,* 733–736.

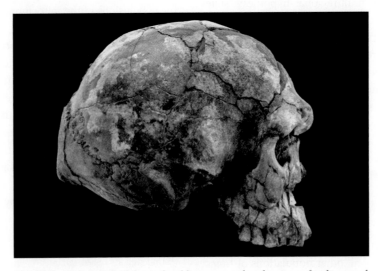

This skull of H. sapiens idaltu *is the oldest near-modern human so far discovered.*
2003 DAVID L. BRILL

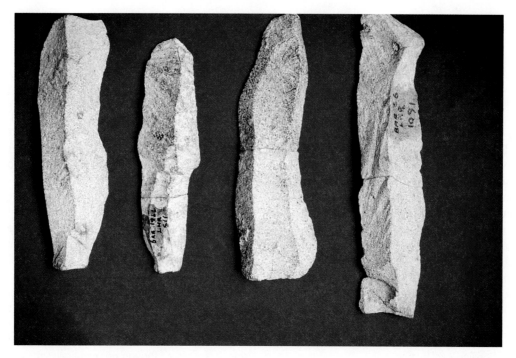

Even older than the blades from the Klasies River mouth are these, from a site in Kenya. Struck from preshaped cores, they are about 240 000 years old, predating any known or possible fossils of anatomically modern humans.

SALLY MCBREARTY

but, as we have already seen, we have no clear evidence for such a replacement. The same is true for East Asia, where evidence for continuity from regional *H. erectus*, through archaic, to anatomical *H. sapiens* populations is even better than it is in Africa. Consistent with this, the archaeological record of East Asia, though distinctly different from Europe, Africa, and Western Asia, shows the same kind of continuity as do the fossils.[39] There is no sign of invasion by people possessing a superior, or even different, technology, as an "Out of Africa" scenario would require.

Given the problems in reconciling the "Out of Africa" hypothesis with the archaeological and fossil records, one may ask: What about the DNA analysis that gave birth to the hypothesis? Here, things are not as certain as proponents of "Out of Africa" maintain.

Other assumptions made by DNA analysts are problematic. For example, it is assumed that rates of mutation are steady, when in fact they can be notoriously uneven. Another assumption is that mtDNA is not subject to selection, when in fact variants have been implicated in epilepsy and a disease of the eye.[40] A third is that DNA is seen as travelling exclusively *from* Africa,

when it is known that, over the past 10 000 years, there has been plenty of movement the other way. In fact, one study of DNA carried on the Y chromosome (and inherited exclusively in the male line) suggests that some DNA seen on the Y chromosome of some Africans was introduced from Asia, where it originated some 200 000 years ago.[41]

Since 1997, studies of mitochondrial DNA have not been limited to living people. In that year, mtDNA was extracted from the original German Neandertal, and several others have since been studied. The Neandertal whose DNA has been substantially sequenced is from Vindija Cave, Croatia. It appears that modern humans and Neandertals share no mitochondrial DNA. This seems to support the view that there can be no Neandertal ancestry in living humans and that Neandertals must constitute a separate species that became extinct. But as

---

[39] Pope, G.C. (1992). Craniofacial evidence for the origin of modern humans in China. *Yearbook of Physical Anthropology*, 35, 291.

[40] Shreeve, p. 121.

[41] Gibbons, A. (1997). Ideas on human origins evolve at anthropology gathering. *Science*, 276, 535–536.

ORIGINAL STUDY

African Origin or Ancient Population Size Differences?

The Eve theory depends on genetic evidence indicating an African origin for modern humanity, because ... the fossil evidence is quite equivocal on this issue. But there is no particular reason to suggest Africa was the place of origin for the current mtDNA [mitochondrial DNA] lineages. The original studies suggesting an African origin were invalid because the computer program used in the analysis was not applied correctly. Then the greater genetic variability in Africans was taken to mean humans evolved there longer: The variation was thought to reflect more mutations and therefore a longer time span for their accumulation. Templeton [a geneticist] has argued that no statistical analysis shows that the genetic variation of Africans actually is greater than that of other populations; but even if it is, there is another, more compelling explanation.

Ancient population sizes expanded first and are larger in Africa than in other regions, which would have the same effect, creating more African variation. Consider what happens in an expanding population. Average family size is greater than two, and all variations have a good chance of being passed on; at least, if they are not selected against, they will probably not get lost by accident. But if a population is decreasing, drift can play a very active role since average family size is less than two. The role of drift is greatly amplified for mtDNA, because for transmission of this molecule the number of female offspring is important. Decreasing populations stand an excellent chance of losing mtDNA lineages.

Now, consider a small but stable population, neither increasing nor decreasing. Here, existing variations may each occur in only one individual. If it is a woman, and she has no female offspring, which can happen one-fourth of the time in a stable population, her unique variation is lost, her mtDNA lineage terminated. But in a large stable population with the same amount of genetic variability, it is likely each mtDNA variant is shared by many individuals. The odds are the same against one woman having no female offspring, but it is very unlikely all the women with a certain mtDNA variant will lack female offspring. It is much harder for mtDNA lines to end by accident in large populations.

These comparisons show that prehistoric population demography, how large or small populations were in the past and how much they fluctuated, can affect mtDNA evolution. Small, fluctuating populations will lose many mtDNA lines. The last common ancestor for the remaining mtDNA variations will be more recent because there is less remaining variation. Large or increasing populations will retain more variation. For them, the roots will be deeper and the last common ancestor will be farther in the past since more variations are retained.

Thus, ancient population size can dictate how long genetic lineages have existed, and therefore when they arose. Because ancient population size differences are an alternate explanation that unlinks the origin of genetic lineages from the origin of a population, it seems as though genetic analysis cannot help solve the problem of whether today's variation reflects African origin or ancient population size differences.

However, genetic analysis can indicate ancient population expansions. Henry Harpending and colleagues studied the probability distributions of pairwise mtDNA comparisons within populations for evidence of past population structure and size expansions. They conclude: "Our results show human populations are derived from separate ancestral populations that were relatively isolated from each other before 50 000 years ago." These studies clearly reveal there have been a series of recent, very significant, population expansions. Some of these are without question associated with the development and spread of agricultural revolutions. But others are earlier.

This means population size history by itself can explain the pattern of mtDNA variation. If, as we believe and as the archaeological record seems to show,

- there were more people living in Africa for most of human prehistory, and
- human populations outside of Africa were smaller and fluctuated more because of the changing ice-age environments,

We would expect just what we do see—African mtDNA has deeper roots, while in other places the coalescent time is more recent. But this explanation does not mean the populations living out of Africa have a more recent origin, or that they originated in Africa. MtDNA history, in other words, is not population history.

John Relethford and Henry Harpending examined the consequences of the possibility that greater African population size, and not greater time depth for modern humans in Africa, may account for their greater variation.

Our results support our earlier contention that regional differences in population size can explain the genetic evidence pertaining to modern human origins. Our work thus far has involved examination of the classic genetic markers and craniometrics, but it also has implications for mitochondrial DNA. The greater mtDNA diversity in sub-Saharan African populations could also be a reflection of a larger long-term African population.

Moreover, they write, a unique African ancestry implies there was a bottleneck for the human species, as moderns would be able to trace their ancestry to only a small portion of humanity, as it existed then.

While this seems at first glance a reasonable notion, it soon becomes apparent that the actual effect of such a [bottleneck] event depends on both the magnitude and duration of a shift in population size. Rogers and Jorde show that given reasonable parameters for our species, the bottleneck would have to be more severe and long-lasting than considered plausible. We have to think of a population of 50 females for 6000 years, for example.

Source: Wolpoff, M.H., & Caspari, R. (1997). *Race and human evolution*. New York: Simon & Schuster, pp. 305–307.

John Relethford (a specialist in anthropological genetics) pointed out before the Vindija Neandertal DNA was sequenced, these conclusions are premature.[42] In fact, the Vindija analysis indicates that there appears to have been some gene flow between modern human males and Neandertal females, although this interpretation needs to be properly tested.

In short, it is definitely premature to read out of the modern human ancestry all populations of archaic *sapiens* save those of Africa. Not even the Neandertals can be excluded. We shall return to this problem in the next chapter, but at the moment, the evidence seems to favour a multiregional emergence of anatomically modern humans. Still, the debate is by no means resolved.

[42] Relethford, J.H. (2001). Absence of regional affinities of Neandertal DNA with living humans does not reject multi-regional evolution. *American Journal of Physical Anthropology*, 115, 95–98.

CHAPTER SUMMARY

At various sites in Europe, Africa, and East Asia, a number of fossils have been found that date between about 800 000 and 130 000 years ago, and that show a mixture of traits of both *Homo erectus/ergaster* and *H. sapiens*. They are indicative of evolution from the older into the younger species. The transitional forms may belong to a separate species, *H. heidelbergensis* although some scholars classify them as archaic *H. sapiens*, the species to which modern humans belong. Their culture was enriched by development of a new technique of tool manufacture known as the Levalloisian. Anatomically modern humans were evolving in Africa by 190 000 years ago.

Homo neanderthalensis was a unique, robust hominin that evolved in Europe and western Asia. Their contemporaries in Asia resembled Neandertals to some extent but were not as robust. Anatomically modern *H. sapiens* were becoming successful in Africa long before the end of Neandertal's dominance in Europe that lasted until about 29 000 years ago.

The brains of Neandertals, their contemporaries in Asia, and early *H. sapiens* were no different in size and organization than our own, although their skulls retained some ancestral characteristics. With a larger brain, they were able to utilize culture as a means of adaptation to a far greater extent than any of their predecessors; they were capable of complex technology and sophisticated conceptual thought.

The cultures of Neandertals and their contemporaries who were not modern humans are known as Middle Palaeolithic, and the best known is the Mousterian of Europe, Northern Africa, and Western Asia. Mousterian tools included handaxes, flakes, scrapers, borers, wood shavers, and spears. These flake tools were lighter and smaller than those of the Levalloisian. Mousterian tools increased the availability and quality of food, shelter, and clothing. Archaeological evidence indicates that Mousterian peoples buried their dead, cared for the disabled, and made a variety of objects for purely symbolic purposes.

All populations after 800 000 are easily derivable from the earlier populations of the *H. erectus* and *H. ergaster* complex. The transition from archaic to anatomically modern *H. sapiens* likely took place in one specific population, probably in Africa. From here, people spread to other regions, replacing older populations as they did so.

QUESTIONS FOR CRITICAL THOUGHT

1. Some scholars believe that the appearance of *H. sapiens* represents the beginning of the end for the genus *Homo*. Why do you suppose this could be the case?

2. What about Neandertals links them closely to modern humans? What about them contrasts with us?

3. If you were able to make contact with living Neandertals, how would you expect to interact given your knowledge of their lives?

INTERNET RESOURCES

Human Origins

http://www.actionbioscience.org/evolution/johanson.html

A comprehensive article written in 2001 that discusses the origin of modern *H. sapiens*; when, where, and how the steps to moderns occurred; and replacement versus regional continuity hypotheses.

Atapuerca, Spain

www.amnh.org/exhibitions/atapuerca

The American Museum of Natural History website explores the research at Atapuerca in northern Spain. The setting, discoveries, and implications of the remains are explored.

Neandertal Culture

www.webster.sk.ca/greenwich/chewchip.htm

One of few descriptive examinations of a bone flute dated to the time of Neandertals.

Neandertals

http://unisci.com/stories/20012/0403012.htm

Presents new evidence regarding whether Neandertals and modern humans interbred.

http://gibraltar.costasur.com/en/neanderthal.html

A descriptive glimpse at the Gibraltar Neandertal skull.

www.ifi.unizh.ch/staff/zolli/CAP/comparingNeand.htm

A comparative analysis of Neandertals and modern humans, including illustrations.

http://news.bbc.co.uk/2/hi/science/nature/6146908.stm

In an attempt to discern the genetic history of early humans, scientists have analyzed the DNA of over a dozen Neandertals. The results of this recent study are shedding light on Neandertal's evolution and their relationship to modern humans.

www.geocities.com/CapeCanaveral/Launchpad/3917/index.html

Discusses the debate concerning Neandertal relations to modern humans. Contains numerous links on same subject.

SUGGESTED READINGS

For a list of suggested readings, visit the textbook's website at www.humanevolution2.nelson.com.

HOMO SAPIENS AND THE UPPER PALAEOLITHIC

The Upper Palaeolithic is defined by changes in technology and evidence of increased human creativity and ingenuity in art and problem solving. The hands and other figures painted on the walls of this cave site in Australia indicate a rich symbolic life. An additional example of the technological capabilities of early Australians can be seen in their ability to arrive on this continent by boat. Early humans crossed many kilometres of open water, distances that Australian palaeoanthropologist Alan Thorne described as "beyond the horizon." What was responsible for the culture changes evident in the archaeological record?

(C) JOHN VAN HASSELT/CORBIS

CHAPTER PREVIEW

1. When Did Anatomically Modern Forms of *Homo sapiens* Appear?

The answer to this question depends on what is meant by "anatomically modern." Because all humans today are members of a single species, all are equally modern. It is generally agreed that by 30 000 years ago, in the Upper Palaeolithic period, populations in all parts of the inhabited world show some resemblance to more recent human populations. The evolution of *H. sapiens* is complex with at least one other species, *H. neanderthalensis*, arising from a probable common ancestor. The extent to which Neanderthals contributed to the modern gene pool is debated.

2. What Was the Culture of Upper Palaeolithic Peoples Like?

Upper Palaeolithic cultures generally include a greater diversity of tools. Techniques of tool-making became widespread, including the manufacture of blades, pressure flaking, and use of burins to fashion implements of bone and antler. In Europe, large game hunting was improved by invention of the spear-thrower, while net hunting allowed effective procurement of small game. In Africa the bow and arrow were invented. There was as well an explosion of creativity, represented by impressive works of art from Africa, Australia, and Europe.

3. What Were the Consequences of the New Upper Palaeolithic Technologies?

First Upper Palaeolithic and then Epipalaeolithic technologies improved people's abilities to adapt through the medium of culture. This resulted in increased regionalism, as people refined their adaptations to local conditions, and further population growth promoted expansion into new regions, most dramatically Australia and the Americas. Biological consequences included reduction of the human face to modern proportions, and the new hunting technologies led to reduction of body mass.

CHAPTER OUTLINE

Upper Palaeolithic Peoples:
   The First Modern Humans
Upper Palaeolithic Tools
Upper Palaeolithic Art
Other Aspects of Upper Palaeolithic Culture

The Spread of Upper Palaeolithic Peoples
Where Did Upper Palaeolithic People
   Come From?
Major Palaeolithic Trends

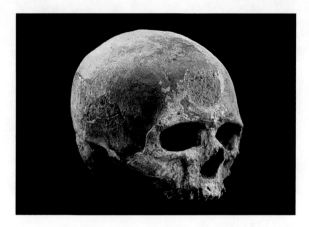

Though the original Cro-Magnon skull shows some resemblance to modern European skulls, it is not identical. **DAVID L. BRILL, ARTIFACT CREDIT, MUSÉE DE L'HOMME, PARIS**

The remains of a Stone Age people who looked much like us were first discovered in 1868 at Les Eyzies in France, in a rock shelter, together with tools of the Upper (late) Palaeolithic. Consisting of eight skeletons, they are commonly referred to as **Cro-Magnons**, after the rock shelter in which they were found. The name was extended to 13 other specimens unearthed between 1872 and 1902 in the caves of the Côte d'Azur near the Italian Riviera and, since then, to other Upper Palaeolithic skeletons discovered in other parts of Europe.

Because Cro-Magnons were found with Upper Palaeolithic tools and seemed responsible for the production of impressive works of art, they were seen as particularly clever, compared to the Neandertals. The idea that the latter were basically dim-witted fit comfortably with the prevailing stereotype of their brutish appearance, and their Mousterian tools were interpreted as evidence of cultural inferiority. Hence the idea was born of an anatomically modern people with a superior culture sweeping into Europe and replacing a primitive, local population.

UPPER PALAEOLITHIC PEOPLES: THE FIRST MODERN HUMANS

Much as Neandertals were stereotyped as particularly brutish, the Cro-Magnons of Europe were stereotyped as having a somewhat godlike appearance, epitomizing modern European ideals of beauty. This image found its way into popular culture, as in a best-selling novel of the 1970s, *The Clan of the Cave Bear.* In this book, the heroine is portrayed as a tall, slender, blonde-haired, blue-eyed beauty. But as Upper Palaeolithic remains (from various parts of

Africa and Asia as well as Europe) have become better understood, it has become clear that the differences from earlier populations have been greatly exaggerated. In the case of Europeans, for example, there is some resemblance between Cro-Magnons and later populations: in braincase shape, high broad forehead, narrow nasal openings, and common presence of chins. But Cro-Magnon faces were shorter and broader than those of modern Europeans, their brow ridges were a bit more prominent, and their teeth and jaws were as large as those of Neandertals. Some (a skull from the original Cro-Magnon site, for instance) even display the distinctive "occipital bun" of the Neandertals on the back of the skull.[1] Nor were Cro-Magnons particularly tall, as their height of 170 to 172 centimetres does not fall outside the Neandertal range.

Although the Cro-Magnons and Upper Palaeolithic people from Africa and Asia are now routinely referred to as anatomically modern, it is surprisingly hard to be precise about what we mean by this. We think of people with brains the size of modern people's, but this had already been achieved by archaic *H. sapiens,* among whom brain size actually peaked at 10 percent larger than ours. The reduction to today's size correlates with a reduction in brawn, as bodies have become less massive overall. Modern faces and jaws are, by and large, less massive as well, but there are exceptions. For example, anthropologists Milford Wolpoff and Rachel Caspari have pointed out that any definition of modernity that excludes Neandertals also excludes substantial numbers of recent and living aboriginal Australians, although they are, quite obviously, a modern people. The fact is, no multidimensional diagnosis of modern humans can be both exclusive of archaic populations and inclusive of all contemporary humans.[2]

The appearance of modern-sized brains in archaic *H. sapiens* no doubt was a consequence of increased reliance on cultural adaptation. Ultimately, this emphasis on cultural adaptation led to the development of more complex tool kits. Among Upper Palaeolithic peoples, as specialized tools increasingly took over the cutting, softening, and clamping functions once performed by

---

[1] Brace, C.L. (1997). Cro-Magnons R us? *Anthropology Newsletter, 38*(8), 1.

[2] Wolpoff, M., & Caspari, R. (1997). *Race and human evolution* (pp. 344–345, 393). New York: Simon & Schuster.

Cro-Magnons. Europeans of the Upper Palaeolithic after about 36 000 years ago.

the front teeth, there followed a reduction in the size of the teeth and, eventually, the jaws. The cooking of food (which began with *H. erectus*) had already favoured some reduction in size of the teeth and muscles involved in chewing; consequently, the jaws diminished in size, and robust sites for muscle attachment disappeared along with features like brow ridges that buttress the skull from the stresses and strains imposed by the action of massive jaw muscles.

Technological improvements also reduced the intensity of selective pressures that had previously favored especially massive, robust bodies. With new emphasis on elongate tools having greater mechanical advantages, more effective techniques of hafting, a switch from thrusting to throwing spears, and development of net hunting, there was a marked reduction in overall muscularity. Moreover, the skeletons of Upper Palaeolithic peoples show far less evidence of trauma than do those of archaic *H. sapiens*, whose bones almost always show evidence of injury.

Homo floresiensis

In 2004 palaeoanthropologists made a controversial discovery that suggested a shocking conclusion: *H. sapiens* was not the only member of the genus surviving after 25 000 years ago. Routine archaeological investigation of the Liang Bua site on Flores Island brought to light at least two adult hominins represented by a mandible in one case and a cranium, mandible, and numerous post-cranial bones of another that stood about a metre tall with a cranial capacity of about 380 cubic centimetres.[3] Subsequent research has found bones of at least seven more individuals. The remains date to about 18 000 years ago. Other archaeological evidence such as stone tools suggest that this hominin lived here from at least 95 000 to 12 000 years ago. When anthropologists analyzed the cranium in particular, it was quite distinct from *Australopithecus* (who also had a small brain) in having a relatively vertical face and smaller teeth. The morphology of the skull, human-like bipedalism, and teeth similar to modern humans all argued for this hominin being a unique member of the genus *Homo* called *H. floresiensis*. Modern humans did not appear on the island until about 10 000 years ago. *H. floresiensis'* stone tools are made of elongate flakes struck from cores as well as flakes from cobbles. A few have been retouched and shaped so that they have pointed projections. These hominins also made fire and hunted. This sophisticated

tool-making behaviour is unlike that of *Australopithecus*, who also had a small brain; therefore, the Flores discovery seems to contradict assumptions about brain size and early human culture. The same kind of tools have been recovered from sites on the island dating to between 750 000 and 950 000 years ago, indicating that the Flores hominin population extends well back to the time that *H. erectus* was in Southeast Asia.[4] One explanation for this unusual population is that an early *Homo* was living on the island when sea levels rose, completely isolating it from its ancestral population. The population subsequently evolved from the larger hominins who were the norm to become a unique, small species of *Homo*. Size reduction is an evolutionary trend found in other species isolated on islands. In the absence of large predators there isn't any advantage to being large, and small size is an advantage when food is scarce in a bounded space like that of an island.

Not everyone agrees that the recent Flores Island discovery represents a new species of *Homo*. T. Jacob and colleagues have examined the bones and propose that they belong to modern humans who suffered abnormal growth and development.[5] The team collected data from the modern population living on the island and found that the chin and molar features thought not to be not present in modern populations are, in fact, present on the island. Among the 140 features examined not one lies outside the range of modern humans. Although the short stature and small brain of the Flores remains are certainly unusual, Jacob's team proposes an explanation for these features: they are consistent with individuals suffering from microcephaly, a disorder caused by genetic abnormalities and environmental factors that influence prenatal and postnatal development. The team also argues that early populations on the island were never completely isolated and the hypothesis of only one migration to the island cannot be justified. An estimated

[3] Brown, P., Sutikna, T., Morwood, M.J., Soejono, R.P., Jatmiko, Saptomo E.W., & Due, R.A. (2004). A new small-bodied hominin from the Late Pleistocene of Flores, Indonesia. *Nature 431*, 1055–1061.

[4] Brumm, A., Aziz, F., van den Bergh, G.D., Morwood, M.J., Moore, M.W., Kurniawan, I., Hobbs, D.R., & Fullagar R. (2006). Early stone technology on Flores and its implications for *Homo floresiensis*. *Nature 441*, 624–628.

[5] Jacob, T., Indriati, E., Soejono, R.P., Hsu, K., Frayer, D.W., Eckhardt, R.B., Kuperavage, A.J., Thorne, A., & Henneberg, M. (2006). Pygmoid Australomelanesian *Homo sapiens* skeletal remains from Liang Bua, Flores: Population affinities and pathological abnormalities. *PNAS*, *103*, 13421–13426.

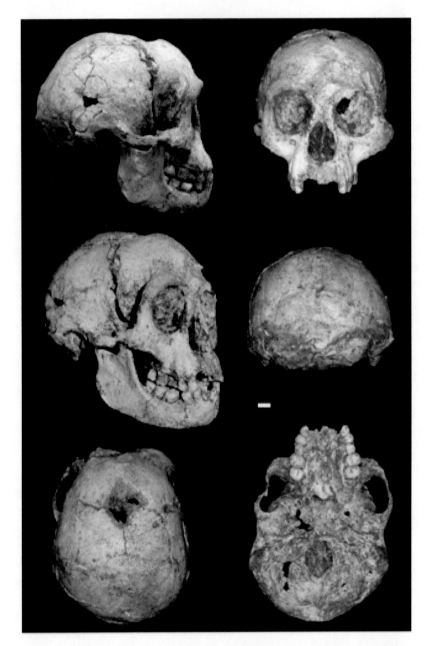

Skull of H. floresiensis *from Flores Island.* FIGURE 1 FROM BROWN P., SUTIKNA T., MORWOOD M.J., SOEJONO R.P., JATMIKO, SAPTOMO E.W., & DUE R.A. (2004). A NEW SMALL-BODIED HOMININ FROM THE LATE PLEISTOCENE OF FLORES, INDONESIA. NATURE 431:1055-1061

population of between 5800 and 7300 individuals would have been all the island could have supported by hunting and gathering, and that was too small a breeding population to survive for the 40 generations they would have been isolated. The two distinct views of just who the Flores people are will be debated for some time and the debate indicates just how difficult it can be to interpret the early human record.

UPPER PALAEOLITHIC TOOLS

The Upper Palaeolithic was a time of great technological innovation. Typical were blades, flint flakes at least twice as long as they are wide. Although Middle Palaeolithic toolmakers, especially in Africa, already made blades (some are illustrated in Chapter 9), they did not do so to the extent that their Upper Palaeolithic successors did. What made this possible were new techniques of core preparation that allowed more intensive production of highly standardized blades. The toolmaker formed a cylindrical core, struck the blade off near the edge of the core, and repeated this procedure, going around the core in one direction until finishing near its centre (Figure 10.1). The procedure is analogous to peeling long leaves off an artichoke. With this **blade technique**, an Upper Palaeolithic flint knapper could get 22 metres of working edge from a 1-kilogram core; a Mousterian knapper could get only 2 metres from the same-sized core.

Other efficient techniques of tool manufacture also came into common use at this time. One such method was **pressure flaking**, in which a bone, antler, or wooden tool was used to press rather than strike off small flakes as the final step in stone tool manufacture. The advantage of this technique was that the toolmaker had greater control over the final shape of the tool than is possible with percussion flaking alone. The so-called Solutrean laurel leaf blades found in Spain and France are examples of this technique. The longest of these blades is 33 centimetres in length but only about 6 millimetres thick. Through pressure flaking, blades could be worked with great precision into a variety of final forms, and worn tools could be effectively resharpened over and over until they were too small for further use.

In Northeast Asia, a blade-core innovation developed. Small, **wedge-shaped microcores** developed from which people prepared **microliths**, also called microblades. The core's most specialized form was made in Japan where bifaces were split down the long axis to produce a long, narrow striking platform. Wedge-shaped cores are found throughout much of Northeast Asia, including China, the Korean Peninsula, and Japan, but

Blade technique. A technique of stone tool manufacture by which long, parallel-sided flakes are struck off the edges of a specially prepared core.

Pressure flaking. A technique of stone tool manufacture in which a bone, antler, or wooden tool is used to press, rather than strike off, small flakes from a piece of flint or similar stone.

Wedge-shaped microcore. A stone that is usually prepared in the shape of a biface, split along the long axis to produce a flat surface or striking platform from which microliths are struck.

Microliths, also called microblades. The small (usually less than a few centimetres long), narrow, parallel-sided flakes removed from microcores.

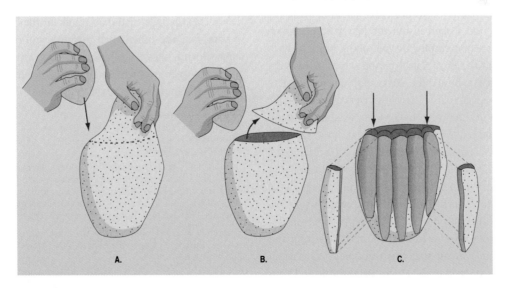

A.   B.   C.

FIGURE 10.1

During the Upper Palaeolithic, a new technique was used to manufacture blades. The stone is flaked to create a striking platform; long, almost parallel-sided flakes then are struck around the sides, providing sharp-edged blades.

In this form of pressure flaking the core is placed in a vice and a hard tip such as a piece of antler is inserted in a handle. The artisan uses his or her core muscles and body weight against the hafted antler piece to punch a long, narrow flake from the core.
GARY CRAWFORD

not in Europe or Western Asia.[6] The widespread use of these microliths in Northeast Asia indicates that it was more than just a novel way of making small tools efficiently. Eventually microliths became a part of the latest Upper Palaeolithic traditions in West Asia, Europe and elsewhere although they were not produced from wedge-shaped cores. The widespread miniaturization of blades likely means that they were an important adaptation to some situation common to northern regions during the last glacial period. Robert Elston and Jeffrey Brantingham have proposed that employing microliths was a way to reduce risk in the cold glacial period when it was very important that a hunter be successful when trying to bring down an animal.[7] Microliths were used to make bone and stone composite tools, which were more useful than a weapon made of a single material. Bone tools are more durable than stone (stone tends to get brittle in the cold and easily breaks when a hunter misses a shot) but take more time to manufacture and don't damage tissue as much as stone does. Composite weapons are superior because they are easily maintained by replacing a missing blade, perform well in cold weather, and are strong and lethal. It is no wonder that this technology saw widespread use by the end of the Upper Palaeolithic and continued in use for some time after (see Chapter 11).

Another common Upper Palaeolithic tool was the **burin**, although it too was invented earlier, in the Middle Palaeolithic. These implements, with their

chisel-like edges, facilitated the working of bone, horn, antler, and ivory into such useful things as fishhooks, harpoons, and eyed needles, all of which made life easier for *H. sapiens*, especially in northern regions. The spear-thrower, too, appeared at this time. Spear-throwers are wooden devices, one end of which is gripped in the hunter's hand, while the other end has a hole or hook, in or against which the end of the spear is placed (Figure 10.2). The spear-thrower is held so as to effectively extend the length of the hunter's arm, thereby increasing the velocity of the spear when thrown. Using a spear-thrower greatly added to the efficiency of the spear as a hunting tool. With handheld spears, hunters had to get close to their quarry to make the kill, and because many of the animals they hunted were quite large and fierce, this was a dangerous business. The need to approach closely, and the improbability of an instant kill, exposed the spear hunter to considerable risk. But with the spear-thrower, the effective killing distance was increased; experiments demonstrate that the effective killing distance of a spear when used with a spear-thrower is between 18 and 27 metres.[8]

Another important innovation, net hunting, appeared some time between 29 000 and 22 000 years ago.[9] Knotted nets, made from the fibres of wild plants such as hemp or nettle, left their impression on the clay floors of huts when people walked on them. These impressions were baked in when the huts later burned, which is how we know that nets existed. Their use accounts for the high number of hare, fox, and other small mammal and bird bones at archaeological sites. Like historically known net hunters, everyone—men, women, and children—probably participated, frightening animals with loud noises to drive them

[6] Lu, L.D. (1998). The microblade tradition in China: Regional chronologies and significance in the transition to neolithic. *Asian Perspectives*, 37, 84–112.

[7] Elston, R.G., & Brantingham, P.J. (2002). Microlithic technology in Northeast Asia: A risk minimizing strategy of the Late Paleolithic and Early Holocene. In R.G. Elston & S.L. Kuhn (Eds.), *Thinking small: Global perspectives on microlithization: Archaeological papers of the American Anthropological Association Number 12,* 103–116.

[8] Frayer, D.W. (1981). Body size, weapon use, and natural selection in the European Upper Paleolithic and Mesolithic. *American Anthropologist, 83,* 58.

[9] Pringle, H. (1997). Ice Age communities may be earliest known net hunters. *Science, 277,* 1203.

Burins. Stone tools with chisel-like edges used for working bone and antler.

FIGURE 10.2

Spear-throwers allowed individual Upper Palaeolithic people to throw spears at animals from a safe distance while still maintaining reasonable speed and accuracy. Contemporary enthusiasts of the Upper Palaeolithic are throwing the atlatl at competitions such as this one organized by the World Atlatl Association.

Shown here is one of the Solutrean laurel leaf bifaces from Europe. Such fine flint work requires a high degree of skill.   GARY CRAWFORD

ANTHROPOLOGY APPLIED

Stone Tools for Modern Surgeons

When anthropologist Irven DeVore of Harvard University was to have some minor melanomas removed from his face, he did not leave it up to the surgeon to supply his own scalpels. Instead, he had graduate student John Shea make a scalpel. Making a blade of obsidian (a naturally occurring volcanic "glass") by the same techniques used by Upper Palaeolithic people to make blades, he then hafted

These microphotographs of an obsidian blade (bottom photo) and a modern steel scalpel (top photo) illustrate the superiority of the obsidian. **WILLIAM A. HAVILAND/UVM PHOTO SERVICE**

this in a wooden handle, using melted pine resin as glue and then lashing it with sinew. After the procedure, the surgeon reported that the obsidian scalpel was superior to metal ones.[1]

DeVore was not the first to undergo surgery in which stone scalpels were used. In 1975, Don Crabtree, then at Idaho State University, prepared the scalpels that his surgeon would use in Crabtree's heart surgery. In 1980, Payson Sheets at the University of Colorado prepared obsidian scalpels that were used successfully in eye surgery. And in 1986, David Pokotylo of the Museum of Anthropology at the University of British Columbia underwent reconstructive surgery on his hand with blades he himself had made (the hafting was done by his museum colleague, Len McFarlane).

The reason for these uses of scalpels modelled on ancient stone tools is that the anthropologists realized that obsidian is superior in almost every way to materials normally used to make scalpels: It is 210 to 1050 times sharper than surgical steel, 100 to 500 times sharper than a razor blade, and three times sharper than a diamond blade (which not only costs much more, but also cannot be made with more than 3 millimetres of cutting edge). Obsidian blades are easier to cut with and do less damage in the process (under a microscope, incisions made with the sharpest steel blades show torn ragged edges and are littered with bits of displaced flesh).[2] As a consequence, the surgeon has better control over what she or he is doing and the incisions heal faster with less scarring and pain. Because of the superiority of obsidian scalpels, Sheets went so far as to form a corporation in partnership with Boulder, Colorado, eye surgeon Dr. Firmon Hardenbergh. Together, they developed a means of producing cores of uniform size from molten glass, as well as a machine to detach blades from the cores.

[1] Shreeve, J. (1995). The Neandertal enigma: Solving the mystery of modern human origins (p. 134). New York: William Morrow.

[2] Sheets, P.D. (1987). Dawn of a New Stone Age in eye surgery. In R.J. Sharer & W. Ashmore (Eds.), Archaeology: Discovering our past (p. 231). Palo Alto, CA: Mayfield.

to where hunters were stationed with their nets. In this way, large amounts of meat could be amassed in ways that did not put a premium on speed or strength.

A further improvement of hunting techniques came with the invention of the bow and arrow, which appeared first in Africa, but not until the end of the Upper Palaeolithic in Europe. The greatest advantage of the bow is that it increases the distance between hunter and prey; beyond 18 to 27 metres, the accuracy and penetration of a spear thrown with a spear-thrower is quite poor, whereas even a poor bow will shoot an arrow farther, with greater accuracy and penetrating power. A good bow is effective even at 91 metres. Thus, hunters were able to maintain an even safer distance between themselves and dangerous prey, dramatically decreasing their chances of being seriously injured by an animal fighting for its life.

These changes in hunting weaponry and techniques likely were responsible for the less robust bodies of Upper Palaeolithic people. Spear hunting, particularly where large, fierce animals are the prey as they often were in Europe, demands strength, power, and overall robustness on the part of the hunter. Without them, the hunter is poorly equipped to withstand the rigours of close-quarter killing. A high nutritional price must be paid, however, for large, powerful, and robust bodies. Therefore, as speed and strength become less important

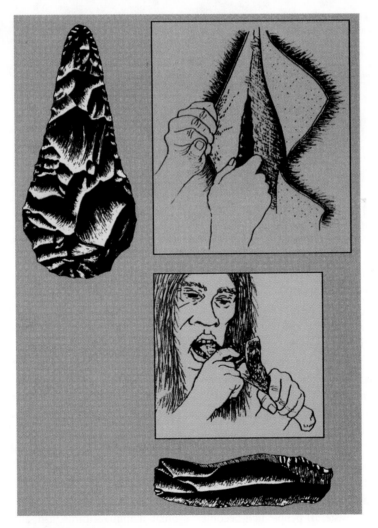

FIGURE 10.3

Two Upper Palaeolithic stone tools, and how they might have been used to skin an animal and cut meat while eating.

The 23 000 year Ohalo II site contains the remains of six brush huts such as the one illustrated here. The site also has a burial of an adult male with a 0.5 m stone platform nearby, and several hearths, all indicating a rich, relatively settled life during the Upper Palaeolithic here.
ZINMAN INSTITUTE OF ARCHAEOLOGY, UNIVERSITY OF HAIFA, MT. CARMEL, 31905, ISRAEL, HTTP://OHALO.HAIFA.AC.IL/

for success, selection for them slacked off, and people tended to become weaker and less robust. As a consequence, nutritional requirements were reduced.

Upper Palaeolithic peoples not only had better tools but also a greater diversity of types than earlier peoples (Figures 10.3 and 10.4). The highly developed Upper Palaeolithic kit included tools for use during different seasons, and regional variation in tool kits was greater than ever before. Thus, it is impossible to speak of an Upper Palaeolithic culture, even in a relatively small peripheral region like Europe; instead, one must make note of the many different traditions that made it possible for people to adapt ever more specifically to the various environments in which they were living. Just how proficient (and even wasteful) people had become at securing a livelihood is indicated by boneyards containing thousands of skeletons. At Solutré in France, for example, Upper Palaeolithic hunters killed 10 000 horses; at Predmost in Czechoslovakia, they were

responsible for the deaths of 1000 mammoths. The favoured big game of European hunters, however, was reindeer, which they killed in even greater numbers.

It would be a mistake to assume that Upper Palaeolithic people consumed only animals and lived relatively mobile lives in order to pursue game animals. Hunting and gathering peoples made extensive use of plants where they were abundant. The Ohalo II site at the southern end of the Sea of Galilee in Israel has revealed that people there harvested at least 147 types of plants including wild barley and wild wheat from about 23 000 years ago, the height of the last glacial period,[10] and archaeologists have recovered over 90 000 plant remains including 19 000 grains of grass. Small mammals, birds, fish, and shellfish were also part of the Ohalo II subsistence.

---

[10] Weiss, E., Wetterstrom, W., Nadel, D., & Bar-Yosef, O. (2004). The broad spectrum revisited: Evidence from plant remains. *PNAS, 101,* 9551–9555.

UPPER PALAEOLITHIC ART

Although the creativity of Upper Palaeolithic peoples is evident in the tools and weapons they made, it is nowhere more evident than in their outburst of artistic expression. Some have argued that this was made possible by a newly evolved biological ability to manipulate symbols and make images, but in view of the modern-sized brains of archaic *sapiens* and increasingly compelling evidence that even the Neandertals were capable of speech, such an idea is hard to maintain. Like agriculture, which came later (see Chapter 11), the artistic explosion may have been no more than a consequence of innovations made by a people who had had the capacity to make them for tens of thousands of years already.

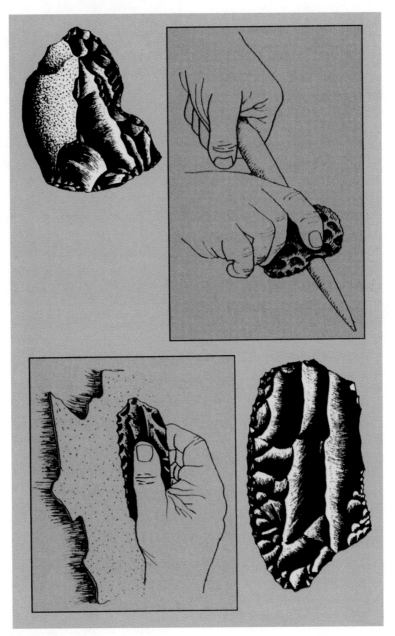

FIGURE 10.4

An Upper Palaeolithic "spokeshave" (top) and scraper (bottom), and the ways they were used.

In fact, just as many of the distinctive tools that were commonly used in Upper Palaeolithic times first appear in the Middle Palaeolithic, so too do objects of art. In Southwest Asia, a crude figurine of volcanic tuff is some 250 000 years old.[11] Although it is unusual, the fact that it exists at all indicates that people had the ability to carve all sorts of things from wood, a substance easier to work than volcanic tuff but rarely preserved for long periods of time. Furthermore, ochre "crayons" from Middle Palaeolithic contexts in various parts of the world must have been used to decorate or mark something. In Southern Africa, for example, regular use of yellow and red ochre goes back 130 000 years, with some evidence as old as 200 000 years.[12] Perhaps pigments were used on people's bodies, as well as objects, as the 50 000-year-old mammoth-tooth *churinga,* discussed and illustrated in Chapter 9, might suggest.

That there was music in the lives of Upper Palaeolithic peoples is indicated by the presence of bone flutes and whistles in sites, some up to 30 000 years old. But again, such instruments may have their origin in Middle Palaeolithic prototypes, such as the probable "Neandertal flute" discussed in Chapter 9. Although we cannot be sure just where and when it happened, some genius discovered that bows could be used not just for killing, but to make music as well. Because the bow and arrow is an Upper Palaeolithic invention, the musical bow likely is as well. We do know that the musical bow is the oldest of all stringed instruments, and its invention ultimately made possible the development of all of the stringed instruments with which we are familiar today.

The earliest evidence of figurative pictures goes back 32 000 years in Europe and is probably equally old in Africa. Both engravings and paintings are known from many rock shelters and outcrops in Southern Africa, where they continued to be made by indigenous peoples of South Africa up until about 100 years ago. Scenes feature both humans and animals, depicted with extraordinary skill, often in association with geometric and other abstract motifs.

Because this rock art tradition continued unbroken into historic times, it has been possible to discover what this art means. There is a close connection between the art and shamanism, and many scenes depict visions seen in states of trance. Distortions in the art, usually of human figures, represent sensations felt by individuals in a state of trance, whereas the geometric designs depict illusions

Crude though it may be, this piece of tuff, carved some 250 000 years ago, looks like a woman if viewed from the right angle. It was found in 1980 on the Golan Heights in the Middle East.
ALEXANDER MARSHACK, NEW YORK UNIVERSITY

that originate in the central nervous system in altered states of consciousness. These **entoptic phenomena** are luminous grids, dots, zigzags, and other designs that seem to shimmer, pulsate, rotate, and expand, and are seen as one enters a state of trance (sufferers of migraines experience similar hallucinations). The animals depicted in this art, often with startling realism, are not the ones most often eaten. Rather, they are powerful beasts like

---

[11] Appenzeller, T. (1998). Art: Evolution or revolution? *Science, 282,* 1452.

[12] Barham, L.S. (1998). Possible early pigment use in south-central Africa. *Current Anthropology, 39,* 709.

Entoptic phenomena. Bright pulsating forms that are generated by the central nervous system and seen in states of trance.

the eland, and this power is important to shamans—individuals skilled at manipulating supernatural powers and spirits for human benefit—who try to harness it for their rain-making and other rituals.

Rock art in Australia goes back at least 45 000 years, with the earliest examples consisting entirely of entoptic motifs. But the Upper Palaeolithic art that is most famous—largely because most students of prehistoric art are themselves of European background—is that of Europe. The earliest of this art took the form of sculpture and engravings, often portraying such animals as reindeer, horses, bears, and ibexes; however, there are also numerous portrayals of voluptuous women with exaggerated sexual and reproductive characteristics. Many appear to be pregnant, and some are shown in birthing postures. These so-called Venus figures have been found at sites from southwestern France to as far east as Siberia. Made of stone, ivory, antler, or baked clay, they differ little in style from place to place, testifying to the sharing of ideas over vast distances. Although some have interpreted the Venuses as objects associated with a fertility cult, others suggest that they may have been exchanged to cement alliances among groups.

Most spectacular are the paintings on the walls of 200 or so caves in southern France and northern Spain,

the oldest of which date from about 32 000 years ago. Most common are visually accurate portrayals of Ice Age mammals, including bison, bulls, horses, mammoths, and stags, often painted one on top of another. Although well represented in other media, humans are not commonly portrayed in cave paintings, nor are scenes or depictions of events at all common. Instead, the animals are often abstracted from nature and rendered two-dimensionally without regard to the conformations of the surfaces they are on—no small achievement for these early artists. Sometimes, though, the artists did make use of bulges and other features of the rock to impart a more three-dimensional feeling. Frequently, the paintings are in hard-to-get-at places while suitable surfaces in more accessible places remain untouched. In some caves, the lamps by which the artists worked have been found; these are spoon-shaped objects of sandstone in which animal fat was burned. Experimentation has shown that such lamps would have provided adequate illumination over several hours.

The techniques used by Upper Palaeolithic people to create their cave paintings were unravelled a decade ago through the experimental work of Michel Lorblanchet. Interestingly, they turn out to be the same ones used by aboriginal rock painters in Australia.

In South Africa, rock art, such as this painting, includes realistic images of animals as well as things seen by dancers while in states of trance. **GARY CRAWFORD**

ORIGINAL STUDY

Palaeolithic Paint Job

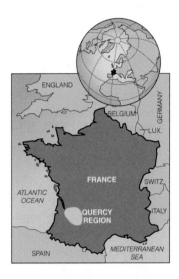

Lorblanchet's recent bid to re-create one of the most important Ice Age images in Europe was an affair of the heart as much as the head. "I tried to abandon my skin of a modern citizen, tried to experience the feeling of the artist, to enter the dialogue between the rock and the man," he explains. Every day for a week in the fall of 1990 he drove the 20 miles from his home in the medieval village of Cajarc into the hills

above the river Lot. There, in a small, practically inaccessible cave, he transformed himself into an Upper Palaeolithic painter.

And not just any Upper Palaeolithic painter, but the one who 18,400 years ago crafted the dotted horses inside the famous cave of Pech Merle.

You can still see the original horses in Pech Merle's vast underground geologic splendor. You enter through a narrow passageway and soon find yourself gazing across a grand cavern to where the painting seems to hang in the gloom. "Outside, the landscape is very different from the one the Upper Palaeolithic people saw," says Lorblanchet. "But in here, the landscape is the same as it was more than 18,000 years ago. You see what the Upper Palaeolithic people experienced." No matter where you look in this cavern, the eye is drawn back to the panel of horses.

The two horses face away from each other, rumps slightly overlapping, their outlines sketched in black. The animal on the right seems to come alive as it merges with a crook in the edge of the panel, the perfect natural shape for a horse's head. But the impression of naturalism quickly fades as the eye falls on the painting's dark dots. There are more than 200 of them, deliberately distributed within and below the bodies and arcing around the right-hand horse's head and mane. More cryptic still are a smattering of red dots and half-circles and the floating outline of a fish. The surrealism is completed by six disembodied human hands stenciled above and below the animals.

Lorblanchet began thinking about re-creating the horses after a research trip to Australia over a decade ago. Not only is Australia a treasure trove of rock art, but its aboriginal people are still creating it. "In Queensland I learned how people painted by spitting pigment onto the rock," he recalls. "They spat paint and used their hand, a piece of cloth, or a feather as a screen to create different lines and other effects. Elsewhere in Australia people used chewed twigs as paintbrushes, but in Queensland the spitting technique worked best." The rock surfaces there were too uneven for extensive brushwork, he adds—just as they are in Quercy.

This spotted horse in the French cave of Pech Merle was painted by an Upper Palaeolithic artist. **(C) JEAN VERTUT**

When Lorblanchet returned home he looked at the Quercy paintings with a new eye. Sure enough, he began seeing the telltale signs of spit-painting—lines with edges that were sharply demarcated on one side and fuzzy on the other, as if they had been airbrushed—instead of the brushstrokes he and others had assumed were there. Could you produce lines that were crisp on both edges with the same technique, he wondered, and perhaps dots too? Archaeologists had long recognized that hand stencils, which are common in prehistoric art, were produced by spitting paint around a hand held to the wall. But no one had thought that entire animal images could be created this way. Before he could test his ideas, however, Lorblanchet had to find a suitable rock face—the original horses were painted on a roughly vertical panel 13 feet across and 6 feet high. With the help of a speleologist, he eventually found a rock face in a remote cave high in the hills and set to work.

Following the aboriginal practices he had witnessed, Lorblanchet first made a light outline sketch of the horses with a charred stick. Then he prepared black pigment for the painting. "My intention had been to use manganese dioxide, as the Pech Merle painter did," says Lorblanchet, referring to one of the minerals ground up for paint by the early artists. "But I was advised that manganese is somewhat toxic, so I used wood charcoal instead." (Charcoal was used as pigment by Palaeolithic painters in other caves, so Lorblanchet felt he could justify his concession to safety.) To turn the charcoal into paint, Lorblanchet ground it with a limestone block, put the powder in his mouth, and diluted it to the right consistency with saliva and water. For red pigment he used ocher from the local iron-rich clay.

He started with the dark mane of the right hand horse. "I spat a series of dots and fused them together to represent tufts of hair," he says, unselfconsciously reproducing the spitting action as he talks. "Then I painted the horse's back by blowing the pigment below my hand held so"—he holds his hand flat against the rock with his thumb tucked in to form a straight line—"and used it like a stencil to produce a sharp upper edge and a diffused lower edge. You get an illusion of the animal's rounded flank this way."

He experimented as he went. "You see the angular rump?" he says, pointing to the original painting. "I reproduced that by holding my hand perpendicular to the rock, with my palm slightly bent, and I spat along the edge formed by my hand and the rock." He found he could produce sharp lines, such as those in the tail and in the upper hind leg, by spitting into the gap between parallel hands. The belly demanded more ingenuity; he spat paint into a V-shape formed by his two splayed hands, rubbed it into a curved swath to shape the belly's outline, then finger-painted short protruding lines to suggest the animals' shaggy hair. Neatly outlined dots, he found, could not be made by blowing a thin jet of charcoal onto the wall. He had to spit pigment through a hole made in an animal skin. "I spent seven hours a day for a week," he says. "Puff ... puff ... puff. ... It was exhausting, particularly because there was carbon monoxide in the cave. But you experience something special, painting like that. You feel you are breathing the image onto the rock—projecting your spirit from the deepest part of your body onto the rock surface."

Was that what the Paleolithic painter felt when creating this image? "Yes, I know it doesn't sound very scientific," Lorblanchet says of his highly personal style of investigation, "but the intellectual games of the structuralists haven't got us very far, have they? Studying rock art shouldn't be an intellectual game. It is about understanding humanity. That's why I believe the experimental approach is valid in this case."

Source: R. Lewin. (1993). Paleolithic paint job. *Discover, 14*(7), 67–69. Copyright ©1993 The Walt Disney Co. Reprinted with permission of *Discover Magazine*.

Hypotheses to account for the early European cave art are difficult because they so often depend on conjectural and subjective interpretations. Some have argued that it is art for art's sake; but if that is so, why were animals so often painted over one another, and why were they so often placed in inaccessible places? The latter might suggest that they were for ceremonial purposes and that the caves served as religious sanctuaries. One suggestion is that the animals were drawn to ensure success in the hunt, another that their depiction was seen as a way to promote fertility and increase the size of the herds on which humans depended. (In Altimira Cave in Northern

Upper Palaeolithic art was quite varied: a carved antler spear-thrower ornamented by two headless ibexes (from Enlene Cave, France); a female Venus figurine of yellow steatite (from a cave at Liguria, Italy); and one of the sandstone lamps by which artists worked in caves (from Lascaux Cave, France). **NEGATIVE NO. K15806, K15872, K15823 COURTESY DEPARTMENT OF LIBRARY SCIENCES, AMERICAN MUSEUM OF NATURAL HISTORY**

Spain, for example, the art shows a pervasive concern for the sexual reproduction of the bison.[13] In cave art generally, though, the painted animals bear little relationship to those most frequently hunted. Furthermore, there are few depictions of animals being hunted or killed, nor are there depictions of animals copulating or with exaggerated sexual parts as there are in the Venus figures.) Another suggestion is that rites by which youngsters were initiated into adulthood took place in the painted galleries. In support of this idea, footprints, most of which are small, have been found in the clay floors of several caves, and at Tuc d'Audoubert in France, they even circle two modelled clay bison dated to about 15 000 years ago. The animals painted, so this argument goes, may have had to do with knowledge being transmitted from the elders to the youths. Furthermore, the transmission of information in a symbolic manner might be implied by countless so-called signs, apparently abstract designs that accompany much Upper

Palaeolithic art. Some have interpreted these as tallies of animals killed, a reckoning of time according to a lunar calendar, or both.

These abstract designs, including such ones as the spots on the Pech Merle horses, suggest yet another possibility. For the most part, these are just like the entoptic designs seen by subjects in experiments dealing with altered states of consciousness, which are so consistently present in the rock art of southern Africa. Furthermore, the rock art of southern Africa shows the same painting of new images over older ones, as well as the same sort of fixation on large, powerful animals instead of the ones most often eaten. Thus, the cave art of Europe may well represent the same depictions of trance experiences, painted after the fact. Consistent with this interpretation, the caves themselves are conducive to the sort of sensory distortion that can induce trance.

[13] Halverson, J. (1989). Review of the book *Altimira revisited and other essays on early art. American Antiquity, 54,* 883.

GENDER PERSPECTIVES

"Venus" Figurines

Since the first "Venus" figurines were discovered in the 1800s, scholars have attempted to interpret the purpose or symbolism of these carvings. Most commonly the objects are associated with a fertility cult, or a Mother Goddess, suggesting that religion and art were inextricably intertwined in the Upper Paleolithic. The exaggerated features were thought symbolic of a pregnant woman, and thus human fertility. Another interpretation suggests that these figurines were erotica, the exaggerated female features being the Paleolithic version of "Playboy bunnies."[1] Other, less well known suggestions include portraits of Paleolithic people; initiation figures; good luck or protective amulets, for example, to ease difficulties in childbirth; puppets; priestesses; witches; and a child's doll.

We see two basic interpretations of the "Venus" figurines. One views the figurines as a representation of idealized womanhood, a symbol of fertility and procreation, within a male-dominated religious system. Today, many archaeologists reject the notion of these figurines representing women as sex objects or breeders. A more recent interpretation, grounded in gendered archaeology, interprets the figurines as symbols of the importance, status, and power of Upper Paleolithic women.

If we examine evidence in the archaeological record, both of these interpretations present problems. First, not all of the figurines are of human form. Indeed, some are so vague it is impossible to determine what they represent. Second, not all of the figurines are female; some are definitely male, and others are indeterminate. In addition, some of the female figurines are quite slim.

Regardless of the explanation, these interpretations tend to be more representative of our own social condition and idealism, and our own gender biases, including unconscious ones, than any reality in the Upper Paleolithic. To suggest female dominance in the Upper Paleolithic based on these figurines is every bit as misleading, inaccurate, and gender-biased as the earlier interpretations.

_____

[1] Kurtén, B. (1986). *How to deep freeze a mammoth*. New York: Columbia University Press.

Source: Adapted from Russell, P. (1998). The Paleolithic mother-goddess: Fact or fiction? In K. Hays-Gilpin, K. and D.S. Whitley, D.S. (Eds.), *Reader in gender archaeology*. (pp. 261–268). New York: Routledge.

Artistic expression, whatever its purpose may have been, was not confined to rock surfaces and portable objects alone. Upper Palaeolithic peoples also ornamented their bodies with necklaces of perforated animal teeth, shells, and beads of bone, stone, and ivory; rings; bracelets; and anklets. Clothing, too, was adorned with beads. This should alert us to the probability that quite a lot of art was executed in perishable materials—wood carving, paintings on bark or animal skins, and the like. Thus, the rarity or absence of Upper Palaeolithic art in some parts of the inhabited world may be more apparent than real, as people elsewhere worked with materials unlikely to survive so long in the archaeological record.

OTHER ASPECTS OF UPPER PALAEOLITHIC CULTURE

Upper Palaeolithic peoples lived not only in caves and rock shelters, but also in structures built out in the open. In Ukraine, for example, the remains have been found of sizable settlements, in which huts were built on frameworks of intricately stacked mammoth bones. Where the ground was frozen, cobblestones were heated and placed in the earth to sink in, thereby providing sturdy, dry floors. Their hearths, no longer shallow depressions or flat surfaces that radiated back little heat, were instead stone-lined pits that conserved heat for extended

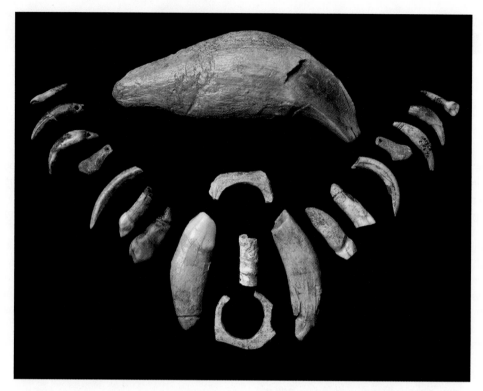

Pendants and beads for personal adornment became common in the Upper Palaeolithic. In Europe, most were made by Cro-Magnons, but some—like those shown here—were made by Neandertals. The earliest undisputed items of personal adornment are some 40 000-year-old beads from Africa made from ostrich egg shell. CLAUDIO VAZQUEZ/DISCOVER MAGAZINE, AUGUST 1999, P 72.

periods and made for more efficient cooking. For the outdoors, Upper Palaeolithic peoples had the same sort of tailored clothing worn in historic times by the indigeneous peoples of Northeast Asia, Alaska, and Canada. They engaged in long-distance trade, as indicated, for example, by the presence of seashells and Baltic amber at sites several hundred kilometres from the sources of these materials. Although Middle Palaeolithic peoples also made use of rare and distant materials, they did not do so with the regularity seen in the Upper Palaeolithic.

THE SPREAD OF UPPER PALAEOLITHIC PEOPLES

Such was the effectiveness of their cultures that Upper Palaeolithic peoples were able to expand into regions previously uninhabited by their archaic forebears (Figure 10.5). Colonization of Siberia began about 42 000 years ago, although it took something like 10 000 years before they reached the northeastern part

of that region. Much earlier, by 60 000 years ago, people managed to get to Australia and New Guinea. To do this, they had to use some kind of watercraft to make the difficult crossing of at least 90 kilometres of water that separated Australia and New Guinea (then a single landmass) from the Asian continent throughout Palaeolithic times. Once in Australia, these people created some of the world's earliest sophisticated rock art, some 15 000 to 10 000 years earlier than the more famous European cave paintings. Other evidence for sophisticated ritual activity in early Australia is provided by the burial of a man at least 40 000 and possibly 60 000 years ago.[14] His fingers were intertwined around his penis and red ochre had been scattered over the body. It may be that this pigment had more than symbolic value; for example, its iron salts have antiseptic and deodorizing properties, and there are recorded instances in which red ochre is associated with prolonging

---

[14] Rice, P. (2000). Paleoanthropology 2000—part 1. *General Anthropology*, 7(1), 11; Zimmer, C. (1999). New date for the dawn of dream time. *Science, 284,* 1243.

Reconstruction of an Upper Palaeolithic hut with walls of interlocked mammoth mandibles.
GORAN BURENHULT, GOTLAND UNIVERSITY, SWEDEN

Epoch
PLEISTOCENE

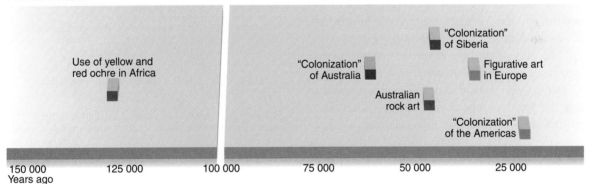

Use of yellow and
red ochre in Africa

"Colonization"
of Australia

Australian
rock art

"Colonization"
of Siberia

Figurative art
in Europe

"Colonization"
of the Americas

| 150 000 | 125 000 | 100 000 | 75 000 | 50 000 | 25 000 |

Years ago

FIGURE 10.5

The spread of people and of creativity.

life and is used medicinally to treat particular conditions or infections. One historically known indigenous Australian society is reported to use ochre to heal wounds, scars, and burns, and a person with internal pain is covered with the substance and placed in the sun to promote sweating. What is especially interesting in view of the impressive accomplishments of indigenous Australians is that the tools used by these people are remarkably similar to those of the Eurasian Middle Palaeolithic. Clearly, simplicity of tool kits does not bespeak absence of sophisticated intellectual capabilities.

Issues surrounding the peopling of the Americas have been a matter of lively debate. Genetic and linguistic evidence suggests that the process of peopling the Americas was anything but simple. Aboriginal peoples of the Americas have the most diverse languages of any continent. At least five distinct genetic groupings have been found among pre-contact and later aboriginal peoples. There may have been many migrations, or there may have been a single one lasting millennia. The timing of the movement of people into the Americas is also at issue. We are far from a clear understanding of these issues.

Most archaeologists agree that aboriginal Americans have their roots in Northeast Asia. The biological affiliations of these early inhabitants of the Americas are not clear. Only a few well-preserved crania older than 8000 years have been found, but none resemble more recent aboriginal peoples in the Americas. This should not be surprising. Before 10 000 years ago East Asian populations had only generalized Asian characteristics. Generalized Asians are known in Southeast Asia during the Palaeolithic.[15] In many ways they are closer to modern Europeans than to contemporary East Asians, but they are definitely not of direct European ancestry. What human biologists consider a typical modern Asian physical type actually arose after 10 000 years ago in Northeast Asia and is considered specialized, or adapted to the local conditions of Northeast Asia[16] The more modern Northeast Asian type is known as **Sinodont**, and the Southeast Asian type is **Sundadont**. The two are distinguished on the basis of eight dental traits. The Ainu of northern Japan are a living example of generalized Sundadont Asians.[17] The first people in the Americas who came through Northeast Asia did so before the Sinodont type developed. Specialized characteristics that represent the Sinodont type are more common in Canada's Far North, indicating that subsequent migration of Asians into the Americas occurred after the specialization evolved in Northeast Asia.

Molecular anthropology is having a significant impact on our understanding of the relationship of peoples of the Americas to each other and to Asian populations. Mitochondrial DNA (mtDNA) analysis indicates the existence of five **haplotypes** found in varying proportions in most populations of First Nations ancestry. Four of the haplotypes are very common while one is exceedingly rare. All are found throughout the Americas. Western and Northern Canadian groups are mainly one group, but the other groups are also present. The fact that all aboriginal American peoples have all types represented among them

means that mixing of populations after several migrations has been considerable, or that there was only one migration. Some mutations are found in the mtDNA of aboriginal peoples, just as they are found in all populations. Assuming a constant mutation rate, the initial emergence of aboriginal ancestral lines took place between 14 000 and 11 000 years ago.[18]

Securely dated remains from Monte Verde, a site in south-central Chile, place people there by 12 500 years ago, if not earlier. People were also exploiting maritime resources at the Quebrada Jaguay site in coastal Peru 11 000 years ago. People were settled at Meadowcroft Rockshelter in Pennsylvania as early as 20 000 years ago. Johanna Nichols's linguistic interpretation is consistent with the archaeological view that the first people to arrive in North America did so by 20 000 years ago. She bases this estimate on the time it took various languages to spread from their homelands—Celtic languages in Europe, Inuit languages in the Arctic, and Athabaskan languages from interior Western Canada to New Mexico and Arizona (Navajo). She concludes that it would have taken at least 7000 years for people to reach south-central Chile.[19]

The conventional wisdom has long been that people first spread into North America over dry land that connected Siberia Northeast Asia to Alaska. This so-called

---

[15] Howells, W.W. (1983). Origins of the Chinese people: Interpretations of the recent evidence. In D.N. Keightly (Ed.), *The origins of the Chinese civilization*. Berkeley: University of California Press.

[16] Lahr, M.M. (1996). *The evolution of modern human diversity: A study of cranial variation*. New York: Cambridge University Press.

[17] Ibid.

[18] Fiedel, S.J. (2000). The peopling of the New World: Present evidence, new theories, and future directions. *Journal of Archaeological Research, 8*, 39–103.

[19] Nichols, J. (1998). The first Americans, ca. 20,000 B.C. *Discover, 19* (6), 24.

Sinodont. The modern Northeast Asian populations typified by a high complexity of dental characteristics such as root number.

Sundadont. Southeast Asian populations with generalized features, particularly less elaborate dental characteristics than in the Sinodont pattern.

Haplotype. A set of closely linked genes on a chromosome that tends to be inherited together as a unit.

land bridge was a consequence of the buildup of great continental glaciers. As these ice masses grew, there was a worldwide lowering of sea levels, causing an emergence of land in places like the Bering Straits, where seas today are shallow. Thus, Alaska became, in effect, an eastward extension of Northeast Asia (Figure 10.6).

The earliest Upper Palaeolithic technology in Northeast Asia is from the Lake Baikal region.[20] Radiocarbon dates indicate a transition from the Middle to Upper Palaeolithic about the same time as in Western Eurasia, that is, shortly before 40 000 years ago. The wedge-shaped core and microlith technology typical of the Northeast Asian Late Upper Palaeolithic is also found in the Americas, although its distribution is limited to Northwest North America. Its earliest manifestation is known as the Northwest Microblade Tradition and dates from 11 000 to 6000 years ago.[21] Some historical relationship likely exists between the technologies in Northwestern North America and Northeast Asia, but the technology does not appear to be ancestral to the Palaeoindian Clovis Tradition.

Palaeoindians hunted big game, such as mammoths, caribou, and now-extinct forms of bison. The earliest Palaeoindians are known as Clovis after the characteristic fluted points they used that were first found in Clovis, New Mexico. The archaeological record for potentially earlier occupants of the New World are usually referred to as "Pre-Clovis" and they are not grouped with Palaeoindians. Fluted points are finely made, with large channel flakes removed from one or both surfaces. This thinned section was inserted into the notched end of a spear shaft for a sturdy haft. Fluted points are found from the Atlantic seaboard to the Pacific coast, and from Alaska down into Panama. So efficient were the hunters who made these points that they may have hastened the extinction of the mammoth and other large Pleistocene mammals. By driving large numbers of animals over cliffs, they killed many more than they could possibly use, thus wasting huge amounts of meat. Palaeoindians did not use wedge-shaped cores. The contrast of the Clovis technology with that of the Northeast Asians is striking.

---

[20] Goebel, T., & Aksenov, M. (1995). Accelerator radiocarbon dating of the Upper Palaeolithic in Siberia. *Antiquity, 69*, 349–357.

[21] LeBlanc, R., & Ives, J.W. (1986). The Bezya site: A wedge-shaped core assemblage from northeastern Alberta. *Canadian Journal of Archaeology 10*, 59–98.

Palaeoindians. The earliest inhabitants of North America.

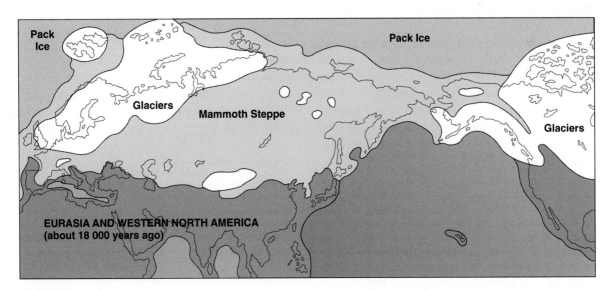

FIGURE 10.6

As this map shows, the land connecting Northeast Asia and Alaska at the height of the last glaciation was not so much a bridge for people to cross into North America as it was a peripheral portion of a region into which human populations in the Upper Palaeolithic spread (Fig. 10.5). Other populations likely moved by boat along the coast, arriving in North America south of the ice. Once the ice barrier between lower North America and Alaska receded, opportunities for gene flow between aboriginal peoples of the Americas and East Asians would have increased.

Although ancient Northeast Asians may indeed have spread eastward, it is now clear that their way south was blocked by massive glaciers until 13 000 years ago at the earliest. Three times during the last glacial period, sea levels were low enough to make Siberia, Alaska, and Yukon Territory one contiguous land mass known as Beringia. Here, archaeologists believe that Upper Palaeolithic people lived as they did elsewhere in Asia, following and hunting animals in their seasonal rounds and moving to collect plants when they were in season for food, teas, medicine, and other purposes. A few occupations on the North American side of Beringia evidence peoples' presence there by at least 15 000 years ago. At the Bluefish Caves in Yukon Territory the discovery of bones and small tools indicates human presence between 15 000 and 12 000 years ago. Pre-Clovis people appear to have already been living further south of the glaciers by this time, however. Thus, the question of how people first came to the Americas has been reopened by the discoveries at such sites as Monte Verde and Quebrada Jaguay in South America that date at least to 12 500 and 11 000 years ago. Monte Verde is at least as old as Clovis and Quebrada Jaguay evidences a coastal adaptation that is unlike Clovis. Beringia may not have been particularly hospitable, suggesting to some archaeologists that regular coastal travel for hunting, fishing, and other activities eventually brought people to North America. Like the first Australians, the first Americans may have come by boat, perhaps travelling between islands or ice-free pockets of coastline, from as far away as the Japanese islands and down North America's Northwest coast. Unfortunately, because sea levels were lower than they are today, coastal sites used by early voyagers would now be under water.

The Palaeoindian fluted-point tradition poses a dilemma because it appears so suddenly in North America, and no fluted points were being manufactured anywhere in the Old World. Curiously, the technology most closely resembling Clovis is found in the Upper Palaeolithic of France and Spain, not Asia. Dennis Stanford of the Smithsonian Institution hypothesizes that small numbers of Upper Palaeolithic people could have easily made it to the Grand Banks, some of which was dry land because of lowered sea levels. From there, migration westward was almost inevitable. A recently documented genetic group, or haplotype, found in about

20 000 indigenous North Americans and in some pre-contact populations is otherwise found only in Europe.[22]

The oldest known site in glaciated Canada is the Debert site in Nova Scotia. Debert was occupied by Palaeoindians who manufactured Clovis points much as their relatives did elsewhere in North America.[23] The site, dating to about 10 200 years ago,[24] may have been situated to exploit migrating caribou, which were common in Nova Scotia at the time. The site was excavated by George MacDonald of the National Museum of Man (now the National Museum of Civilization). This was shortly after the glaciers started to recede from this part of Canada. Since Clovis peoples were well established in unglaciated North America, mainly what is now the United States, they would have had to migrate from these unglaciated areas to the newly exposed land in what is now Canada. One of the closest Clovis sites outside Nova Scotia is the Vail site in Maine, and it appears to date several centuries earlier than Debert.[25] The artifacts at Debert are spread over 9 hectares. All evidence points to the people having been relatively mobile, so the site does not represent a large town; small groups returning seasonally used the locale. Another important Nova Scotia Palaeoindian location was excavated in 1990. The Belmont site is about the same size as Debert and is a Clovis site as well.

Debert and Bluefish Caves lie thousands of kilometres apart at opposite ends of Canada, and few sites in Canada rival them in age. One is Kilgii Gwaay on Ellen Island, British Columbia.[26] Dating from about 9500 to 9400 years ago, it is among the oldest sites in the coastal Americas and suggests the people had a

[22] Stanford, D., & Bradley, B. (1999). Constructing the Solutrean solution. Retrieved July 27, 2007, from the World Wide Web: www.clovisinthesoutheast.net/stanford.html.

[23] MacDonald, G. (1969). *Debert: A Palaeo-indian site in Central Nova Scotia*. Anthropology Papers, No. 16. Ottawa: National Museum of Man.

[24] Ellis, C. (2004). Understanding "Clovis" fluted point variability in the Northeast: A perspective from the Debert Site, Nova Scotia. *Canadian Journal of Archaeology, 28.*

[25] Gramly, R. (1982). *The Vail site: A Palaeo-Indian encampment in Maine.* Buffalo: Buffalo Society of Natural Sciences, Bulletin Series, Volume 30.

[26] Fedje, D.W., Wigen, R.J., Mackie, Q., Lake, C., & Sumpter, I. (2001). Preliminary results from investigations at Kilgii Gwaay: An early Holocene archaeological site on Ellen Island, Haida Gwaii, British Columbia. *Canadian Journal of Archaeology, 25,* 98–120.

Fluted points, such as these, tipped the spears of Palaeoindian hunters in North America about 12 000 years ago. **GARY CRAWFORD**

long-standing relationship with coastal habitats, that is, that their history in the area is older than this site. People ate primarily shellfish, deep-water and shallow-water fish (but not much salmon), and bear. Tools include stone flakes and evidence of toolmaking but no bifaces or microblades. People also modified bone to be used as tools. Another site is Charlie Lake Cave, in Northeastern British Columbia. It was excavated by Jon Driver and Knut Fladmark of Simon Fraser University. Human activity there dates from 10 500 to 9500 years ago.[27] In contrast to Kilgii Gwaay on the coast, the occupants made microblades around 9500 years ago.[28] The earliest occupants made projectile points that are descended from the fluted-point tradition of the Palaeoindians, so the first Charlie Lake inhabitants came from the South. People seem to have taken advantage of a sheltered area between a cliff face and a large slab of sandstone that had broken away from the same cliff. The 3-metre gap between the cliff face and the slab provided just enough space for people to seek shelter or hide while hunting bison. At least, this is one interpretation. The evidence of human use of the site is slim to say the least. People may have lived above the cliff face and

dropped their garbage into the gully between the slab and the cliff. Nevertheless, the artifacts here suggest that the site was first used only for a few hours or days.

The picture currently emerging, then, is of people, who did not look like modern aboriginal people, arriving by boat, spreading southward and eastward over time. They may have met people who had arrived by boat via the Pacific and the North Atlantic, although this is still not certain. There is no reason to suppose that contact back and forth between North America and Northeast Asia ever stopped. In all probability, it became more common as the glaciers melted. As a consequence, through gene flow as well as later arrivals of people from the East, those living in the Americas came to have the broad faces, prominent cheekbones, and round cranial vaults that characterize aboriginal people today.

---

[27] Driver, J. (1999). Raven skeletons from Paleoindian contexts, Charlie Lake Cave, British Columbia. *American Antiquity, 64.*

[28] Fladmark, K.R. (1996). The prehistory of Charlie Lake Cave. In R.L. Carlson & L. Dalla Bona (Eds.), *Early human occupation in British Columbia* (pp. 11–20). Vancouver: UBC Press.

Where Did Upper Paleolithic People Come From?

As noted in Chapter 9, scholars still debate whether the transition from archaic to anatomically modern *H. sapiens* took place in one specific population or was the result of several populations living in Africa, Asia, and even Europe between 100 000 and 40 000 years ago evolving together. In Europe, where the argument for replacement of archaic by modern *sapiens* has been most strongly made, the most recent Neandertals display modern features, whereas the most ancient moderns show what appear to be Neandertal holdovers. For example, the Saint Césaire skull has the high forehead and chin of moderns. Similarly, the late Neandertal from Vindija, northern Croatia, shows a thinning of brow ridges toward their outer margins. Conversely, early Upper Paleolithic skulls from Brno, Mladec, and Predmosti, in the Czech Republic, retain heavy brow

ridges and Neandertal-like muscle attachments on their backs.[29] As noted early in this chapter, some of the skulls from the Cro-Magnon rock shelter look Neandertal-like from the back. Of course, these features could all be the result of interbreeding between two populations that overlapped in time, rather than simple evolution from one into the other. Or, they could represent a single varied population whose average characteristics were shifting in a more "modern" direction. In either case, they do not fit with the idea of the complete extinction of the older population. Looking at the larger picture, what we see in all regions of the Old World, since the time of *H. erectus/ergaster,* is more and more emphasis placed on cultural, as opposed to biological, adaptation. To handle environmental stress, reliance was placed

---

[29] Bednarik, R.G. (1995). Concept-mediated marking in the Lower Paleolithic. *Current Anthropology, 36,* 627; Minugh-Purvis, N. (1992). The inhabitants of Ice Age Europe. *Expedition, 34* (3), 33–34.

Palaeoindians and their descendants were such accomplished hunters that they could kill large numbers of animals using methods such as stampeding them over a cliff in a calculated manner. Head-Smashed-In, Alberta, has evidence of such techniques being used from about 6000 years ago until relatively recently.
GARY CRAWFORD

ANTHROPOLOGY APPLIED

Kennewick Man

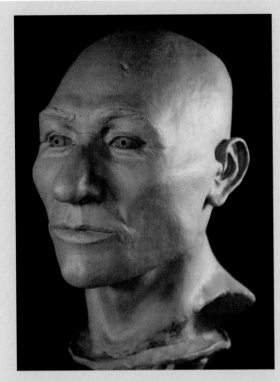

(C) AP/WIDE WORLD PHOTOS

"The Ancient One," or the "Kennewick Man," refers to the 9300-year-old skeletal remains that were found in 1996 below the surface of Lake Wallula, part of the Columbia River, in Kennewick, Washington. This discovery has been the centre of increasing controversy since it was made: Who owns these human remains? Who can determine what shall be done with them? This particular conflict involves three major parties.

Because the skeleton was found on a location for which the U.S. Army Corps of Engineers is responsible, this federal agency first took possession of the remains. Appealing to a new federal law, the *Native American Graves Protection and Repatriation Act* of 1990 (NAGPRA), a nearby American Indian group named the Confederated Tribes of the Umatilla Indian Reservation (representing the region's Umatilla, Cayuse, and Walla Walla nations) claimed the remains. Because Kennewick Man was found within their ancestral homeland, they argue that they are "culturally affiliated" with the individual they refer to as "The Ancient One." Viewing these human bones as belonging to an ancestor, they wish to return them to the earth in a respectful ceremony.

This claim was challenged in federal court by a group of scientists in 1996, including some archaeologists and biological anthropologists. They view these human remains, among the oldest ever discovered in the Western hemisphere, as scientifically precious, with potential to shed light on the earliest population movements in the Americas. By means of DNA analysis, for instance, these scientists expect to determine possible prehistoric linkages between this individual and ancient human remains found elsewhere, including Asia. Moreover, scientific analysis may determine whether there actually exists any biological connection between these remains and currently living aboriginal peoples, including individuals residing on the Umatilla Indian Reservation. Fearing the loss of a unique scientific specimen, the group filed a lawsuit in federal court to prevent reburial before these bones are researched and analyzed. Their legal challenge was not based on "cultural affiliation," which is a very difficult concept when it concerns such ancient human remains, but focuses on the fact that the region's aboriginal peoples cannot prove they are direct lineal descendants. Unless such ties have been objectively established, they argue, Kennewick Man should be released for scientific study. In 2002 the courts ruled in favour of those who wished to study the remains. The ruling makes it clear that "the term 'Native American' requires, at a minimum, a cultural relationship between remains or other cultural items and a present-day tribe, people, or culture indigenous to the United States." No evidence was produced that could establish this relationship.

BIOGRAPHY

Knut Fladmark and Chen Shen

Knut Fladmark is a professor in the Department of Archaeology at Simon Fraser University. His interests lie in the archaeology of Northern and Northwestern North America, from its initial peopling to the early fur-trade period. He has paid special attention to (1) the effects of Late Quaternary palaeoenvironments and palaeoecology on precontact aboriginal cultures; (2) the general prehistory of the Northern Northwest Coast, especially the Queen Charlotte Islands, and Western Subarctic, especially Northern Interior British Columbia; and (3) the archaeology of early European visitors to the Northwest Coast and Western Subarctic. Fladmark considers one of his major research contributions to have been proposing a theoretical perspective on Northwest Coast prehistory, centred on the cultural ecological effects of changing sea levels. He has also determined that a chain of small unglaciated "biotic refugia" that existed along the Northwest Coast during part or all of the last Pleistocene glaciation could have been used by early people moving south from the Bering Strait region. Fladmark has demonstrated the potential significance of microdebitage (extremely small stone flakes) and other "micro-artifacts" for archaeology, and discovered and investigated Charlie Lake Cave, the first excavated Early Palaeoindian "fluted point" site in British Columbia, which is still the oldest radiocarbon-dated site in the province. Fladmark published the first general synthesis of British Columbia prehistory in 1982 and later worked the material into a book, entitled *British Columbia Prehistory*, for a popular audience.

Chen Shen is the Bishop White Curator of Far Eastern Archaeology at the Royal Ontario Museum (ROM). He began his archaeological career in China but moved to the United States to begin his graduate work. After graduating from Wuhan University he decided to study with one of the leading authorities on use-wear analysis at the University of Tulsa. He applied what he learned in Tulsa to his Ph.D. research at the University of Toronto. His doctoral dissertation was written on stone tool technology and function during the shift to agriculture in Ontario. Shen's expertise lies in the analysis of stone tools, particularly their function, by analyzing the scratches and polishes on tools and understanding what processes resulted in the wear patterns.

Shen's research is designed to investigate the development of microblades during the Upper Palaeolithic of north-central China from 30 000 to 8 000 B.C. Microblade technology in its cultural and archaeological context has never been studied adequately in North China. By investigating the wedge-shaped core microblade tradition in north-central China, Shen hopes to not only gain insight into events in China during the Upper Palaeolithic, but also investigate the technological connections to Northwestern North America. The project is in its initial stages, so much remains to be accomplished.

Shen is also a member of a team exploring human evolution in China. In recent years he has developed an interest in the Bronze Age in China, and he has mounted an exhibition of Chinese bronzes from the Sanxingdui site at the ROM.

increasingly on the development of appropriate tools, clothes, shelter, use of fire, and so forth, as opposed to alteration of the human organism itself. This was true whether human populations lived in hot or cold, wet or dry, forest or grassland areas. Because culture is learned and not carried by genes, it is ultimately based on what might loosely be called "brain power" or, more formally, **cognitive capacity**. Although this includes intelligence in the IQ sense, it is broader than that, for it also includes such aptitudes as educability, concept formation, self-awareness, self-evaluation, reliability of performance under stress, attention span, sensitivity in discrimination, and creativity.

> **Cognitive capacity.** A broad concept including intelligence, educability, concept formation, self-awareness, self-evaluation, reliability of performance under stress, attention span, sensitivity in discrimination, and creativity.

Glaciers such as this one in Alberta are now shrinking rapidly as the climate warms. During the Pleistocene, glaciers such as this one grew so much that they coalesced with others to form massive continental-scale ice sheets that covered most of Canada 18 000 years ago. **GARY CRAWFORD**

The major thrust in the evolution of the genus *Homo,* then, has been toward improved cognitive capacity through the evolution of the brain regardless of the environmental and climatic differences among the regions in which populations of the genus lived. Hence, there has been a certain similarity of selective pressures in all regions. At the same time, gene flow among populations would have spread whatever genes happen to relate to cognitive capacity. In an evolving species, in the absence of isolating mechanisms, genes having survival value anywhere tend to spread from one population to another. As a case in point, wolves, like humans, have a wide distribution, ranging all the way from the Atlantic coast of Europe eastward across Eurasia and North America to Greenland. Yet, wolves constitute a single species—*Canis lupus*—and never in its 5- to 7-million-year evolutionary history has more than a single species coexisted.[30] That wolves never split into multiple species relates to the size of territories occupied by successful packs and the exchange of mates between packs. Both promoted gene flow across the species' entire range.

It is impossible to know just how much gene flow took place among ancient human populations, but that some took place is consistent with the sudden appearance of novel traits in one region later than their appearance somewhere else. For example, Upper Palaeolithic remains

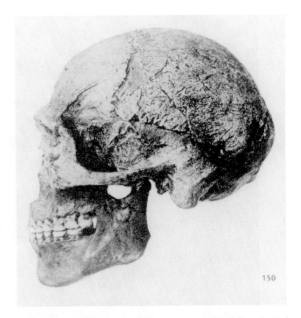

The bulge on the back of this Upper Palaeolithic skull from Predmosti in the Czech Republic, along with its still-prominent brow ridges, is reminiscent of the earlier Neandertals. **COURTESY OF ANTHROPOS INSTITUTE, BRNO**

30 Brace, C.L. (2000). *Evolution in an anthropological view* (p. 341). Walnut Creek, CA: Altamira.

from North Africa exhibit the kind of mid-facial flatness previously seen only in East Asian fossils; similarly, various Cro-Magnon fossils from Europe show the short upper jaws, horizontally oriented cheekbones, and rectangular eye orbits previously seen in East Asians. Conversely, the round orbits, large frontal sinuses, and thin cranial bones seen in some archaic *sapiens* skulls from China represent the first appearance there of traits that have greater antiquity in the West.[31] What appears to be happening, then, is that genetic variants from the East are being introduced into Western gene pools and vice versa. Support for this comes from studies of the Y chromosome in humans (found only in males). These studies indicate that some DNA carried by this chromosome originated in Asia at least 200 000 years ago and spread from there to Africa.[32] Such gene flow is not only consistent with the remarkable tendency historically known humans have to "swap genes" between populations, even in the face of cultural barriers to gene flow, but also consistent with the tendency of other primates to produce hybrids when two

subspecies (and sometimes even species) come into contact.[33] Moreover, without such gene flow, multiregional evolution inevitably would have resulted in the appearance of multiple species of modern humans, something that clearly has *not* happened. In fact, the low level of genetic differentiation among modern humans can be explained easily as a consequence of high levels of gene flow.[34]

MAJOR PALAEOLITHIC TRENDS

Certain trends stand out from the information anthropologists have gathered about the Old Stone Age in most parts of the world. One was toward increasingly more

---

[31] Pope, G.C. (1992). Craniofacial evidence for the origin of modern humans in China. *Yearbook of Physical Anthropology, 35,* 287–288.

[32] Gibbons, A. (1997). Ideas on human origins evolve at anthropology gathering. *Science, 276,* 535–536.

[33] Simons, E.L. (1989). Human origins. *Science, 245,* 1349.

[34] Relethford, J.H., & Harpending, H.C. (1994). Craniometric variation, genetic theory, and modern human origins. *American Journal of Physical Anthropology, 95,* 265.

In 1998, this skeleton of a four-year-old child was found in a Portuguese rock shelter, where it had been ritually buried. A controversy surrounds this burial. Many specialists accept it as a modern human but the discoverers believe the child displays a mix of Neandertal and Cro-Magnon traits. Its 25 000-year-old date would make it too recent to be the product of a chance encounter between two populations (by then, Neandertals were long gone). Instead, if it is a hybrid, it bespeaks earlier extensive interbreeding, or else is an example of an Upper Palaeolithic European showing evidence of Neandertal ancestry. JOSE ZILHAO, COPYRIGHT INSTITUTO PORTUGUES ARQUEOLOGIA

sophisticated, varied, and specialized tool kits. Tools became progressively lighter and smaller, resulting in the conservation of raw materials and a better ratio between length of cutting edge and weight of stone. Tools became specialized according to region and function. Instead of crude all-purpose tools, more effective particularized devices were made to deal more effectively with the differing conditions of savanna, forest, and shore.

This more efficient tool technology enabled human populations to grow and spill over into more diverse environments; it also was responsible for the loss of heavy physical features, favouring instead decreased size and weight of face and teeth, the development of larger and more complex brains, and ultimately a reduction in body size and robustness. This dependence on intelligence rather than bulk provided the key for humans' increased reliance on cultural rather than physical adaptation. As the brain became modernized, conceptual thought developed, as evidenced by symbolic artifacts and signs of ritual activity.

By the Upper Palaeolithic, the amount of sexual dimorphism, too, was greatly reduced, as size differences between men and women were relatively slight compared to what they were in *Australopithecus*, *H. habilis*, or (to a lesser extent) *H. erectus*. This has important implications for gender relations. As noted in earlier chapters, among primates marked sexual dimorphism is associated with male dominance over females. Lack of sexual dimorphism, by contrast, correlates with a lack of such dominance. In evolving humans, it appears that a loss of male dominance went hand in hand with the ever-increasing importance of cooperative relationships. (Paradoxically, humans reinvented male dominance in the context of civilization, a relatively recent development that is the subject of Chapter 12.)

Through Palaeolithic times, at least in the colder parts of the world, there appeared a trend toward the importance of and proficiency in hunting. Humans' intelligence enabled them to develop tools that exceeded other animals' physical equipment, as well as the improved social organization and cooperation so important for survival and population growth. As discussed in the next chapter, this trend was reversed during the Epipalaeolithic, when hunting lost its preeminence, and the gathering of wild plants and seafood became increasingly important.

As human populations grew and spread, regionalism also became more marked. Tool assemblages developed in different ways at different times in different areas. General differences appeared between North and South, East and West. Although there are some indications of cultural contact and intercommunication, such as the development of long-distance trade in the Upper Palaeolithic, regionalism was a dominant characteristic of Palaeolithic times. The persistence of regionalism was probably due to two factors: a perceived need to distinguish symbolically one's own people from others and the need to adapt to differing environments. Palaeolithic peoples eventually spread over most of the world, including Australia and the Americas, and as they did so, changes in climate and environment called for new kinds of adaptations. Thus Palaeolithic tool kits had to be altered to meet the requirements of many varying locations. In forest environments, people needed tools for working wood; on the open savanna and plains, they came to use the bow and arrow to hunt the game they could not stalk closely; the people in settlements that grew up around lakes and along rivers and coasts developed harpoons and hooks; in the subarctic regions they needed tools to work the heavy skins of seals and caribou. The fact that culture is first and foremost an adaptive mechanism meant that it was of necessity a regional thing.

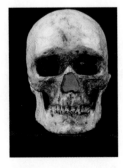 

These Upper Palaeolithic skulls from China (left) and Africa (right) are easily derivable from earlier archaic sapiens skulls in the same region. PROFESSOR WU XINZHI, BEIJING, CHINA (LEFT) DRAWING FROM UP FROM THE APE BY ERNEST A. HOOTON. COPYRIGHT 1931, 1946 BY THE MACMILLAN COMPANY, NEW YORK. (RIGHT)

CHAPTER SUMMARY

The Cro-Magnons and the other Upper Palaeolithic peoples of the world, in addition to a full-sized brain, possessed a physical appearance somewhat similar to our own. The modernization of the face of Upper Palaeolithic peoples is a result of a reduction in the size of the teeth and the muscles involved in chewing and relates to the fact that teeth were no longer being used as tools. Similarly, bodies became somewhat less massive and robust as improved technology reduced the need for brute strength.

Upper Palaeolithic cultures evolved out of the Middle Palaeolithic cultures of Africa, Asia, and Europe. The typical Upper Palaeolithic tool was the blade. The blade technique of toolmaking was less wasteful of flint than Middle Palaeolithic methods. Other efficient Upper Palaeolithic toolmaking techniques were pressure flaking of stone and using chisel-like tools called burins to fashion bone, antler, horn, and ivory into tools. The cultural adaptation of Upper Palaeolithic peoples became specific; they developed different tools in different regions. Northern Upper Palaeolithic cultures supported themselves by the hunting of large herd animals and catching smaller animals in nets. Hunting with the bow and arrow developed in Africa, spreading later to Europe and other regions. Upper Palaeolithic cultures are the earliest in which artistic expression is common.

The emphasis in evolution of the genus *Homo* in all parts of the world was toward increasing cognitive capacity through development of the brain. This took place regardless of environmental or climatic conditions under which the genus lived. In addition, evolution of the genus *Homo* undoubtedly involved gene flow among populations. Lack of much genetic differentiation among human populations today bespeaks high levels of gene flow among populations in the past.

Three trends are evident in the Palaeolithic period. First was a trend toward more sophisticated, varied, and specialized tool kits. This trend enabled people to increase their population and spread to new environments. It also had an impact on human anatomy, favouring decreased size and weight of face and teeth; the development of larger, more complex brains; and ultimately a reduction in body size, mass, and degree of sexual dimorphism. Second was a trend toward the importance of and proficiency in hunting. Third was a trend toward regionalism, as people's technology and life habits increasingly reflected their association with a particular environment.

People arrived by boat in Australia between 60 000 and 40 000 years ago. The Americas were populated by at least 20 000 years ago, and by 11 000 years ago the Palaeoindian culture, unique to the region, had developed. Most of Canada was first peopled from the south after the glaciers retreated. Subsequently, people from Northeast Asia moved into the Canadian Arctic, where other regional cultures developed.

QUESTIONS FOR CRITICAL THOUGHT

1. How do archaeology and human biology work together to inform us about the peopling of Canada?

2. What makes the first modern humans "modern"? Did their potential as people differ from ours?

3. Considering what we know about human evolution, technology, and migrations during the Upper Palaeolithic, to what extent is it appropriate to define one's ancestry to be from someone else's?

INTERNET RESOURCES

Palaeoindian

www.adamsheritage.com/pre/preont1.htm
Details of the Palaeoindian and other cultures in ancient Ontario.

http://museum.gov.ns.ca/places/debert/debert.htm
Canada's national museum provides details on the Debert site in Nova Scotia. Links to related sites are provided, as well as a bibliography.

www.ele.net
An archaeological site geared toward examining the various Palaeoindian tool traditions found in North America. Includes discussions on Clovis and Folsom projectile points.

www.flheritage.com/facts/reports/contexts/paleo.cfm
A large site, with many links, that looks at the Palaeoindian period. Provides maps, photos of tool traditions, and clear concise information.

Palaeolithic

www.bradshawfoundation.com/index.html
A visual treat; features the clay bison at Tuc D'Audoubert, France and cave rock art from Australia to Africa, some of which dates back to the Palaeolithic.

www.culture.fr/culture/arcnat/lascaux/en/
To protect the magnificent cave art at Lascaux Cave, only six people per day can go inside. To share this national treasure more widely, the French government built an entire replica of the site as well as this website for a virtual tour.

www.johnerwin.org/fdl.htm
A description of a large, well-preserved prehistoric Dorset soapstone quarry in Fleur de Lys, Newfoundland.

http://anthropology.uwaterloo.ca/ArcticArchStuff/index.html
A large site introducing archaeological research in the Arctic; includes numerous links of related interest.

www.hf.uio.no/iakk/roger/lithic/MOUST/upperPal2.html#anchor75523
Excellent illustrations of tool traditions in the Upper Palaeolithic.

www.mnh.si.edu/arctic/html/peopling_siberia.html
Attempts to answer common questions about Upper Palaeolithic peoples using DNA evidence: When did people first settle in Siberia? Where did they come from? When did they first cross the Bering Strait?

www.he.net/~archaeol/9607/newsbriefs/brazil.html
A discussion of a cave near the Amazon River in northern Brazil that provides evidence that people migrated from North to South America some 11 000 years ago.

Head-Smashed-In Buffalo Jump

www.head-smashed-in.com
Further details on the archaeology and background of this World Heritage Site.

Microblades in Canada

www.socsci.mcmaster.ca/anthro/faculty/cannon.cfm#interests
An excellent paper on microblade manufacturing in British Columbia with illustrations of an extremely small microblade

SUGGESTED READINGS

For a list of suggested readings, visit the textbook's website at www.humanevolution2.nelson.com.

Cultivation and Domestication

Beginning about 11 000 years ago, some of the world's people embarked on a new way of life based on food production. Though farming has changed dramatically in the millennia since then, all of the crops we rely on today originated with those earliest farmers.

GARY CRAWFORD

CHAPTER PREVIEW

1. When and Where Did the Change from Food Foraging to Food Production Begin?

Independent centres of early plant and animal domestication exist in Africa, China, Mesoamerica, North and South America, as well as Southwest and Southeast Asia. From these places, food production spread to most other parts of the world. It began roughly at the end of the Pleistocene in these different places (with slightly different timing), a bit earlier in Southwest Asia, and a bit later in eastern North America.

2. Why Did the Change Take Place?

Because food production by and large requires more work than hunting and gathering, it creates new health and social problems, it can be assumed that people probably did not become food producers through choice. Of various theories that have been proposed, the most likely is that food production came about as a consequence of a chance convergence of separate natural events and cultural developments.

3. What Were the Consequences of the Change to Food Production?

Although food production generally provides less leisure time than food foraging, it does permit some reallocation of the workload. Some people can produce enough food to support others who undertake other tasks such as the construction of large tombs and buildings. In addition, food production facilitates a sedentary way of life in villages, with more substantial housing. Finally, the new modes of work and resource allocation require new ways of organizing people, generally into lineages, clans, and common-interest associations.

CHAPTER OUTLINE

The Postglacial Roots of Farming and Pastoralism

The Neolithic Revolution

Why Humans Became Food Producers

Other Centres of Domestication

The Spread of Food Production

Culture of Neolithic Settlements

Neolithic Culture in the New World

The Neolithic and Human Biology

The Neolithic and the Idea of Progress

Human societies throughout history have used a variety of **subsistence strategies** such as hunting and gathering, pastoralism, swidden or slash-and-burn agriculture, and industrialized agriculture. During the Palaeolithic, people depended exclusively on wild sources of food for their survival. In cold northern regions, they came to rely on the hunting of large animals such as the mammoth, bison, and horse, but especially reindeer, as well as smaller animals such as hares, foxes, and birds. Elsewhere, they hunted, fished, or gathered whatever nature provided. There is no evidence (yet) in Palaeolithic remains to indicate that livestock was kept or plants cultivated. Palaeolithic people followed wild herds and gathered wild plant foods, relying on their wits and muscles to acquire what nature provided. Whenever favoured sources of food became scarce, as sometimes happened, people adjusted by increasing the variety of food eaten and incorporating less favoured food into their diets.

About 12 000 years ago, the subsistence strategy of some people began to change in ways that were to transform radically their way of life, although no one involved had any way of knowing it at the time. Not until these changes were well advanced could people realize that their mode of subsistence differed from that of other cultures—that they had become farmers, rather than food foragers.[1] This change in the means of obtaining food had important implications for human development. Many of the risks of foraging could be reduced or eliminated, although new risks were introduced. Moreover, by reorganizing the workload, some people could be freed from the food quest to devote their energies to other tasks. With good reason, the **Neolithic period,** when this change took place, has been called a revolutionary one in human history. This period, and the changes that took place within it, are the subjects of this chapter.

THE POSTGLACIAL ROOTS OF FARMING AND PASTORALISM

By 12 000 years ago, glacial conditions in the world were moderating, causing changes in human habitats. Throughout the world, sea levels were on the rise,

ultimately flooding many areas that had been above sea level during periods of glaciation, such as the Bering Strait, parts of the North Sea, and an extensive area that had joined the eastern islands of Indonesia to Southeast Asia. In north temperate regions, milder climates brought about marked changes as, in some regions, tundras were replaced by forests. In the process, the herd animals upon which northern Palaeolithic peoples had depended for much of their food, clothing, and shelter disappeared from many areas. Some, like the reindeer and musk ox, moved to colder climates; others, like the mammoths, died out completely. Thus, the temperate Northerners especially were forced to adapt to new conditions. In the new forests, animals were more solitary in their habits and so not as easy to hunt as they had been, and large, cooperative hunts were less productive than before. Such hunts continued in parts of the Near East and other regions where forests did not cover the whole landscape. However, plant food was more abundant, and there were new and abundant sources of fish and other food around lakeshores, bays, and rivers. Hence, human populations came to rely more on ingenious ways to catch and kill a variety of smaller birds and animals, while at the same time they devoted more energy to fishing and the collection of a broad spectrum of wild plant foods. This way of life is first seen as early as 23 000 years ago at Ohalo II in Israel (Chapter 10) but by the end of the Palaeolithic this new way of life was more the rule than the exception. No single tradition emerges from the Palaeolithic due to the varied conditions around the world. Some archaeologists prefer to

---

[1] Rindos, D. (1984). *The origins of agriculture: An evolutionary perspective* (p. 99). Orlando: Academic Press.

Subsistence strategy. Decisions and actions that affect food and raw material procurement of a society.

Neolithic period. The New Stone Age; began about 11 000 years ago in Southwest Asia when the first domesticated plants appear; in East Asia the period refers to the time when pottery was used and begins 17 000 to 15 000 years ago.

call this period the **Mesolithic** or Middle Stone Age, while others prefer the term **Epipalaeolithic** or post-Palaeolithic. "Mesolithic" is a term generally associated with Europe and adjacent regions, and "Epipalaeolithic" is used to refer to cultures in West and East Asia. Just as archaeologists do not use the term "Palaeolithic" for New World cultures (instead using "Palaeoindian"), the immediate post-Palaeoindian groups are usually known as **Archaic** cultures.

Early Postglacial Tools and Weapons

New technologies were developed for the changed postglacial environment. Ground stone tools, shaped and sharpened by grinding the tool against an abrasive stone (often along with sand or other grit such as volcanic tuff), made effective axes and adzes. Such implements, though they take longer to make, are less prone to breakage under heavy-duty usage than are those made of chipped stone. Ground stone tools are easier to sharpen than chipped stone. Thus, they were helpful in clearing forest areas and in the woodwork needed for the creation of dugout canoes and skin-covered boats. Although some kind of water craft had been developed early enough to get humans to the island of Flores (and probably Italy and Spain) by 800 000 years ago, sophisticated boats become prominent after the Upper Palaeolithic, indicating that hominin foraging for food frequently took place on the water as well as the land. Thus, it was possible to make use of deep-water resources as well as those of coastal areas.

Epipalaeolithic, Mesolithic, and Archaic. Cultures at the end of the Palaeolithic that survived into early post-glacial times. They are usually marked by the manufacture and use of small blades and cores. Mesolithic normally refers to these cultures in Europe while Epipalaeolithic is normally specific to the Near East while Archaic is reserved for the New World. Sometimes both Epipalaeolithic and Mesolithic are used with reference to the Old World in general.

Two examples of ground stone tools used for heavy woodworking: an adze and a gouge. The adze was used much like an axe for cutting wood. Gouges like this one were used to make dugout canoes. GARY CRAWFORD

The microliths that had begun to be manufactured in Central Africa by about 40 000 years ago[2] and Northeast Asia by 20 000 years ago,[3] became the characteristic tool in the Old World soon after 12 000 years ago. The risk-reduction advantages of microliths discussed in Chapter 10 likely had less impact at this time but microliths could be mass-produced because they were small and easy to make. Also, they could be attached to arrow shafts by using melted resin or asphalt as a binder. Thus, the bow and arrow with the microlith arrowhead became the deadliest and most common weapon in some parts of the world such as Europe.

The widespread adoption of microlith technology that was first developed in the Upper Palaeolithic, particularly in Northeast Asia, enabled late glacial and postglacial populations to devise a wider array of composite tools made out of stone and wood or bone (Figure 11.1). Thus, they could make sickles, harpoons, arrows, and daggers by fitting microliths into slots in wood or bone handles. Later experimentation with these forms led to more sophisticated tools and weapons.

It appears that people became more sedentary in the immediate post-glacial compared to earlier eras. Although dwellings were not new (see the Ohalo II site in Chapter 10), dwellings from this period seem more substantial, an indication of permanency. Indeed, this is a logical development. Most hunting and gathering cultures, especially those depending on herd animals, are nomadic: To be successful, one must follow the game. This is not necessary for people who subsist on a diet of seafood and plants, as the location of shore and vegetation remains relatively constant. Microlith production that had begun during the Upper Palaeolithic to reduce risk for a variety of reasons was quite compatible with this less mobile lifestyle. People were ranging over smaller areas so quality stone would have been less accessible. With more efficient tool production methods, their raw materials would last much longer.

Another important innovation at this time was pottery manufacturing. Pottery was significant among many Epipalaeolithic and nonagricultural people in East Asia, North Africa, Borthern Europe, and parts of the Americas, to name a few. In Central and Eastern Canada, pottery was an important part of nonagricultural people's technology. Pottery developed well after the advent of food production in the Eastern Mediterranean region. The oldest undisputed pottery in the world dates to

[2] Bednarik, R.G. (1995). Concept-mediated marking in the Lower Paleolithic. *Current Anthropology, 36,* 606.

[3] Lu, T.D. (1998). The microblade tradition in China: Regional chronologies and significance in the transition to the Neolithic. *Asian Perspectives, 37,* 84–112.

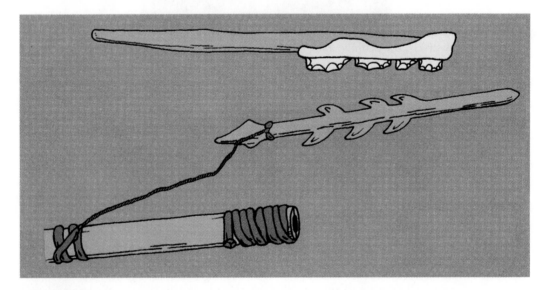

FIGURE 11.1

This drawing shows a European Mesolithic composite tool consisting of microliths set into a wooden handle. Also shown is a bone harpoon head with the end of its wooden shaft. Harpoons actually came into use before the Epipalaeolithic.

between 17 000 and 15 000 years ago in Japan, the Russian Far East, and China.[4] Thus, a cause-effect relationship between pottery and agriculture does not explain the appearance of the new technology.

Archaeologists are not clear how or why the first steps to potting were made. The manufacture of pottery is a difficult art and requires a high degree of technological sophistication. To make a useful vessel requires knowledge of clay, how to remove impurities from it, how to shape it into desired forms without it slumping, and how to dry it without cracking. Proper firing is tricky as well; the object must be heated sufficiently that the clay will harden and resist future disintegration from moisture, but care must be taken to prevent the object from cracking or even exploding as it heats and later cools. The first pottery brought about new food preparation and storage methods. Because pottery vessels are impervious to damage by insects, rodents, and dampness, they could be used for storing small grain, seeds, and other materials. Moreover, food can be boiled in pottery vessels directly over the fire rather than by such ancient techniques as dropping stones heated directly in the fire into the food being cooked. Pottery is decorated in various ways. For example, designs can be engraved on the vessel before firing, or special rims, legs, bases, and other details may be made separately and fastened to the finished pot. Painting is the most common form of pottery decoration, and there are literally thousands of painted designs found among the pottery remains of ancient cultures. Pottery probably also immediately took on social meaning, because the earliest pots are decorated, and regionally specific pottery designs appear. One's social group membership could be symbolized by the pottery decorations. Pottery also became a commodity for exchange and the decorations would clearly signify the source of the pots. Social roles changed as well. Women likely invented the first pottery, so gender roles also took on new dimensions as women continued to make and be the primary users of pots.

Cultural Diversity in the Postglacial Period

In the warmer parts of the world, the collection of wild plant foods had been more of an equal partner with hunting in subsistence activities in the Upper Palaeolithic than had been the case in the colder north.

Hence, in areas like Southwest Asia, the Epipalaeolithic represents less of a changed way of life than was true in the European Mesolithic.

The **Natufian culture**, a variant of the Near Eastern Epipalaeolithic, flourished between 12 500 and 10 200 years ago at the eastern end of the Mediterranean Sea in caves, rock shelters, and small villages with stone- and mud-walled houses. Nearby, their dead were buried in communal cemeteries, usually in shallow pits without grave goods or decorations. A small shrine is known from one of their villages, a 10 500-year-old settlement at Jericho. Basin-shaped depressions in the rocks found outside homes at Natufian sites are thought to have been storage pits. Plastered storage pits beneath the floors of the houses were also found, indicating that the Natufians were the earliest Epipalaeolithic people known to have stored plant foods. Certain tools found among Natufian remains bear evidence that they were used to cut grain. These Epipalaeolithic sickles, for that is what they were, consisted of small stone blades set in straight handles of wood or bone.

In the New World, microlith technology derived from Northeast Asia spread from the Western Arctic into British Columbia, Alberta, and the Eastern Arctic. Elsewhere on the Americas, cultures comparable to Mesolithic and Epipalaeolithic cultures of the Old World developed, but here they are referred to as **Archaic cultures**. Outside the Arctic, microlithic tools were not prominent as they in the rest of the world, but ground stone tools such as axes, adzes, gouges, plummets, and spear-thrower weights were common. Archaic cultures were widespread in the Americas. One of the better documented is the **Maritime Archaic culture**, which

---

[4] Kuzmin, Y.V. (2006). Chronology of the earliest pottery in East Asia: progress and pitfalls. *Antiquity, 80*, 362–371.

Natufian culture. An Epipalaeolithic culture of Israel, Lebanon, and Western Syria, between about 12 500 and 10 200 years ago.

Archaic cultures. Term used to refer to Mesolithic cultures in the Americas.

Maritime Archaic culture. An Archaic culture of northeastern North America, centred on the Gulf of St. Lawrence, that emphasized the utilization of marine resources.

began to develop about 7000 years ago around the Gulf of St. Lawrence. Maritime Archaic people developed an elaborate assortment of bone and ground slate tools with which they hunted a wide variety of sea mammals, including whales; fish, including swordfish; and sea birds. To get some of these, they regularly paddled their dugout canoes far offshore. To appreciate the skills this required, one need only recognize the difficulty of landing a 500-pound swordfish, extremely aggressive fish known historically to have driven their swords through the hulls of substantial wooden vessels. The Maritime Archaic people also developed the first known elaborate burial ceremonialism in North America, involving the use of red ocher ("red paint") and the placement of finely made grave goods with the deceased.

In eastern North America other Archaic cultures adapted to the riverine woodlands. For example, in Kentucky, Tennessee, and Illinois the rich resources permitted more sedentary communities to develop. The Indian Knoll culture is among the best known of these groups.[5] Their technology included an array of projectile points, drills, knives, and scrapers. Ground stone adzes and axes that would have been essential in woodworking and tree cutting were common. Reliance on fish, shellfish, small mammals, and deer meant people could stay in the same settlements for generations. The garbage heaps left by these people formed what are known as **shellmounds** next to the rivers. The Indian Knoll people exchanged materials over long distances, and used a wide variety of plant foods with an emphasis on acorns and hickory nuts. Small-seeded plants such as knotweeds, goosefoot, and wild beans were also collected.[6] A small, native squash or egg-gourd was also exploited, probably for its usefulness as fishing net floats. Elsewhere in the Eastern Woodlands Archaic people were beginning to domesticate several plants such as marsh elder and sunflower. Archaic people lived relatively rich lives in this time of innovation.

The Archaic of the Eastern Woodlands exemplifies a trend seen in many regions of the world: domesticated plants or animals were first added to hunting-gathering regimes, providing additional resources and security. However, these resources did not signal an inevitable and rapid shift to agriculture. These **low-level food producers**, as Bruce Smith calls them, are neither hunting-gathering nor farming societies.[7] Instead, they represent stable adaptations along a continuum between foraging and balanced agriculture. Some Epipalaeolithic societies such as

the Natufian were just such low-level food producers. In other cases, aquatic resources and plants were so abundant that people's lives came to resemble those of farmers. Low-level food production includes a variety of wild plant and animal management strategies. First Nations communities in British Columbia are one example of people who relied on rich resources and management techniques that included burning and limited transplanting. Others harvested productive wild plants from habitats created by a process called **anthropogenesis** with the same result. Anthropogenesis includes such human-initiated changes as burning, flooding, or, in modern times, urban development or the creation of walking trails.

One of the longest-lived low-level food producing traditions was the Jomon of the Japanese islands dating from about 13 000 years ago to 3000 years ago in the south and 1500 years ago in the north. Many archaeologists prefer to view the Jomon as **affluent foragers** with a way of life similar to First Nations in coastal British Columbia (see Chapter 10) but this does not accurately reflect the complexities of the Jomon economy, which eventually involved

---

[5] Marquardt, W.H., Watson, P.J., & University of Florida. Institute of *Archaeology and Paleoenvironmental Studies. (2005). Archaeology of the Middle Green River Region, Kentucky*. Gainesville: Institute of Archaeology and Paleoenvironmental Studies, University of Florida.

[6] Crawford, G.W. (2005). Green River Archaic Paleoethnobotany. In W.M. Marquardt & P.J. Watson (Eds.) p. 181–212). Archaeology of the Middle Green River Area, Kentucky: University of Alabama Press.

[7] Smith, B.D. (2001). Low-level food production. *Journal of Archaeological Research*, 9, 1–43.

Shellmound. An extensive deposit of refuse including quantities of shell left behind by people. These deposits include artifacts and it is not unusual to find burials in them.

Low-level food producers. People who use management techniques to secure resources; may include nonintensive growing of domesticated organisms.

Anthropogenesis. The process whereby humans modify their environment, consciously or not.

Affluent forager. Also known as complex hunter-gatherers, are nonagricultural, substantially sedentary people with hierarchical social organization and food storage.

domestication and some crops. Initially, the Jomon began as an elaboration of the late East Asian Upper Palaeolithic that was characterized by microliths. Pottery was added to the technological repertoire and microliths eventually dropped out of use. Ground stone and bifacial stone tools became common. Jomon people soon settled in pit-house villages that appeared as early as 10 000 years ago; by 5000 years ago these communities were becoming quite large and elaborate. Extraordinary pottery decorated with complex cord impressions and sometimes painted with lacquer, and a wide range of ground, polished, and flaked stone tools and objects, basketry, and wooden tools formed their material legacy. Rich cemeteries surrounded by earthworks as well as stone circles have also been found. Many of these are characteristics of agricultural societies, but the Jomon had only a few domesticated resources such as barnyard millet, bottle gourd, and dogs. The wild resources the Jomon harvested were mainly products of anthropogenic environments such as village-forest boundaries (forest edges), and open habitats associated with villages such as abandoned pit-houses that were filled with debris and earth producing rich, sunlit soils perfect for plant growth.[8] This way of life succeeded for millennia and tells us that balanced and intensive agriculture was not always inevitable. It also tells us that classifying cultures as hunting and gathering or farming is not our goal; we do so here in order to sketch general patterns of culture change.

Varied though cultures immediately after the Upper Palaeolithic were, this new, agricultural way of life generally offered more secure supplies of food and therefore an increased margin of survival. In some parts of the world, people started living in larger and more sedentary groups and cooperating with others outside the sphere of family or hunting band. They became settled village dwellers, and some of these settlements were shortly to expand into the first farming villages, towns, and (ultimately) cities.

THE NEOLITHIC REVOLUTION

The Neolithic, or New Stone Age, was characterized by the transition from foraging for food to dependence upon domesticated plants and animals. It was by no means a smooth or rapid transition; in fact, the switch to food production spread over many centuries—even millennia—and was a direct outgrowth of the preceding Epipalaeolithic. Where to draw the line between the two periods is not always clear.

The term "New Stone Age" is derived from the polished stone tools that are characteristic of this period. But more important than the presence of these tools is the transition from a hunting, gathering, and fishing economy to one based on food production, representing a major change in the subsistence practices of early peoples. One of the first regions to undergo this transition, and certainly the most intensively studied, was Southwest Asia. The remains of domesticated plants and animals are known from parts of Israel, Jordan, Syria, Turkey, Iraq, and Iran, all before 8000 years ago.

Domestication: What Is It?

Domestication is an evolutionary process whereby humans modify, either intentionally or unintentionally, the genetic makeup of a population of plants or animals, sometimes to the extent that members of the population are unable to survive and/or reproduce without human assistance. As such, it constitutes a special case of a kind of relationship between different species frequently seen in the natural world, as in the case of one species that has come to depend for its protection and reproductive success on some other that feeds upon it. A particularly dramatic example is offered by species of New World ants that grow fungi in their nests, providing the ants with most of their nutrition. Like human farmers, the ants add manure to stimulate fungal growth and eliminate competing weeds both mechanically and through use of antibiotic herbicides. They propagate their crops vegetatively, as do humans for some of their crops (bananas, for example), and even share crops, as when one ant species borrows from another's nest or when several nests become disturbed and mixed. Finally, like human farming, ant farming did not develop just once, but at least five different times.[9]

---

[8] Crawford, G.W. (1997). Anthropogenesis in prehistoric northeastern Japan. In K. Gremillion (Ed.), *People, plants, and landscapes: Studies in paleoethnobotany* (pp. 86–103). University of Alabama Press.

[9] Diamond, J. (1998). Ants, crops, and history. *Science, 281,* 1974–1975.

> **Domestication.** An evolutionary process whereby humans modify, either intentionally or unintentionally, the genetic makeup of a population of plants or animals, sometimes to the extent that members of the population are unable to survive and/or reproduce without human assistance.

BIOGRAPHY

Jean-Luc Pilon

Jean-Luc Pilon is Curator of Ontario Archaeology at the Canadian Museum of Civilization. His work has involved putting together exhibits at the CMC ("Kitchi Sibi"—Ottawa Valley ancient history and "Gather Around this Pot"—ancient Canadian ceramics) and participating in teams developing larger permanent exhibits (the First People's Hall). Pilon is also a member of the archaeology committee of the Pan-American Institute of Geography and History, thereby establishing links with the archaeological community of Central and South America. His research takes place in the north, well away from the crowded archaeological fields of Southern Ontario. Instead, he is investigating early sites near Sioux Lookout in northwestern Ontario, Late Archaic sites in Eastern Ontario, and Laurel sites near Thunder Bay. He is also beginning fascinating research into a North West Company fur-trade post in the Mackenzie Valley where his ancestor died of starvation in the winter of 1810–11.

Jean-Luc Pilon first began his archaeological career in the Ungava Peninsula. He continued to work in various parts of northern Quebec and eventually pursued his Ph.D. research near the shores of Hudson Bay in northern Ontario. Since then, he has been working on a long-term project aimed at obtaining baseline data on the prehistory of the lower Mackenzie Valley. Pilon is unique in having firsthand experience in the Eastern, Central, and Western Subarctic. This vast region holds more landmass than any other physiographic/culture area in North America, yet is still poorly understood. Acidic soils, frequent forest fires, and a high reliance on perishable raw materials by the inhabitants makes this a challenging region in which to conduct archaeological research.

Looked at from the perspective of the fungi, the benefit gained is protection and ensured reproductive success. Turning from fungi to plants, we find that there are numerous species that rely on some type of animal—in some cases birds, in others mammals, and in yet others insects—for protection and dispersal of their seeds. The important thing is that both parties benefit from the arrangement; reliance on animals for seed dispersal ensures that the latter will be carried further afield than would otherwise be possible, thereby cutting down on competition for sun and nutrients between young and old plants and reducing the likelihood that any diseases or parasites harboured by one will be transmitted to the others.

Evidence of Early Plant Domestication

The characteristics of plants under human domestication that set them apart from their wild ancestors and have made them attractive to those who eat them include increased size, at least of edible parts; reduction or loss of natural means of seed dispersal; reduction or loss of protective devices such as husks or distasteful chemical compounds; loss of delayed seed germination (important to wild plants for survival in times of drought or other adverse conditions of temporary duration); and development of simultaneous ripening of the seed or fruit. Many of these characteristics can be seen in plant remains from archaeological sites; thus, archaeobotanists can often tell the seed or fruit of a wild plant species from a domesticated one, for example, by studying the seed of cereal grasses, such as barley, wheat, and maize (corn). Wild cereals have brittle stalks called **rachis** that attach the grain to the grass plant. Domesticated ones have non-brittle rachis nodes. Under natural conditions, plants with brittle grain stalks scatter their seed by naturally severing the grain from the plant, whereas those with non-brittle rachis nodes do not. Instead, people have to break the grain from the plant. This means that people can cut the grain with sickles and carry the plants back to the village without losing the grain and then remove the grain at one time by threshing it. At sites where the first domesticated grasses have been found, rachis fragments have been recovered too. The rachis bases show ragged tears where they were torn from the plant.

Worker ants have made a path as they go out to cut pieces of leaf that they bring back to their nest to make the soil in which they plant their fungus gardens. WILLIAM A. HAVILAND/UVM PHOTO SERVICE

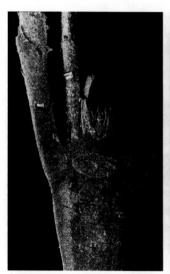 

The wild barley rachis on the left shows a smooth, eliptical break in the centre of the photo but the rachis from the domesticated counterpart on the right shows a fragment attached at the connecting node. SMITH, BRUCE (1998). THE EMERGENCE OF AGRICULTURE. SCIENTIFIC AMERICAN LIBRARY, P. 77. USED WITH PERMISSION.

The structural change from a soft to a tough stem in early domesticated plants involves a genetic change, undoubtedly the result of what Darwin referred to as **unconscious selection**: the preservation of valued individuals and the

> **Unconscious selection.** The preservation of valued variants of a plant or animal species and the destruction of less valued ones, with no thought as to the long-range consequences.
>
> **Rachis.** The main stalk attaching the grass fruit (grain) to the plant.

destruction of less valued ones, with no thought as to long-range consequences.[10] When the grain stalks were harvested, their soft stem would shatter at the touch of sickle or flail, and many of their seeds would be lost. Inevitably, most of the seeds that people harvested would have been taken from the tough plants. Early domesticators probably also tended to select seed from plants having few husks or none at all—eventually breeding them out—because husking prior to pounding the grains into meal or flour was much too time consuming. Size of plants is another good indicator of the presence of domestication. For example, the large ear of corn (maize) we know today is a far cry from the tiny ears (about an inch long) characteristic of early maize. Small and

primitive though these were (an entire ear contained less nourishment than a single kernel of modern maize), they were radically different in structure from the ears of teosinte (see Figure 11.2).

Evidence of Early Animal Domestication

Domestication also produced changes in the skeletal structure of some animals. For example, the horns of wild goats and sheep differ from those of their

---

[10] Rindos, p. 86.

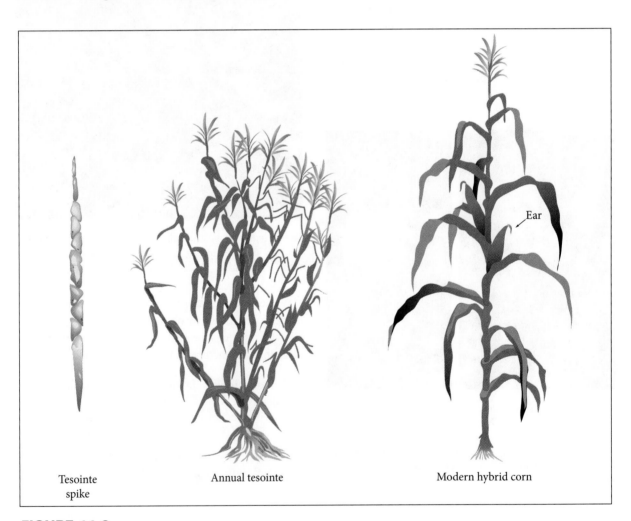

Ear

| Tesointe spike | Annual tesointe | Modern hybrid corn |

FIGURE 11.2

Modern corn has a single main stalk with its seeds (kernels) packaged in a just a few, easily harvested cobs. The wild ancestor of corn, teosinte, has many stalks on a single plant, each stalk with its own small grain head.

A modern wild sunflower fruit (left) is compared with an archaeological example (right) from an Iroquoian site in Ontario. The useful parts of domesticated plants are usually larger than those of their wild counterparts. **GARY CRAWFORD**

Beginnings of Domestication

Over the past 30 years, a good deal of information has accumulated about the beginnings of domestication, primarily in Southwest Asia as well as Central and South America. We still do not have all the answers about how and why it took place. Nonetheless, some observations of general validity can be made that help us to understand how the switch to food production may have taken place.

The first of these observations is that the switch to food production was not the result of discoveries such as that seeds, if planted, grow into plants. Food foragers are far from ignorant about the forces of nature and are perfectly aware of the role of seeds in plant growth, that plants grow better under certain conditions than others, and so forth. Physiologist Jared Diamond calls such peoples "walking encyclopedias of natural history with individual names for as many as a thousand or more plant and animal species, and with detailed knowledge of those species' biological characteristics, distribution and potential uses."[12] What's more, they frequently apply their knowledge so as to manage actively the resources on which they depend. For example, people living in the northern part of Alberta put to use a sophisticated knowledge of the effects of fire to create local environments of their own design. Similarly, aboriginal peoples in California used fire to perpetuate oak woodland savanna, to promote hunting and the collection of acorns. In northern Australia, runoff channels of creeks were deliberately altered so as to flood extensive tracts of land, converting them into fields of wild grain. People do not remain food foragers through ignorance, but through choice.

A second observation is that a switch from food foraging to food production does not free people from hard work. The available ethnographic data indicate just the opposite—that farmers, by and large, work far longer hours than do most food foragers.

domesticated counterparts (domesticated female sheep have none). Another structural change that occurred in domestication involves the size of the animal or its parts. For example, certain teeth of domesticated pigs are smaller than those of wild ones.

A study of age and sex ratios of butchered animals at a site may indicate whether or not animal domestication was practised. Investigators have assumed that if the age and/or sex ratios at the site differ from those in wild herds, the imbalances are due to conscious selection. For example, at 10 000-year-old sites in the Zagros Mountains of Iran and Iraq, there was a sharp rise in the numbers of young male goats killed. Evidently, people were slaughtering the young males for food and saving the females for breeding. Although such herd management does not prove that the goats were fully domesticated, it does indicate a first step in the domestication process.[11]

In Peru, the prominence of bones of newborn llamas at archaeological sites (up to 72 percent at some), dating to around 6300 years ago, is probably indicative of at least incipient domestication. Such high mortality rates for newborn animals are uncommon in wild herds but are common where animals are penned up. Under confined conditions, the inevitable buildup of mud and filth harbours bacteria that cause diarrhea and enterotoxemia, both of which are fatal to newborn animals.

[11] Zeder, M.A., & Hesse, B. (2000). The initial domestication of goats (*Capra hircus*) in the Zagros Mountains 10,000 years ago. *Science, 287,* 2254–2257.

[12] Diamond, J. (1997). *Guns, germs and steel* (p. 143). New York: Norton.

A final observation is that food production is not necessarily a more secure means of subsistence than food foraging. Seed crops in particular— of the sort domesticated in Southwest Asia, Mexico, and Peru—are highly productive but very unstable on account of low species diversity. Without constant human attention, their productivity suffers.

From all of this, it is little wonder that food foragers do not necessarily regard farming and animal husbandry as superior to hunting, gathering, and fishing. Thus, there are some people in the world who have remained food foragers up to the present time, although it has become increasingly difficult for them as food-producing peoples have deprived them of more and more of the land base necessary for their way of life. But as long as existing practices worked well, there was no need to abandon them. After all, their traditional way of life gave them all the food they needed and an eminently satisfactory way of living in small, intimate groups. Free from tedious routine, their lives were often more exciting than those of farmers. Food could be hunted, gathered, or fished for as needed, but in most environments they could relax when they had enough to eat. Why raise crops through backbreaking work when the whole family could camp under a tree bearing tasty and nutritious nuts? Farming brings with it a whole new system of human relationships that offers no easily understood advantages and disturbs an age-old balance between humans and nature as well as the people who live together.

WHY HUMANS BECAME FOOD PRODUCERS

In view of what has been said so far, we may well ask: Why did any human group abandon food foraging in favour of food production?

Several theories have been proposed to account for this change in human subsistence practices. One older theory, championed by V. Gordon Childe, is the desiccation, or oasis, theory based on climatic determinism. Its proponents advanced the idea that the glacial cover over Europe and Asia caused a southern shift in rain patterns from Europe to Northern Africa and Southwest Asia. When the glaciers retreated northward, so did the rain patterns. As a result, northern Africa and Southwest

Asia became drier, and people were forced to congregate at oases for water. Because of the scarcity of wild animals in such an environment, people were driven by necessity to collect the wild grasses and seeds growing around the oases. Eventually they had to cultivate the grasses to provide enough food for the community. According to this theory, animal domestication began because the oases attracted hungry animals, such as wild goats, sheep, and also cattle, which came to graze on the stubble of the grain fields. People, finding these animals too thin to kill for food, began to fatten them up.

In spite of its initial popularity, evidence in support of the oasis theory was not immediately forthcoming. Moreover, as systematic fieldwork into the origins of domestication began in the late 1940s, other theories gained favour. One of the pioneers in this work was Robert Braidwood of the University of Chicago, who proposed what is sometimes called the "hilly flanks" theory. Contrary to Childe, Braidwood argued that plants and animals were domesticated by people living in the hill country surrounding the Fertile Crescent (Figure 11.3). They had reached the point in their evolutionary development where they were beginning to "settle in"—that is, become more sedentary—a situation that allowed them to become intimately familiar with the plants and animals around their settlements. Given the human capacity and enthusiasm for experimentation, it was inevitable that they would have experimented with grasses and animals, bringing them under domestication. Problems with this theory include the ethnocentric notion that nonsedentary food foragers are not intimately familiar with the plants and animals on which they rely for survival and its projection onto all human cultures of the great value Western culture places on experimentation and innovation for its own sake. In short, the theory was culture-bound, strongly reflecting the notions of progress in which people in the Western world had such faith in the period following World War II.

Population pressure is yet another theory that became popular in the 1960s. In Southwest Asia, so this theory goes, people adapted to the cool, dry conditions of the last glacial period by developing a mixed pattern of resource utilization: They hunted such animals as were available, harvested wild cereal grasses, gathered nuts, and collected a wide variety of birds, turtles, snails, crabs, and mussels. They did so well that their populations grew, requiring the development of new ways of

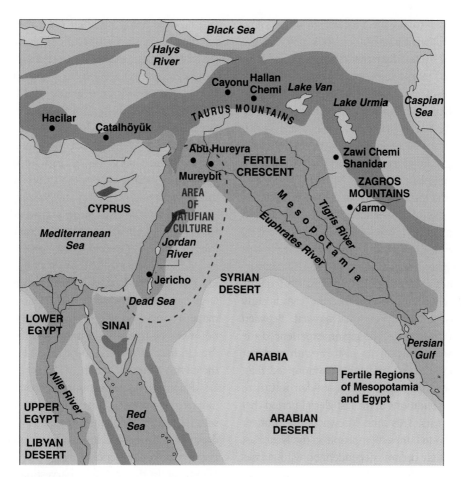

FIGURE 11.3

The Fertile Crescent of Southwest Asia and the area of the Natufian culture.

providing sufficient food. The result, especially in marginal situations where wild foods were least abundant, was to improve productivity through the domestication of plants and animals.

Just as there are problems with Braidwood's theory, so are there problems with this one. The most serious is that it requires an intentional decision on the part of the people involved to become producers of domestic crops, whereas, as we have already seen, domestication (as illustrated by ant farmers) does not require intentional design. Furthermore, prior to domestication, people could have had no way of knowing that plants and animals could be so radically transformed as to permit a food-producing way of life (even today, the long-term outcome of plant breeding cannot be predicted). Finally, even if people had wanted to become producers of their own food, there is no way such a decision could have had

an immediate and perceptible effect; in fact, a complete switch to food production took more than 1000 years to accomplish. Although this may seem a relatively short period of time compared to the 200 000 or 300 000 years since the appearance of *H. sapiens,* it was still too long to have made any difference to people faced with immediate food shortages. Under such conditions, the usual response among food foragers is to make use of a wider variety of foods than before, which acts as a brake on domestication by diverting attention from potential domesticates, while alleviating the immediate problem.

Another theory—in accord with the evidence as we now know it but also more in accord with the role played by chance both in evolution (Chapters 3 and 5) and in cultural innovation—takes us back to some of the ideas of Childe, who, as it turns out, guessed what the environmental circumstances were, even though he didn't fully understand the process. We now know that the earliest plant domestication took place in the lands just east of the Mediterranean Sea (Figure 11.3). As early as 11 500 years ago people living at a site (Abu Hureyra) east of Aleppo, Syria, were growing domestic rye, although they otherwise continued to rely heavily on wild plants and animals for food. Not until 3 millennia later did they become full-fledged farmers.[13] By 10 300 years ago, however, others in the region were also domesticating plants.

Evidently, the process was a consequence of a chance convergence of independent natural events and cultural developments.[14] The process is exemplified by the Natufians, whose culture we looked at earlier in this chapter. These people lived at a time of dramatically changing climates in the region. With the end of the last glaciation, climates not only became significantly warmer, but also markedly seasonal as well. Between 12 000 and 6000 years ago, the region experienced the most extreme seasonality in its history, with summer aridity significantly longer and more pronounced than today. This period had began with a sudden return to the cold and dry conditions of the last glacial period that lasted for 1000 years. This time, known as the Younger Dryas, had a profound impact on people in the Near East who had increasingly become dependent on wild grasses and other plants for food.[15] The region's plant cover changed dramatically. In particular at the Abu Hureyra site, the plants people preferred for food withdrew to areas a long distance from the community. Furthermore, those plants best adapted to environmental instability and seasonal aridity were annuals, including wild cereal grains and legumes (plants that fix nitrogen in the soil, including peas, lentils, chickpeas, and bitter vetch). Such plants can evolve very quickly under unstable conditions, because they complete their life cycle in a single year. Moreover, they store their reproductive abilities for the next wet season in abundant seeds, which can remain dormant for prolonged periods.

The Natufians, who lived where these conditions were especially severe, adapted by modifying their subsistence strategies in two ways: They probably regularly fired the landscape to promote browsing by red deer and gazelles, the main focus of their hunting activities; and they placed greater emphasis on wild seeds from the annual plants that could be effectively stored to see people through the dry season. Evidence from Abu Hureyra indicates that the inhabitants turned more

and more to managing their plant resources, including planting them nearby, to artificially create stands of preferred plants that otherwise were disappearing from the natural vegetation around them due to the rapid onset of cold and dry weather (Figure 11.4). The importance of stored and cultivated foods, coupled with the scarcity of reliable water sources, promoted more sedentary living patterns, reflected in the substantial villages of late Natufian times. The greater importance of seeds in Natufian subsistence was made possible by the fact that they already possessed sickles for harvesting grain and grinding stones for processing seeds. The grinding stones were used originally to process a variety of wild foods, whereas the sickles may originally have served to procure nonfood plants such as the sedges or reeds used to make baskets and mats (Natufian sites yielding large numbers of sickles tend to be located near coastal marshes and swamps).[16] Thus, these implements were not invented to enable people to become farmers, even though they turned out to be useful for that purpose as the environment changed.

Planting and managing plants combined with sickle harvesting provided just the right environment for selecting traits in plants that made them increasingly dependent on people for their reproduction. This had important consequences, again unexpected, for the Natufians. In the course of harvesting, it was inevitable that many easily dispersed seeds would be "lost" at the harvest site, whereas those from plants that did not readily scatter their seeds would mostly be carried back to where people processed and stored them.[17] Genetic mutations against easy dispersal would inevitably arise in the wild stocks, but they would be at a competitive disadvantage compared to variants that could readily disperse their seeds. However, the rate of this and other mutations potentially useful to human consumers

[13] Pringle, H. (1998). The slow birth of agriculture. *Science, 282,* 1449.

[14] McCorriston, J., & Hole, F. (1991). The ecology of seasonal stress and the origins of agriculture in the Near East. *American Anthropologist, 93,* 46–69.

[15] Moore, A.M.T., Hillman, G.C., & Legge, A.J. (2000). *Village on the Euphrates: From foraging to farming at Abu Hureyra.* Oxford: Oxford University Press.

[16] Olszewski, D.I. (1991). Comment. *Current Anthropology, 32,* 43.

[17] Blumer, M.A., & Byrne, R. (1991). The ecological genetics and domestication and the origins of agriculture. *Current Anthropology, 32,* 30.

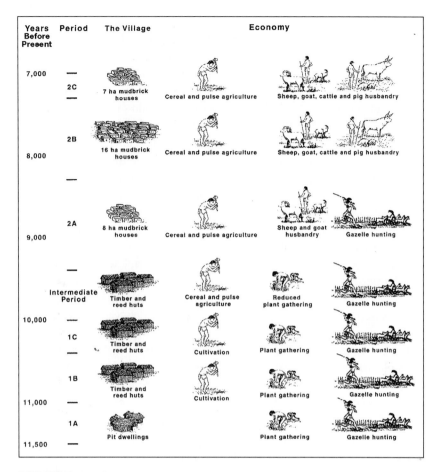

FIGURE 11.4

At Abu Hureyra the archaeological evidence documents a sequence of economic and social developments leading to agriculture.

might have been unknowingly increased by the periodic burning of vegetation carried out to promote the deer and gazelle herds, for heat is known to be an effective mutagenic agent, and fire can drastically and quickly change gene frequencies. In any event, with seeds for nondispersing variants being carried back to settlements, it was inevitable that some lost seeds would germinate and grow there on dump heaps and other disturbed sites (latrines, areas cleared of trees, or burned over).

As it turns out, many of the plants that became domesticated were colonizers, which do particularly well in disturbed habitats. Moreover, with people becoming increasingly sedentary, disturbed habitats became more extensive as resources in proximity to settlements were depleted over time; thus variants of plants particularly susceptible to human manipulation had more and more opportunity to flourish where

people were living and where they would inevitably attract attention. Under such circumstances, it was inevitable that people sooner or later would begin to actively promote their growth, even by deliberately sowing them, especially as people otherwise had to travel farther afield to procure the resources that were depleted near their villages. One consequence of intensive human manipulation was the shift in the Hardy-Weinberg equilibrium of grain populations that, in the wild, have a very low representation of non-brittle stalks to a population almost entirely with non-brittle stalks. For example, barley, which in its wild state can be tremendously productive but difficult to harvest and process, had developed the tougher stems that make it easier to harvest by 9000 years ago; by 8000 years ago "naked" barley, which is easier to process, was common, and by 7500 years ago six-row barley, which is more productive than the original two-row, was widespread. Sooner or later, people realized that they could play a more active role in the process by deliberately trying to breed more useful strains. With this, domestication may be said to have shifted from a process that was unintentional to one that was intentional.

The development of animal domestication in Southwest Asia seems to have proceeded along somewhat similar lines but in the hilly country of southeastern Turkey, northern Iraq, and the Zagros Mountains of Iran (Figure 11.4). In the latter two regions were to be found large herds of wild sheep and goats, as well as much environmental diversity. From the low, alluvial plains of the valley of the Tigris and Euphrates rivers, for example, travel to the north or east takes one into the high country through three other zones: first steppe, then oak and pistachio woodlands, and, finally, high plateau country with grass, scrub, or desert vegetation. Valleys that run at right angles to the mountain ranges afford relatively easy access between these zones. Today, a number of pastoral peoples in the region practise a pattern of **transhumance,** in which they graze their herds of sheep and goats on the low steppe in the winter and move to high pastures on the plateaus in the summer.

Moving 12 000 years backward in time to the Epipalaeolithic, we find that the region was inhabited by peoples whose subsistence pattern, like that of the Natufians, was one of food foraging. Different plants were found in different ecological zones, and, because of the difference in altitude, plant foods matured at different times in different zones. The animals hunted for meat and hides by these people included several species, among them bear, fox, boar, and wolf. Most notable, though, were the hoofed animals: deer, gazelles, wild goats, and wild sheep. Their bones are far more common in human refuse piles than those of other animals. This is significant, for most of these animals are naturally transhumant in the region, moving back and forth from low winter pastures to high summer pastures. People followed these animals in their seasonal migrations, making use along the way of other wild foods in the zones through which they passed: dates in the lowlands; acorns, almonds, and pistachios higher up; apples and pears higher still; wild grains maturing at different times in different zones; woodland animals in the forested zone between summer and winter grazing lands. All in all, it was a rich, varied fare.

There was in hunting, then, a concentration on hoofed animals, including wild sheep and goats, which provided meat and hides. At first, animals of all ages and sexes were hunted. But, beginning about 11 000 years ago, the percentage of immature sheep eaten, for example, increased to about 50 percent of the total. At the same

Transhumance. Among pastoralists, the grazing of sheep and goats in low steppe lands in the winter and then moving to high pastures on the plateaus in the summer.

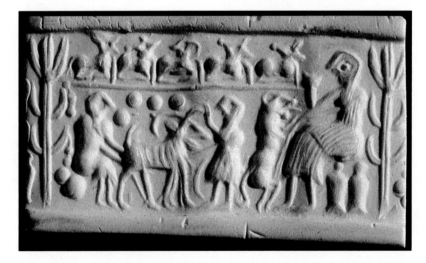

Although sheep and goats were first valued for their meat, hides, and sinew, the changes wrought by domestication made them useful for other purposes as well. This impression, from a 4500-year-old seal, shows a goat being milked. **PIERRE BOULAT/WOODFIN CAMP & ASSOCIATES**

time, the percentage of females among animals eaten decreased. Apparently, people were learning that they could increase yields by sparing the females for breeding, while feasting on ram lambs. This marks the beginning of human management of sheep. As this management of flocks became more and more efficient, sheep were increasingly shielded from the effects of natural selection. Eventually, they were introduced into areas outside their natural habitat. So we find sheep and goats being kept by farmers at ancient Jericho, in the Jordan River Valley, 8000 years ago (by which time farming, too, had spread widely, into Turkey to the north and into the Zagros Mountains in the east). As a consequence of this human intervention, variants that usually were not successful in the wild were able to survive and reproduce. Although variants that were perceived as being of immediate advantage would have attracted peoples' attention, they did not arise out of need, but independently of it at random, as mutations do. In such a way did those features characteristic of domestic sheep—such as greater fat and meat production, excess wool (Figure 11.5), and so on—begin to develop. By 9000 years ago, the bones of domestic sheep had become distinguishable from those of wild sheep.

At about the same time that these events were happening, similar developments were taking place in Southeastern Turkey, where pigs were the focus of attention.[18] Here, an increase in pig bones in human trash, coupled with a heavy bias in favour of very young animals, is indicative of a taste for suckling pigs and the beginning of stock management by 10 500 years ago.

To sum up, the domesticators of plants and animals sought only to maximize the food sources available to them. They were not aware of the revolutionary consequences their actions were to have. But as the process continued, the productivity of the domestic species increased relative to wild species. Thus, they became increasingly more important to subsistence, resulting in further intensification of interest in, and management of, the domesticates. Inevitably, the result would be further increases in productivity.

OTHER CENTRES OF DOMESTICATION

In addition to Southwest Asia, the domestication of plants and, in some cases, animals took place independently in Southeast Asia, parts of the Americas (Southern

---

[18] Pringle, p. 1448.

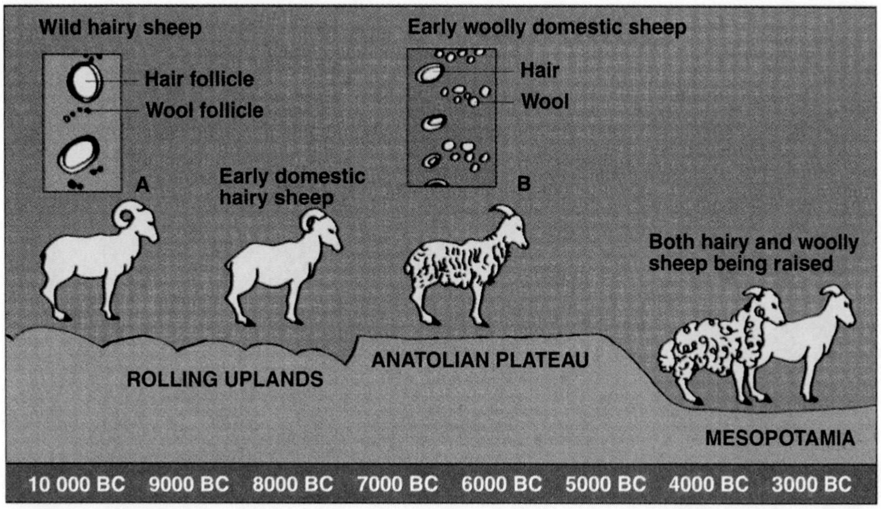

FIGURE 11.5

Domestication of sheep resulted in evolutionary changes that created more wool. Drawing A shows a section, as seen through a microscope, of skin of wild sheep, showing the arrangement of primary (hair) and secondary (wool) follicles. Drawing B shows a section of similarly enlarged skin of domestic sheep, showing the changed relationship and the change in size of follicles that accompanied the development of wool.

Mexico, Peru, the tropical forests of South America, and eastern North America), South-Central and Northern China, and Africa (Figure 11.6).

East Asia is the source of hundreds of domesticated plants and animals, among which are two of the most important crops in the modern world, rice and soybean.[19] Water buffalo and the East Asian pig are two significant animals domesticated here. The earliest stages of food production are poorly known, but enough is known to sketch out what happened. There were at least two areas of domestication, one in the north from the Yellow River Valley to the Liao River in the cool, dry Northeast, and the second centred in the moist and mild Yangtze River basin. Foxtail millet, broomcorn millet, and hemp are among the main early Northern crops. Low-level food production probably characterized adaptations from 11 000 to 8500 years ago but little is known about this time period in China. The Xinglongwa site, dating to about 8000 years ago in Southeastern Inner Mongolia is a large pit-house village surrounded by a ditch. Some of the oldest domesticated millets in China are from the Xinglongwas culture. The oldest domesticated rice is about 8500 to 8000 years old.[20] It is found at several sites south of the Yellow River. The first rice harvesting appears to have been carried out by people occupying caves and shelters near seasonally inundated marshes. Productive rice agriculture requires wet fields or paddies that mimic the natural habitat of rice. At first, people probably managed rice in marshes and on lake margins. Such low-level food producers appear to have been doing just that at the Diaotonghuan site, where wild rice remains date to at least 11 000 years ago.

One species of domestic squash may have been grown as early as 10 000 years ago in the coastal forests of Ecuador at the same time another species was being grown in an arid region of highland Mexico.[21]

---

[19] Crawford, G.W. (2006). East Asian plant domestication. In M. T. Stark (Ed.) *Archaeology of Asia*, (pp. 77–95). Malden: Blackwell Publishing.

[20] Crawford, G.W., & Shen, C. (1998). The origins of rice agriculture: Recent progress in East Asia. *Antiquity, 72*, 858–866.

[21] Smith, B.D. (1998). *The emergence of agriculture*. New York: Scientific American Library.

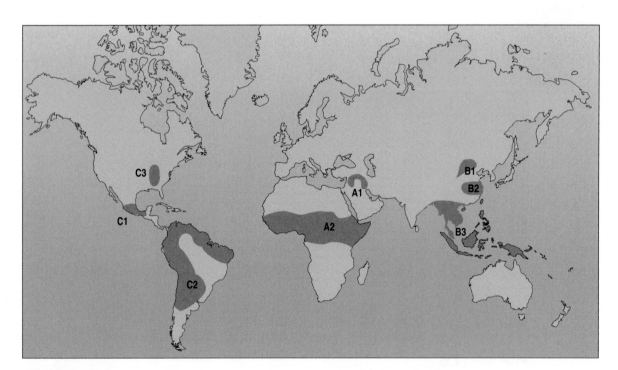

FIGURE 11.6

Early plant and animal domestication took place in such widely scattered areas as Southwest Asia (A1), Central Africa (A2), Northern China (B1), South-Central China (B2), Southeast Asia (B3), Mesoamerica (C1), South America (C2), and North America (C3).

Evidently, these developments were independent of one another. Other crops were eventually added later; the earliest occurrence of maize, for example, is from a site on the Gulf Coast of the Mexican state of Tabasco dated 7700 years ago.[22] Because genetic evidence puts its place of origin somewhere in the highlands of Western Mexico, it must have appeared somewhat earlier there. Ultimately, aboriginal peoples in the Americas domesticated over 300 food crops, including two of the five most important ones in the world today: potatoes and maize (the other three are wheat, rice, and soy bean). In fact, 60 percent of the crops grown in the world today were domesticated by aboriginal Americans, who not only remain the developers of the world's largest array of nutritious foods but also are the primary contributors to the world's varied cuisines.[23] After all, where would Italian cuisine be without tomatoes? Thai cooking without peanuts? Northern European cooking without potatoes? Or Chinese cooking without sweet potatoes (the daily food of peasants, but also used to make noodles rivalling in popularity those made of wheat)? Small wonder aboriginal Americans have been called the world's greatest farmers.

Archaeological evidence for the beginning of farming in Mexico comes from the highland valleys of Oaxaca, Puebla, and Tamaulipas. In the Tehuacan Valley of Puebla, for example, crops such as maize, beans, and squash very gradually came to make up a greater percentage of the food eaten (Figure 11.7). Like the hill country of Southwest Asia, the Tehuacan Valley is environmentally diverse, and the people living there had a cyclical pattern of hunting and gathering that made use of the resources of different environmental zones. In the course of their seasonal movements, people carried the wild precursors of future domesticates out of their native habitat, exposing them to different selective pressures. Under such circumstances, potentially useful (to humans) variants that did not do well in the native habitat would, by chance, do well in novel settings, again (as in Southwest Asia) attracting human attention.

The change to food production also took place in South America, including the highlands of Peru—again, an environmentally diverse region. Although a number of crops first grown in Mexico eventually came to be grown here, there was greater emphasis on root crops, the best known being potatoes (of which about 3000 varieties were grown, versus the mere 250 grown today in North

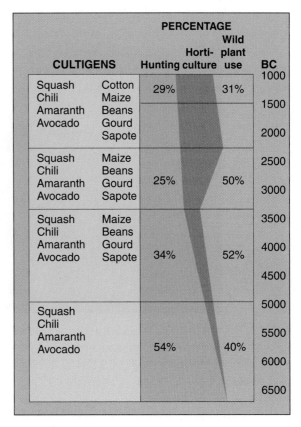

FIGURE 11.7

Subsistence trends in Tehuacan Valley show that here, as elsewhere, dependence on horticulture came about gradually, over a prolonged period of time.

America), sweet potatoes, and manioc (originally developed in the tropics). South Americans domesticated guinea pigs, llamas, alpacas, and ducks, whereas the Mexicans never did much with domestic livestock. They limited themselves to dogs, turkeys, and bees.

Although the aboriginal peoples living north of Mexico ultimately adopted several crops, such as maize and beans, from their southern neighbours, this occurred after they developed some of their own indigenous domesticates. These included local varieties of squash and sunflower. Other native crops such as lamb's-quarter and sumpweed reverted to the wild as preferred foods appeared from Mexico.

---

[22] Piperno, D.R. (2001). On maize and the sunflower. *Science, 292,* 2260.

[23] Weatherford, J. (1988). Indian givers: *How the Indians of the Americas transformed the world* (pp. 71, 115). New York: Fawcett Columbine.

This view from Diaotonghuan Cave in Southern China, from where some of the earliest evidence of domesticated rice has come, overlooks rich farmland today. Thousands of years ago this area was a wetland supporting stands of wild rice and other aquatic resources. **GARY CRAWFORD**

Considering all of the separate innovations of domestic plants, it is interesting to note that in all cases people developed the same categories of foods. Everywhere, starchy grains (or root crops) are accompanied by one or more legumes—wheat and barley with peas, chickpeas, bitter vetch, and lentils in Southwest Asia—maize with various kinds of beans in Mexico, for example. The starchy grains are the core of the diet and are eaten at every meal in the form of bread, some sort of food wrapper (like a tortilla), or a gruel or thickening agent in a stew along with one or more legumes. Being rather bland, these sources of carbohydrates and proteins are invariably combined with flavour-giving substances that help the food go down. In Mexico, for example, the flavour enhancer par excellence is the chili pepper; in other cuisines it may be a bit of meat, a dairy product, mushrooms, or whatever.

Anthropologist Sidney Mintz refers to this as the core-fringe-legume pattern (CFLP), noting that only recently has it been upset by the worldwide spread of processed sugars and high-fat foods.[24]

THE SPREAD OF FOOD PRODUCTION

Agriculture had its **primary origins** in at least eight regions throughout the world. In these settings, hunters and gatherers domesticated local crops and/or animals and made the shift to an agricultural way of life on their own. Although population growth and the need to feed more people cannot explain the origin of the food-producing way of life, it does have a lot to do with its subsequent spread. Many **secondary** shifts to agriculture followed

[24] Mintz, S. (1996). A taste of history. In W.A. Haviland & R.J. Gordon (Eds.), *Talking about people* (2nd ed., pp. 81–82). Mountain View, CA: Mayfield.

Primary origins. When hunters and gatherers transform organisms from wild to domesticated and take up agriculture.

Secondary origins. When agriculture expands from its original region of origin by migration of farmers or by the adoption of an agricultural way of life by hunter-gatherers who are in contact with farmers.

Domestic plants were useful for purposes other than food. Although cotton was independently domesticated three times—in the Old World, Mesoamerica, and Peru—95 percent of the cotton grown in the world today is the Mesoamerican species, owing to its superiority. **GARY CRAWFORD**

primary origins, spreading agriculture to much of the rest of the world. Crops in Europe, the Southwestern United States, Korea, Japan, and Ontario were adopted from outside by local hunters and gatherers. In northwestern Europe, domestic animals were also introduced from the Western Mediterranean. Knowledge of how to plant, manage, and harvest the introduced crops and raise the new animals likely came along as well. Sometimes crops were added one by one; however, in some instances they were introduced as a group. Migration of farmers into the territories of hunters and gatherers was also a mechanism for the spread of farming.

As already noted, domestication inevitably leads to higher yields, and higher yields make it possible to feed more people. In addition, unlike most food foragers, farmers have available a variety of foods that are soft enough to be fed to infants. Hence, farmers do not need to nurse their children so intensively nor for so many years. In humans, prolonged nursing, as long as it involves frequent stimulation of the nipple by the infant, has a dampening effect on ovulation. As a result, women in food-foraging societies are less likely to become fertile as soon after childbirth as they are in

food-producing societies. Coupled with this, having too many children to care for at once interferes with the foraging activities of women in hunting, gathering, and fishing societies. Among farmers, however, numerous children are frequently seen as assets, to help out with the many household chores. Small wonder, then, that increased dependence on farming is associated with increased fertility across human populations.[25]

Paradoxically, although domestication increases productivity, it also increases instability. This is so because those varieties with the highest yields become the focus of human attention, while other varieties are less valued and ultimately ignored. As a result, farmers become dependent on a rather narrow range of resources, compared to the wide range utilized by food foragers. Modern agriculturists, for example, rely on a mere dozen species for about 80 percent of the world's annual tonnage of all crops.[26] By contrast, the Ju/'hoansi of Africa's Kalahari Desert regard more than 100 species

[25] Sellen, D.W., & Mace, R. (1997). Fertility and mode of subsistence: A phylogenetic analysis. *Current Anthropology, 38*, 886.

[26] Diamond, p. 132.

as edible. This dependence upon fewer varieties means that when a crop fails, for whatever reason, farmers have less to fall back on than do food foragers. Furthermore, the likelihood of failure is increased by the common farming practice of planting crops together in one locality, so that a disease contracted by one plant can easily spread to others. Moreover, by specializing in one or two crops, farmers put themselves at increased risk. If some virus, bacterium, or fungus is able to destroy one plant, it will likely destroy them all. This happened in the famous Irish potato famine of 1845–46, which sent waves of Irish immigrants to North America.

The advantages of agriculture in primary regions would not have been lost on hunters and gatherers where conditions were also right for food production. Increased productivity and vulnerability of agriculture such as in the potato famine example may also contribute to the geographic spread of agriculture when people try to re-establish the subsistence practices with which they were familiar in a new area. Migration would be the mechanism of spread in such cases. How and when the spread occurred can be understood in terms of the local dietary, demographic, and other impacts of primary agricultural developments as well as the adaptive success of neighbouring hunting and gathering populations. Thus, once farming came into existence, it was more or less guaranteed that it would spread to neighbouring regions (Figure 11.8). From Southwest Asia, for instance, it spread to Southeastern Europe by 8000 years ago, reaching Central Europe and the Netherlands by 4000 years ago, and England between 4000 and 3000 years ago. Those who brought crops to Europe brought other things as well, including new alleles for human gene pools. As a consequence, those modern Europeans who most resemble their Upper Palaeolithic predecessors are to be found around the northern fringes of the region.[27] Early farmers likely introduced languages ancestral to most of today's European languages as well, leaving Basque (spoken today on the Atlantic coast where France and Spain meet) as the sole survivor of languages once spoken by earlier Epipalaeolithic people.

From Southwest Asia, farming also spread westward to North Africa and eastward to India. Here, crops domesticated in the West met those spreading from Southeast Asia, some of which spread farther West. Facilitating this East-West exchange was the fact that localities shared the same seasonal variations in day length and more or less the same diseases, temperature, and rainfall.

In sub-Saharan Africa, a similar spread occurred and accounts for the modern distribution of speakers of Bantu languages. Crops including sorghum (so valuable today it is grown in hot, dry areas on all continents), pearl millet, watermelon, black-eyed peas, African yams, oil palms, and kola nuts (source of modern cola drinks) were first domesticated in West Africa but began spreading east by 5000 years ago.

Between 3000 and 2000 years ago Bantu speakers with their crops reached the east coast, and a few centuries later, reached the Great Fish River, 800 kilometres east of Capetown. Being well adapted to summer rains, African crops spread no farther, for the Cape has a Mediterranean climate with winter rains.

---

[27] Brace, C.L. (1997). Cro-Magnons Я us *Anthropology Newsletter, 38* (8), 2.

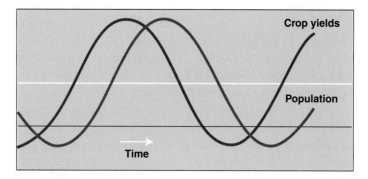

FIGURE 11.8

Population growth has a tendency to follow increases in farming yields. Inevitably, this results in too large a population to be fed when crops fail, as they periodically do. The result is an outward migration of people to other regions.

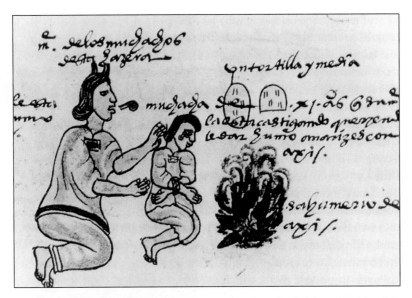

In Mexico, chili peppers enhanced the flavour of foods and aided digestion. (They help break down cellulose in diets heavy in plant foods.) They had other uses as well: This illustration from a 16th-century manuscript shows an Aztec woman threatening her child with punishment by being exposed to smoke from chili peppers. Chili smoke was also used as a kind of chemical weapon in warfare. BETTMANN/CORBIS

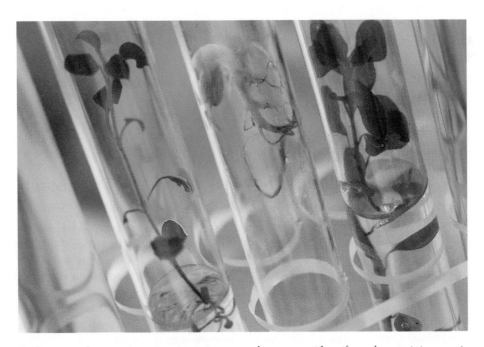

To the extent that genetic engineering strives to produce crops with uniform characteristics, genetic homogeneity will make them vulnerable to plant diseases and predators. BSIP/CHASSENET/PHOTO RESEARCHERS, INC.

In other areas, a combination of adoption by hunter-gatherers and migration took place. In Ontario, for example, the earliest farmers settled into the Grand River valley flats where it appears no one was living at the time (see Original Study box). The first maize was probably grown in small gardens around A.D. 500. People became less mobile, settling into more substantial settlements. Fishing, hunting, and collecting continued to be important.

Chinese developments ultimately transformed cultures in the Korean Peninsula and Japan. Millet from China made its way into Korea by at least 5500 years ago.[28] Populations in Korea were already relatively settled in small villages and had been making pottery for thousands of years. The introduction of crops is almost imperceptible and initially may have done nothing more than add some security for people living in an extremely seasonal climate. More crops were adopted as contact with China increased, leading to Koreans committing to farming by 3000 years ago. While farming was becoming established in Korea, crops were diffusing to Japan where the extremely successful Jomon were living as low-level food producers. Following this first step, as-yet undocumented events led to a relatively constant flow of migrants to Japan who brought intensive grain agriculture, including wet rice production, on a massive scale. By 2600 years ago, southern Japan was agricultural, transformed by migrants, and by 1400 years ago northern populations had taken up food production, although people such as the Ainu of Hokkaido never entirely gave up hunting, gathering, and collecting.[29]

In coastal Peru, the earliest domesticates were the nonedible bottle gourd (like the one shown here) and cotton. They were used to make floats and nets, respectively, to catch fish, which was an important source of food. **HARVEY FINKLE**

[28] Crawford, G.W., & Lee, G.-A. (2003). Agricultural origins in the Korean Peninsula. *Antiquity, 77.*

[29] Crawford, G.W. (1992). The transition to agriculture in Japan. In A.B. Gebauer & T.D. Price (Eds.), *Transitions to agriculture in prehistory: Monographs in world archaeology No. 4* (pp. 117–132). Madison, WI: Prehistory Press.

ORIGINAL STUDY

Pre-Contact Agriculture in Ontario: The Iroquoians

In Ontario, agricultural origins are closely tied to the development of local Iroquoian people. The Huron, Neutral, and Petun are Iroquoian peoples in Ontario who had an agricultural way of life. Their social relations were matrilineal, extended families lived in longhouses, and the longhouses formed villages of hundreds of people. Longhouse villages changed locations every 10 to 20 years, so were not as permanent as Canadian towns today; however, they were more permanent than earlier hunter-gatherer camps. The

only domesticated animal was the dog. Iroquoian peoples in Ontario grew corn, bean, sunflower, tobacco, and squash or pumpkin. Their agriculture production was impressive, often growing enough food to store for several years. Some of the produce was traded to hunting and gathering groups to the north.

Disease was common among Iroquoians, and warfare was a constant threat, much as in other agricultural societies. Sites were often fortified with palisades. Gathering, fishing, and hunting were important activities necessary to round out the diet and to provide raw materials for tools, clothing, medicine, and other nonfood purposes. Men were often away from the community for months fishing in distant locations such as the Gulf of St. Lawrence, hunting, as well as raiding other groups. Women managed village life when the men were absent, and to a large extent even when they were present.

We are fortunate that contact and pre-contact Iroquoians are known from a combination of archaeological research, ethnohistory and oral history.[1] The first Europeans in the region recorded observations about contact-period Iroquoian peoples. Oral histories are still maintained, so the combination of information from a variety of sources provides a rich view of Iroquoian life between A.D. 1100 and 1650. Archaeology tells us that Iroquoian tools were made of stone, bone, wood, and other perishable items. Clay was made into pottery and smoking pipes. The pottery was relatively plain, but the rims of most pots were decorated. Iroquoian settlements are found nearly everywhere agriculture is feasible today in Ontario and southern Quebec. Archaeologists are also aware that Iroquoian culture is dynamic and many changes occurred through the centuries before contact.

Systematic collection of plant remains by flotation for palaeoethnobotanical research has been extremely informative. Charred remains of domesticated plants are common at Iroquoian sites. Wild plants at these sites include nuts and berries. Most of these wild plants flourish in disturbed habitats, particularly locations disturbed by people. Local agriculture, therefore, not only provided the crops but altered the local habitats so that new and useful wild plant associations formed. Deer, rodents, and other animals would have had more food available to them as well. The large populations supported by agriculture in the area did not decimate the game by any means. In fact, game populations were probably higher than they had been before agriculture.

It is difficult to say just when Iroquoian culture began in Ontario. Iroquoian is actually a language family with northern and southern subdivisions. Northern Iroquoian consists of 12 languages in four subgroups: Huronian, Five Nations and Susquehannock, Laurentian, and Nottoway and Tucarora.[2] Cherokee is southern Iroquoian. These languages are mutually unintelligible. Nevertheless, they share many features that allow linguists to include them in one language family, suggesting a common ancestry for all Iroquoians. Language

families are impossible to recognize in the archaeological record, of course. However, the physical hallmarks of Iroquoian settlements appear in Ontario around A.D. 1100 when the first longhouse villages begin to appear. By A.D. 1100 archaeological sites have plenty of corn on them. Beans do not appear on sites until after A.D. 1300. Sunflower, squash, and tobacco appear sometime between A.D. 1000 and 1300. Crops appear to have been introduced individually rather than as a group.

None of the crops grown by Iroquoians are native to Ontario. The fact that these crops were introduced into pre-contact Ontario means that the area was the setting for secondary agricultural origins. Until at least A.D. 400, people lived in relatively impermanent settlements. People fished, hunted, and collected wild plant resources. The plants that they ate included nuts and a few berries, but not nearly the range of plants that we find at Iroquoian archaeological sites. No doubt, plants played an important role in the hunting and gathering lifestyle in Ontario, but not in the same way they did for Iroquoians.

Sometime between A.D. 400 and A.D. 1100 the dramatic change from hunting and gathering to agriculture occurred in Ontario. One group immediately preceding the Iroquoians is known as the Princess Point culture. This culture is generally limited to the Grand River and the western end of Lake Ontario. The Princess Point Project is directed by Gary Crawford and David Smith of the University of Toronto. They are concerned with the timing of agricultural origins, the community structure and settlement pattern, as well as Princess Point technology. They are also concerned with developing a reconstruction of the local environment in the 700 years preceding Iroquoian culture in Ontario. All of this is designed to help us understand how the transition to agriculture occurred.

Systematic archaeological investigations along the Grand River south of Brantford, Ontario, proved particularly difficult because, in contrast with Iroquoian peoples, Princess Point peoples preferred to live on floodplains. As a result, their archaeological sites are buried under substantial layers of alluvium. Just why Princess Point peoples preferred to live in such settings is an important issue. Iroquoian villages, in contrast, are generally found in upland areas near small creeks rather than lowlands near larger rivers. If the Princess Point people were living on floodplains, wouldn't they have needed to cope with annual flooding? In fact, flooding during Princess Point times was not nearly as

(Continued)

extensive as it is today. Lake Erie was several metres lower at the time, allowing relatively rapid drainage of the Grand River during wet periods. Runoff was also inhibited by extensive vegetation growing along the Grand River. Contemporary people have cleared most of the natural vegetation, encouraging rapid runoff and erosion, so that flooding tends to be more extreme today. Shallow channels flowed behind the floodplains at the base of terraces, allowing what flood waters did rise to flow around the communities.

The sites do not appear to be nucleated like Iroquoian villages. Nevertheless, Princess Point communities appear to have been quite large and bounded only by the limits of the floodplain. The importance of the floodplain was central to Princess Point settlement. The rich alluvium and the well-watered floodplain provided the perfect setting for the first agriculture in Ontario.

Excavations document the earliest corn in northeastern North America. Flotation samples contained burned remains of corn cob fragments as well as kernels. Cob fragments have been directly radiocarbon-dated to as early as A.D. 450, and the crop was grown throughout the Princess Point region by A.D. 700 to 800. By the end of Princess Point, people also grew sunflower. Unlike the predecessors of Princess Point, the plant assemblage found at Princess Point sites looks similar to the plant assemblage found at Iroquoian communities. Clearly an agricultural ecology was beginning to develop in Ontario as early as the 5th century A.D.

---

[1] Heidenreich C.E. (1971). Huronia: A History and Geography of the Huron Indians, 1600–1650. Toronto: McClelland and Stewart.

[2] Lounsbury, F.G. (1978). Iroquoian languages. In B.G. Trigger (Ed.), Handbook of North American Indians: Northeast (pp. 334–343). Washington, DC: Smithsonian Institution.

Source: Crawford, G.W. & Smith, D.G. (2002). Early Late Woodland in Southern Ontario: An update. In J. Hart & C. Rieth (Eds.), Northeast subsistence-settlement change: A.D. 700–A.D. 1300 (pp. 117–133). Albany: New York State Museum.

CULTURE OF NEOLITHIC SETTLEMENTS

A number of Neolithic settlements have been excavated, particularly in Southwest Asia. The structures, artifacts, and food debris found at these sites reveals much about the daily activities of their former inhabitants as they pursued the business of making a living.

Earliest Full-Fledged Farming Settlements

The earliest known sites containing domesticated plants and animals found in Southwest Asia date mostly between 10 300 and 9000 years ago. These sites occur in a region extending from the Jordan Valley northward across the Taurus Mountains into Turkey, eastward across the flanks of the Taurus Mountains into northeastern Iran, and southward into Iraq and Iran along the hilly flanks of the Zagros Mountains. The sites contain evidence of domesticated barley, wheat, peas, chickpeas, bitter vetch, lentils, flax, goats, sheep, dogs, and pigs.

These sites are generally the remains of small village farming communities—small clusters of houses built of mud, with each house having its own storage pit and clay oven. Occupants continued to use stone tools of Epipalaeolithic type, plus a few new types of use in farming. Probably the people born into these communities spent their lives in them in a common effort to make their crops grow and their animals prosper. At the same time, they participated in long-distance trade networks. Obsidian found at Jarmo, Iraq, for instance, was imported from 480 kilometres away.

The transition to agriculture in Western Asia is best represented at Abu Hureyra, Syria, where two sequential settlements spanned the period from 11 500 to 7400 years ago. The first settlement is Epipalaeolithic and the second is Neolithic. Abu Hureyra is situated in the Euphrates River Valley where the alluvial soils are well suited to agriculture. Easy access to two environment zones, park-woodland and steppe, meant that people here had a variety of resources from which to choose. We have a clear picture of these resources because Abu Hureyra has been subjected to extraordinary scrutiny. In particular, Andrew Moore of the Rochester Institute of Technology, who directed the project, carried out extensive flotation of soils and has amassed the largest collection of plant and animal remains for this period anywhere.[30] The first settlers numbered a few hundred and lived in pit-dwellings. Despite the wide array of wild resources in the area, the inhabitants intensively used a small fraction of them; they mainly hunted gazelle and collected nuts, wild grains, and river valley plants.

Within 500 years the first crop, rye, was grown. The only domestic animal at first was the dog, probably an important hunting partner. At the same time, people stopped collecting park-woodland resources and de-emphasized wild grains but continued to hunt gazelle as they always had. The turn to farming coincided with the onset of a cool, dry period that lasted from 11 000 to 10 000 years ago. When warmer, moister times returned, the settlement reorganized, at first as an open village whose houses were of perishable material, then as a village of rectangular, multiroomed mud-brick houses packed closely together. Initially the Neolithic residents continued to hunt, gather, and farm, but by 8000 years ago they had turned to farming of rye, wheat, barley, and legumes; raising pigs; and herding sheep, goats, and cattle. The population, now fully engaged in agriculture, grew to 20 times that of the first settlement. People were engaged in trade over long distances, but the community appears to have been relatively isolated.

Women spent much more time in their houses, specializing in household duties; their toe bones were deformed from endless hours of kneeling at grinding stones. Even after death they stayed in the homes, more often than not buried under the house floors.

The Abu Hureyra research tells us that the transition to agriculture took place quickly here, allowing people to survive a climate change that brought less than optimal conditions for agriculture but nonetheless did not limit its development. Hunting patterns were maintained much longer than wild plant collecting, but hunting gazelle abruptly stopped around 9400 years ago and domestic animals appeared. Burials at Abu Hureyra were elaborate, with considerable veneration of ancestors evident. Skulls were routinely separated from the bodies in a pattern that continued from Epipalaeolithic times. The new settlement style of large groups of crowded housing meant that a new form of social organization had arisen so that community business could be regulated by a subset of people in the society.

---

[30] Moore, A.M.T., Hillman, G.C., & Legge, A.J. (2000). *Village on the Euphrates: From foraging to farming at Abu Hureyra.* New York: Oxford University Press.

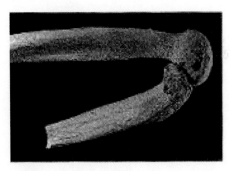

These bones from Abu Hureyra are the knee of a woman in the highly flexed position it would have been in when kneeling at a grinding stone. The knee is arthritic and the thighbone is curved more than normal. MOORE A.M.T., HILLMAN, G.C., & LEGGE, A.J. (2000). VILLAGE ON THE EUPHRATES: FROM FORAGING TO FARMING AT ABU HUREYRA. OXFORD: OXFORD UNIVERSITY PRESS. P. 315

Neolithic Technology

Early harvesting tools were made of wood or bone into which serrated flints were inserted. Later tools continued to be made by chipping and flaking stone, but during the Neolithic period, stone that was too hard to be chipped was ground and polished for tools (Figure 11.9). People developed scythes, forks, hoes, and plows to replace their simple digging sticks. Pestles and mortars were used for preparation of grain. Plows were later redesigned when, after 8000 years ago, domesticated cattle became available for use as draft animals.

Pottery Renaissance

In addition to the domestication of plants and animals, one of the characteristics of the Neolithic period is the significant expansion of the manufacture and use of pottery. Although pottery was first invented by food foragers, it was perfected and elaborated by farmers. New techniques would eventually include kilns and the potter's wheel. In food-foraging societies, most people are involved in the food quest. In food-producing societies, even though people have to work longer at subsistence activities than food foragers, the whole community need not be involved in the food quest. Hard work on the part of those producing the food may support other members of the society who devote their energies to other craft specialties. Different forms of pottery were created for transporting and storing food, artifacts, and other material possessions. Pottery was also used for pipes, ladles, lamps, and other objects, and some cultures used large vessels for disposal of the dead. Significantly, pottery containers remain important for much of humanity today. Painting is the most common form of pottery decoration, and there are literally thousands of painted designs found among the pottery remains of ancient cultures.

Housing

Food production and the new sedentary lifestyle engendered another technological development—house building. Permanent housing is of limited interest to most food foragers, who frequently are on the move. For them, cave shelters, pits dug in the earth, and simple lean-tos made of hides and tree limbs serve the purpose of keeping

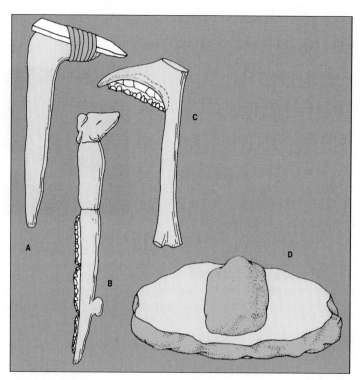

FIGURE 11.9

In Southwest Asia, many tools fabricated by Neolithic peoples made use of flint microliths in bone or wood handles, as well as ground and polished stone.

the weather out. In the Neolithic, however, dwellings became more complex in design and more diverse in type. Some, like Swiss lake dwellings, were constructed of wood, housed several families per building, had doors, and contained beds, tables, and other furniture. In other places, more elaborate shelters were made of stone, sun-dried brick, or branches plastered together with mud or clay.

Although permanent housing frequently goes along with food production, there is evidence that one can have substantial houses without food production. For example, on the northwestern coast of North America, people lived in substantial houses made of heavy planks hewn from cedar logs. Yet their food consisted entirely of wild plants and animals, especially fish.

Clothing

During the Neolithic, for the first time in human history, clothing was made of woven textiles. The raw materials and technology necessary for the production of clothing came from several sources: flax and cotton from farming, wool from domesticated sheep, silk from silk worms, and the spindle for spinning and the loom for weaving from the inventive human mind.

Social Structure

Evidence of all the economic and technological developments listed thus far has enabled archaeologists to draw inferences concerning the organization of early Neolithic society. The general absence of elaborate buildings in all but a few settlements may suggest that neither religion nor government was yet a formally established institution

This pottery vessel from Turkey was made around 7600 years ago. Pigs were under domestication as early as 10 500 to 11 000 years ago in Southeastern Turkey. ANKARA ARCHAOLOGICAL MUSEUM/ ARA GULER, ISTANBUL

able to wield real social power. Although there is evidence of ceremonial activity, little evidence of a centrally organized and directed religious life has been found. Burials, for example, show a marked absence of patterning; variation seems to have been common. Because early Neolithic graves were rarely constructed of or covered by stone slabs and rarely included elaborate grave goods, it is believed differences in social status were not great; evidently, no person had attained the kind of exalted status that would have required an elaborate funeral. The smallness of most villages suggests that the inhabitants knew one another very well, so that most of their relationships were probably highly personal ones, charged with emotional significance.

The general picture that emerges is one of a relatively egalitarian society with minimal division of labour and probably little development of new and more specialized social roles. Villages seem to have comprised several households, each providing for most of its own needs. The organizational needs of society beyond the household level were probably met by kinship groups and common-interest associations.

By late Neolithic times the picture is somewhat different. Agriculture facilitated population growth and towns grew much larger than they were in the early Neolithic. Burials often have elaborate grave goods. Stone monuments and earthworks are found from the British Isles to Japan. Record keeping is evident, particularly in the Near East where tokens and clay balls with notations date to relatively early times. Stone structures such as Stonehenge in England are astronomically aligned to serve some form of calendrical purpose. Earthworks in eastern North America also had special alignments. The timing of planting and harvesting could mean the difference between eating and starving so some form of calendar was important. Agricultural activities are often accompanied by religious rituals such as first-fruit ceremony. These rituals began during the Neolithic. The Late Neolithic heralded profound changes in sociopolitical arrangements that are taken up in Chapter 12.

NEOLITHIC CULTURE IN THE NEW WORLD

Outside Mesoamerica (southern Mexico and northern Central America) and Peru, hunting, fishing, and the gathering of wild plant foods remained important elements in the economy of Neolithic peoples in the New World.

Apparently, most aboriginal North Americans never made a complete change from a food-foraging to a food-producing mode of life, even though maize and other domestic crops came to be cultivated just about everywhere that climate permitted. Farming developed independently of Europe and Asia, with different crops and different technologies.

The Neolithic developed even more slowly in the New World than in the Old. For example, Neolithic agricultural villages were common in Southwest Asia between 9000 and 8000 years ago, but similar villages did not appear in the New World until about 4500 years ago, in Mesoamerica and Peru. Neither the potter's wheel nor the loom and spindle were used by early Neolithic people in the New World. Both pottery and textiles were manufactured by hand; evidence of the loom and spindle does not appear in the New World until 3000 years ago. None of these absences indicate any backwardness on the part of New World peoples, who, as we have already seen, were highly sophisticated farmers and plant breeders. Rather, the effectiveness of existing practices was such that they continued to be satisfactory.

THE NEOLITHIC AND HUMAN BIOLOGY

Although we tend to think of the invention of food production in terms of its cultural impact, it obviously had a biological impact as well. From studies of human skeletons from Neolithic burials, biological anthropologists have found evidence for a somewhat lessened mechanical stress on people's bodies and teeth. Although there are exceptions, the teeth of Neolithic peoples show less wear, their bones are less robust, and osteoarthritis (the result of stressed joint surfaces) is not as marked as in the skeletons of Palaeolithic and Epipalaeolithic peoples. On the other hand, there is clear evidence for a marked deterioration in health and longevity of Palaeolithic and Neolithic peoples. Anthropologist Anna Roosevelt sums up our knowledge of this in the following Original Study.

For the most part, the crops on which Neolithic peoples came to depend were selected for their higher productivity and storability rather than their nutritional value. Moreover, as already noted, the crops' nutritional shortcomings would have been exacerbated by their susceptibility to periodic failure, particularly as populations grew in size. Thus, the worsened health and mortality of Neolithic peoples is not surprising. Some researchers have gone so far as to assert that the switch from food foraging to food production was the worst mistake that humans ever made!

Another key contributor to the increased incidence of disease and mortality was probably the new mode of life in Neolithic communities. First, sedentary life in fixed villages brings with it sanitation problems as

Sometimes Neolithic villagers got together to carry out impressive communal works. Shown here is Stonehenge, the famous ceremonial and astronomical centre in England, which dates back to about 2500 B.C. Its construction relates to the new attitudes toward the earth and forces of nature associated with food production. GETTY IMAGES

ORIGINAL STUDY

History of Mortality and Physiological Stress

Although there is a relative lack of evidence for the Palaeolithic stage, enough skeletons have been studied that it seems clear that seasonal and periodic physiological stress regularly affected most prehistoric hunting-gathering populations, as evidenced by the presence of enamel hypoplasias (horizontal linear defects in tooth enamel) and Harris lines (horizontal lines near the ends of long bones). What also seems clear is that severe and chronic stress, with high frequency of hypoplasias, infectious disease lesions, pathologies related to iron-deficiency anemia, and high mortality rates, is not characteristic of these early populations. There is no evidence of frequent, severe malnutrition, and so the diet must have been adequate in calories and other nutrients most of the time. During the Epipalaeolithic, the proportion of starch in the diet rose, to judge from the increased occurrence of certain dental diseases, but not enough to create an impoverished diet. At this time, diets seem to have been made up of a rather large number of foods, so that the failure of one food source would not be catastrophic. There was a possible slight tendency for Palaeolithic people to be healthier and taller than Epipalaeolithic people, but there was no apparent trend toward increasing physiological stress during the Epipalaeolithic. Thus, it seems that both hunter-gatherers and incipient agriculturalists regularly underwent population pressure, but only to a moderate degree.

During the periods when effective agriculture first came into use, there seems to be a temporary upturn in health and survival rates in a few regions: Europe, North America, and the Eastern Mediterranean. At this stage, wild foods were still consumed periodically and a variety of plants were cultivated, suggesting the availability of adequate amounts of different nutrients. Based on the increasing frequency of tooth disease related to high carbohydrate consumption, it seems that cultivated plants probably increased the storable calorie supply, removing for a time any seasonal or periodic problems in food supply. In most regions, however, the development of agriculture seems not to have had this effect, and there seems to have been a slight increase in physiological stress.

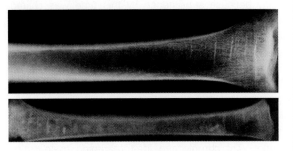

Harris lines near the ends of these youthful thighbones, found in a prehistoric farming community in Arizona, are indicative of recovery after growth arrest, caused by famine or disease. **ALAN H. GOODMAN/HAMPSHIRE COLLEGE**

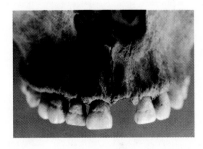

Enamel hypoplasias, such as those shown on these teeth, are indicative of arrested growth caused by disease or famine. The teeth are from an adult who lived in an ancient farming community in Arizona. **ALAN H. GOODMAN/HAMPSHIRE COLLEGE**

Stress does not seem to have become common and widespread until after the development of high degrees of sedentism, population density, and reliance on intensive agriculture. At this stage in all regions the incidence of physiological stress increased greatly, and average mortality rates increased appreciably. Most of these agricultural populations had high frequencies of porotic hyperostosis and cribra orbitalia (bone deformities indicative of chronic iron-deficiency anemia), and there was a substantial increase in the number and severity of enamel hypoplasias and pathologies associated with infectious disease. Stature in many populations appears to have been considerably lower than would be expected if genetically determined height maxima had been reached, which suggests that the growth arrests documented by pathologies were causing stunting. Accompanying these indicators of
(Continued)

poor health and nourishment, there was a universal drop in the occurrence of Harris lines, suggesting a poor rate of full recovery from the stress. Incidence of carbohydrate-related tooth disease increased, apparently because subsistence by this time was characterized by a heavy emphasis on a few starchy food crops. Populations seem to have grown beyond the point at which wild food resources could be a meaningful dietary supplement, and even domestic animal resources were commonly reserved for farm labour and transport rather than for diet supplementation.

It seems that a large proportion of most sedentary prehistoric populations under intensive agriculture underwent chronic and life-threatening malnutrition and disease, especially during infancy and childhood.

The causes of the nutritional stress are likely to have been the poverty of the staple crops in most nutrients except calories, periodic famines caused by the instability of the agricultural system, and chronic lack of food due to both population growth and economic expropriation by elites. The increase in infectious disease probably reflects both a poorer diet and increased interpersonal contact in crowded settlements, and it is, in turn, likely to have aggravated nutritional problems.

Source: Adapted from Roosevelt, A.C. (1984). Population, health, and the evolution of subsistence: Conclusions from the conference. In M.N. Cohen & G.J. Armelagos (Eds.), *Paleopathology at the origins of agriculture* (pp. 572–574). Orlando: Academic Press.

Crops bred for higher productivity and storability, rather than nutritional value, contributed to the poor health of Neolithic people. Even today, plants are still bred for nonnutritional characteristics: long shelf life, appearance, and the like. This is true, too, of genetically engineered crops, which are altered to survive massive applications of herbicides and pesticides and to not produce viable seed (the latter solidifies corporate control of the food system). One may only wonder what the long-term consequences of such practices will be. **SEPP SEITZ/WOODFIN CAMP & ASSOCIATES**

garbage and human waste accumulate. These are not a problem for small groups of people who move about from one campsite to another. Second, airborne diseases are more easily transmitted where people are gathered into villages. Third, the close association between humans and their domestic animals was conducive to the transmission of some animal diseases to humans. A host of life-threatening diseases, including smallpox, chicken pox, and in fact all of the infectious diseases of childhood that were not overcome by medical science until the latter half of the 20th century, were transmitted to humans through their close association with domestic animals (Table 11.1).

Another example of the biological impact of food production on human biology is that of the abnormal hemoglobin responsible for sickle-cell anemia, discussed in Chapter 3. Other abnormal hemoglobins are associated with the spread of farming from Southwest Asia westward around the Mediterranean as well as eastward to India, and also with the spread of farming in Southeast Asia. In all these regions, changes in human gene pools occurred as a biological response to malaria, which had become a problem as a result of farming practices.

Higher mortality rates in Neolithic villages were offset by increased fertility, for population growth accelerated dramatically at precisely the moment that health and mortality worsened. The factors responsible for this increased natality have already been discussed in this chapter.

TABLE 11.1 Diseases Acquired from Domesticated Animals

HUMAN DISEASE	ANIMAL WITH MOST CLOSELY RELATED PATHOGEN
Measles	Cattle (rinderpest)
Tuberculosis	Cattle
Smallpox	Cattle (cowpox) or other livestock with related pox viruses
Influenza	Pigs, ducks
Pertussis ("whooping cough")	Pigs, dogs

Some of the diseases that humans have acquired from domestic animals. Close contact with animals provides a situation in which variants of animal pathogens may establish themselves in humans.

Source: Diamond, J. (1997). Guns, germs, and steel (p. 207). New York: Norton.

THE NEOLITHIC AND THE IDEA OF PROGRESS

One of the more deeply held biases of Western culture is that human history is basically a record of steady progress over time. The transition from food foraging to food production is generally viewed as a great step upward on a supposed ladder of progress. To be sure, farming allowed people to increase the size of their populations, to live together in substantial sedentary communities, and to reorganize the workload in ways that permitted craft specialization. If one chooses to regard this as progress, that is fine—progress is, after all, whatever it is defined as, and different cultures define it differently.

Whatever the benefits of food production, however, a substantial price was paid. As anthropologists Mark Cohen and George Armelagos put it:

Taken as a whole, indicators fairly clearly suggest an overall decline in the quality—and probably in the length—of human life associated with the adoption of agriculture. This decline was offset in some regions, but not in others, by a decline in physical demands on the body. The studies support recent ethnographic statements and theoretical arguments about the relatively good health and nutrition of hunter-gatherers. They also suggest that hunter-gatherers were relatively well buffered against episodic stress. These data call in [sic] question simplistic popular ideas about human progress. They also call in question

models of human population growth that are based on assumed progressive increases in life expectancy. The data suggest that the well documented expansion of early farming populations was accomplished in spite of general diminution of both child and adult life expectancy rather than being fueled by increased survivorship.[31]

Rather than imposing ethnocentric notions of progress on the archaeological record, it is best to view the advent of food production as but one more factor contributing to the diversification of cultures, something that had begun in the Palaeolithic. Although some societies continued to practise hunting, gathering, and fishing, others became **horticultural**—small communities of gardeners working with simple hand tools and using neither irrigation nor the plow. Horticulturists typically cultivate a variety of crops in small gardens they have cleared by hand. Some horticultural societies, however, developed **intensive agriculture**. Technologically more

[31] Cohen, M.N., & Armelagos, G.J. (1984). Paleopathology at the origins of agriculture: Editors' summation. In *Paleopathology at the origins of agriculture* (p. 594). Orlando: Academic Press.

Horticulture. Cultivation of crops carried out with hand tools such as digging sticks or hoes.

Intensive agriculture. Intensive farming of large plots of land, employing fertilizers, plows, and/or extensive irrigation.

complex than the horticulturalists, intensive agriculturalists employ such techniques as irrigation, fertilizers, and the wooden or metal plow pulled by two harnessed draft animals, such as oxen or water buffalo, to produce food on larger plots of land. The distinction between horticulturalist and intensive agriculturalist is not always an easy one to make. For example, the Hopi Indians of the North American Southwest traditionally employed irrigation in their farming while at the same time using simple hand tools.

GENDER PERSPECTIVES

Division of Labour among Agriculturalists

When people became agriculturalists, gender roles began to alter. Food systems and social relations (for example, the relationships between men and women) are linked, so if food systems change so will gender roles.[1] Evidence of these changes is difficult to discern in the archaeological record, so attempts at reconstruction of the division of labour rely on ethnographic data. Such data tell us that plants are usually the business of women.[2] The division of labour at the onset of agriculture likely did not change all that dramatically from that of Palaeolithic hunter-gatherers: Men still dealt with the animal world, hunting and herding where animals were domesticated; women's attention to plants continued through gathering and food preparation. With food production, women also took care of planting, weeding, and harvesting. As agriculture continued to develop, women's lives became increasingly linked to the household.

Many archaeologists suggest that because of the close links between women and plants in the Palaeolithic and Neolithic, women domesticated the first crops. Patty Jo Watson and Mary Kennedy hypothesize that domestication of plants was a conscious decision on the part of women.[3] Using bioarchaeological evidence, Patricia Bridges found that Mississippian agriculturalists in the U.S. Midwest, particularly the women, exhibited stronger, denser bones, due to the physical strength required.[4] In more recent times, as agricultural enterprises grew larger, men became more active in them, and when plow agriculture (intensive agriculture) took hold, men became the primary farmers.

As agriculture intensified, there may have been a corresponding decrease in the political status of women as their contributions to food production became increasingly part of the domestic world. There may also have been a shift toward monogamous marriages, rather than the more common polygynous marriages. Finally, there also seems to be a tendency toward a shorter adolescence. Children of agriculturalists are required to contribute to the farm work, especially during planting and harvesting seasons. This tendency is still evident in rural communities in Western countries such as Canada.

[1] Hastorf, C. (1991). Gender, space, and food in prehistory. In J.M. Gero & M.W. Conkey (Eds.), Engendering archaeology: Women and prehistory (pp. 132–159). Oxford: Basil Blackwell.

[2] Watson, P.J., & Kennedy, M.C. (1991). The development of horticulture in the Eastern Woodlands of North America: Women's role. In J.M. Gero & M.W. Conkey (Eds.), Engendering archaeology: Women and prehistory (pp. 255–275). Oxford: Basil Blackwell.

[3] Ibid.

[4] Bridges, P.S. (1989). Changes in activities with the shift to agriculture in the southeastern United States. Current Anthropology, 30, 385–394.

Sources: Gilchrist, R. (1999). Gendered hierarchies? Labour, "prestige" and production. In R. Gilchrist (Ed.), Gender and archaeology: Contesting the past (pp. 31–53). London: Routledge; and Smith, P.E.L. (1976). Food production and its consequences. Menlo Park, CA: Cummings Publishing.

Some societies became specialized **pastoralists** in environments that were too dry, too grassy, too steep, or too cold for effective horticulture or intensive agriculture. For example, the Russian steppes, with their heavy grass cover, were not suitable to farming without a plow, but they were ideal for herding. Thus, a number of peoples living in the arid grasslands and deserts that stretch from northwestern Africa into Central Asia kept large herds of domestic animals, relying on their neighbours for plant foods. A comparable development took place in the high, intermountain basins of Peru and Bolivia.

> **Pastoralists.** People who rely on herds of domestic animals for their subsistence.

CHAPTER SUMMARY

The end of the glacial period saw great physical changes in human habitats. Sea levels rose, vegetation changed, and herd animals disappeared from many areas. The European Mesolithic period marked a shift from big game hunting to the hunting of smaller game and gathering of a broad spectrum of plants and aquatic resources. Increased reliance on seafood and plants made the post-Upper Palaeolithic a more sedentary period for people. Ground stone tools, including axes and adzes, responded to postglacial needs for new technologies. Many Epipalaeolithic and Mesolithic tools in the Old World were made with microliths—small, hard, sharp blades of flint or similar stone that could be hafted with others to produce implements like sickles.

The change to food production, which (in Southwest Asia) was becoming widespread by 9000 years ago, took place as Epipalaeolithic people there were becoming more sedentary and allowed reorganization of the workload so that some people could pursue other tasks. From the end of the Epipalaeolithic, human groups became larger and more permanent as people turned to animal breeding and crop growing.

A domesticated plant or animal is one that has become genetically modified as an intended or unintended consequence of human manipulation. Analysis of plant and animal remains at a site will usually indicate whether or not its occupants were food producers. Wild cereal grasses, for example, usually have fragile stems, whereas cultivated ones have tough stems. Domesticated plants can also be identified because their edible parts are usually larger than those of their wild counterparts. Domestication produces skeletal changes in some animals. The horns of wild goats and sheep, for example, differ from those of domesticated ones. Age and sex imbalances in herd animals may also indicate manipulation by human domesticators.

Several theories have been proposed to account for the changes in the subsistence patterns of early humans. One theory, the "oasis" or "desiccation" theory, is based on climatic determination. Domestication began because the oasis attracted hungry animals, which were domesticated instead of killed by early humans. Although once popular, this theory fell out of favour as systematic studies of the origins of domestication were begun in the

late 1940s. One alternative idea was that domestication began in the hilly flanks of the Fertile Crescent because culture was ready for it. This somewhat culture-bound idea was replaced by theories, popular in the 1960s, that saw domestication as a response to population growth. However, this would require a deliberate decision on the part of people who could have had no prior knowledge of the long-range consequences of domestication. The most probable theory is that domestication came about as a consequence of a chance convergence of separate natural events and cultural developments. This happened independently even if at more or less similar times in Southwest and Southeast Asia, highland Mexico and Peru, South America's Amazon forest, eastern North America, China, and Africa. In all cases, however, people developed food complexes based on starchy grains and/ or roots that were consumed with protein-containing legumes plus some other flavour enhancers.

Two major consequences of domestication are that crops become more productive but also more vulnerable. This combination periodically causes population to outstrip food supplies, whereupon people are apt to move into new regions. In this way, farming has often spread from one region to another, as into Europe from Southwest Asia. Sometimes, food foragers will adopt the cultivation of crops from neighbouring peoples, in response to a shortage of wild foods, as happened in ancient coastal Peru.

Among the earliest known sites containing domesticated plants and animals, about 11 500 to 7000 years old, are those of Southwest Asia (e.g. Abu Hureyra). These sites were mostly small villages of mud huts with individual storage pits and clay ovens. There is evidence not only of cultivation and domestication but also of trade. At ancient Jericho, remains of tools, houses, and clothing indicate the oasis was occupied by Neolithic people as early as 10 350 years ago. At its height, Neolithic Jericho had a population of 400 to 900 people. Comparable villages developed independently in Mexico and Peru by about 4500 years ago.

During the Neolithic, stone that was too hard to be chipped was ground and polished for tools. People developed scythes, forks, hoes, and plows to replace simple digging sticks. The Neolithic was also characterized by the extensive manufacture and use of pottery. The widespread use of pottery is a good indicator of a sedentary community; pottery is found in all but a few of the earliest Neolithic settlements. The manufacture of pottery requires a knowledge of clay and the techniques of firing or baking. Other technological developments that accompanied food production and the sedentary life were the building of permanent houses and the weaving of textiles.

Archaeologists have been able to draw some inferences concerning the social structure of Neolithic society. No evidence has been found indicating that religion or government was yet a centrally organized institution. Society was probably relatively egalitarian, with minimal division of labour and little development of specialized social roles.

The development of food production had biological, as well as cultural, consequences. New diets, living arrangements, and farming practices led to increased incidence of disease and higher mortality rates. Increased fertility of women, however, more than offset mortality.

QUESTIONS FOR CRITICAL THOUGHT

1. How does knowledge of plants recovered from archaeological sites help us understand life at the time these sites were occupied? What would the evidence of plants where you live tell an archaeologist 1000 years from now about your society?

2. The initiation of agriculture has been called the worst mistake humans have made, causing changes in health, population growth, settlement, warfare, and the environment, among other things. What do you think are the reasons for this strong statement?

3. We have a much better idea of what was happening at the onset of agriculture than we did 20 years ago. If you were to undertake an investigation of agricultural origins today, what type of project would you design? What types of data would your investigation try to recover?

INTERNET RESOURCES

The Archaic

www.pc.gc.ca/lhn-nhs/nl/portauchoix/natcul/maritime_E.asp

www.thecanadianencyclopedia.com/index.cfm?PgNm=TCE&Params=A1ARTA0004526
Excellent descriptions of two Maritime Archaic sites in Newfoundland and Labrador.

Canadian Agriculture

www.angelfire.com/ns/canadianagriculture
Presents information on many aspects of Canadian agriculture, including the history of Canadian agriculture and its present form.

Domestication

www.umanitoba.ca/faculties/arts/anthropology/manarchnet/chronology/archaic
A discussion of the Archaic period (6000 B.C. to 1 A.D.) by Brian Schwimmer from the University of Manitoba.

www.maizegenetics.net/index.php?page=domestication/index.html
Discusses the genetics of maize domestication.

www.llamapaedia.com/origin/domestic.html
The story of llamas domesticated by the Incas around 4000 B.C.

www.sciencedaily.com/releases/2005/03/050326004537.htm
The domestication of the pig from the wild boar in a number of different locales is outlined.

www.wsu.edu/gened/learn-modules/top_agrev/agrev-index.html
A comprehensive site from Washington State University that addresses the agricultural revolution. Provides detailed discussion of hunting and gathering, emergence of animal domestication (i.e., pastoralism), and the emergence of agriculture, including swidden (slash-and-burn) horticulture.

www.carleton.ca/~bgordon/Rice
A comprehensive collection of information and original articles, most translated from Chinese, on the archaeology of ancient rice.

Near East Archaeology from the Epipalaeolithic through Neolithic and later periods

www.chass.utoronto.ca/~banning/Ziqlab
Professor Ted Banning of the University of Toronto describes the results of his research in Jordan.

Epipalaeolithic

http://witcombe.sbc.edu/ARTHprehistoric.html
A large home page with links to prehistoric as well as historic art sites. Includes several links to prehistoric art in general, and other sites specializing in Palaeolithic, Epipalaeolithic, and Neolithic art. Provides historical information as well as visual images of this art.

www.gallica.co.uk/celts/portland.htm
This site presents findings from excavations at an Epipalaeolithic habitation site at Portland, Dorset. This habitation site may be the oldest known permanent residence in Britain. Provides good reconstructive photos of the site.

Near East Neolithic

www.jewishmag.com/31MAG/jericho/jericho.htm
www.mnsu.edu/emuseum/archaeology/sites/middle_east/jericho.html
Visit these sites to see the ruins and get a sense of what the ancient city of Jericho is like today.

Neolithic

www.princeton.edu/~bogucki/saa1997.html
Discusses the agricultural dispersal in Europe between 8000 and 5000 years ago, the reasons for it, and the consequences.

www.civilization.ca/cmc/archeo/oracles/ontario/10.htm
Canada's national museum website provides an overview of Ontario prehistory including the Iroquoian agricultural period.

Swidden Horticulture

www.geocities.com/RainForest/3134/agricult.html
A description of the Lacandon Maya sustainable swidden or slash-and-burn horticulture. Links to other information on the Maya.

www.nusantara.com/heritage/swid/index.html
A small site with pictures displaying the six stages of swidden horticulture described in the site.

SUGGESTED READINGS

For a list of suggested readings, visit the textbook's website at www.humanevolution2.nelson.com.

The Rise of Cities and Civilization

Social complexity is commonly exemplified by urban centres or cities. One of the hallmarks of a city is a well-defined nucleus. Shown here is Machu Picchu, an ancient Inca city in the Peruvian Andes. This site has residences, public buildings, temples, and storage facilities. The pit house community at Keatley Creek in British Columbia, although not a city, was occupied by a complex society with a social hierarchy that included wealthy and not-so-wealthy people. The pectin shells were imported to the site and are a prestige item.

KATHERINE GOODES, DR. BRIAN HAYDEN

CHAPTER PREVIEW

1. When and Where Did the World's First Cities Develop?

Cities—urban settlements with well-defined nuclei and populations that are large, dense, and diversified both economically and socially—are characteristic of civilizations that developed initially between 6000 and 4500 years ago in China, the Indus and Nile valleys, Mesopotamia, Meso-america, and Peru. The world's oldest cities were those of Mesopotamia, but one of the world's largest was located in Mesoamerica.

2. What Changes in Culture Accompanied the Rise of Cities?

Four basic culture changes mark the transition from Neolithic village life to that in civilized urban centres. These are agricultural innovation, as new farming methods were developed; diversification of labour, as more people were freed from food production to pursue a variety of full-time craft specialties; the emergence of centralized governments to deal with the new problems of urban life; and the emergence of social classes as people were ranked according to the work they did or the position of the families into which they were born.

3. Why Did Civilizations Develop in the First Place?

A number of theories have been proposed to explain why civilizations develop. For example, some civilizations may have developed as populations grew, causing competition for space and scarce resources, which favoured the development of centralized authority to control resources and organize warfare. Some civilizations, though, appear to have developed as a result of certain beliefs and values that brought people together. In some cases, too, the actions of powerful individuals to promote their own interests may have played a role. Thus, it may be that civilizations arose in different places for somewhat different reasons.

CHAPTER OUTLINE

What Civilization Means

Tikal: A Case Study

Cities and Cultural Change

The Making of Civilization

Civilization and Its Discontents

A walk down a street of a busy North American city brings us in contact with numerous activities that are essential to the well-being of North American society. The sidewalks are crowded with people going to and from offices and stores. The traffic of cars, taxis, and trucks is heavy, sometimes almost at a standstill. In a brief two-block stretch, there may be a department store; shops selling clothing, appliances, or books; a restaurant; a newsstand; a gasoline station; and a movie theatre. Perhaps there will also be a museum, a police station, a school, a hospital, or a library. That is quite a number of services and specialized skills to find in such a small area.

Each of these services or places of business is dependent on others. A butcher shop, for instance, depends on slaughterhouses and beef ranches. A clothing store depends on designers, farmers who produce cotton and wool, and workers who manufacture synthetic fibres. Restaurants depend on refrigerated trucking and vegetable and dairy farmers. Hospitals depend on a great variety of other institutions to meet their more complex needs. All institutions, finally, depend on the public utilities—the telephone, gas, water, and electric companies. Although interdependence is not immediately apparent to the passerby, it is an important aspect of modern cities.

The interdependence of goods and services in a big city is what makes so many products readily available to people. For example, refrigerated air transport makes it possible to buy fresh Prince Edward Island lobsters in Vancouver. This same interdependence, however, has undesirable effects if one service stops functioning, for example, because of strikes, bad weather, accidents, or acts of violence. Thus, every so often, major North American cities have had to do without services as vital as newspapers, subways, schools, and garbage removal. The question is not so much "Why does this happen?" but rather "Why doesn't it happen more often, and why does the city continue to function as well as it does when one of its services stops?" The answer is that services are not only interdependent, but also adaptable. When one breaks down, others take over its functions.

On the surface, city life seems so orderly that we take it for granted; but a moment's reflection reminds us that the intricate fabric of city life did not always exist, and the goods that are widely accessible to us were once simply not available.

WHAT CIVILIZATION MEANS

This complicated system of goods and services available in such a small space is a mark of civilization itself. The history of civilization is intimately bound up with the history of cities. This does not mean that civilization is to be equated with modern industrial cities or with present-day European or North American society. People as diverse as the ancient preindustrial Aztecs of Mexico and the industrial North Americans of today are included in the term "civilization," but each represents a very different kind. It was with the development of the earliest preindustrial cities, however, that civilization first developed (Figure 12.1). In fact, the word comes from the Latin *civis,* which refers to one who is an inhabitant of a city, and *civitas,* which refers to the community in which one dwells. The word *civilization* contains the idea of "citification," or "the coming-to-be of cities."

Civilization is one of those words that is used in different ways by different people. In everyday usage, it carries the notion of refinement and progress, two ethnocentric concepts that mean whatever a culture holds them to mean. In anthropology, by contrast, the term has a very precise meaning that avoids such culture-bound notions. As used by anthropologists, **civilization** refers to societies in which large numbers of people live in cities, are socially stratified, and are governed by centrally organized political systems called states. We shall elaborate on all of these points in the course of this chapter.

The world's first cities sprang up in some parts of the world as Neolithic villages of the sort discussed in Chapter 11 grew into towns, some of which in turn grew into cities. This happened first in Mesopotamia (in modern-day Iraq), then in Egypt and the Indus Valley, between 6000 and 4500 years ago. The inhabitants of Sumer, in southern Mesopotamia, developed the world's first civilization about 5500 years ago. In China, civilization was under way by 5000 years ago. Independent of these developments in the Old World, the first cities appeared in Peru between 5000 and 4000 years ago, and in Mesoamerica about 2000 years ago.

> **Civilization.** In anthropology, a type of society marked by the presence of cities, social classes, and the state.

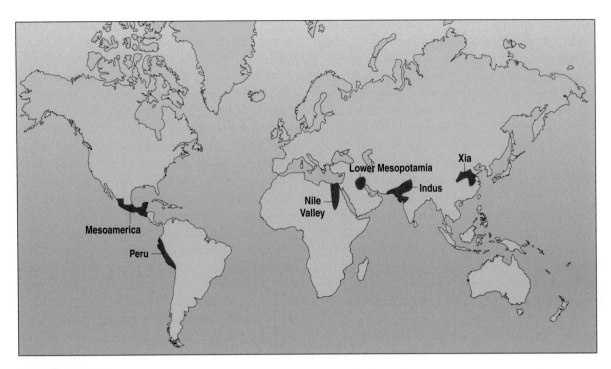

FIGURE 12.1

The major early civilizations sprang from Neolithic villages in various parts of the world. Those of North and South America developed wholly independently of those in Africa and Asia; Chinese civilization seems to have developed independently of Southwest Asia (including the Nile and Indus) civilizations.

Civilization does not suddenly appear after the Neolithic, although sites grow in size and show evidence that the status of individuals has begun to vary from low to high. Late Neolithic societies often exhibit some, but not all, of the characteristics of civilization. In the Mississippi Valley, the Mississippian culture had large communities were constructed around temples built on high, flat-topped mounds, and supported by a mixed economy. These communities do not appear to have been organized as a state. Nor does civilization as we define it appear to have developed in pre-contact Canada. Public works in the form of earthworks are found from British Columbia to New Brunswick, but they are not associated with intensive agriculture, urbanization, centralized authority, and social ranking. On the Canadian East Coast, research directed by Chris Turnbull at Augustine Mound, New Brunswick, constructed about 2500 years ago, points to the spread of religious and perhaps other influences (or people) from the Adena culture in Ohio that began about 3000 years ago. Among the numerous cremation burials in the mound are materials and artifacts from the U.S. Midwest.[1] The legacy of this culture

in New Brunswick is unknown. On the West Coast, complex social institutions developed in the absence of agriculture, although the coastal environment provided rich terrestrial and aquatic resources, some of which were managed. Archaeologically, this is known as the "Developed Northwest Coast Pattern," recognized by its villages of large, planked houses.[2] These villages were occupied by hundreds of people for many months, although not year-round. For the period that these large groups were together, they formed a loose confederacy. However, extended families, not the confederacy, held rights to resources. Individuals owned property, but ownership essentially meant that the owner's permission was required for the land to be used by someone else and the permission was always granted.[3] The household

---

[1] Keenleyside, D.L. (2001). Glimpses of Atlantic Canada's past. Retrieved November 30, 2002, from the World Wide Web: www.civilization.ca/academ/articles/keen1_3e.html.

[2] Matson, R.G., & Coupland, G.G. (1995). *The prehistory of the northwest coast.* San Diego: Academic Press.

[3] Drucker, P. (1966). Rank, wealth, and kinship in northwest coast society. In T. MeFeat (Ed.), *Indians of the north Pacific coast* (pp. 134–146). Seattle: University of Washington Press.

consisted of a group of people closely related to the chief (nobles), commoners who had no rights to resources and ceremonies, and slaves. Except for slaves and non-slaves, social classes did not exist. Ethnographers point out that individuals actually fit into a graduated series from low to high status. We know from such North American groups such as the Natchez that the chief is the head of a large extended family and the position has prestige and wealth associated with it. Archaeological research is examining the history of this pattern in relation to environment and resources. Northwest Coast archaeology can contribute to our understanding of power structures, economic and social change, and intensification, all important issues related to the rise of civilization.

What characterized the first cities? Why are they called the birthplaces of civilization? The first characteristic of cities—and of civilization—is their large size and population. But is this all that a city is? Consider the case of Çatalhöyük, a 9500-year-old settlement in south-central Turkey (see Figure 12.2).[4] Home to 5000 or more people, its houses were so tightly packed together in an area of roughly 12 hectares that there were no streets. To get into one's own house, one dropped through a hole in the roof, after having traversed the roofs of neighbouring houses. For subsistence, people grew crops and tended livestock, but because the village was located in the middle of a swamp, these activities were carried out at locations at least 12 kilometres away. But there is no evidence for intensification of agriculture; furthermore, people's diets included significant amounts of food from wild plants and animals.

The reason for Çatalhöyük's location in the middle of a swamp may have been to exploit the lime-rich clay that people used to plaster their walls, floors, and ovens. Walls were covered with all sorts of paintings, often of small men confronting outsize beasts, as well as reliefs of leopards, bulls, and female breasts. But there was little division of labour, nor is there any evidence of centralized authority. The houses are all pretty much alike, and there is no known public architecture. It is as if a number of what otherwise would be separate Neolithic villages were all crammed together in one place.

One may compare Çatalhöyük with Teotihuacan, the Americas' first great experience in planned urbanism (Figure 12.3). Located in central Mexico, in the first 400 years after its founding 2200 years ago, its population grew rapidly, until it reached perhaps 80 000 people. Slower growth thereafter brought this figure to around 100 000, all packed within an area of about 20 square kilometres. As revealed by regional surveys, one reason for the early rapid growth was that the population of the entire 5000-square-kilometre Basin of Mexico (where modern Mexico City is located today) was removed and relocated to Teotihuacan, apparently as a result of a large volcanic eruption that for reasons not well understood focused the survivors' attentions on the location that became the site of Teotihuacan. Furthermore, the layout of the city was planned from the very start. At its centre is what is known as the Street of the Dead, a grand north-south axis along which are located the huge Sun and Moon pyramids as well as a royal palace compound (associated with the planet Venus) and other monumental construction. The Sun pyramid was built above a cave, seen as a portal to the underworld, home of deities associated with death. The street itself was deliberately oriented to an astronomical alignment of 15.5 degrees east of true north. Surrounding this core were thousands of apartment compounds, separated from one another by narrow streets laid out in a grid,

FIGURE 12.2

Location of Çatalhöyük

---

[4] Material on Çatalhöyük is drawn from Balter, M. (1998). Why settle down? The mystery of communities. *Science, 282,* 1442–1444; Balter, M. (1999). A long season puts Çatalhöyük in context. *Science, 286,* 890–891; Balter, M. (2001). Did plaster hold Neolithic society together? *Science, 294,* 2278–2281; and Kunzig, R. (1999). A tale of two obsessed archaeologists, one ancient city and nagging doubts about whether science can ever hope to reveal the past. *Discover, 20* (5), 84–92.

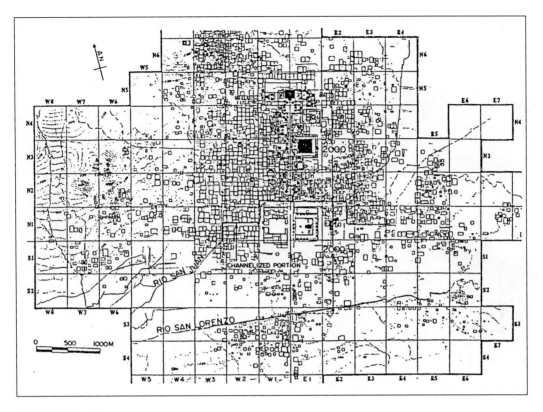

FIGURE 12.3

The founders of Teotihuacan imposed an audacious plan on several square kilometres of landscape in central Mexico. At the centre is the Avenue of the Dead, running from the Temple of the Moon (near top), past the Temple of the Sun and, south of the Rio San Juan, the palace compound. Note the gridded layout of surrounding apartment compounds, and the channelized Rio San Juan.

maintaining the east-of-north orientation throughout the city. Key linear dimensions of construction and distance between compounds seem to have translated calendrical numbers into a unified spatial pattern. So rigid was this layout that the Rio San Juan, where it runs through the city, was channelized to conform with the grid. Finally, there is clear evidence for both social and economic diversity. Some six levels of society can be recognized by variation in size and quality of apartment rooms. Those at and near the top of the social scale lived on or near the Street of the Dead. Exotic goods and raw materials were imported from afar to be worked by Teotihuacano artisans, and at least two enclaves housed people with foreign affiliations, one to Oaxaca, the other ("merchant's barrio") to the Gulf and Maya lowlands. Also resident in the city were farmers, whose labour in fields (some of them irrigated) supplied the food on which the city dwellers relied.[5]

As this comparison shows, early cities were far more than expanded Neolithic villages. The changes that took place in the transition from village to city were so great that the emergence of urban living is considered by some to be one of the great revolutions in human culture. The following case study gives us a glimpse of another of the world's ancient cities, how it was studied by archaeologists, and how it may have grown from a smaller farming community.

Social Complexity

The concept of "civilization" in anthropology has a history of controversy and the way the term is used in this text may oversimplify the issue of societal complexity. "Civilization"

---

[5] Cowgill, G.L. (1997). State and society at Teotihuacan, Mexico. *Annual Review of Anthropology, 26,* 129–161.

This photo looks south down Teotihuacan's principal avenue, the Street of the Dead, an urban axis unequalled in its scale until construction of such modern-day avenues as the Champs Elysées in Paris. **RICHARD REED/ANTHRO-PHOTO**

is by no means the only way of characterizing this complexity. However we choose to conceptualize complex societies, their study is situated in comparative studies.[6] Comparative studies seek an understanding of societies by examining their similarities and differences. Early civilizations can be studied only through archaeological research so the details of what they actually represent are difficult to assess. Archaeologists have at one time or another tried to compare and classify early cultures with reference to the materials they produced, and we still see these names in use in the Stone, Bronze and Iron Age classification. These labels are so general as to be almost useless today.

Other schemes have been introduced and one that still enjoys popularity among anthropological archaeologists is one detailed by Elman Service.[7] He considers a variety of factors such as the nature of social stratification and authority, distribution of goods, specialization of production and other activities, and presence and nature of monuments. Bands were egalitarian groups of hunter-gatherers, tribes were kinship-based organizations of populations that were larger than found in bands and

they were usually farming or mixed-economy groups with situational leaders but no permanent institutions or formal specializations. Chiefdoms have even larger populations and are stratified or class-based groups whose leaders belong to a kin group whose authority is religious. That is, they form what is called a theocracy. Their economy involves the redistribution of goods from specialists through trade and markets. Although there may be communities that appear to be small cities, there is no secular power base. States are also stratified societies but their power base includes secular leaders, a full-time military, taxation, and secular laws. Craft specialization is well developed, and the economy is more expansive than in chiefdoms. The archaeological signs of bands, tribes, chiefdoms, and states are debated and not always clear. How do archaeologists tell the difference between a chiefdom and a state, for example? We

[6] Trigger B.G. (2003). *Understanding early civilizations: A comparative study*. Cambridge UK: Cambridge University Press.

[7] Service E.R. (1975). *Origins of the state and civilization: The process of cultural evolution*. New York: Norton.

might look for secular government-related architecture, written laws, and the like, but it is not a simple matter most of the time.

Service's scheme is evolutionary and unilineal. Such schemes are rejected by many anthropologists according to Bruce Trigger[8] because they seem to deny human behavioural diversity and the role of culturally based ideas to create even more diversity. There can be no denying that we have descended from Upper Palaeolithic cultures who became farmers who then formed modern societies. This text is organized on that principle. Comparative studies indicate that Service's scheme also oversimplifies reality. Anthropologists studying African societies point out that social complexity developed to a high degree in the absence of urbanization,[9] and that power based on centralization and hierarchies is not universal when the African situation is considered. Control in many African societies tends to be over people rather than territory. In this case, highly complex societies can exist without monumental architecture. Archaeologists are considering alternative models of complexity, and many prefer the terms "ranked society" or "complex society" over the terms "chiefdom" or "state."

TIKAL: A CASE STUDY

The ancient city of Tikal, one of the largest lowland Maya centres in existence, is situated in Central America about 300 kilometres by air north of Guatemala City. Tikal was built on a broad limestone terrace in a rain forest. Here the Maya settled in the 1st millennium B.C., and their civilization flourished until about A.D. 869 (dates were recorded by the Maya in their own calendar, which can be precisely correlated with our own).

At its height, Tikal covered about 120.5 square kilometres, and its nucleus, or "epicentre," was the Great Plaza, a large, paved area surrounded by about 300 major structures and thousands of houses. Starting from a small, dispersed population, the population of Tikal swelled to large proportions. By A.D. 550, the density of Tikal was on the order of 600 to 700 persons per square kilometre, six times that of the surrounding regions.

From 1956 through the 1960s, Tikal and the surrounding region were intensively explored under the joint auspices of the University of Pennsylvania Museum and the Guatemalan government. Until 1959, the Tikal Project had investigated only major temple and palace structures found in the vicinity of the Great Plaza, at the site's epicentre. It became evident, however, that in order to gain a balanced view of Tikal's development and composition, considerable attention would have to be devoted to hundreds of small mounds, thought to be the remains of dwellings, which surround the larger buildings. Just as one cannot get a realistic view of present-day London or Paris by looking at the monumental public buildings alone, so one cannot obtain a realistic view of Tikal without examining the full range of ruins in the area.

It became evident that a long-range program of excavation of small structures, most of which were probably houses, was necessary at Tikal. Such a program would provide some basis for an estimate of the city's population size and density—information critical for testing the conventional assumption that the Maya could not have sustained large concentrations of population because their subsistence practices were not adequate. Extensive excavation would also provide a sound basis for a reconstruction of the everyday life of the Maya, a people up until then known almost entirely through a study of ceremonial remains. Moreover, the excavation might shed light on the social organization of the Maya. For example, differences in house construction and in the quality and quantity of associated remains might suggest social class differences; or features of house distribution might reflect the existence of extended families or other types of kin groups. The excavation of both large and small structures could reveal the variations in architecture and associated artifacts and burials; such variations might reflect the social structure of the total population of Tikal.[10]

Surveying the Site

By the time the first excavations of small structures were undertaken, 6 square kilometres surrounding the Great Plaza had already been extensively surveyed by mapping crews (see Figure 12.3). For this mapping, aerial photography was worthless because the tree canopy in this area

[8] Trigger B.G. (2003). *Understanding early civilizations: A comparative study.*

[9] McIntosh S.K. (1999). *Beyond chiefdoms: Pathways to complexity in Africa.* Cambridge, UK Cambridge University Press.

[10] Haviland, W.A. (2003). Settlement, society and demography at Tikal. In J. Sabloff (Ed.), *Tikal.* Santa Fe: School of American Research.

is often 30 metres above the ground and obscures all but the tallest temples; many of the small ruins are practically invisible even to observers on the ground. The only effective way to explore the region is on foot. Even after four years of careful mapping, the limits of the site still had not been revealed; ancient Tikal was far larger than the 6 square kilometres surveyed until then. More time and money were required to continue surveying the area in order to define the city's boundaries. To simplify this problem, straight survey trails oriented toward the four cardinal directions, with the Great Plaza as the centre point, were cut through the forest, measured, and staked by government surveyors. The distribution of ruins was plotted, using the trails as reference points, and the overall size of Tikal was calculated.[11]

The area selected for the first small-structure excavation was surveyed in 1957 while it was still covered by forest. A map was drafted, and two years later the first excavations were undertaken.[12] Six structures, two plazas, and a platform were investigated. The original plan was to strip each of the structures to bedrock in order to obtain every bit of information possible. Three obstacles prevented this procedure, however. First was the discovery of new structures not visible before excavation; second, the structures turned out to be far more complex architecturally than anyone had expected; and, finally, the enormous quantity of artifacts found then

had to be washed and catalogued, a time-consuming process. Consequently, not every structure was completely excavated, and some remained uninvestigated.

Evidence from the Excavation

Following this initial work, over 100 additional small structures were excavated in different parts of the site in order to ensure that a representative sample was investigated. Numerous test pits were sunk in various other small structure groups to supplement the information gained from more extensive excavations.

Excavation at Tikal revealed evidence of trade in nonperishable items. Granite, quartzite, hematite, pyrite, jade, slate, and obsidian all were imported, either as raw materials or finished products. Marine materials came from Caribbean and Pacific coastal areas. Tikal itself is located on a source of abundant flint, which may have been exported in the form of raw material and finished objects. The site also happens to be located between two river systems to the east and west, and so may have been on a major overland trade route between the two. There is indi-

---

[11] Puleston, D.E. (1983). *The settlement survey of Tikal*. Philadelphia: University Museum.

[12] Haviland, W.A., et al. (1985). *Excavations in small residential groups of Tikal: Groups 4F-1 and 4F-2*. Philadelphia: University Museum.

At Tikal, only the tallest temples are visible above the forest canopy. The two farthest temples are at either end of the Great Plaza, the civic and ceremonial heart of the city. (Those familiar with the original Star Wars movie will recognize this view.) **WILLIAM A. HAVILAND**

rect evidence that trade went on in perishable goods such as textiles, feathers, salt, and cacao. We can safely conclude that there were full-time traders among the Tikal Maya.

In the realm of technology, specialized woodworking, pottery, obsidian, and shell workshops have been found. The skillful stone carving displayed on stone monuments suggests that this was done by occupational specialists. The same is true of the fine artwork exhibited on ceramic vessels. Those who painted these had to envision what their work would look like after their pale, relatively colourless slips had been fired. The complex Maya calendar required astronomers, and in order to control the large population, estimated to have been at least 50 000 people, there must have been some form of bureaucratic organization. We do know that the government was headed by a hereditary ruling dynasty, and that it had sufficient power to organize the construction and continuing maintenance of a massive system of defensive ditches and embankments on the northern and southern edges of the city (the longest of these ran for a distance of perhaps 19, if not 28 kilometres). Although we do not

Carved monuments like this were commissioned by Tikal's rulers to commemorate important events in their reigns. Portrayed on this one is a king who ruled between A.D. 768 and A.D. 790 or a bit later. Such skilled stone carving could have been accomplished only by a specialist. (For a translation of the inscription on the monument's left side, see Figure 12.5. on page 351.) **ANITA DE LAGUNA HAVILAND**

have direct evidence, there are clues to the existence of textile workers, dental workers, makers of bark cloth "paper," scribes, masons, and other occupational specialists.

The religion of the Tikal Maya probably developed initially as a means to cope with the uncertainties of agriculture. When people are faced with problems unsolvable by technological or organizational means, they resort to manipulation of magic and the supernatural. Soils at Tikal are thin, and there is no water except that which can be collected in ponds. Rain is abundant in season, but its onset tends to be unreliable. Once the wet season arrives, there may be dry spells of varying duration that can seriously affect crop productivity. Or there may be too much rain, so that crops rot in the fields. Other risks include storm damage, locust plagues, and incursions of wild animals. To this day, the native

This painting from Cacaxtla in southern Mexico shows a deity with the typical backpack of a Maya merchant. **ENRICO FERORELLI**

inhabitants of the region display great concern about these very real risks involved in agriculture over which they have no direct control.

The Maya priesthood devoted much of its time to calendrical matters; the priests tried not only to placate the deities in times of drought but also to propitiate them in times of plenty. Priests determined the most auspicious time to plant crops and were concerned with other agricultural matters. The dependence of the population in and around Tikal upon their priesthood to manipulate supernatural beings and forces in their behalf, in order that their crops would not fail, tended to keep the crops in or near the city, although a slash-and-burn method of agriculture, which was probably the prevailing method early in Tikal's history, requires the constant shifting of plots and consequently tended to disperse the population over large areas.

As the population increased, land for agriculture became scarcer, and the Maya were forced to find new methods of food production that could sustain the dense population concentrated at Tikal. To slash-and-burn agriculture as their main form of subsistence they added the planting and tending of fruit trees and other crops that could be grown around their houses in soils enriched by human waste (unlike houses at Teotihuacan, those at Tikal were not built close to one another). Along with increased reliance on household gardening went the construction of artificially raised fields in areas that were flooded each rainy season. In these fields, crops could be intensively cultivated year after year, as long as they were carefully maintained. Measures also were taken to maximize catchment of water for the dry season, by converting low areas into reservoirs and constructing channels to carry runoff from plazas and other architecture into these reservoirs. As these changes were taking place, a class of artisans, craftspeople, and other occupational specialists emerged to serve the needs first of religion, then of an elite consisting of the priesthood and a ruling dynasty. The arts flourished, and numerous temples, public buildings, and houses were built.

For several hundred years, Tikal was able to sustain its ever-growing population. Then the pressure for food and land reached a critical point, and population growth halted. At the same time, warfare with other cities was becoming increasingly destructive. All of this is marked archaeologically by abandonment of houses on prime land in rural areas, by the advent of nutritional problems as evidenced by the bones from burials, and by the construction of the previously mentioned defensive ditches and embankments. In other words, a period of readjustment set in, which must have been directed

ANTHROPOLOGY APPLIED

Economic Development and Tropical Forests

Prime targets for development in the world today, in the eyes of governments and private corporations alike, are vast tracts of tropical forests. On a global basis, forests are being rapidly cleared for lumber and fuel, as well as to make way for farms, ranches, mines, and other forms of economic development. The world's largest uninterrupted tracts are the forests of the Amazon and Orinoco watersheds of South America, which are being destroyed at about the rate of 4 percent a year. Just what the rate is for the world as a whole no one is quite sure, but it is clearly accelerating. Already there are signs of trouble, as extensive tracts of once-lush growth have been converted to semidesert. Essential nutrients are lost, either through erosion (which increases by several orders of magnitude under deforestation) or by leaching too deeply, as soils are exposed to the direct force of the heavy tropical rains.

The problem is that developers, until recently, have lacked reliable models by which the long-term impact of their actions might be assessed. At least one model, and recently a possible second, exist, thanks to the efforts of archaeologists. The first is unravelling the mystery of how the ancient Maya, in a tropical rain forest setting, carried out large-scale urban construction and sustained huge numbers of people successfully for two millennia. The key to the Maya success was their implementation of sophisticated practices to reduce regionwide processes of nutrient loss, deterioration of soil structure, destabilization of water flows, soil erosion, and loss of productive components of their environment.[1] These included construction of terraces, canals, and raised fields, the fertility of which was maintained through mulching with water plants and the addition of organic wastes. Coupled with all this, crops were planted in such a way as to produce complex patterns of foliage distribution, canopy heights, and nutrient demands. Far different from "modern" mono-crop agriculture, this reduced the impact on the soils of intensive farming, while making maximum use of nutrients and enhancing their cycling in the system.

In Mexico, where population growth has threatened the country's ability to provide sufficient food for its people, archaeologists and agriculturalists are already cooperating to apply our knowledge of ancient Maya techniques to the problems of modern food production in the tropics. Application of these techniques in other tropical forested countries, like Brazil, could do much to alleviate food shortages.

A second example is from the Amazon basin in Brazil. This research is somewhat controversial because it is also calling into question our assumption of pristine tropical Amazon forests only now being impacted by

humans. In fact, between 1200 and 1600 A.D. people lived in large settlements with earthworks and roads in a 1000-square-kilometre area of the Xingu region where they made large-scale changes to the environment.[2] All of the vegetation in the area appears to have been significantly affected by people before European contact. Dark, rich soils called "Indian black earth" are associated with the settlements and are well known to the local Kuikuro people. Agriculture seems to have dominated the landscape for over four centuries. Archaeologists are studying just how this system was maintained for so long without devastating the local ecology. The soils, for example, appear to have been artificially enriched in such a manner that they are still preferred for agriculture. Unlocking the secrets of this Amazonian system could potentially provide important alternative to land-use strategies in the region.

---

[1] Rice, D.S., & Rice, P.M. (1984). Lessons from the Maya. *Latin American Research Review, 19* (3), 24–28.

[2] Heckenberger, M.J., Kuikuro, A., Kuikuro, U.T., Russell, J.C., Schmidt, M., Fausto, C., & Franchetto, B. (2003). Amazonia 1492: Pristine Forest or Cultural Parkland? *Science, 301,* 1710–1714.

by an already strong central authority. Activities then continued as before, but without further population growth for another 250 years or so.

CITIES AND CULTURAL CHANGE

If someone who grew up in a small village in New Brunswick, Saskatchewan, or northern Ontario were to move to Montreal, Toronto, or Vancouver, that person would experience a number of marked changes in his or her way of life. The same sorts of changes in daily life would have been felt 5000 years ago by a Neolithic village dweller upon moving into one of the world's first cities in Mesopotamia. Of course, the differences would be less extreme today. In the 21st century, every North American village, however small, is part of civilization; back when cities first developed, *they* were civilization, and the villages for the most part represented a continuation of Neolithic life. Four basic culture changes mark the transition from Neolithic village life to life in the first urban centres.

Agricultural Innovation

The first culture change characteristic of life in cities—hence, of civilization itself—occurred in farming methods. The ancient Sumerians, for example, built an extensive system of dikes, canals, and reservoirs to irrigate their farmlands. With such a system, they could control water resources at will; water could be held and then run off into the fields as necessary. Irrigation was an important factor affecting an increase of crop yields. Because farming could now be carried on independently of the seasons, more crops could be harvested in one year. On the other hand, this intensification of agriculture did not necessarily mean that people ate better than before. Under centralized governments, intensification was generally carried out with less regard for human health than when such governments did not exist.[13]

---

[13] Roosevelt, A.C. (1984). Population, health, and the evolution of subsistence: Conclusions from the conference. In M.N. Cohen & G.J. Armelagos (Eds.), *Paleopathology at the origins of agriculture* (p. 568). Orlando: Academic Press.

The ancient Maya who lived at Tikal developed systems of tree cultivation and constructed raised fields in seasonally flooded swamplands to supplement their earlier slash-and-burn farming. The resultant increase in crop yields provided for a higher population density. Increased crop yields, resulting from agricultural innovations such as those of the ancient Maya and Sumerians, were undoubtedly a factor contributing to the high population densities of all civilized societies.

Diversification of Labour

The second culture change characteristic of civilization is diversification of labour. In a Neolithic village that possessed neither irrigation nor plow farming, the members of every family were primarily concerned with the raising of crops. However, in cities, the high crop yields made possible by new farming methods and the increased population meant that a sizable number of people were available to pursue nonagricultural activities on a full-time basis. In the early cities, some people still farmed (as at Tikal and Teotihuacan), but a substantial number of the inhabitants were skilled workers or craftspeople.

Ancient public records indicate there was a considerable variety of such skilled workers. For example, an early Mesopotamian document from the city of Lagash lists the artisans, craftspeople, and others paid from crop surpluses stored in the temple granaries. Among them were coppersmiths, silversmiths, sculptors, merchants, potters, tanners, engravers, butchers, carpenters, spinners, barbers, cabinetmakers, bakers, clerks, and brewers. At the ancient Maya city of Tikal we have evidence for traders, potters, woodworkers, obsidian workers, painters, scribes, and sculptors, and perhaps textile workers, dental workers, shell workers, and paper makers.

With specialization came the expertise that led to the invention of new and novel ways of making and doing things. In the Old World, civilization ushered in what archaeologists often refer to as the **Bronze Age**, a period marked by the production of tools and ornaments of this metal. Metals were in great demand for the manufacture of farmers' and artisans' tools, as well as for weapons. Copper and tin—the raw materials from which bronze is made—and eventually iron were smelted, separating them from their ores, then purified, and cast to make plows, swords, axes, and shields. In wars over border disputes or to extend a state's territory, stone knives, spears, and slings could not stand up against bronze spears, arrowheads, swords, or armour.

> **Bronze Age.** In the Old World, the period marked by the production of tools and ornaments of bronze; began about 2000 B.C. in China, 3000 B.C. in Southwest Asia, and about 500 years earlier in Southeast Asia.

The earliest objects of bronze, such as this one, come from Ban Chiang, Thailand.
BAN CHIANG PROJECT, COURTESY OF THE UNIVERSITY OF PENNSYLVANIA MUSEUM

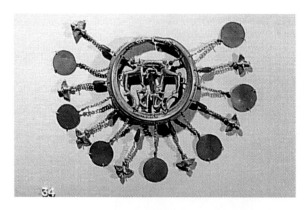

This ear pendant from Greece dating to about 1200 B.C. is a fine example of the artistry that became possible with the introduction of bronze. RONALD SHERIDAN/ANCIENT ART & ARCHITECTURE

The indigenous civilizations of the Americas also used metals—in South America, for tools as well as ceremonial and ornamental objects; in Mesoamerica mostly for ceremonial and ornamental objects. Why people like the Aztecs and Maya continued to rely on stone for their everyday tools has puzzled those who assume that metal is inherently superior. The answer, however, is simple: The ready availability of obsidian (a glass formed by volcanic activity), its extreme sharpness (many times sharper than the finest steel), and the ease with which it could be worked made it perfectly suited to their needs. With obsidian, these people fabricated tools with the sharpest cutting edges ever made.

In order to procure the raw materials needed for their technologies, extensive trade systems were developed by the early civilizations. The city of Teotihuacan, for example, controlled most of the obsidian trade in central Mexico. Trade agreements were maintained with distant peoples, not only to secure basic raw materials but also to provide luxury items.

Boats gave greater access to trade centres; they could easily carry back to cities large loads of imports at less cost than if they had been brought back overland. A one-way trip from Egypt to the northern city of Byblos in Phoenicia (now Lebanon) took only four to eight days by rowboat. With a sailboat, it took even less.

Egyptian pharaohs sent expeditions to the Sinai Peninsula for copper; to Nubia for gold; to Arabia for spices and perfumes; to Asia for lapis lazuli (a blue semi-precious stone) and other jewels; to Lebanon for cedar, wine, and funerary oils; and to central Africa for ivory, ebony, ostrich feathers, leopard skins, cattle, and slaves.

With technological innovation, along with increased contact with foreign peoples through trade, came new

Aztec spears tipped and edged with obsidian blades are shown in this 16th-century drawing of a battle with the Aztecs' Spanish conquerors. Though superior to steel for piercing, cutting, and slashing, the brittleness of obsidian placed the Aztecs at a disadvantage when faced with Spanish swords. NEGATIVE NO. 330878, COURTESY DEPARTMENT OF LIBRARY SCIENCES, AMERICAN MUSEUM OF NATURAL HISTORY

knowledge. It was within the early civilizations that sciences such as geometry and astronomy were first developed. Geometry was used by the Egyptians for such purposes as measuring the area of a field or staking off an accurate right angle at the corner of a building.

Astronomy grew out of the need to know when to plant and harvest crops or to hold religious observances and to find exact bearings on voyages. Astronomy and mathematics were used to devise calendars. The Maya calculated that the solar year was 365 days (actually, it is 365 1/4 days), accurately predicted the appearances over time of the planet Venus as morning and evening "star," predicted eclipses, and tracked other astronomical events. As one scholar comments, "Maya science, in its representation of numbers, and its empirical base, is in many respects superior to the science of their European contemporaries."[14]

---

[14] Frake, C.O. (1992). Lessons of the Mayan sky: A perspective from medieval Europe. In A.F. Aveni (Ed.), *The sky in Mayan literature* (p. 287). New York: Oxford University Press.

Paper making, invented in China 2000 years ago, is an example of technological innovation by which farming societies evolved into civilizations. **HEATHER ANGEL/BIOFOTOS**

Central Government

The third culture change characteristic of civilization is the emergence of a governing elite, a strong central authority required to deal with the many problems arising within the new cities because of their size and complexity. The new governing elite saw to it that different interest groups, such as farmers, craft specialists, or money lenders, provided the services that were expected of them and did not infringe on one another's rights (to the extent that they had rights). It ensured that the city was safe from its enemies by constructing fortifications (such as those at Tikal) and raising an army. It levied taxes and appointed tax collectors so that construction workers, the army, and other public expenses could be paid. It saw to it that merchants, carpenters, or farmers who made legal claims received justice (however "justice" was defined). It guaranteed safety for the lives and property of ordinary people and assured that any harm done one person by another would be justly handled. In addition, surplus food had to be stored for times of scarcity, and public works such as extensive irrigation systems or fortifications had to be supervised by competent, disinterested individuals. The mechanisms of government served all these functions.

Evidence of Centralized Authority

Evidence of centralized authority in ancient civilizations comes from such sources as law codes, temple records, and royal chronicles. Excavation of the city structures themselves provides further evidence. For example, archaeologists believe that the cities of Mohenjo-Daro and Harappa in the Indus Valley, which flourished between 4800 and 3700 years ago, were governed by a centralized authority because they show definite signs of city planning. Both cities stretch out over a 5-kilometre distance; their main streets are laid out in a rectangular grid pattern; and both contain citywide drainage systems. Similar evidence for centralized planning comes from Teotihuacan where, in addition, the sudden relocation of people from the Basin of Mexico also attests to strong, centralized control.

Monumental buildings and temples, palaces, and large sculptures are usually found in civilizations. The Maya city of Tikal contained over 300 major structures, including temples, ball courts, and "palaces" (residences of the aristocracy). The Pyramid of the Sun in the pre-Aztec city of Teotihuacan is over 200 metres long and more than 60 metres high. Its interior is filled by more than 764 000 cubic metres of sun-dried bricks. The

Construction of large-scale public works such as the Great Wall of China reflects the power of a centralized government to mobilize and supervise the labour necessary to carry out such monumental undertakings. **COURTESY OF CHEN SHEN**

tomb of the Egyptian pharaoh Khufu, known as the Great Pyramid, is 230 metres long and 146 metres high. It contains about 2 300 000 stone blocks, each with an average weight of over 2 tonnes. The Greek historian Herodotus reports that it took 100 000 men 20 years to build this tomb. Such gigantic structures could be built only because the considerable labour force, engineering skills, and raw materials necessary for their construction could be harnessed by a powerful central authority.

Another indicator of the existence of centralized authority is writing, or some form of recorded information (Figure 12.4). With writing, central authorities could disseminate information and store, systematize, and deploy

memory for political, religious, and economic purposes. In Mesopotamia, early governments found it useful to keep records of state affairs, such as accounts of their food surplus, tribute records, and other business receipts. The earliest documents appear to be just such records—lists of vegetables and animals bought and sold, tax lists, and storehouse inventories. Being able to record information was an extremely important invention, because governments could keep records of their assets instead of simply relying upon the memory of administrators.

Before 5500 years ago, records consisted initially of "tokens," ceramic pieces with different shapes indicative of different commercial objects. Thus, a cone shape

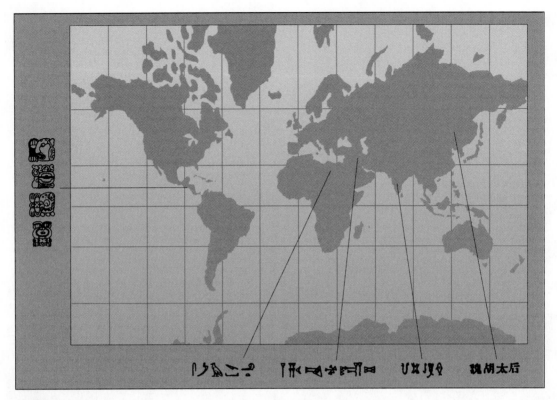

FIGURE 12.4

The impermanence of spoken words contrasts with the relative permanence of written records. In all of human history, writing has been independently invented no more than five times.

could represent a measure of grain, or a cylinder an animal. As the system developed, tokens represented different animals; processed foods such as oil, trussed ducks, or bread; and manufactured or imported goods such as textiles and metal.[15] Ultimately, these tokens were replaced by clay tablets with impressed marks representing objects.

In the Mesopotamia city of Uruk, by 5100 years ago, a new writing technique emerged, which used a reed stylus to make wedge-shaped markings on a tablet of damp clay. Originally, each marking stood for a word. Because most words in this language were monosyllabic, the markings came, in time, to stand for syllables. There were about 600 signs, half of them ideograms, the others functioning either as ideograms or as syllables.

In the New World, systems of writing came into use among various Mesoamerican peoples, but the most sophisticated was that of the Maya. Their hieroglyphic system had less to do with keeping track of state belongings than with "dynastic bombast." Maya lords glorified themselves by recording their dynastic genealogies, important conquests, and royal marriages; by using grandiose titles to refer to themselves; and by associating their actions with important astrological events (Figure 12.5). Often, the latter involved complicated mathematical calculations. So important was the written word in reinforcing the power and authority of Maya kings that scribes were high-ranking members of royal courts. So closely tied to kings were they that, when a king was defeated in warfare, his scribes were captured, tortured, and then sacrificed. The torture was highly symbolic, involving finger mutilation that destroyed their ability to produce politically persuasive texts for any rival of the victor.

_____

[15] Lawler, A. (2001). Writing gets a rewrite. _Science, 292,_ 2419.

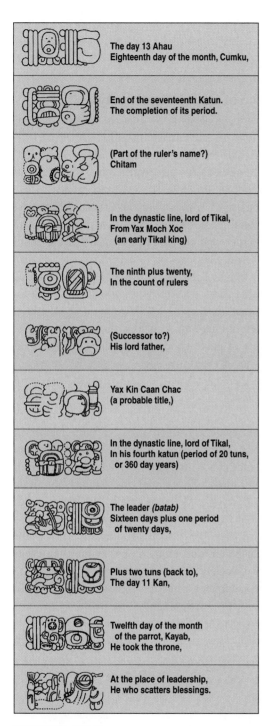

	The day 13 Ahau Eighteenth day of the month, Cumku,
	End of the seventeenth Katun. The completion of its period.
	(Part of the ruler's name?) Chitam
	In the dynastic line, lord of Tikal, From Yax Moch Xoc (an early Tikal king)
	The ninth plus twenty, In the count of rulers
	(Successor to?) His lord father,
	Yax Kin Caan Chac (a probable title,)
	In the dynastic line, lord of Tikal, In his fourth katun (period of 20 tuns, or 360 day years)
	The leader (batab) Sixteen days plus one period of twenty days,
	Plus two tuns (back to), The day 11 Kan,
	Twelfth day of the month of the parrot, Kayab, He took the throne,
	At the place of leadership, He who scatters blessings.

FIGURE 12.5

The translation of the text on the monument shown above gives some indication of the importance of dynastic genealogy to Maya rulers. The "scattering" mentioned may refer to bloodletting as part of the ceremonies associated with the end of one 20-year period, or Katun, and the beginning of the next.

The Earliest Governments

The government of the earliest cities was typically headed by a king and his special advisers. In addition, there were sometimes councils of lesser advisers. Formal laws were enacted, and courts sat in judgment over the claims of rival litigants or the criminal charges brought by the government against an individual.

Of the many ancient kings known, one stands out as truly remarkable for the efficient government organization and highly developed legal system that characterized his reign. This is Hammurabi, the Babylonian king who lived sometime between 1950 and 1700 B.C. He promulgated a set of laws for his kingdom, known as the Code of Hammurabi, which is notable for its thorough detail and standardization. It prescribes the correct form for legal procedures and determines penalties for perjury, false accusation, and injustice done by judges. It contains laws applying to property rights, loans and debts, family rights, and damages paid for malpractice by a physician. There are fixed rates to be charged in various trades and branches of commerce. The poor, women, children, and slaves are protected against injustice. The code was publicly displayed on huge stone slabs so that no one accused could plead ignorance. Even the poorest citizen was supposed to know his or her rights.

Some civilizations flourished under a ruler with extraordinary governing abilities, such as Hammurabi. Other civilizations possessed a widespread governing bureaucracy that was very efficient at every level. Teotihuacan was probably of this sort, but the government of the Inca civilization is better known.

The Inca empire of Peru reached its zenith 500 years ago, just before the arrival of the Spanish in A.D. 1528. In the mid-1400s A.D., the Inca kingdom probably did not extend more than 32 kilometres beyond the modern-day city of Cuzco, which was then its centre. However, within a 30-year period, in the late 1400s, the Inca kingdom enlarged a thousand times its original size. By A.D. 1528, it stretched 4000 kilometres miles from north to south and 800 kilometres from east to west, making it at the time the greatest empire on the face of the earth. Its population numbered in the millions, composed of people of various ethnic groups. In the achievements of its governmental and political system, Inca civilization surpassed every other civilization of the New World and most of those of the

Old World. At the head of the government was the emperor, regarded as semidivine, followed by the royal family, the aristocracy, imperial administrators, the lower nobility, and the masses of artisans, craftspeople, and farmers.

The empire was divided into four administrative regions, further subdivided into provinces, and so on down to villages and families. Planting, irrigation, and harvesting were closely supervised by government agricultural and tax officials. Teams of professional relay runners could carry messages up to 400 kilometres in a single day over a network of roads and bridges that remains impressive even today. The Inca are unusual in that they had no writing that we know about; public records and historical chronicles were kept in the form of an ingenious system of coloured beads, knots, and ropes known as quipu, the Quechua word for "knot." The number and spacing of knots on strings attached to a main string carried commercial information, names, and other information. Unfortunately, the details of quipu recording are not well known.

Social Stratification

The rise of large, economically diversified populations presided over by centralized governing authorities brought with it the fourth culture change characteristic of civilization: social stratification, or the emergence of social classes. Thus, we note that symbols of special status and privilege appeared in the ancient cities of Mesopotamia, and people were ranked according to the kind of work they did or the family into which they were born.

People who stood at or near the head of government were the earliest holders of high status. Although economic specialists of one sort or another—metal workers, tanners, traders, or the like—generally outranked farmers, such specialization did not necessarily bring with it high status. Rather, people engaged in economic activity were either of the lower class or outcasts.[16] The exception was those merchants who were in a position to buy their way into some kind of higher class. With time, the possession of wealth and the influence it could buy became in itself a requisite for high status.

Evidence of Social Stratification

How do archaeologists know that there were different social classes in ancient civilizations? One way they are revealed is by burial customs. Graves excavated at early Neolithic sites are mostly simple pits dug in the ground, containing few, if any, grave goods. Grave goods consist of things such as utensils, figurines, and personal possessions, which are placed in the grave in order that the dead person might use them in the afterlife. The lack of much variation between burials in terms of the wealth implied by grave goods in Neolithic sites indicates an essentially classless society. Graves excavated in civilizations, by contrast, vary widely in size, mode of burial, and the number and variety of grave goods. This indicates a stratified society—one divided into social classes. The graves of important persons contain not only a great variety of artifacts made from precious materials, but sometimes, as in some early Egyptian burials, even the remains of servants evidently killed to serve their master in the afterlife. The skeletons from the burials may also give evidence of stratification. At Tikal, skeletons from elaborate tombs indicate that the subjects of these tombs had longer life expectancy, ate better food, and enjoyed better health than the bulk of that city's population. In stratified societies, the elite usually live longer, eat better, and enjoy an easier life than other members of society.

As an example of what upper-class burials may look like, and what more they can tell us about the customs of the people placed in them, we may look at a spectacular tomb from one of the civilizations that preceded that of the Incas in Peru.

---

[16] Sjoberg, G. (1960). *The preindustrial city* (p. 325). New York: Free Press.

ORIGINAL STUDY

Finding the Tomb of a Moche Priestess

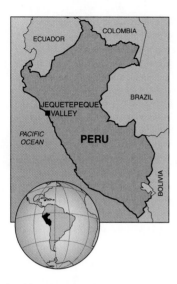

The Moche kingdom flourished on the north coast of Peru between A.D. 100 and 800. Although the Moche had no writing system, they left a vivid artistic record of their beliefs and activities on beautifully modelled and painted ceramic vessels. Because of the realism and detail of these depictions, we are able to reconstruct various aspects of Moche society such as religious ceremonies and mythology, as well as activities like hunting, weaving, and combat rarely preserved in the archaeological record.

During the past 20 years we have developed a major photographic archive of Moche art at the University of California, Los Angeles, which serves as an important resource for the study of their culture. Our goal has been to reconstruct aspects of Moche culture by combining systematic studies of their art with archaeological fieldwork in Peru. Our analyses of sites, including residential compounds, palaces, temples, and cemeteries, and the artifacts associated with them, have allowed us to document archaeologically some of the complex scenes illustrated in Moche art, and to understand aspects of their culture that are not portrayed in the art.

During the past 10 years our research has focused on the Jequetepeque Valley, located in the northern portion of the territory occupied by the Moche. In this region we have undertaken several lines of research, concentrating our efforts on the relationship between Moche ceremonial activities and socioeconomic organization. In June 1991, UCLA began excavations at San José de Moro, a major ceremonial centre in the lower Jequetepeque Valley. It was clear from its various ceramic styles that the site had a long history of occupation and thus would be ideal for answering questions about the cultural sequence of the region. Moreover, the quantity and variation in monumental construction at the site strongly suggested that it had served as a major ceremonial centre through most of its occupation and thus could provide us with good insights about the nature of Moche ceremonial activity.

During our first field season we excavated three complex late-Moche tombs—each consisting of a room-sized burial chamber made of mud bricks. The tomb chambers had originally been roofed with large wooden beams. The principal occupant of each tomb was lying face up in an extended position, with the remains of complete llamas, humans, or both, at their feet. In two of the tombs the principal occupants were flanked by other individuals. Hundreds of ceramic vessels and metal objects, including ceremonial knives, lance points, sandals, cups, masks, and jewellery, had been placed in the tombs as offerings.

The most elaborate of the three tombs was that of a high-status adult female. It is the richest Moche female burial ever scientifically excavated and clearly demonstrates that in Moche society extraordinary wealth and power were not the exclusive domain of males. The tomb chamber was approximately 2 by 4 metres. The walls, which were made of mud brick, had niches—six on each side and four at the head of the tomb—in which ceramic vessels and parts of llamas had been placed. Additional ceramic vessels had been stacked on the floor of the tomb chamber.

(Continued)

A silver-copper alloy mask (left) was found near the priestess's skull. Her body (right) was covered with hammered metal arms and legs. DR. CHRISTOPHER B. DONNAN/UCLA FOWLER MUSEUM OF CULTURAL HISTORY

Some of the artifacts associated with this burial provide clear evidence that the Moche were involved in long-distance trade and that their elite expended a great deal of effort to obtain precious materials. Included among the offerings were three imported ceramic vessels—a plate of Cajamarca style, which must have been brought to San José de Moro from the highland area located more than 112 kilometres to the east, and two exotic ceramic bottles of Nieveria style, a type of pottery that was made in the area of Lima, more than 560 kilometres to the south. Two other kinds of materials associated with the tomb provide further evidence of long-distance trade. Over the woman's chest and hands were *Spondylus princeps* shells that had been brought from Ecuador to the north, and around her neck were cylindrical beads of lapis lazuli that had been brought from Chile to the south.

The most remarkable aspect of this woman's tomb, however, was that the objects buried with her allow us to identify her as a specific priestess who is depicted in Moche art. This priestess was first identified in the Moche Archive at UCLA in 1975, at which time she was given the name "Figure C." Five years later, Anne Marie Hocquenghem and Patricia Lyon convincingly demonstrated that this individual was female. She was one of the principal participants in the "Sacrifice Ceremony," an event depicted in Moche art where prisoners of war were sacrificed and their blood ritually consumed in tall ceremonial goblets.

Figure C is always depicted with her hair in wrapped braids that hang across her chest, and wearing a long dresslike garment. Also characteristic of Figure C is her headdress, which is unique in having two prominent tassels. The tomb of the woman at San José de Moro contained an identical headdress with two huge tassels made of a silver copper alloy.

In one corner of the tomb was a large blackware ceramic basin containing cups and a tall goblet. An identical blackware basin with cups in it is shown associated with Figure C in a famous mural at the site of Pañamarca, a ceremonial centre located in the Nepeña Valley. Furthermore, the tall goblet contained in the ceramic basin was of the type used in the Sacrifice Ceremony. It is decorated with a scene of anthropomorphized clubs and shields drinking blood from similar goblets. The tall goblet is a prominent feature in all depictions of the Sacrifice Ceremony, and it is often seen being presented by Figure C. Finding the tall goblet in her grave thus supports her identification as Figure C.

The Moche Sacrifice Ceremony

The Sacrifice Ceremony, an event at which prisoners of war are sacrificed and their blood ritually consumed, is a common iconographic theme in Moche art. One of the better-known representations of this ceremony appears on a stirrup spout bottle. The scene, centre, shows four principal figures and attendants. Below them are bound captives having their throats slashed. During recent excavations at San José de Moro and at Sipán, the remains of several people who participated in this ceremony have been identified. Figure C, a priestess, was discovered at San José de Moro, while Figure A, a warrior-priest, and Figure B, a bird-warrior, were excavated at Sipán.

A goblet, recovered during the excavation of the priestess's tomb at San José de Moro, is decorated with a scene of anthropomorphic war clubs and shields drinking the blood of captives from tall goblets. A similar goblet is being passed between Figure A and Figure B in the drawing below.

DR. CHRISTOPHER B. DONNAN/ UCLA FOWLER MUSEUM OF CULTURAL HISTORY

Silver-copper alloy tassels worn by the principal occupant of the tomb allowed her to be identified as the priestess depicted in the Sacrifice Ceremony. The tassels are identical to those worn by Figure C in both the drawing and the Pañamarca mural, bottom.

DR. CHRISTOPHER B. DONNAN/UCLA FOWLER MUSEUM OF CULTURAL HISTORY

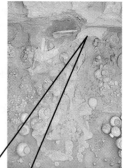

DR. CHRISTOPHER B. DONNAN/UCLA FOWLER MUSEUM OF CULTURAL HISTORY

The Pañamarca mural, right, painted on an adobe wall at a Moche ceremonial centre in the Nepeña Valley, shows Figure C accompanied by several attendants bearing goblets. Pictured too are three bound captives with their throats slashed and a ceramic basin containing cups. A similar basin, below, was found in the priestess's tomb.

DR. CHRISTOPHER B. DONNAN/ FOWLER MUSEUM OF CULTURAL HISTORY

REPRODUCTION BY GONZALO DE REPARAZ, PAINTING BY FELIX CAYCHO. FROM ARCHAEOLOGY (NOV/DEC 1992). REPRODUCED WITH PERMISSION.

(Continued)

The tomb of Figure C at San José de Moro has profound implications for Moche studies. Excavations by Walter Alva at Sipán, located in a valley to the north of San José de Moro, have revealed the tombs of two other participants, Figure A and Figure B, in the Sacrifice Ceremony. The richest of these tombs is that of the Lord of Sipán, Figure A. He was buried with his characteristic crescent-shaped headdress, crescent-shaped nose ornament, large circular ear ornaments, and warrior's backflap, and was holding a rattle like that shown in representations of Figure A. The occupant of another tomb appears to be Figure B, a bird-warrior who is frequently shown as companion to Figure A. He was found wearing a headdress adorned with an owl. Although no grave of Figure C has yet been excavated at Sipán, it seems likely that someone who performed this role was also buried at that site.

How do the tombs at Sipán relate to the tomb of Figure C at San José de Moro? First, it should be noted that the two tombs at Sipán date to approximately A.D. 300, and those at San José de Moro at least 250 years later—sometime after A.D. 550. Clearly, the Sacrifice Ceremony had a long duration in Moche culture, with individuals consistently dressing in traditional garments and headdresses to perform the roles of specific members of the priesthood.

Second, the Sacrifice Ceremony was also wide-spread geographically. The Pañamarca mural, which clearly depicts this ceremony, was found in the Nepeña Valley, in the southern part of the Moche kingdom. San José de Moro is more than 240 kilometres to the north of Pañamarca, and Sipán is another 64 kilometres further north. Moreover, in the 1960s rich tombs containing artifacts with Sacrifice Ceremony iconography were looted from the site of Loma Negra in the Piura Valley, more than 480 kilometres north of Pañamarca.

The four sites where evidence of the Sacrifice Ceremony has been found have characteristics in common. Each is located on an elevated area that rises naturally above the intensively cultivated valley floor and is near, but not immediately adjacent to, a river. Each was a major ceremonial complex, with multiple pyramids that for centuries served as staging areas for religious activities. Perhaps each of the other river valleys that made up the Moche kingdom also had a central ceremonial precinct where the Sacrifice Ceremony was enacted.

The fact that the Sacrifice Ceremony was so widespread in both time and space strongly implies that it was part of a state religion, with a priesthood in each part of the kingdom comprising individuals who dressed in prescribed ritual attire. When members of the priesthood died, they were buried at the temple where the Sacrifice Ceremony took place, wearing their ceremonial paraphernalia and accompanied by the objects they had used to perform the ritual. Subsequently, other men and women were chosen to replace them, to dress like them, and to perform the same ceremonial role.

The careful excavation of the tomb of Figure C at San José de Moro has provided important new insights into the nature of Moche religious practices. As our excavations continue at this remarkable site, we expect to find additional archaeological evidence that will refine and improve upon these insights.

Source: Adapted from Donnan, C.B., & Castillo, L.J. (1992). Finding the tomb of a Moche priestess. *Archaeology, 45* (6), 38–42.

In addition to burials, there are three other ways by which archaeologists may recognize the stratified nature of ancient civilizations:

1. ***The Size of Dwellings***. In early Neolithic sites, dwellings tended to be uniformly small in size. Even at Çatalhöyük, there was little difference in size between houses. In the oldest excavated cities, however, some dwellings were notably larger than others, well spaced, and located together in one district, whereas dwellings in other parts of the city were much smaller, sometimes little more than hovels. In the city of Eshnunna in Mesopotamia, archaeologists excavated houses that occupied an area of 200 square metres situated on main thoroughfares and huts of but 50 square metres located along narrow back alleys. The rooms in the larger houses often contained impressive artwork, such as friezes or murals. At Tikal, and other Maya cities, the elite lived in large, multiroomed, masonry houses, mostly in the city's centre, whereas lower-class people lived in small, peripherally scattered houses of one or two rooms, built partly or wholly of pole and thatch materials.

2. **Written Documents**. Preserved records of business transactions, royal chronicles, or law codes of a civilization reveal much about the social status of its inhabitants. Babylonian and Assyrian texts reveal three main social classes—aristocrats, commoners, and slaves. The members of each class had different rights and privileges. This stratification was clearly reflected by the law. If an aristocrat put out another aristocrat's eye, then the first person's eye was to be put out too; hence, the saying "an eye for an eye." If the aristocrat broke another's bone, then the first aristocrat's bone was to be broken in return. If the aristocrat put out the eye or broke the bone of a commoner, however, the punishment was to pay a mina of silver.[17]

Even in the absence of written information, people may record much about their society in other ways. As the Original Study demonstrates, the Moche recorded much information about their society in their art. The stratified nature of this ancient society is clearly revealed by the scenes painted on ceramic vessels.

3. **Correspondence**. European documents describing the aboriginal cultures of the New World as seen by early European explorers and adventurers also offer evidence of social stratification. Letters written by the Spanish conquistadors about the Aztec empire indicate that they found a social order divided into three main classes: nobles, commoners, and serfs. The nobles operated outside the lineage system on the basis of land and serfs allotted them by the ruler from conquered peoples. The commoners were

divided into lineages, on which they were dependent for land. Within each of these, individual status depended on the degree of descent from the founder; those more closely related to the lineage founder had higher status than those whose kinship was more distant. The third class in Aztec society consisted of serfs bound to the land and porters employed as carriers by merchants. Lowest of this class were the slaves. Some had voluntarily sold themselves into bondage; others were captives taken in war.

Informative though accounts of other civilizations by Europeans may be, they are not without their problems. For example, the explorers, missionaries, and others did not always understand what they saw; moreover, they had their own interests (or those of their sponsors) to look out for, and were not above falsifying information to further those interests. These points are of major importance, given the tendency of Western peoples, with their tradition of literacy, to assume that written documents are reliable. In fact, they are not always reliable, and must be checked for accuracy against other sources of information. The same is true of ancient documents written by people about themselves, for they, too, had their particular agendas. Ancient Maya inscriptions, for example, were often propagandistic in their intent, which was to impress people with particular rulers' importance.

THE MAKING OF CIVILIZATION

From Mesopotamia to China to the South American Andes, we witness the enduring achievements of the human intellect: magnificent palaces built high above ground; sculptures so perfect as to be unrivalled by those of contemporary artists; engineering projects so vast and daring as to awaken in us a sense of wonder. Looking back to the beginnings of written history, we can see a point at which humans transform themselves into "civilized" beings; they begin to live in cities and to expand the scope of their achievements at a rapid pace. How is it, then, that humans at a certain moment in history became consummate builders, harnessing mighty rivers so that they could irrigate crops, developing a system whereby their thoughts could be preserved in writing? The fascinating subject of the development of civilization

This "palace," which housed members of Tikal's ruling dynasty, may be compared with the lower-class house in the photo on p. 458.
ANITA DE LAGUNA HAVILAND

---

[17] Moscati, S. (1962). *The face of the ancient orient* (p. 90). New York: Doubleday.

Lower-class residents of Tikal lived in the same sort of houses in which most Maya live today.
WILLIAM HAVILAND

has occupied the minds of philosophers and anthropologists alike for a long time. We do not yet have the answers, but a number of theories have been proposed.

Theories of Civilization's Emergence

Each of the theories sees the appearance of centralized government as the point at which there is no longer any question whether or not a civilization exists. So, the question they pose is: What brought about the appearance of a centralized government? Or, stated another way: What caused the transition from a small, egalitarian farming village to a large urban centre in which population density, social inequality, and diversity of labour required a centralized government?

Irrigation Systems

One popular theory concerning the emergence of civilization was given its most forceful statement by Karl Wittfogel,[18] and variants of this theory are still held by some anthropologists. Simply put, the irrigation or **hydraulic theory** holds that Neolithic farmers in ancient Mesopotamia and Egypt, and later in the Americas, noticed that the river valleys that were periodically flooded contained better soils than those that were not; but they also noted that violent floods destroyed their planted fields and turned them into swamps. So the farmers built dikes and reservoirs to collect the

floodwater and save it until it was needed. Then they released it into canals and ran it over the fields. At first, these dikes and canals, built by small groups of neighbouring farmers, were very simple. The success of this measure led to larger, more complex irrigation systems, which eventually necessitated the emergence of a group of "specialists"—people whose sole responsibility was managing the irrigation system. The centralized effort to control the irrigation process blossomed into the first governing body and elite social class, and civilization was born.

There are several objections to this theory. One of them is that some of the earliest large-scale irrigation systems we know about anywhere in the world developed in highland New Guinea, where strong centralized governments never emerged. Conversely, actual field studies of ancient Mesopotamian irrigation systems reveal that by 4000 years ago, by which time many cities had already

[18] Wittfogel, K.A. (1957). *Oriental despotism, a comparative study of total power.* New Haven, CT: Yale University Press.

Hydraulic theory. The theory that sees civilization's emergence as the result of the construction of elaborate irrigation systems, the functioning of which required full-time managers whose control blossomed into the first governing body and elite social class.

flourished, irrigation was still carried out on a small scale, consisting of small canals and diversions of natural waterways. If there were state-managed irrigation, it is argued, such a system would have been far more extensive than excavations show it really was. Moreover, documents indicate that irrigation was regulated by officials of local temples and not by centralized government. The oldest irrigation system in the Americas is at Caral, in the coastal desert of Peru. By 4600 years ago, a shallow channel had been cut to a river, where a simple headgate controlled the flow. The system was far simpler than later irrigation works in Peru, and one can argue here, as elsewhere in South America and Mesoamerica, that large-scale irrigation works were a consequence of civilization's development, rather than a cause.

Trade Networks

Some anthropologists argue that trade was a decisive factor in the development of civilizations. In regions of ecological diversity, so the argument goes, trade mechanisms are necessary to procure scarce resources. In Mexico, for example, maize was grown just about everywhere; but chilis were grown in the highlands, cotton and beans were planted at intermediate elevations, certain animals were found only in the river valleys, and salt was obtained along the coasts.

This theory holds that some form of centralized authority was necessary in order to organize trade for the procurement of these and other commodities. Once procured, some system was necessary in order to redistribute commodities throughout the population. Redistribution, like procurement, must have required a centralized authority, promoting the growth of a centralized government. Teotihuacan supplied most of the obsidian tools found in the Valley of Mexico beginning probably during the first century A.D. However, Michael Spence of the University of Western Ontario points out that this was not the result of heavy-handed state control. The Teotihuacan state only facilitated the relatively independent obsidian industry.[19]

Although trade may have played an important role in the development of some civilizations, it did not invariably do so. For example, the aboriginal peoples of northeastern North America traded widely with one another for at least 6000 years without developing civilizations comparable to those of Mexico or Peru. In the course of this trade, copper from deposits around Lake Superior wound up in such faraway places as New England, as did chert from Labrador and marine shells from the Gulf of Mexico. Wampum, made on the shores of Long Island Sound, was carried westward, and obsidian from the Yellowstone region has been found in mounds in Ohio.[20]

Environmental and Social Circumscription

In a series of papers, Robert Carneiro[21] has advanced the theory that civilization develops where populations are hemmed in by such things as mountains, seas, or other human populations. As such populations grow, they have no space in which to expand, and so they begin to compete for increasingly scarce resources. Internally, this results in the development of social stratification, in which an elite controls important resources to which lower classes have limited access. Externally, this leads to warfare and conquest, which, to be successful, require elaborate organization under a centralized authority.

Religion

The three theories just summarized exemplify ecological approaches to explaining the development of civilization. Such theories emphasize the interrelation between people and what they do on the one hand and the environment in which they live on the other. Theories of the emergence of civilization have commonly taken some such approach. Although few anthropologists would deny the importance of the human–environment interrelationship, a growing number of them are dissatisfied with theories that do not take into account the beliefs and values that regulate the interaction between people and their environment.[22]

An example of a theory that does take into account the role of beliefs is one that seeks to explain the emergence of Maya civilization in Mesoamerica.[23] This theory holds that Maya civilization was the result of a process

[19] Spence, M. (1981). Obsidian production and the state of Teotihuacan. *American Antiquity, 46,* 769–788.

[20] Haviland, W.A., & Power, M.W. (1994). *The original Vermonters* (2nd ed., Chap. 3 & 4). Hanover, NH: University Press of New England.

[21] Carneiro, R.L. (1970). A theory of the origin of the state. *Science, 169,* 733–738.

[22] Adams, R.M. (2001). Scale and complexity in archaic states. *Latin American Antiquity, 11,* 188.

[23] Haviland, W.A. (1975). The ancient Maya and the evolution of urban society. *University of Colorado Museum of Anthropology, Miscellaneous Series,* no. 37.

of urbanization that occurred at places like Tikal. In the case study on Tikal earlier in this chapter, it is suggested that Maya religion probably developed initially as a means of coping with the uncertainties of agriculture. In its early days, Tikal seems to have been an important religious centre. Because of its religious importance, people sought to settle there, with the result that its population grew in size and density. A similar process may be seen at Çatalhöyük. As noted early in this chapter, this village was located so as to be near sources of lime-rich clay. This material was required to plaster the walls of houses, the medium for paintings and other art of apparently ritual significance. This seems to have been of such importance as to take precedence over convenient proximity to agricultural fields. Perhaps the inconvenience of having to travel so far to get to one's fields was a reason that Çatalhöyük never developed into a true city.

At Tikal, by contrast, the process went further. Because the concentration of a growing population was incompatible with the prevailing slash-and-burn agriculture, which tends to promote dispersed settlement, new subsistence techniques—such as raised fields—were developed. By chance, these were sufficiently productive to permit further population growth, and, by 1500 years ago, Tikal had become an urban settlement of at least 50 000 people. By then, craft specialization had developed, at first in the service of religion but soon in the service of an emerging social elite as well. This social elite was concerned at first with calendrical ritual, but through the control of ritual it developed into the centralized governing elite that could control a population growing larger and more diversified in its interests.

Developing craft specialization itself served as another factor to pull people into Tikal, where their

BIOGRAPHY

Louise I. Paradis

Louise I. Paradis has been a member of the Department of Anthropology, University of Montreal, since 1972, and has had the opportunity to be a visiting professor at McGill, Yale, and the Université de Paris. She became interested in Mesoamerican archaeology as a graduate student in Montreal and then at Yale where she was awarded her Ph.D. (1974). Her first research was in the Basin of Mexico, where she explored the Preclassic period. She then turned to another area, Guerrero, to do more or less the same thing, which was to document, contextualize, and understand the presence of Olmec-styled artifacts in the area.

Paradis has dedicated most of the last 20 years to a regional study of the pre-Hispanic history of the Mezcala area, still in Guerrero. Paradis and her students were able to document the history of the occupation of the area, from 800 b.c. to the Conquest, to learn about their lapidary tradition, and to understand their local economics and politics as well as their relationships with the rest of Mesoamerica. She has also been researching other topics such as symbolic systems, religion, and politics (human sacrifice). Paradis has dedicated most of the last 20 years to a regional study of

the pre-Hispanic history of the Mezcala area, still in Guerrero. Paradis and her students were able to document the history of the occupation of the area, from 800 b.c. to the Conquest, to learn about their lapidary tradition, and to understand their local economics and politics as well as their relationships with the rest of Mesoamerica.

Sources: Paradis, L.I., & Tolstoy, P. (1970). Early and middle Preclassic cultures in the Basin of Mexico. Science, 167, 344–351.

Paradis, L.I. (2000). Guerrero region. In S.T. Evans & D.L. Webster (Eds.), The archaeology of ancient Mexico and Central America: An encyclopedia. New York: Garland.

Paradis, L.I. (2000). La mort blanche. Actes du Colloque 5. Montréal: Département d'anthropologie, Université de Montréal.

Paradis, L.I. (1999). Le soleil Aztèque était-il un vampire? Frontières, 11, 25–30.

Paradis, L.I. (1998). Tollan et les Toltèques, chacun sa vérité. Anthropologie et Histoire, Actes du Colloque 4 (pp. 19–26). Montréal: Département d'anthropologie, Université de Montréal.

Paradis, L.I. (1981). Guerrero and the Olmec. In E. Benson (Ed.), The Olmec and their neighbors (pp. 195–208). Washington, DC: Dumbarton Oaks.

products were in demand. It also required further development of trade networks, if only to provide exotic raw materials. More long-distance trade contacts, of course, brought more contact with outside ideas, including some from as far afield as Teotihuacan. In other words, what we seem to have is a complex system with several factors—religious, economic, and political—acting to reinforce one another, with religion playing a central role in getting the system started in the first place.

A criticism that may be levelled at all of the above theories is that they fail to recognize the capacity of aggressive, charismatic leaders to shape the course of human history. Accordingly, anthropologists Joyce Marcus and Kent Flannery have developed what they call **action theory**.[24] This recognizes the systemic nature of society and the impact of the environment in shaping social and cultural behaviour but recognizes as well that forceful leaders in any society strive to advance their material or political positions through self-serving actions. In so doing, they may create change. Applying this to the Maya, for example, local leaders, who once relied on personal charisma for the economic and political support needed to sustain them in their

positions, may have seized upon religion to solidify their grip on power. They did this by developing an ideology endowing them and their descendants with supernatural ancestry. Only they were seen as having the kind of access to the gods on which their followers depended. In this case, the nature of the existing system presented a situation in which certain individuals could monopolize power and emerge as divine kings, using their power to subjugate any rivals.

As the above example makes clear, the context in which a forceful leader operates is critical. In the case of the Maya, it was the combination of existing cultural and ecological factors that opened the way for emergence of political dynasties. Thus, explanations of civilization's emergence are likely to involve multiple causes, rather

---

[24] Marcus, J., & Flannery, K.V. (1996). *Zapotec civilization: How urban society evolved in Mexico's Oaxaca Valley.* New York: Thames & Hudson.

Action theory. The theory that self-serving actions by forceful leaders play a role in civilization's emergence.

At Çatalhöyük, as at Tikal, religion seems to have been the initial impetus for nucleation. Here we see a reproduction of some wall paintings, likely with religious meaning, from Çatalhöyük. The site was located near the source of the material used for the wall plaster. **JAMES MELLAART**

than just one. Furthermore, we may also have the cultural equivalent of what biologists call "convergence," where somewhat similar forms come about in quite different ways. Consequently, a theory that accounts for the rise of civilization in one place may not account for its rise in another.

CIVILIZATION AND ITS DISCONTENTS

Living in the context of civilization ourselves, we are inclined to view its development as a great step upward on some sort of ladder of progress. Whatever benefits civilization has brought, though, the cultural changes it represents produced new sorts of problems. Among them is the problem of waste disposal. Actually, waste disposal probably began to be a problem in settled, farming communities even before the emergence of civilization. But as villages grew into towns and towns grew into cities, the problem became far more serious, as the buildup of garbage and sewage created optimum environments for such diseases as bubonic plague and typhoid. The latter is an intestinal disease caused by a *Salmonella* bacterium. In northern Europeans, mutation of a gene on Chromosome 7 that deletes three DNA bases (out of the gene's total of 250 000) makes carriers of this allele virtually immune to typhoid and other bacterial diarrheas.[25] Because of the mortality imposed by these diseases, selection favoured spread of the allele among northern Europeans. But as with sickle-cell anemia, protection comes at a price. That price is cystic fibrosis, a usually fatal disease of the lungs and intestines contracted by those who are homozygous for the altered gene.

Quite apart from sanitation problems and their attendant diseases, the rise of towns and cities brought the problem of acute, infectious diseases. In a small population, such diseases as chicken pox, influenza, measles, mumps, pertussis, polio, rubella, and smallpox will kill or immunize so high a proportion of the population that the virus cannot continue to propagate. Measles, for example, is likely to die out in any human population with fewer than half a million people.[26] Hence, such diseases, when introduced into small communities, spread immediately to the whole population and then die out. Their continued existence depends upon the presence of large population aggregates, such as towns and cities provide.

This mosaic death mask of greenstone, pyrite, and shell was worn by a king of the Maya city of Tikal who died about A.D. 527. Obviously the product of skilled craft work, such specialization developed first to serve the needs of religion, but soon served the needs of an emerging elite as well. **VICTOR R. BOSWELL/NGS IMAGE COLLECTION**

Another disease that became a serious problem in towns and cities (and is becoming so again in the 21st century) is tuberculosis. Here again it has triggered a genetic response not unlike what we have seen in response to malaria (sickle cell and other abnormal hemoglobins) and bacterial diarrheas (the cystic fibrosis gene). Among the Ashkenazi Jews of Eastern Europe, a genetic variant that causes Tay-Sachs disease in homozygotes became comparatively common. Crammed into urban ghettos over several centuries, the Ashkenazim were especially exposed to tuberculosis, but those individuals heterozygous for the Tay-Sachs allele were protected from this disease.[27]

---

[25] Ridley, M. (1999). *Genome, the autobiography of a species in 23 chapters* (p. 142). New York: HarperCollins.

[26] Diamond, J. (1997). *Guns, germs and steel* (p. 203). New York: Norton.

[27] Ridley, p. 191.

Unlike most ancient cities, Mohenjo-Daro, a 4000-year-old metropolis in the Indus River Valley, had an extensive system of drains. Lack of adequate drains in cities contributed to poor public health. **DAVE AGEE/ANTHRO-PHOTO**

In essence, early cities tended to be disease-ridden places, with relatively high death rates. At Teotihuacan, for instance, very high infant and child mortality rates set a limit to the city's growth. Not until relatively recent times did public health measures reduce the risk of living in cities, and had it not been for a constant influx of rural peoples, they would have been hard pressed to maintain their population size, let alone increase it. Europe's urban population, for example, did not become self-sustaining until early in the 20th century.[28] One might wonder, then, what would have led people to go live in such unhealthy places? The answer is, they were attracted by the same sorts of things that lure people to cities today: They are vibrant, exciting places that also provide people with opportunities not available in rural communities. Of course, their experience in the cities did not always live up to advance expectations, any more than is true today.

In addition to health problems, early cities faced social problems strikingly similar to those found in modern North America. Dense population, class systems, and a strong centralized government created internal stress. The slaves and the poor saw that the wealthy had all the things that they themselves lacked. It was not just a question of luxury items; the poor did not have enough food or space in which to live with comfort and dignity.

Evidence of warfare in early civilizations is common. Cities were fortified; documents list many battles, raids, and wars between groups; cylinder seals, paintings, and sculpture depict battle scenes, victorious kings, and captured prisoners of war. Increasing population and the accompanying scarcity of good farming land often led to boundary disputes and quarrels over land between civilized states or between so-called tribal peoples and a state. Open warfare often developed. People tended to crowd into walled cities for protection and to be near irrigation systems.

[28] Diamond, p. 205.

Signs of warfare are common in ancient civilizations. China's first emperor wanted his army to remain with him—in the form of 7000 life-sized terra-cotta figures of warriors. **CULTURAL RELICS BUREAU, BEIJING**

The class system also caused internal stress. As time went on, the rich became richer and the poor poorer. In early civilizations one's place in society was relatively fixed. Wealth was based on free labour from slaves. For this reason there was little or no impetus for social reform. Records from the Mesopotamian city of Lagash indicate that social unrest due to exploitation of the poor by the rich grew during this period. Members of the upper class received tracts of farmland some 20 times larger than those granted the lower class. An upper-class reformer, Urukaginal, saw the danger and introduced changes to protect the poor from exploitation by the wealthy, thus preserving the stability of the city.

The period of growth and innovation at Tikal, decribed earlier in the chapter, is an example of a regional culture known as the Classic Maya (A.D. 250–900). The end of population growth and outright abandonment of centres, and evidence of increased warfare and nutritional problems, has become associated with a phenomenon known as the Classic Maya Collapse. A complete collapse of southern centres apparently led to a reestablishment of the Maya, called the Postclassic, in the north.[29] Exactly what happened is a matter of controversy. Some see it as another example of pressures leading to the inevitable demise of such societies. The collapse of the Roman empire and Harappa in the Indus Valley are other examples. Nevertheless, before archaeologists can generalize about such events, they need to be clear about what actually occurred. Did population growth outstrip production? Did the environment change? Did extensive warfare seal the fate of the Classic Maya? These questions assume that the Classic Maya did indeed undergo a collapse, but did this happen? A project developed by archaeologists at the Royal Ontario Museum in Toronto illuminates the issues surrounding Maya civilization's development, as well as what happened after the Classic period.

In cooperation with archaeologists in Belize, David Pendergast (now affiliated with Trent University in Peterborough, Ontario) and Elizabeth Graham (now at University College London) have been able to investigate Lamanai, the longest continuous Maya occupation ever studied.[30] The team has not only been investigating the settlement history, architecture, and technology, but also is particularly interested in health and diet. If health and diet were deteriorating through time, then it would confirm that life was getting harder as time passed. We might discern an increasingly despotic ruling class who treated their subjects more harshly as time went on by comparing the diet and health of the commoners and rulers.

The first substantial evidence of houses and public structures at Lamanai dates to about 700 to 500 B.C.[31] According to Christine White of the University of Western Ontario, the first settlers were dependent on corn.[32] In fact, for a considerable period their dependence on corn changed little. Their diet also likely included a range of invertebrates such as conchs, marine and freshwater fish, reptiles, turkey and other birds, as well as a range of mammals.[33]

A major transformation appears to have taken place around 100 B.C. when a major plaza group was built along with a single temple. Evidence of a hereditary ruling class at Lamanai comes from the discovery of two elaborate tombs. Two people buried here were surrounded by wooden objects, pottery vessels, and a variety of jade and shell mosaic ear ornaments and pendants.[34] The two individuals provided an opportunity to explore the suspicion that there was a close relationship between socioeconomic status and diet. In ranked societies, the ruling group would have had differential access to resources such as better food. Confirmation that such differential access existed in this community comes from observations of the health of their teeth. The two elite rulers have no dental cavities (caries) whatsoever.[35] Dental health and diet are closely related; agricultural peoples with a high dependency on starchy foods usually have extremely high rates of caries. In fact, the rest of the people at Lamanai have high rates of cavi-

---

[29] Pendergast, D. (1990). Up from the dust: The Central Lowlands postclassic as seen from Lamanai and Marco Gonzales. In F.S. Clancy & P.D. Harrison (Eds.), *Vision and revision in Maya studies* (pp. 169–177). Albuquerque: University of New Mexico Press.

[30] Ibid.

[31] Pendergast, D., & Graham, E. (1998). The history of excavations at Lamanai. Retrieved from the World Wide Web: www.yorku.ca/anthro/Belize/history.html.

[32] White, C.D. (1997). Ancient diet at Lamanai and Pacbitun: Implications for the ecological model of collapse. In S.L. Whittington & D.M. Reed (Eds.), *Bones of the Maya: Studies of ancient skeletons* (pp. xi, 290). Washington, DC: Smithsonian Institution Press.

[33] Powis, T., Stanchly, N., White, C.D., Healy, P., Awe, J., & Longstaff, F. (1999). A reconstruction of Middle Preclassic Maya subsistence economy at Cahal Pech, Belize. *Antiquity, 73,* 377–393.

[34] Pendergast.

[35] Pendergast & Graham.

ties consistent with agricultural diets. The rulers were not only relatively healthy, but also appear to have eaten less corn than the rest of the people. This suggests that corn was not a food with high social value. The rulers were using other foods, but just what they were eating is not known.

In the ninth and tenth centuries, evidence of the Classic Maya disintegration is widespread in the south. Remarkably, Lamanai survived and continued to thrive. This is not to say that the effects of the events unfolding in the Maya region were not felt at Lamanai. Some buildings began to decay. Maintenance of the major temples in central Lamanai was curtailed but development continued elsewhere at the site and there are no signs of population decline. The problem here is to account for the continued success of the Lamanai community in the face of events unfolding around it. Inexplicable dietary changes occurred. The rate of caries among the general population was reduced by the end of the Classic period so everyone, not just the rulers, had healthy teeth. Apparently, the consumption of corn was reduced considerably by the end of the Classic period. Pendergast, Graham, and White have not found a good explanation for the decline of corn in the diet. One possibility is that an ecological collapse forced a shift to alternate and less desirable food resources. However, the Lamanai residents in the still-thriving community were otherwise healthy.

The changing emphasis on corn in the diet appears to correlate with a shift in political alliances. By the twelfth century, the residents were interacting economically with other regions. Products such as pottery made at Lamanai are found in the Yucatan region. Clothing and ornaments were coming from western Mexico. With the disappearance of so many communities with which Lamanai had commercial relations, ties had to be forged elsewhere. Although the local temple was disintegrating, people were still making offerings. People also returned to a diet dominated by corn.

If an ecological collapse and the failure of agriculture were responsible for the Classic Maya collapse, it is not evident at Lamanai. In fact, the first evidence for physiological stress among the local residents appears much later, at the turn of the 16th century. Children were particularly vulnerable. The introduction of diseases by the newly arrived Spanish appears to be responsible for this vulnerability. A Christian church and related structures were incorporated into the local settlement as the Spanish were trying to convert the local people to Christianity. The church was built over a Mayan temple, thereby replacing Mayan spiritual authority with Christian authority.

Given the problems associated with civilization, it is perhaps not surprising that a recurring phenomenon is their collapse. Nonetheless, the rise of cities and civilization laid the basis for modern life. It is discouraging to note that many of the problems associated with the first civilizations are still with us. Waste disposal, pollution-related health problems, crowding, social inequities, and warfare continue to be serious problems. Through the study of past civilizations, we now stand a chance of understanding why such problems persist. Such an understanding will be required if the problems are ever to be overcome. One would hope the next cultural revolution would see the human species transcending these problems. If this comes about, anthropology, through its comparative study of civilizations, will have played a key role.

CHAPTER SUMMARY

The world's first cities grew out of Neolithic villages between 6000 and 4500 years ago, first in Mesopotamia, then in Egypt and the Indus Valley. In China, the process was under way by 5000 years ago. Somewhat later, and completely independently, similar changes took place in Mesoamerica and Peru. Four basic culture changes mark the transition from Neolithic village life to life in civilized urban centres. The first culture change is agricultural innovation as new farming methods were developed. For example, the ancient Sumerians built an irrigation system that enabled them to control their water resources and thus increase crop yields.

The second culture change is diversification of labour. With the growth of large populations in cities, some people could provide sufficient food for others to devote themselves fully to specialization as artisans and craftspeople. With specialization came the development of new technologies, leading to the beginnings of extensive trade systems. An outgrowth of technological innovation and increased contact with foreign people through trade was new knowledge; within the early civilizations sciences such as geometry and astronomy were first developed.

The third culture change that characterized urban life is the emergence of central government with authority to deal with the complex problems associated with cities. Evidence of a central governing authority comes from such sources as law codes, temple records, and royal chronicles. With the invention of writing, governments could keep records of their transactions and/or boast of their own power and glory. Further evidence of centralized government comes from monumental public structures and signs of centralized planning.

Typically, the first cities were headed by a king and his special advisers. The reign of the Babylonian King Hammurabi, sometime between 1950 and 1700 B.C., is well known for its efficient government organization and the standardization of its legal system. In the New World the Inca empire in Peru reached its culmination 500 years ago. With a population of several million people, the Inca state, headed by an emperor, possessed a widespread governing bureaucracy that functioned with great efficiency at every level.

The fourth culture change characteristic of civilization is social stratification, or the emergence of social classes. In the early cities of Mesopotamia, symbols of status and privilege appeared for the first time, and individuals were ranked according to the work they did or the position of their families. Archaeologists have been able to verify the existence of social classes in ancient civilizations in four ways: by studying burial customs, as well as skeletons, through grave excavations; by noting the size of dwellings in excavated cities; by examining preserved records in writing and art; and by studying the correspondence of Europeans who described the great civilizations that they destroyed in the New World.

A number of theories have been proposed to explain why civilizations developed. The hydraulic theory holds that the effort to build and control an irrigation system required a degree of social organization that eventually led to civilization. There are several objections to this theory, however. One might argue simply that sophisticated irrigation systems were a result of the development of civilization rather than a cause. Another theory suggests that in the multicrop economies of both the Old and New Worlds, some kind of system was needed to distribute the various food products throughout the population. Such a procedure would have required a centralized authority, leading to the emergence of a centralized government. A third theory holds that civilization develops where populations are circumscribed by environmental barriers or other societies. As such populations grow, competition for space and scarce resources leads to the development of centralized authority to control resources and organize warfare.

These theories all emphasize the interrelation of people and what they do on the one hand and the environment in which they live on the other. A theory that lays greater stress on the beliefs and values that regulate the interaction between people and their environment seeks to explain the emergence of Maya civilization in terms of the role religion may have played in keeping the Maya in and about cities like Tikal. Finally, action theory focuses attention on the actions of forceful leaders, whose efforts to promote their own interests may play a role in social change. Probably, several factors acted together, rather than singly, to bring about civilization's rise.

Sanitation problems in early cities, coupled with large numbers of people living in close proximity, created environments in which infectious diseases were rampant. Early urban centres also faced social problems strikingly similar to our own. Dense population, class systems, and a strong centralized government created internal stress. Warfare was common; cities were fortified, and armies served to protect the state. Nevertheless, a recurrent phenomenon in all civilizations has been their ultimate collapse.

QUESTIONS FOR CRITICAL THOUGHT

1. How does information about the diet of the occupants of an archaeological site help archaeologists to understand social and political processes?

2. Do the lessons of studying early cities apply to us? Why or why not?

3. Discuss the view that all urban societies inevitably collapse versus the argument that they exist until they are pushed to collapse.

4. Reflect on the design of the city or town you live in. To what extent is its design and administration similar to the earliest cities?

INTERNET RESOURCES

Civilization in the Americas

www.destination360.com/tikal.htm
Experience life in this large city over 2000 years ago through this 360-degree virtual tour of the site. Learn about the cultural practices of this great ancient civilization through the artifacts and ruins.

http://archaeology.la.asu.edu/teo
Visit the Teotihuacan home page to learn about this incredible pre-Aztec city. Stroll down the Avenue of the Dead and visit the pyramids of the Sun and the Moon.

www.dartmouth.edu/~izapa/CS-MM-Chap.%205.htm
Learn about the reasons behind the 15.5 degrees east of north alignment of Teotehuacan.

www.pacmusee.qc.ca/pages/musee/mot_directrice/mot_directrice_generale.aspx?lang=EN-CA
The Pointe-à-Callière Museum celebrates the cultural diversity of Montreal. The website is a wonderful introduction to the archaeology and history of the city.

http://discovermagazine.com/2002/may/featamazon
An interview with archaeologist Anna Roosevelt on her work in the Amazon River basin.

www.smm.org/catal
An interactive exploration of the Çatalhöyük Neolithic site in Turkey.

www.beyondtouring.com/Lamanai/lamanai_history.htm
Learn about the work at Lamanai including project history, discoveries and research team.

SUGGESTED READINGS

For a list of suggested readings, visit the textbook's website at www.humanevolution2.nelson.com.

Modern Human Diversity

One of the notable characteristics of the human species today is its great variability. Human diversity has long fascinated people, but unfortunately, it also has led to discrimination and even bloodshed.

© ARTIGA PHOTO/CORBIS

CHAPTER PREVIEW

1. What Are the Causes of Physical Variability in Modern Animals?

In a species like *H. sapiens,* there are various alleles for any given physical characteristic. When such a species is divided into geographically dispersed populations, forces such as drift and natural selection cause the store of genetic variability to be unevenly expressed. For example, alleles for dark skin are found in high frequency in human populations native to regions of heavy ultraviolet radiation, whereas alleles for light skin have a high incidence in populations native to regions of reduced ultraviolet radiation.

2. Is the Concept of Race Useful for Studying Human Physical Variation?

No. Because races are arbitrarily defined, it is impossible to agree on any specific classification. The problem is compounded by the tendency for "racial" characteristics to occur in gradations from one population to another without sharp breaks. Furthermore, because genes are assorted independently of one another, one characteristic may be distributed in a north-south gradient while another may occur in an east-west gradient. For these and other reasons, most anthropologists have actively worked to get rid of race as a biological category.

3. Are There Differences in Intelligence from One Population to Another?

No, although some populations receive lower average scores on IQ tests than others, many individuals in "lower-scoring" populations score higher than some in the "higher-scoring" populations. There is no agreement on what intelligence really is, but there is agreement that intelligence involves several different talents and abilities. Certainly, there are genes affecting these, but like other genes, they may be independently assorted, and their expression is affected significantly by environmental factors.

CHAPTER OUTLINE

Variation and Evolution	The Concept of Human Races
Physical Variability	The Social Significance of Race: Racism
The Meaning of Race	Evolutionary Medicine
Race as a Biological Concept	Continuing Human Biological Evolution

What a piece of work is man," said Hamlet. "How noble in reason, how infinite in faculties, in form and moving how express and admirable, in action how like an angel, in apprehension how like a god: the beauty of the world, the paragon of animals! And yet to me what is this quintessence of dust?"

What people are to one another is the province of anthropology: Biological anthropology reveals what we are; cultural anthropology reveals what we think we are. Our dreams of ourselves are as varied as our languages and our physical bodies. We are the same, but we differ. We speak English or another language, our hair is curly or straight, our skin is lightly to heavily pigmented, and in height we range from short to tall. Human genetic variation generally is distributed in such a continuous range, with varying clusters of frequency. The significance we give our variations, the way we perceive them—in fact, whether we perceive them at all—is determined by our culture. For example, in many Polynesian countries, where skin colour is not a determinant of social status, people really pay little attention to this physical characteristic; in Canada and the United States, it is one of the first things people do notice.

VARIATION AND EVOLUTION

Many behavioural traits—reading, for instance—are learned or acquired by living in a society; other characteristics, such as blue eyes, are passed on physically by heredity. Environment affects both. A person growing up surrounded by books learns to read. If the culture insists that brown-eyed people watch TV and blue-eyed people read, the brown-eyed people may end up making videotapes while the blue-eyed people are writing books. These skills or tastes are acquired characteristics. Changes in such things within one population but not another are capable of making the two distinct in learned behavioural characteristics within relatively few generations.

PHYSICAL VARIABILITY

The physical characteristics of both populations and individuals, as we saw in Chapter 3, are a product of the interaction between genes and environments. Thus, one's genes predispose one to a particular skin colour, for example, but the skin colour one actually has is strongly

affected by environmental factors such as the amount of solar radiation. In this case, phenotypic expression is strongly influenced by environment; in some others, such as one's A-B-O blood type, phenotypic expression closely reflects genotype.

For most characteristics, there are within the gene pool of *H. sapiens* variant forms of genes, known as alleles. In the colour of an eye, the shape of a hand, the texture of skin, many variations can occur. This kind of variability, found in many animal species, signifies a rich potential for new combinations of characteristics in future generations. Such a species is called **polymorphic** (meaning "many shapes"). Our blood types, determined by the alleles for Types A, B, and O blood, are an example of polymorphism, which in this case may appear in any of four distinct phenotypic forms. A polymorphic species faced with changing environmental conditions has within its gene pool the possibility of producing individuals with traits appropriate to its altered life. Many may not achieve reproductive success, but those whose physical characteristics enable them to do well in the new environment will usually reproduce, so that their genes will become more common in subsequent generations. Thus, humankind, being polymorphic, has been able to occupy a variety of environments.

A major expansion into new environments was under way by the time *H. erectus/ergaster* appeared on the scene (Chapter 8). These hominins and subsequently *H. sapiens* were living in Africa, Southeast Asia, Europe, and China. Each of these places constitutes a different **faunal region**, which is to say that each possesses its own distinctive assemblage of animal life, not precisely like that of other regions. This differentiation of animal life is the result of selective pressures that, through the Pleistocene, differed from one region to another. For example, the conditions of life were quite different in China, which lies in the temperate zone, than they were in tropical Southeast Asia. Coupled with differing selective pressures were geographic features that restricted or prevented gene flow between populations of different faunal regions.

Polymorphic. A species with alternative forms (alleles) of particular genes.

Faunal region. A geographic region with its own distinctive assemblage of animal life, not precisely like that of other regions.

When a polymorphic species is divided into geographically dispersed populations, it usually is **polytypic** (many types); that is, the store of genetic variability is unevenly expressed. Genetic variants will be expressed in different frequencies in different populations. For example, in the Old World, populations of *H. sapiens* living in the tropics had a higher frequency of alleles for dark skin colour than did those living in more northerly regions. In blood type, *H. sapiens* is polymorphic, with four distinct groups (A, B, O, or AB). In the distribution of these types, the species is again polytypic. The frequency of the O allele is highest in aboriginal peoples of the Americas, especially among some populations native to South America; the highest frequencies of the allele for Type A blood tend to be found among certain European populations (although the highest frequency of all is found among the Blackfoot and Blood people of North America); the highest frequencies of the B allele are found in some Asian populations (Figure 13.1).

THE MEANING OF RACE

Early anthropologists tried to explore the polytypic nature of the human species by systematically classifying *H. sapiens* into subspecies, or **races**, based on geographic location and phenotypic (physical) features such as skin colour, body size, head shape, and hair texture. Such classifications were continually being challenged by the presence of individuals who did not fit the categories, such as light-skinned Africans or dark-skinned "Caucasoids"; to get around the problem,

Polytypic. The expression of genetic variants in different frequencies in different populations of a species.

Race. In biology, a population of a species that differs in the frequency of the variants of some gene or genes from other populations of the same species.

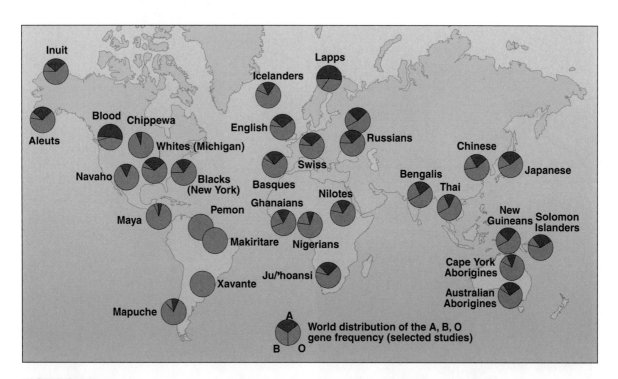

FIGURE 13.1

Frequencies of the three alleles for the A, B, and O blood groups for selected populations around the world demonstrate the polytypic nature of *H. sapiens*.

it was assumed that these individuals were hybrids or the product of racial mixtures. Lack of concordance among traits—for example, the fact that long prominent noses are not only common among Europeans but also have a high frequency in various East African populations as well—was usually explained away in a similar manner. The fact is, generalized references to human types such as "Asiatic" or "Mongoloid," "European" or "Caucasoid," and "African" or "Negroid" were at best mere statistical abstractions about populations in which certain physical features appeared in higher frequencies than in other populations; no example of "pure" racial types could be found. These categories turned out to be neither definitive nor particularly helpful. The visible traits were found to occur not in abrupt shifts from population to population but in a continuum that changed gradually, with few sharp breaks. To compound the problem, one trait might change gradually over a north-south gradient, whereas another might show a similar change from east to west. Human skin colour, for instance, becomes progressively darker as one moves from Northern Europe to Central Africa, whereas blood Type B becomes progressively more common as one moves from Western to Eastern Europe.

Finally, there were many variations within each group, and those within groups were often greater than those between groups. In Africa, the skin colour of someone from the Kalahari Desert might more closely resemble that of a person of East Indian extraction than the darkly pigmented Nilotic Sudanese who was supposed to be of the same race.

The Negroid was characterized as having dark skin, thick lips, a broad nose, and tightly curled hair; the Mongoloid, straight hair, a flat face, a flat nose, and spread nostrils; and the Caucasoid, pale skin, a narrow

Among the tallest people in the world are the Tutsi (left), whereas among the smallest are the Efe (right). Both are from central Africa and illustrate the wide range of variation seen in a (supposedly) single racial category. ELIOT ELISOFON ARCHIVES, NATIONAL MUSEUM OF AFRICAN ART/LAURE COMMUNICATIONS (LEFT), JEAN-PIERRE HALLET/THE PYGMY FUND (RIGHT)

BIOGRAPHY

Ashley Montagu (1905–1999)

Born Israel Ehrenberg to a working-class immigrant Jewish family living in London's East End, Ashley Montagu (a name he adopted in the 1920s) went on to become a pioneering critic of the race concept and one of the best-known anthropologists of his time. An avid reader as a child, in 1922 he attended University College of London, where he studied anthropology and psychology. It was at this time that he changed his name in response to the strong ethnic and class prejudice he experienced. Among his professors were founders of the eugenics movement—a proposal to improve humanity by identifying those with supposedly undesirable hereditary characteristics and removing them from the breeding population. Canada was not immune to such ideas. In 1956, for example, the now defunct Eugenics Board of the Alberta government declared 11-year-old Lellani Muir a "moron" and had her sterilized at the same time she had her appendix removed. She was never told of the Board's decision.

Also, in the 1920s, Montagu studied under the founders of British social anthropology at the London School of Economics. In 1927, however, he left for the United States, where he considered the society to be more congenial to social justice. At Columbia University, he studied under Franz Boas and other pioneers of North American anthropology, earning his doctorate in 1937 with a dissertation on knowledge of paternity among Australian Aborigines.

Having felt the sting early on of ethnic and class prejudice himself, it is not surprising that Montagu became a strong critic of eugenics and other racist doctrines. As early as 1926, he focused on the mistake of viewing races as typological, bounded categories. This put him at odds with many of his old professors and colleagues, but, as he put it, he learned early on "not to let the shadows of great men block out the

AP/WIDE WORLD PHOTOS

light." All his life, Montagu fought racism in his writing, in academic and public lectures, and in the courts.

Ashley Montagu wrote over 60 books and hundreds of articles, including a series in *Ladies Home Journal.* These ranged over subjects from primate anatomy to the importance of nurturance in human development, and even the history of human swearing. Of all his works, none is more important than his book *Man's Most Dangerous Myth: The Fallacy of Race.* Published in 1942, it took the lead in exposing, on purely scientific grounds, the fallacy of human races as biological entities. The book has since gone through six editions, the last in 1999. Although Montagu's once controversial ideas have since become mainstream, the book remains the most comprehensive treatment of its subject.

Source: Sperling, S. (2000). Ashley Montagu (1905–1999). *American Anthropologist, 102,* 584.

nose, and varied eye colour and hair form. The classification then expanded to take in North American indigenous peoples, Australians, and Polynesians, but even the expanded system failed to account for dramatic differences in appearance among individuals, or even populations, in each racial category; for example,

Europeans, Arabs, and South Asians were all lumped together as Caucasoids.

In an attempt to encompass such variations, schemes of racial classification proliferated. In 1926, J. Deniker classified 29 races according to texture of hair, presumably improving upon Roland B. Dixon's

1923 classification based on three indexes of body measures. Hair texture and body build were the characteristics used for another set of racial categories proposed in 1930. By 1947, Earnest Hooton had proposed three new composite races resulting from the interbreeding of "primary" races. Despite these classificatory attempts on the part of Western anthropologists, no definitive grouping of distinct, discontinuous biological groups was found for modern humanity.

While many anthropologists struggled with the problem of defining human races, others began to question the whole exercise. Most notable was Ashley Montagu, whose effective criticism of race as a valid biological concept began to influence people's thinking on the subject.

Also influential was a book, published in 1950, called *Races* by Carleton Coon, Stanley Garn, and Joseph Birdsell. Unlike Ashley Montagu, they did not reject the race concept, and like their predecessors, they too tried to classify modern humans into a number of racial groups, 30 in their case. They did, however, reject a trait-list approach. Instead, they recognized races as populations that owed certain common characteristics to environmental, primarily climatic, adaptation, which continued to change in response to evolutionary forces such as gene flow and altered selective pressures. Although this book certainly had its weaknesses—its

continued assumption that races existed, for one—it did represent a significant departure from previous attempts at racial classification and was influential in paving the way for a sounder understanding of human variation.

RACE AS A BIOLOGICAL CONCEPT

To understand why the racial approach to human variation has been so unproductive, we must first understand the race concept in strictly biological terms. In biology, a race is defined as a population of a species that differs in the frequency of different variants of some gene or genes from other populations of the same species. Simple and straightforward though such a definition may seem, there are three very important things to note about it. First, it is arbitrary; there is no agreement on how many genetic differences it takes to make a race. For some who are interested in the topic, different frequencies in the variants of one gene are sufficient; for others, differences in frequencies involving several genes are necessary. Ultimately, it proved impossible to reach agreement on the number of genes and precisely which ones are the most important for defining races.

The arbitrariness of racial classification is well illustrated by the following Original Study.

The "openness" of races to gene flow is illustrated by this picture of an Asian and African-American couple with their children. **LAWRENCE MIGDALE**

ORIGINAL STUDY

Race Without Colour

Science often violates simple common sense. Our eyes tell us that the Earth is flat, that the sun revolves around the Earth, and that we humans are not animals. But we now ignore that evidence of our senses. We have learned that our planet is in fact round and revolves around the sun, and that humans are slightly modified chimpanzees. The reality of human races is another commonsense "truth" destined to follow the flat Earth into oblivion.

What Could Be More Objective?

The commonsense view of races goes somewhat as follows. All native Swedes differ from all native Nigerians in appearance: There is no Swede whom you would mistake for a Nigerian, and vice versa. Swedes have lighter skin than Nigerians do. They also generally have blond or light brown hair, while Nigerians have very dark hair. Nigerians usually have more tightly coiled hair than Swedes do, dark eyes as opposed to eyes that are blue or grey, and fuller lips and broader noses.

In addition, other Europeans look much more like Swedes than like Nigerians, while other peoples of sub-Saharan Africa—except perhaps the Khoisan peoples of southern Africa—look much more like Nigerians than like Swedes. Yes, skin colour does get darker in Europe toward the Mediterranean, but it is still lighter than the skin of sub-Saharan Africans. In Europe, very dark or curly hair becomes more common outside Scandinavia, but European hair is still not as tightly coiled as in Africa. Since it's easy then to distinguish almost any native European from any native sub-Saharan African, we recognize Europeans and sub-Saharan Africans as distinct races, which we name for their skin colours: whites and blacks, respectively.

As it turns out, this seemingly unassailable reasoning is not objective. There are many different, equally valid procedures for defining races, and those different procedures yield very different classifications. One such procedure would group native Italians and Greeks with most Africans. It would classify Xhosas—the South African group to which Nelson Mandela belongs—with native Swedes rather than Nigerians. Another equally valid procedure would place Swedes with Fulani (a Nigerian group) and not with Italians, who would again be grouped with most other Africans. Still another procedure would keep Swedes and Italians separate from all Africans but would throw the Swedes and Italians into the same race as New Guineans and indigenous Americans. Faced with such differing classifications, many anthropologists today conclude that one cannot recognize any human races at all.

If we were just arguing about races of nonhuman animals, essentially the same uncertainties of classification would arise. But the debates would remain polite and would never attract attention outside the halls of academia. Classification of humans is different "only" in that it shapes our views of other peoples, fosters our subconscious differentiation between "us" and "them," and is invoked to justify political and socioeconomic discrimination. On this basis, many anthropologists therefore argue that even if one could classify humans into races, one should not.

To understand how such uncertainties in classification arise, let's steer clear of humans for a moment and instead focus on warblers and lions, about which we can easily remain dispassionate. Biologists begin by classifying living creatures into species. A species is a group of populations whose individual members would, if given the opportunity, interbreed with individuals of other populations of that group. But they would not interbreed with individuals of other species that are similarly defined. Thus all human populations, no matter how different they look, belong to the same species because they do interbreed and have interbred whenever they have encountered each other. Gorillas and humans, however, belong to two different species because—to the best of our knowledge—they have never interbred despite their coexisting in close proximity for millions of years.

We know that different populations classified together in the human species are visibly different. The same proves true for most other animal and plant species as well, whenever biologists look carefully. For example, consider one of the most

(Continued)

familiar species of bird in North America, the yellow-rumped warbler. Breeding males of eastern and western North America can be distinguished at a glance by their throat colour: white in the east, yellow in the west. Hence they are classified into two different races, or subspecies (alternative words with identical meanings), termed the myrtle and Audubon races, respectively. The white-throated eastern birds differ from the yellow-throated western birds in other characteristics as well, such as in voice and habitat preference. But where the two races meet, in western Canada, white-throated birds do indeed interbreed with yellow-throated birds. That's why we consider myrtle warblers and Audubon warblers as races of the same species rather than different species.

Racial classification of these birds is easy. Throat colour, voice, and habitat preference all vary geographically in yellow-rumped warblers, but the variation of those three traits is "concordant"—that is, voice differences or habitat differences lead to the same racial classification as differences in throat colour because the same populations that differ in throat colour also differ in voice and habitat.

Racial classification of many other species, though, presents problems of concordance. For instance, a Pacific island bird species called the golden whistler varies from one island to the next. Some populations consist of big birds, some of small birds; some have black-winged males, others green-winged males; some have yellow-breasted females, others grey-breasted females; many other characteristics vary as well. But, unfortunately for humans like me who study these birds, those characteristics don't vary concordantly. Islands with green-winged males can have either yellow-breasted or grey-breasted females, and green-winged males are big on some islands but small on other islands. As a result, if you classified golden whistlers into races based on single traits, you would get entirely different classifications depending on which trait you chose.

Classification of these birds also presents problems of "hierarchy." Some of the golden whistler races recognized by ornithologists are wildly different from all the other races, but some are very similar to one another. They can therefore be grouped into a hierarchy of distinctness. You start by establishing the most distinct population as a race separate from all other populations. You then separate the most

distinct of the remaining populations. You continue by grouping similar populations, and separating distinct populations or groups of populations as races or groups of races. The problem is that the extent to which you continue the racial classification is arbitrary, and it's a decision about which taxonomists disagree passionately. Some taxonomists, the "splitters," like to recognize many different races, partly for the egotistical motive of getting credit for having named a race. Other taxonomists, the "lumpers," prefer to recognize few races. Which type of taxonomist you are is a matter of personal preference.

How does that variability of traits by which we classify races come about in the first place? Some traits vary because of natural selection: That is, one form of the trait is advantageous for survival in one area, another form in a different area. For example, in the United States and Canada northern hares and weasels develop white fur in the winter, but southern ones retain brown fur year-round. The white winter fur is selected in the north for camouflage against the snow, while any animal unfortunate enough to turn white in the snowless southern United States would stand out from afar against the brown ground and would be picked off by predators.

Other traits vary geographically because of sexual selection, meaning that those traits serve as arbitrary signals by which individuals of one sex attract mates of the opposite sex while intimidating rivals. Adult male lions, for instance, have a mane, but lionesses and young males don't. The adult male's mane signals to lionesses that he is sexually mature, and signals to young male rivals that he is a dangerous and experienced adversary. The length and colour of a lion's mane vary among populations, being shorter and blacker in Indian lions than in African lions. Indian lions and lionesses evidently find short black manes sexy or intimidating; African lions don't.

Finally, some geographically variable traits have no known effect on survival and are invisible to rivals and to prospective sex partners. They merely reflect mutations that happened to arise and spread in one area. They could equally well have arisen and spread elsewhere—they just didn't.

Nothing that I've said about geographic variation in animals is likely to get me branded a racist. We don't attribute higher IQ or social status to black-winged whistlers than to green-winged whistlers. But now let's consider geographic variation in humans.

We'll start with invisible traits, about which it's easy to remain dispassionate.

Many geographically variable human traits evolved by natural selection to adapt humans to particular climates or environments—just as the winter colour of a hare or weasel did. Good examples are the mutations that people in tropical parts of the Old World evolved to help them survive malaria, the leading infectious disease of the Old World tropics. One such mutation is the sickle-cell gene, so-called because the red blood cells of people with that mutation tend to assume a sickle shape. People bearing the gene are more resistant to malaria than people without it. Not surprisingly, the gene is absent from northern Europe, where malaria is nonexistent, but it's common in tropical Africa, where malaria is widespread. Up to 40 percent of Africans in such areas carry the sickle-cell gene. It's also common in the malaria-ridden Arabian Peninsula and southern India, and rare or absent in the southernmost parts of South Africa, among the Xhosas, who live mostly beyond the tropical geographic range of malaria.

The geographic range of human malaria is much wider than the range of the sickle-cell gene. As it happens, other antimalarial genes take over the protective function of the sickle-cell gene in malarial Southeast Asia and New Guinea, and in Italy, Greece, and other warm parts of the Mediterranean basin. Thus human races, if defined by antimalarial genes, would be very different from human races as traditionally defined by traits such as skin colour. As classified by antimalarial genes (or their absence), Swedes are grouped with Xhosas but not with Italians or Greeks. Most other peoples usually viewed as African blacks are grouped with Arabia's "whites" and are kept separate from the "black" Xhosas.

Not all the effects of natural selection are as invisible as sickle cells. Environmental pressures have also produced more noticeable differences among peoples, particularly in body shapes. Among the tallest and most long-limbed peoples in the world are the Nilotic peoples, such as the Dinkas, who live in the hot, dry areas of East Africa. At the opposite extreme in body shape are the Inuit, who have compact bodies and relatively short arms and legs. The reasons have to do with heat loss. The greater the surface area of a warm body, the more body heat that's lost, since heat loss is directly proportional to surface area. For people of a given weight, a long-limbed, tall shape maximizes surface area, while a compact, short-limbed shape minimizes it. Dinkas and Inuit have opposite problems of heat balance: The former usually need desperately to get rid of body heat, while the latter need desperately to conserve it. Thus natural selection moulded their body shapes oppositely, based on their contrasting climates.

Other visible traits that vary geographically among humans evolved by means of sexual selection. We all know that we find some individuals of the opposite sex more attractive than other individuals. We also know that in sizing up sex appeal, we pay more attention to certain parts of a prospective sex partner's body than to other parts. Men tend to be inordinately interested in women's breasts and much less concerned with women's toenails. Women, in turn, tend to be turned on by the shape of a man's buttocks or the details of a man's beard and body hair, if any, but not by the size of his feet.

But all those determinants of sex appeal vary geographically. Khoisan and Andaman Island women tend to have much larger buttocks than most other women. Nipple colour and breast shape and size also vary geographically among women. European men are rather hairy by world standards, while Southeast Asian men tend to have very sparse beards and body hair.

What's the function of these traits that differ so markedly between men and women? They certainly don't aid survival: It's not the case that orange nipples help Khoisan women escape lions, while darker nipples help European women survive cold winters. Instead, these varying traits play a crucial role in sexual selection. Women with very large buttocks are a turn-on, or at least acceptable, to Khoisan and Andaman men but look freakish to many men from other parts of the world. Bearded and hairy men readily find mates in Europe but fare worse in Southeast Asia. The geographic variation of these traits, however, is as arbitrary as the geographic variation in the colour of a lion's mane.

There is a third possible explanation for the function of geographically variable human traits, besides survival or sexual selection—namely, no function at all. A good example is provided by fingerprints, whose complex pattern of arches, loops, and whorls is determined genetically. Fingerprints also vary geographically: for example, Europeans' fingerprints tend to have many loops, while aboriginal Australians' fingerprints tend to have many whorls.

(Continued)

Fingerprints' patterns of loops, whorls, and arches are genetically determined. Grouping people on this basis would place most Europeans, sub-Saharan Africans, and East Asians together as "loops," Australian Aborigines and the people of Mongolia together as "whorls," and central Europeans and the Ju/'hoansi of southern Africa together as "arches." **GETTY IMAGES (CENTRE), WADSWORTH PUBLISHING (LEFT, RIGHT)**

If we classify human populations by their fingerprints, most Europeans and Africans would sort out together in one race, Jews and some Indonesians in another, and aboriginal Australians in still another. But those geographic variations in fingerprint patterns possess no known function whatsoever. They play no role in survival: Whorls aren't especially suitable for grabbing kangaroos, nor do loops help bar mitzvah candidates hold on to the pointer for the Torah. They also play no role in sexual selection: While you've undoubtedly noticed whether your mate is bearded or has brown nipples, you surely haven't the faintest idea whether his or her fingerprints have more loops than whorls. Instead it's purely a matter of chance that whorls became common in aboriginal Australians, and loops among Jews. Our rhesus factor blood groups and numerous other human traits fall into the same category of genetic characteristics whose geographic variation serves no function.

Source: Adapted from Diamond, J. (1994). Race without color. *Discover, 15* (11), 83–88.

After arbitrariness, the second thing to note about the biological definition of race is that it does not mean that any one race has exclusive possession of any particular variant of any gene or genes. In human terms, the frequency of the allele for blood group O may be high in one population and low in another, but it is present in both. Races are genetically "open," meaning that gene flow takes place between them. Because they are genetically open, they are apt to be impermanent and subject to reamalgamation. Thus, one can easily see the fallacy of any attempt to identify pure races; if gene flow cannot take place between two populations, either directly or indirectly through intermediate populations, then they are not races but separate species.

The third thing to note about the biological definition of race is that individuals of one race will not necessarily be distinguishable from those of another. In fact, as we have just noted with respect to humans, the differences among individuals within a population are generally greater than the differences among populations. As the science writer James Shreeve puts it, "most of what separates me genetically from a typical African or Eskimo also separates me from another average American of European ancestry."[1] This follows from the genetic "openness" of races; no one race has an exclusive claim to any particular gene or allele.

THE CONCEPT OF HUMAN RACES

As a device for understanding polytypic variation in humans, the biological race concept has serious drawbacks. One is that the category is arbitrary to begin with, which makes agreement on any given classification difficult, if not impossible. For example, if one researcher emphasizes skin colour while another emphasizes blood group differences, they will not classify people in the same way. Perhaps if the human species were divided into a number of relatively discrete breeding populations, this wouldn't be such a problem, but even this is open to debate. What has happened, though, is that human populations have grown in the course of human evolution, and with this growth have come increased opportunities for contact and gene flow between populations. Since the advent of food production, the process has accelerated as higher birthrates and periodic food

[1] Shreeve, J. (1994) Terms of estrangement. *Discover, 15* (11), 60.

shortages (discussed in Chapter 11) have prompted the movement of farmers from their homelands to other places. In East Asia, for example, the development of farming, followed by the invention of bronze and a host of other technologies in China, resulted in expansion of northern Chinese populations and displacement of southern Chinese peoples into Southeast Asia. This expansion effectively "swamped" the original populations of this region, except in a few out-of-the-way places like the Andaman Islands.[2]

Things are even more complicated because humans are complicated genetically. Thus, the genetic underpinnings of the phenotypic traits upon which traditional racial classifications are usually based are poorly understood. Compounding the problem, "race" exists as a cultural, as well as a biological, category. In various different ways, cultures define religious, linguistic, and ethnic groups as races, thereby confusing linguistic and cultural traits with physical traits. For example, in many Central and South American countries, people are commonly classified as "Indian," "Mestizo" (mixed), or "Ladino" (of Spanish descent). But despite the biological connotations of these terms, the criteria used for assigning individuals to these categories consist of things such as whether they wear shoes, sandals, or go barefoot; speak Spanish or some aboriginal language; live in a thatched hut or a European-style house; and so forth. Thus, a person—by speaking Spanish, wearing Western-style clothes, and living in a house in a Ladino neighbourhood—ceases to be an "Indian," no matter how many genetic traits he or she may possess that are typically aboriginal.

This sort of confusion of nonbiological characteristics with what are spoken of as biological categories is by no means limited to Central and South American societies. To one degree or another, such confusion is found in most Western societies, including those of Europe and North America. The Canadian census no longer uses the term "race," but the concept is still implicit in the 2001 survey and reflects how Canadian society views diversity. A separate question asks if the respondent is a member of an Indian Band/First Nation, clearly exposing the social and political significance of the diversity issue to the Canadian federal government. The Chinese category is not as homogeneous as the census implies either, because a large number of groups defined by the Chinese government are also physically diverse. In addition to Chinese, Asian groups are split into a variety of categories including Japanese, Korean, South Asian,

[2] Diamond, J. (1996). Empire of uniformity. *Discover, 17* (3), 83–84.

The Andaman Islanders (left) are a remnant of the original inhabitants of Southeast Asia; the Vietnamese (right) are descendants of people from southern China who spread into the region after the invention of agriculture. In the process there was mixing of gene pools. DINODIA PHOTO LIBRARY (LEFT), A. RAMEY/PHOTO EDIT (RIGHT)

Southeast Asian, Filipino, West Asian, and Arab in the census. The differences are primarily cultural/linguistic and span a broad continuum of biological variation. To compound the confusion, inclusion in one or another of these categories is usually based on self-identification. In short, what we are dealing with here are not biological categories at all, but rather social constructs.

To make matters even worse, this confusion of social with biological factors is frequently combined with attitudes that are then taken as excuses to exclude whole categories of people from certain roles or positions in society. In North America, for example, the idea of race originated in the 18th century to refer to the diverse peoples—European settlers, First Nations, and Africans imported as slaves—that were brought together in colonial North America. This racial worldview assigned some groups to perpetual low status on the basis of their supposedly biological inferiority, whereas access to privilege, power, and wealth was reserved for favoured groups of European descent.[3]

Different ways in which this discrimination plays out may be illustrated with two quite different examples. An old stereotype is that Africans are born with rhythm, which somehow is thought to give them a natural affinity for jazz, soul music, rap, and related forms of musical expression. A corollary of this myth is that African Americans are unsuited "by nature" for symphonic music. Hence, until recently, one did not find an African American at the head of any major symphony orchestra in the United States, even though African-American conductors such as James de Priest, Paul Freeman, and Dean Dixon made distinguished careers for themselves in Canada and Europe.

A particularly evil consequence of the racial worldview occurred when the Nazis declared the superiority of the "Aryan race" (which is really a linguistic grouping and not a race at all), and the inferiority of the Gypsy and Jewish "races" (really ethno-religious categories), and then used this distinction as an excuse to exclude Roma (Gypsies) and Jews from life altogether. In all, 11 million people (Jews, Roma, Africans, homosexuals, and other supposedly inferior people) were deliberately put to death.

Tragically, such programs of extermination of one group by another continue to occur in many parts of the world today, including parts of South America, Africa, Europe, and Asia. Holocausts are by no means things of the past, nor are Roma and Jews their only victims. The well-meant vow "never again" contrasts with the reality of "frequently again."

Augie Fleras and Jean Elliott point out that Canada has gained a reputation for being the world's "least imperfect society"[4] because of the country's social ideals. Canada became officially multicultural in 1971, setting out a context in which Canadian society would account for human diversity. The policy "confirms how dissimilar peoples can share land, power, and resources while respecting and sustaining their differences."[5] Of course, Canadian society has its flaws, and implementation of a multicultural policy is difficult. Nonetheless, education and knowledge can help correct the flaws that still exist, and this is where anthropology can make a significant contribution.

Pressures exist in the scientific community to apply the concept of human biological races despite the fact that there are none. In the United States, the Food and Drug Administration advocates the collection of race and ethnicity data for clinical drug trials but many scientists want individual genomic data collected instead.[6] In forensic investigations, Canadian and U.S. scientists have differing approaches to documenting the biological background of human remains. In Canada, forensic anthropologists do not determine race from skeletal remains. Instead, they are concerned with ancestry.[7] In contrast, their U.S. counterparts will classify an individual set of remains according to the U.S. census categories and will often use the term "race." Despite the lack of biological justification for doing so, the U.S. forensic community is pressured to identify an individual according to socially defined racial categories. However, certain general morphological traits such as blood type, body shape, limb length, face shape (e.g., nose), hair forms (e.g., oblong, round), wear patterns on teeth, and

---

[3] American Anthropological Association. (1998). Statement on "race." Accessed July 27, 2007, from the World Wide Web: www.aaanet.org/stmts/racepp.htm.

[4] Fleras, A., & Elliott, J.L. (2002). *Engaging diversity: Multiculturalism in Canada*. Toronto: Nelson.

[5] Ibid, p. 253.

[6] Bamshad, M.J., & Olsen, S.E. (2003). Does race really exist? *Scientific American, 289*, 78–85.

[7] Rogers, T.L. (1999). The attribution of ancestry for European and Indian (South Asian) individuals within a forensic context. Burnaby, BC: Simon Fraser University, Department of Archaeology.

morphology of incisors can tell forensic anthropologists much about the ancestry of the remains.[8] As an example, First Nations people *tend* to possess a rounded nasal aperture, as compared to a European's narrow or elongated nasal aperture. Likewise, aboriginal American incisors are usually shovel-shaped, while Europeans have blade-shaped incisors.

Considering all the problems, confusion, and evil consequences, it is small wonder that there has been a lot of debate not just about how many human races there may be, but about what race is and is not. Often forgotten is the fact that a race, even if it can be defined biologically, is the result of the operation of evolutionary processes. Because it is these processes rather than racial categories themselves in which we are really interested, most anthropologists have abandoned the race concept as being of no particular utility in understanding human biological variation. Instead, they have found it more productive to study the distribution and significance of specific, genetically based characteristics, or else the characteristics of small breeding populations that are, after all, the smallest units in which evolutionary change occurs.

Some Physical Variables

Attempts to classify people into races have proved futile and counterproductive, and it has also become apparent that the amount of genetic variation in humans is relatively low, compared to that of other primate species. Nonetheless, human biological variation is a fact of life, and biological anthropologists have learned a great deal about it. Much of it is related to climatic adaptation. For example, a correlation has been noted between body build and climate. Generally, people native to regions with cold climates tend to have greater body bulk (not to be equated with fat) relative to their extremities (arms and legs) than do people native to regions with hot climates, who tend to be long and slender. Interestingly, these differences show up as early as the time of *H. erectus/ergaster,* as already noted. Anthropologists generally argue that such differences of body build represent a climatic adaptation; certain body builds are better suited to particular living conditions than others. A person with larger body bulk and shorter extremities may suffer more from summer heat than someone whose extremities are long and whose body is slender. But that person will conserve needed body heat under cold conditions.

Studies of body build and climatic adaptation are complicated by the intervening effects on physique of diet, because dietary differences will cause variation in body build. Another complicating factor is clothing. Thus, much of the way people adapt to cold is cultural, rather than biological. For example, Inuit peoples live in a region where it is cold much of the year. To cope with this, they long ago developed efficient clothing to keep the body warm. Because of this, the Inuit are provided with what amount to artificial tropical environments inside their clothing. In spite of such considerations, it remains true that in northerly regions of the world, bulky body builds predominate, whereas the reverse is true in the tropics.

Anthropologists have also studied such body features as nose and eye shape and hair textures in relation to climate. A wide flaring nose, for example, is common in populations living in tropical forests; here the air is warm and damp, and so the warming and humidifying functions of the nose are secondary. Longer, more prominent noses, common among cold dwellers, are helpful in humidifying and warming cold air before it reaches the lungs. They are also useful in cleaning and humidifying dry, dusty air in hot climates, which is why long prominent noses are not restricted to places like Europe. Coon, Garn, and Birdsell once proposed that the "Mongoloid face," common in populations native to East and Central Asia, as well as arctic North America, exhibits features adapted to life in very cold environments.[9] The **epicanthic eye fold**, which minimizes eye exposure to the cold, a flat facial profile, and extensive fatty deposits may help to protect the face against frostbite. Although experimental studies have failed to sustain the frostbite hypothesis, it is true that a flat facial profile generally goes with a round head. A significant percentage of body heat may be lost from the head; however, a round head, having less surface area relative to volume, loses less heat than a longer, more elliptical head. As one would

---

[8] Nafte, M. (2000). *Flesh and bone: An introduction to forensic anthropology.* Durham, NC: Carolina Academic Press.

[9] Ibid.

Epicanthic eye fold. A fold of skin at the inner corner of the eye that covers the true corner of the eye; common in Asiatic populations.

predict from this, long-headed populations are generally found in hotter climates; round-headed ones are more common in cold climates.

Skin Colour: A Case Study in Adaptation

In North America, race is most commonly equated with skin colour. Perhaps this is not surprising, because it is a highly visible trait. Skin colour is subject to great variation, and there are at least four main factors associated with it: transparency or thickness of the skin, a copper-coloured pigment called carotene, reflected colour from the blood vessels (responsible for the rosy colour of lightly pigmented people), and the amount of **melanin** found in a given area of skin. Exposure to sunlight increases the amount of melanin, a dark pigment, causing the skin to darken. Melanin is known to protect skin against damaging ultraviolet solar radiation;[10] consequently, darkly pigmented peoples are less susceptible to skin cancers and sunburn than are those whose skin has less melanin. They also seem to be less susceptible to photo-destruction of certain vitamins. Because the highest concentration of dark-skinned people tends to be found in the tropical regions of the world, it appears that natural selection has favoured heavily pigmented skin as a protection against the strong solar radiation of equatorial latitudes, where ultraviolet radiation is most intense. Because skin cancers generally do not develop until later in life, they are unlikely to have interfered with the reproductive success of lightly pigmented individuals in the tropics, and so are unlikely to have been the agent of selection. On the other hand, severe sunburn, which is especially dangerous to infants, causes the body to overheat and interferes with its ability to sweat, by which it might rid itself of excess heat. Furthermore, it makes one susceptible to other kinds of infection. In addition to all this, decomposition of folate, an essential vitamin sensitive to heavy doses of ultraviolet radiation, can cause anemia, spontaneous abortion, and infertility.[11]

Although dark skin pigmentation has enjoyed a selective advantage in the tropics, the opposite is true in northern latitudes, where skins have generally been lightly pigmented. This lack of heavy amounts of melanin enables the weak ultraviolet radiation of northern latitudes to penetrate the skin and stimulate formation of vitamin D, necessary for calcium regulation. Dark

The epicanthic eye fold is common among people native to East Asia and arctic North America. Still, a comparison of this individual with those shown on p. 379 shows the absurdity of lumping all Asians in a single category. **GARY CRAWFORD**

pigmentation interferes with this process. Without access to external sources of vitamin D, once provided by cod liver oil but now more often provided in vitamin D–fortified milk, individuals incapable of synthesizing enough of this vitamin in their own bodies were selected against, for they contracted rickets, a disease that seriously deforms children's bones. At its worst, rickets

[10] Neer, R.M. (1975). The evolutionary significance of vitamin D, skin pigment, and ultraviolet light. *American Journal of Physical Anthropology, 43,* 409–416.

[11] Branda, R.F., & Eatoil, J.W. (1978). Skin color and photolysis: An evolutionary hypothesis. *Science, 201,* 625–626.

Melanin. The chemical responsible for dark skin pigmentation, which helps protect against damage from ultraviolet radiation.

These photos of people from Spain, Scandinavia, Senegal, and Indonesia illustrate the range of variation in human skin colour. Generally, the closer to the equator populations live, the darker the skin colour. BERYL GOLDBERG (TOP), FARRELL GREHAN/PHOTO RESEARCHERS, INC. (LEFT), RICHARD WOOD (CENTRE), E.R. DEGGINGER/COLOR-PIC, INC. (RIGHT)

prevents children from reaching reproductive age; at the least, it interferes with a woman's ability to give birth if she does reach reproductive age (Figure 13.2).

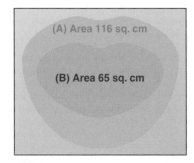

FIGURE 13.2

The outline of a normal pelvic inlet (A) compared with that of a woman with rickets (B), which would interfere with her capacity to give birth. Rickets is caused by a deficiency of vitamin D. In the absence of artificial sources of this vitamin among people living in northern latitudes, lightly pigmented people are least likely to contract rickets.

Darkly pigmented skins likely are quite ancient considering that the earliest hominins evolved in tropical latitudes. Consistent with this, the enzyme tyrosinase, which converts the amino acid tyrosine into the compound that forms melanin, is present in lightly pigmented peoples in sufficient quantity to make them very "black." The reason it does not is that they have genes that inactivate or inhibit it.[12] Human skin is more liberally endowed with sweat glands than is the skin of other mammals; in combination with our lack of heavy body hair, this makes for effective elimination of excess body heat in a hot climate. This would have been especially advantageous to early hominins on the savanna, who could have avoided confrontations with carnivorous animals by carrying out most of their activities in the heat of the day. For the most part, carnivores rest during this period, being active from dusk until early morning.

_____

[12] Wills, C. (1994). The skin we're in. *Discover, 15*(11), 79.

Without much hair to cover early hominin bodies, selection would have favoured dark skins; hence all humans appear to have had a "black" ancestry, no matter how "white" some of them may be today.

One should not conclude that, because it is newer, lightly pigmented skin is better, or more highly evolved, than heavily pigmented skin. The latter is clearly more highly evolved to the conditions of life in the tropics, although with protective clothing, hats, and sunscreen lotions, lightly pigmented peoples can survive there. Conversely, the availability of supplementary sources of vitamin D allows heavily pigmented peoples to do quite well away from the tropics. In both cases, culture has rendered skin colour differences largely irrelevant.

An interesting question is how long it took for light pigmentation to develop in populations living outside the tropics. We now know that the first people to reach Australia did so about 60 000 years ago. They came there from tropical Southeast Asia and, as we would expect, had darkly pigmented skin. In Australia, those populations that spread south of the tropics (where, as in northern latitudes, ultraviolet radiation is less intense) underwent some reduction of pigmentation. But for all that, their skin colour is still far darker than that of Europeans or East Asians (remember that most of today's Southeast Asian population spread there from southern China following the invention of farming—hence their relatively light pigmentation). The obvious conclusion is that 60 000 years is not enough to produce advanced depigmentation, and that Europeans and East Asians lived outside the tropics for a far longer period.[13]

The inheritance of skin colour is not well understood, except that several genes (rather than variants of a single gene), each with several alleles, must be involved. Nevertheless, its geographical distribution, with few exceptions, tends to be continuous, like that of other human traits (Figure 13.3). The exceptions have to do with the movement of certain populations from their original homelands to other regions or the practice of selective mating, or both. For example, there have been repeated invasions of the Indian subcontinent by peoples from the north, who were then incorporated into the Hindu caste system. Still today, the higher the caste, the lighter its skin colour. This skin colour gradient is maintained by strict in-group marriage rules. In the United States, statistical studies

Although Tasmania is as far south of the equator as Europe is north of it, indigenous Tasmanians were more darkly pigmented. Although the ancestors of both Europeans and Tasmanians lived in tropical regions, populations did not arrive in Tasmania until a good deal later than they reached Europe. Consequently, Tasmanians have not been subject to selection for light pigmentation for as long as have Europeans. **ROYAL ANTHROPOLOGICAL INSTITUTE PHOTOGRAPHIC COLLECTION**

have shown that there has been a similar trend among African Americans, with African-American women of higher status choosing to marry lighter-skinned males, reflecting the culture's emphasis on the supposed superiority of people with light skin. It is quite possible that the Black Pride movement, which places positive value on features common among those of West African descent—such as dark skins, tightly curled hair, and broad, flat noses—is leading to a reversal of this cultural selection factor.

---

[13] Ferrie, H. (1997). An interview with C. Loring Brace. *Current Anthropology, 38,* 864.

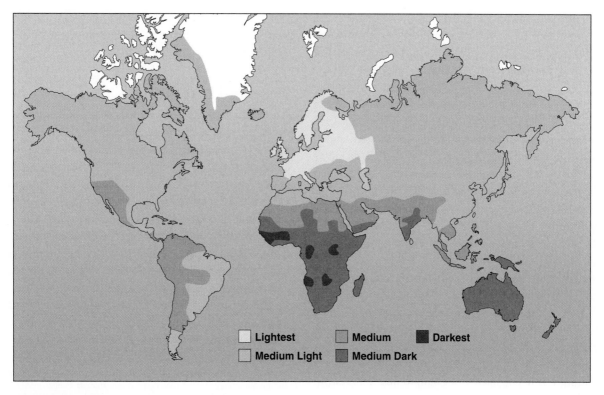

FIGURE 13.3

This map illustrates the pre-Columbian distribution of dark and light human skin pigmentation. Medium-light skin colour in Southeast Asia reflects the spread into that region of people from southern China, whereas the medium darkness of people native to southern Australia is a consequence of their tropical Southeast Asian ancestry. Lack of a dark skin pigmentation among tropical populations of North American First Nations reflects their ancestry in Northeast Asia a mere 20 000 years ago.

THE SOCIAL SIGNIFICANCE OF RACE: RACISM

Scientific facts, unfortunately, have been slow to change what people think about race. **Racism** can be viewed solely as a social problem, although at times it has been used by politicians as a purportedly scientific tool. It is an emotional phenomenon best explained in terms of collective psychology. Racial conflict results from long-suppressed resentments and hostilities. The racist responds to social stereotypes, not to known scientific facts.

Race and Behaviour

Many people in contemporary society cling tenaciously to the assumption that there are behavioural differences among human races. Throughout history, certain "races" have been attributed certain characteristics that assume a variety of names—national character, spirit, temperament—all of them vague and standing for a number of concepts totally unrelated to any biological concept of race. Common myths involve the "coldness" of Scandinavians or the "martial" character of Germanics or the "indolent" nature of Africans. These generalizations serve to characterize a people unjustly; German citizens do not advocate genocide, nor do Africans hate to work. The term "race" has a precise biological meaning, but in popular usage, as we have already seen, the term often acquires a meaning unrelated to that given by scientists, often with disastrous results.

> **Racism.** A doctrine of racial superiority by which one group asserts its superiority over another.

To date, no innate behavioural characteristic can be attributed to any group of people that the nonscientist would most probably term a "race" that cannot be explained in terms of cultural practices. If the Chinese happen to exhibit exceptional visuospatial skills, it is probably because the business of learning to read Chinese characters requires a visuospatial kind of learning that is not needed to master Western alphabets.[14] If African Canadians and First Nations members are not as well represented in managerial positions as their fellow citizens, it is because for a long time they were allowed neither the necessary training nor the opportunity (nor is the problem fully rectified today). All such differences or characteristics can be explained in terms of culture.

Similarly, high crime rates among certain groups can be explained with reference to culture rather than biology. Individuals alienated and demoralized by poverty, injustice, and inequality of opportunity tend to display what the dominant members of society regard as antisocial behaviour more frequently than those who are culturally well integrated. For example, aboriginal North Americans, when equipped and allowed to compete on an equal footing with other North Americans, have not suffered from the high rate of alcoholism exhibited by those living under conditions of poverty.

Race and Intelligence

A question frequently asked by those unfamiliar with the deficiencies of the race concept is whether some races are inherently more intelligent than others. Intelligence tests carried on in the United States by European-American investigators among people of African and European descent have often shown that European Americans attain higher scores. During World War I, a series of IQ tests known as Alpha and Beta were regularly given to U.S. draftees. The results showed that the average score attained by European Americans was higher than that obtained by African Americans. Even though many African Americans scored higher than some European Americans, and some African Americans scored higher than most European Americans (African Americans from

---

[14] Chan, J.W.C., & Vernon, P.E. (1988). Individual differences among the peoples of China. In J.W. Berry (Ed.), *Human abilities in cultural context* (pp. 340–357). Cambridge, UK: Cambridge University Press.

BIOGRAPHY

Emoke J.E. Szathmáry

Biological anthropologist Emoke J.E. Szathmáry is the 10th President and Vice-Chancellor of The University of Manitoba and a Member of the Order of Canada. She specializes in the genetics of aboriginal North Americans. Her work has addressed the causes of type-2 diabetes in aboriginal North Americans, the genetic relationships within and between peoples of North America and Asia, and microevolution of the peoples of the subarctic and arctic. Her field research was conducted among Ottawa, Ojibwa, and Dogrib peoples in Ontario and the Northwest Territories. Szathmáry, like many of us, started on a different academic path than the one she now finds herself on. As a medical student at the University of Toronto, an encounter with anthropology provided her with a "defining moment." She learned that all people share intrinsic needs but that different societies have different ways of meeting those needs. The obvious conclusion from this, that no group was inferior to any other, motivated her to register in the honours anthropology program. Her interest in human genetics, particularly the genetics of aboriginal North Americans, led to her doctoral research on gene flow from Europeans into aboriginal North Americans. Szathmáry remains deeply concerned about what she calls the "European hegemony" in human genome research. Biological anthropologists with their concerns for investigating diversity should be at the forefront of the study of the genetics of indigenous peoples.

Source: Szathmáry, E.J.E. (2001). A comment on the series "A view on the science: Physical anthropology at the millennium." *American Journal of Physical Anthropology, 114*, 1–3.

northern states, for instance, scored better on average than southern European Americans), many people took this as proof of the intellectual superiority of "white people." But all the tests really showed was that, on the average, European Americans outperformed African Americans in certain social situations. The tests did not measure "intelligence" per se, but the ability, conditioned by culture, of certain individuals to respond to certain socially conditioned problems. These tests had been conceived by European Americans for comparable middle-class European Americans. Although people of colour coming from similar backgrounds generally did well (Chinese and Japanese Americans, for example, generally outperformed European Americans), African Americans as well as people of colour coming from other backgrounds to meet the challenge of these tests were clearly at a disadvantage. It would be unrealistic to expect individuals unfamiliar with European American middle-class values and linguistic behaviour to respond to a problem based on a familiarity with these.

Many large-scale intelligence tests continue to be administered in the United States. Notable among these are several series that attempt to hold environmental factors constant. Where this is done, African and European Americans tend to score equally well.[15] This isn't surprising; because genes assort themselves independently of one another, there is no reason to suppose that whatever alleles may be associated with intelligence are likely to be concordant with the ones for skin pigmentation. Intelligence tests, however, have increasingly become the subject of controversy. There are many psychologists as well as anthropologists who are convinced that their use is overdone. Intelligence tests, they say, are of limited use, because they are applicable only to particular cultural circumstances. Only when these circumstances are carefully met can any meaningful generalizations be derived from the use of tests.

Notwithstanding the foregoing, there continue to be some who insist that there are significant differences in intelligence among human populations. Recent proponents of this view are the psychologist Richard Herrnstein and Charles Murray, a social scientist who is a fellow of the American Enterprise Institute, a conservative think-tank. Their argument, in a lengthy (and highly publicized) book entitled *The Bell Curve,* is that a well-documented 15-point difference in IQ exists between African and European Americans, with the latter scoring higher, though not quite as high as Asian Americans. Furthermore, Herrnstein and Murray assert that these differences are mostly determined by genetic factors and are therefore immutable.

Herrnstein and Murray's book has been justly criticized on many grounds, including violation of basic rules of statistics and their practice of utilizing studies, no matter how flawed, that appear to support their thesis while ignoring or barely mentioning those that contradict it. But does this mean that they are wrong? On purely theoretical grounds, could we not suppose that, just as we see a spectrum of inherited variations in physical traits—skin colour, hair texture, height, or

---

[15] Sanday, P.R. (1975). On the causes of IQ differences between groups and implications for social policy. In M.F.A. Montagu (Ed.), *Race and IQ* (pp. 232–238). New York: Oxford.

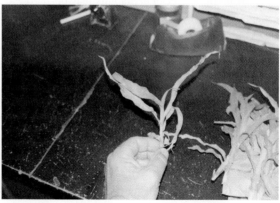

These photos show how important the environment is in the expression of genetic traits. The same strain of corn that flourishes in one set of circumstances may do quite poorly in another. DR. CLOYCE G. COFFMAN/TEXAS A&M UNIVERSITY

whatever—there may be similar variation in innate intellectual potential of different populations? It is likely that just as there are genes affecting the development of such things as blue eyes, curly hair, or heavily pigmented skin, there are others affecting the development of intelligence. Of course, even if genes affecting intelligence do exist, we would still need to ask why their distribution should be any more concordant with those for skin colour than with ones that determine whether one has A, B, or O blood, normal or abnormal (antimalarial) hemoglobin, or whatever.

A number of studies have appeared to indicate an appreciable degree of hereditary control of intelligence. First, there is a general tendency for those pairs of individuals who are most genetically similar (identical twins) to be most similar in intelligence, even when reared in different environments. Furthermore, the scores on IQ tests of biological parents and their children are correlated and tend to be similar, whereas foster parents and their foster children show less of this tendency. There are, however, enormous problems in attempting to separate genetic components from environmental contributors.[16] As biologists Richard Lewontin and Steven Rose with psychologist Leon Kamin observe, twin studies are plagued by a host of problems: inadequate sample sizes, biased subjective judgments, failure to make sure that "separated twins" really were raised separately, unrepresentative samples of adoptees to serve as controls, untested assumptions about similarity of environments. In fact, children reared by the same mother resemble her in IQ to the same degree, whether or not they share her genes.[17] Clearly, we do not know what the heritability of intelligence really is.[18]

Whatever the degree of heritability may be, it is clear that the effects of environment are important for intelligence. This should not surprise us, as even traits of high heritability are strongly influenced by environmental factors. Height in humans, for example, is genetically determined while being dependent both upon nutrition and health status (severe illness in childhood arrests growth, and renewed growth never makes up for this loss). With respect to intelligence, in the early 1900s, new immigrants to the United States, many of whom were Jews, scored lower on IQ tests than U.S.–born whites. Today, the descendants of those Jewish immigrants score 10 points higher on average than whites. In

fact, as in most industrial countries including Canada, IQ scores of all groups have risen some 15 points in the last 40 years, some faster than others. The gap between African and European Americans, for example, is narrower today than in the past. Nor is this surprising, for there are studies showing impressive IQ scores for African-American children from poor backgrounds who have been adopted into affluent and intellectual homes. It is now known that disadvantaged children adopted into affluent and stable families can boost their IQs by 20 points. It is also well known that IQ scores rise with the amount of schooling the test takers have. More such cases could be cited, but these suffice to make the point: The assertion that IQ is fixed and immutable is clearly false. Just as millions of people routinely overcome deficiencies of vision that are far more heritable than *anyone* claims intelligence to be, so may enriched education increase intelligence.

Intelligence: What Is It?

A question that must now be asked is: What do we mean by the term "intelligence"? To some, the answer is: that which is measured by IQ tests. Unfortunately, there is no general agreement as to what abilities or talents actually make up what we call intelligence, even though there are some psychologists who insist that it is a single quantifiable thing. Many more psychologists have come to believe intelligence to be the product of the interaction of different sorts of cognitive abilities: verbal, mathematical-logical, spatial, linguistic, musical, bodily kinesthetic, social, and personal.[19] Each may be thought of as a particular kind of intelligence, unrelated to the others. This being so, they must be independently inherited (to the degree they are inherited), just as height, blood type, skin colour, and so forth are independently inherited. Thus, the various abilities that

---

[16] Andrews, L.B., & Nelkin, D. (1996). The bell curve: A statement. *Science, 271*, 13.

[17] Lewontin, R.C., Rose, S., & Kamin, L.J. (1984). *Not in our genes* (pp. 100, 113, 116). New York: Pantheon.

[18] Ibid., pp. 9, 121.

[19] Jacoby, R., & Glauberman, N. (Eds.). (1995). *The bell curve debate* (pp. 7, 55–56, 59). New York: Random House.

constitute intelligence may be independently distributed as are, for example, the previously discussed skin colour and blood type (compare Figures 13.3 and 13.4).

The next question is: If we are not exactly sure what IQ tests are measuring, how can we be sure of the validity of such tests—that is, can we be sure an IQ test measures what it is supposed to measure? The answer, of course, is that we cannot be sure. But, even at best, an IQ test measures performance (something that one does) rather than genetic disposition (something that lies within the individual). Reflected in one's performance are one's past experiences and present motivational state, as well as one's innate ability. In sum, it is fair to say that an IQ test is not a reliable measure of innate intelligence.

Attempts to prove the existence of significant differences in intelligence among human populations have been going on as long as people have been talking about race. But in spite of all, the hypothesis remains unproved. Nor is it ever likely to be proved, in view of what we saw in Chapter 10 as the major thrust in the evolution of the genus *Homo*. Over the past 2.5 million years, in all populations of this genus, the emphasis has been on cultural adaptation—actively inventing solutions to the problems of existence, rather than passively relying on biological adaptation. Thus, we would expect a comparable degree of intelligence in all present-day human populations. But even if this were not the case, it would mean only that dull and bright people are to be found in all human populations, though in different frequencies. Remember: Within-group variation is greater than between-group variation. Thus, geniuses can and do appear in any population, regardless of what that population's average intelligence may be. The fact of the matter is that the only way to be sure that individual human beings develop their innate abilities and skills, whatever they may be, to the fullest is to make sure they have access to the necessary resources and the opportunity to do so. This certainly cannot be accomplished if whole populations are assumed at the outset to be inferior.

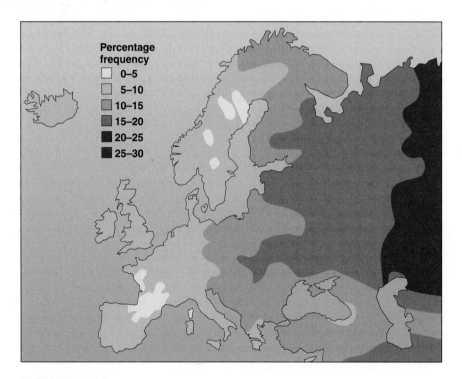

FIGURE 13.4

The east-west gradient in the frequency of the Type B blood in Europe contrasts with the north-south gradient in skin colour shown in Figure 13.3. Whatever genes are involved in the various abilities lumped together as "intelligence" must be independently assorted as well.

On one IQ test designed to be fair to both African American and European American students, they are asked to identify either of two famous scientists, Albert Einstein or George Washington Carver. Unfortunately, in the United States Carver is mostly a European American person's African American hero, so a European American is more likely to identify either than is an African American (see Mark Cohen, 1995, "Anthropology and race: The bell curve phenomenon," General Anthropology 2(1), p. 3). **AP/WIDE WORLD PHOTOS**

EVOLUTIONARY MEDICINE

Can knowledge of evolution make better medical clinicians? Evolutionary medicine is the perspective that human ills are related to incompatibility between the lifestyles and environments in which humans currently live and environments under which human biology evolved.[20] If evolution is the foundation for our understanding of biology, then treatment of medical problems can be informed by a knowledge of evolution. Links between human evolutionary adaptations and illness may be difficult to rigorously demonstrate but according to Randolphe Nesse, Stephen Stearns, and Gilbert Omenn, training in evolutionary thinking can help researchers and clinicians ask questions they might not otherwise consider.[21] Organisms are a result of innumerable evolutionary compromises that have also produced certain vulnerabilities. Our resistance to infection is a result of a long and complex adaptive process. Certain symptoms such as cough, fever, and diarrhea are useful to our bodies and clinicians need to know under what

circumstances it is best to stop them. A typical response to a fever, for example, is to lower it by administering medication; however, an elevated temperature is a biological response that creates a hostile environment for bacteria and viruses so lowering a fever may not always be the best response. Fetal nutritional stress triggers a response that protects against starvation. If a modern diet is introduced to such individuals the body can respond by developing obesity, high blood pressure, and diabetes. An important aspect of being human is that biological processes are given cultural meaning and cultural practices in turn affect human biology.

Take infant crying for example. Many parents, particularly in industrialized European North America, differentiate short periods of crying that can be soothed by

---

[20] McKenna, J.J., Smith, E.O., & Trevathan, W. (1999). *Evolutionary medicine*. New York: Oxford University Press.

[21] Nesse, R.M., Stearns, S.C., & Omenn, G.S. (2006). Medicine needs evolution. *Science, 311*, 1071.

comforting or feeding, and crying because of a physical problem from colic, a type of prolonged crying that has no apparent underlying cause. Frustrated parents have harmed their infants out of frustration with prolonged crying so a lack of understanding of colic can have severe negative consequences. This is a cultural response to the infant's behaviour. Clinical studies of colic are inconclusive so an evolutionary approach might be helpful.[22] Instead of thinking about colic as an ailment that infants "have," Ronald Barr suggests that it is something infants "do" and that the inconclusive studies that have tried to link colic to consumption of cows milk or to "gas" mean that it should not necessarily be distinguished from other forms of infant crying. Crying in the absence of a physical problem is a fitness-maximizing behaviour on the part of an infant that brings the parent to feed, sooth, or otherwise to be in contact. Prolonged crying may correlate with the modern Western custom of prolonged separation of parent and child in a setting in which a quiet household and parental freedom tend to be preferred. Parents who are always in contact with their infant and feed the baby frequently are often considered in a negative light as being indulgent. Infants are often in physical contact with their mother throughout the day in hunting and gathering societies and many non-Western cultures such as the Japanese who also feed throughout the day rather than at prescribed times. An understanding that prolonged infant crying makes sense and that a wide range of parenting styles that include parental responsiveness and frequent feeding is acceptable may be all that parents need to reduce their frustration and the possibility of negative consequences.

CONTINUING HUMAN BIOLOGICAL EVOLUTION

In the course of their evolution, humans in all parts of the world came to rely on cultural rather than biological adaptation for their survival. Nevertheless, as they spread beyond their tropical homeland into other parts of the world, they did develop considerable physical variation from one population to another. The forces responsible for this include genetic drift—especially at the margins of their range where small populations were easily isolated for varying amounts of time—and biological adaptation to differing climates.

Although much of this physical variation can still be seen in human populations today, the increasing effectiveness of cultural adaptation has often reduced its importance. For instance, the consumption of cod liver oil or vitamin D–fortified milk has cancelled out the selective advantage of lightly pigmented skins in northern peoples. At the same time, culture has also imposed its own selective pressures, as we have seen in preceding chapters. Just as the invention of the spear-thrower was followed by a reduction in overall muscularity, or just as the transition to food production was followed by worsened health and mortality, so cultural practices today are affecting the human organism in important, often surprising, ways.

The probability of alterations in human biological makeup induced by culture raises a number of important questions. By trying to eliminate genetic variants for balanced polymorphic traits, such as the sickle-cell trait discussed in Chapter 3, are we also removing alleles that have survival value? Are we weakening the gene pool by allowing people with hereditary diseases and defects to reproduce? Are we reducing chances for genetic variation by trying to control population size?

We do not have answers to all of these questions. If we are able to wipe out sickle-cell anemia, we also may be able to wipe out malaria; thus, we would have eliminated the condition that made the sickle-cell trait advantageous. On the other hand, antimalarial campaigns have had no more than limited success, as the disease afflicts some 270 million people around the world. In 1997, 1.5 million to 2.7 million deaths were caused by malaria, making it the fifth largest infectious killer in the world. Moreover, as a consequence of global warming, the disease could spread (with a number of others) into more northerly regions. Although it is not certain, it is at least possible that over the next century, an average temperature increase of $3°C$ could result in 50 million to 80 million new malaria cases per year.[23] Nor is it strictly true that medical science is weakening the gene pool by letting those with disorders for which there may be a genetic predisposition, such as diabetes, reproduce.

---

[22] Barr, R. (1999). Infant crying behavior and colic. In J.J. McKenna, E.O. Smith,, & W. Trevathan (Eds.), *Evolutionary Medicine* (pp. 27–52). New York: Oxford University Press.

[23] Stone, R. (1995). If the mercury soars, so may health hazards. *Science, 267,* 958.

This photo of African, Asian, aboriginal American, and other winners of the Nobel Peace Prize was taken in 1998. It illustrates the point that individuals of exceptional ability can and do appear in any human population. **BILL CLARK/THE DAILY PROGRESS**

In the present environment, where medication is easily available, such people are as fit as anyone else. However, if such people are denied access to the needed medication, their biological fitness is lost and they die out. In fact, one's financial status affects one's access to medication, and so, however unintentional it may be, one's biological fitness in North American society may be decided by one's financial status.

Examples of culture enabling individuals to reproduce even though they suffer from genetic disorders are familiar. Perhaps less familiar are the cases in which medical technology selects against some individuals by removing them from the reproducing population. One example can be seen in South Africa. About 1 percent of South Africans of Dutch descent have a gene that, in its dominant form, causes porphyria, a disorder that renders the skin of its victims sensitive to light and causes skin abrasions. If these Afrikaners remain in a rural environment, they suffer only minor skin abrasions as a result of their condition. However, the allele renders them very sensitive to modern medical treatment, such as they might receive in a large urban centre like Johannesburg.

If they are treated for some problem unrelated to porphyria, with barbiturates or similar drugs, they suffer acute attacks and very often die. In a relatively quiet rural environment where medical services are less readily accessible, the Afrikaners with this peculiar condition are able to live normal lives; it is only in an urban context, where they are more likely to receive medical attention, that they suffer physical impairment or loss of life.

Another example of culture acting as an agent of biological selection has to do with lactose tolerance: the ability to assimilate **lactose**, the primary constituent of fresh milk. This ability depends on the presence of a particular enzyme, **lactase**, in the small intestine. Failure to retain lactase into adulthood, although controlled by recessive alleles, is characteristic of mammals in general, as well as most human populations—especially Asian, aboriginal Australian, North American First Nations, and

Lactose. The primary constituent of fresh milk.

Lactase. An enzyme in the small intestine that enables humans to assimilate lactose.

The routine use of antibiotics to prevent disease and reduce the amount of feed needed to fatten animals has produced lethal strains of bacteria (previously harmless to humans) that resist antibiotic treatment. One example is the emergence of enterococci as a threat to public health. These bacteria usually dwell peacefully in the human gut, but new strains have emerged that poison organs and cause the immune system to go haywire. Because of the bacteria's resistance to antibiotics, thousands of people die each year. **AP/WIDE WORLD PHOTOS**

many (but not all) African populations. Hence, only 10 to 30 percent of Americans of African descent and 0 to 30 percent of adult Asians retain lactase into adulthood and so are lactose tolerant.[24] By contrast, lactase retention and lactose tolerance are normal for over 80 percent of adults of northern European descent. Eastern Europeans, Arabs, and some East Africans are closer to northern Europeans in lactase retention than they are to Asians and other Africans. Generally speaking, a high retention of lactase is found in populations with a long tradition of fresh milk as an important dietary item. In such populations, selection has in the past favoured those individuals with the dominant allele that confers the ability to assimilate lactose, selecting out those without this allele.

In developing countries, milk supplements are used in the treatment of acute protein-calorie malnutrition. Tube-fed diets of milk are used in connection with other medical procedures. Quite apart from medical practices, powdered milk has long been a staple of economic aid to other countries. Such practices in fact discriminate against the members of populations in which lactase is not commonly retained into adulthood. At the least, those

individuals who are not lactose tolerant will be unable to utilize the nutritive value of milk; frequently they will suffer diarrhea, abdominal cramping, and even bone degeneration, with serious results. In fact, the shipping of powdered milk to victims of South American earthquakes in the 1960s caused many deaths among them.

Among Europeans, the evolution of lactose tolerance is linked with evolution of a nonthrifty genotype.[25] Until about 6000 years ago all humans were characterized by a **thrifty genotype**. This permitted efficient storage of fat to draw on in times of food shortage, and in times of scarcity conserved glucose (a simple sugar)

[24] Harrison, G.G. (1975). Primary adult lactase deficiency: A problem in anthropological genetics. *American Anthropologist, 77,* 815–819.

[25] Allen, J.S., & Cheer, S.M. (1996). The non-thrifty genotype. *Current Anthropology, 37,* 831–842.

> **Thrifty genotype.** Human genotype that permits efficient storage of fat to draw on in times of food shortage and conservation of glucose and nitrogen.

for use in brain and red blood cells (as opposed to other tissues such as muscle), as well as nitrogen (vital for growth and health) through the body's diminished exertion. Regular access to lactose, a source of glucose, led to selection for the nonthrifty genotype as protection against adult-onset diabetes, or at least its onset relatively late in life (at a nonreproductive age). By contrast, populations that are lactose intolerant retain the thrifty genotype. As a consequence, when they are introduced to Western-style diets, characterized by abundance, particularly of foods high in sugar content, the incidence of diabetes skyrockets.

In recent years, there has been considerable concern about human activities that damage the earth's ozone layer. A major contributor to the ozone layer's deterioration has been the use of chlorofluorocarbons in aerosol sprays, refrigeration and air conditioning, and the manufacture of Styrofoam. Because the ozone layer screens out some of the sun's ultraviolet rays, its continued deterioration will expose humans to increased ultraviolet radiation. As we saw earlier in this chapter, some ultraviolet radiation is necessary for the production of vitamin D, but excessive amounts lead, among other things, to an increased incidence of skin cancers. Hence a rising incidence of skin cancers is not surprising, as the ozone layer continues to deteriorate.

Although a ban on the use of chlorofluorocarbons in aerosol sprays was imposed some years ago, the destruction of the ozone layer continued about twice as quickly as scientists had predicted it would, even without the ban. Subsequently, an international treaty further limiting the use of chlorofluorocarbons was negotiated, but this ban has merely slowed, rather than halted, further deterioration. In fact, the ozone hole over Antarctica in October 1994 was the severest ever recorded in 35 years. Most immediately affected by the consequent increase in ultraviolet radiation are the world's lightly pigmented peoples, but ultimately, all will be affected.

Ozone depletion is merely one of a host of problems confronted by humans today that ultimately have an impact on human gene pools. In view of the consequences for human biology of such seemingly benign innovations as dairying or (as discussed in Chapter 11) farming, we may wonder about many

recent practices—for example, the effects of increased exposure to radiation from increased use of X-rays and CT scans, nuclear accidents, increased production of radioactive wastes, and the like. To be sure, we are constantly reassured by various experts that we are protected by adequate safety regulations, but one is not reassured by discoveries, such as the one announced by the U.S. National Academy of Sciences in 1989, that what were accepted as safe levels of radiation were in fact too high; or the earlier discovery that the supposedly safe treatment of sinus disorders in the 1940s by massive doses of X-ray radiation produced a bumper crop of thyroid cancers in the late 1960s. But it is not only increased exposure to radiation that we confront but also to other known mutagenic agents, including a wide variety of chemicals, such as pesticides. Despite repeated assurances about their safety, there have been tens of thousands of cases of poisonings in North America alone (probably more in so-called underdeveloped countries, where controls are even less effective and where substances banned in North America are routinely used), and thousands of cases of cancer related to the manufacture and use of pesticides. All this on top of the several million birds killed each year (many of which would otherwise have been happily gobbling down bugs and other pests), serious fish kills, honey bee kills (bees are needed for the efficient pollination of many crops), and the like. In all, pesticides alone (never mind other agricultural chemicals) are responsible for an estimated $8 *billion* worth of environmental and public health damage in the United States each year.[26]

Aside from pesticides, there are other dangerous substances, like hormone-disrupting chemicals. In 1938, a synthetic estrogen known as DES was developed and subsequently prescribed for a variety of ailments ranging from acne to prostate cancer. Moreover, tons of it are routinely added to animal feeds. It was not until 1971, however, that the first indication that DES causes vaginal cancer in young women came to light. Subsequent research has shown that DES causes problems with the male reproductive system and deformities of the female reproductive tract. DES mimics the natural hormone, binding with appropriate receptors in and on cells and

---

[26] Pimentel, D. (1991). Response. *Science, 252,* 358.

thereby turns on biological activity associated with the hormone. As one group of scientists observes:

> *The synthetic hormone has two troublesome traits. First, it triggers certain parts of the reproductive system more effectively than does estradiol, one of the body's own estrogens. … Even more important, it manages to circumvent a mechanism that protects the fetus from the developmentally disruptive effects of excessive estrogen exposure. Normally, special maternal and fetal blood proteins soak up almost all excess circulating estrogen. But they do not recognize DES. As a consequence, DES in the fetal blood supply remains biologically active.[27]*

DES is not alone in its effects: At least 51 chemicals—many of them in common use—are now known to disrupt hormones, and even this could be the tip of the iceberg. Some of these chemicals mimic hormones in the manner of DES, whereas others interfere with other parts of the endocrine system, such as thyroid and testosterone metabolism. Included are such supposedly benign and inert substances as plastics widely used in laboratories and chemicals added to polystyrene and polyvinyl chloride (PVCs) to make them more stable and less breakable. These plastics are widely used in plumbing, food processing, and food packaging. Hormone-disrupting chemicals are also found in many detergents and personal care products, contraceptive creams, the giant jugs used to bottle drinking water, and plastic linings in cans.

The implications of all these developments are sobering. We know that pathologies result from extremely low levels of exposure to harmful chemicals. Yet, besides those used in North America, millions of kilograms are exported (over 18 million kilograms in 1991 alone).[28] It is quite possible that hormone disruptions are at least partially responsible for certain trends that have recently become causes for concern among scientists. These range from increasingly early onset of puberty in human females to dramatic declines in human sperm counts. With respect to the latter, some 61 separate studies confirm that sperm counts have dropped almost 50 percent from 1938 to 1990 (Figure 13.5). Most of these studies

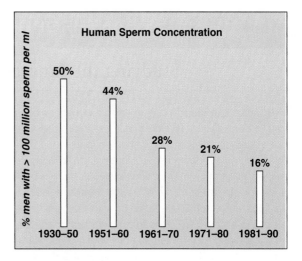

FIGURE 13.5

A documented decline in human male sperm counts worldwide may be related to widespread exposure to hormone-disrupting chemicals.

were carried out in North America and Europe, but some from Africa, Asia, and South America show that this is essentially a worldwide phenomenon. If this trend continues, it will have profound results.

It is not that the experts who assure us of the safety of such things are deliberately misleading us. (Although there are cases of that too, one notorious example being the case of asbestos. As early as 1902 it was included in a list of dusts known to be hazardous. By 1933 it was well documented as a cause of lung cancer, yet in the 1960s, corporate executives denied ever hearing of the dangers.) For the most part, experts are convinced of the validity of what they say; the difficulty is that serious problems, such as those having to do with radiation or exposure to various chemicals, have a way of not being apparent until years, or even decades later. By then, of course, serious financial interests are at stake.

What is clear, then, is that cultural practices, probably as never before, are currently having an impact on human gene pools. Unquestionably, this impact is deleterious to those individuals who suffer the effects of negative selection, whose misery and death are the

---

[27] Colburn, T., Dumanoski, D., & Myers, J.P. (1996). Hormonal sabotage. *Natural History*, (3), 45–46.

[28] Ibid., 47.

ANTHROPOLOGY APPLIED

Studying the Emergence of New Diseases

Ever since the Neolithic, humans have had to cope with a host of new diseases that got their start as a consequence of changes in human behaviour. This has become a renewed source of concern following a recent resurgence of infectious diseases and appearance and spread of a host of new and lethal diseases. All told, more than 30 diseases new to medicine have emerged in the past 25 years, of which perhaps the best known is AIDS. This has now become number 4 among infectious killers of humans, with 5.8 million people infected in 1998 alone.[1] But there are others—like Ebola, which causes victims to hemorrhage to death, blood pouring from every orifice; hemorrhagic fevers like Dengue fever, Lassa fever, and Hantavirus; Invasive Streptococcus A, which consumes the victims' flesh; Legionnaire's disease; and Lyme disease. What has sparked the appearance and spread of these and other new diseases has been a considerable mystery, but one theory is that some are the result of human activities. In particular, the intrusion of people into new ecological settings, such as rain forests, along with construction of roads allows viruses and other infectious microbes to spread rapidly to large numbers of people. It is now generally accepted that the HIV virus responsible for AIDS transferred to humans from chimpanzees in the forests of the Democratic Republic of Congo as a consequence of hunting and butchering these animals for food. For the first 30 years, few people were affected; it was not until people began congregating in cities like Kinshasa that conditions were ripe for an epidemic.

To gain a better understanding of the interplay between ecological disturbance and the emergence of new diseases, anthropologist Carol Jenkins, whose specialty is medical anthropology, obtained a grant from the MacArthur Foundation in 1993. From her base at the Papua New Guinea Institute of Medical Research, she is following what happens to the health of local people in the wake of a massive logging operation, begun in 1993. From this should come a better understanding of how disease organisms spread from animal hosts to humans. Since most of the "new"

viruses that have suddenly afflicted humans are in fact old ones that have been present in animals like monkeys (monkey pox), rodents (Hanta virus), deer (Lyme disease), and insects (West Nile virus), it appears that something new has enabled them to jump from their animal hosts to humans. A recent example comes from the Democratic Republic of Congo. Here civil war created a situation where villagers in the central part of the country were faced with starvation. Their response was to increase the hunting of animals, including monkeys, squirrels, and rats that carry a disease called monkey pox. Related to smallpox, the disease transfers easily to humans, resulting in the largest outbreak of this disease ever seen among humans. What makes this outbreak even more serious is an apparently new strain of the infection, enabling it to spread from person to person, instead of only from an animal host.[2]

Large-scale habitat disturbance is an obvious candidate for such disease transfers, but this needs to be confirmed and the process understood. So far, it is hard to make more than a circumstantial case, by looking back after a disease outbreak. The work of Jenkins and her team is unique in that she was able to get baseline health data on local people before their environment was disturbed. Thus, she is in a position to follow events as they unfold.

It will be some time before conclusions can be drawn from Jenkins's study. Its importance is obvious; in an era of globalization, as air travel allows more and more tropical diseases to spread beyond the tropics, we need a fuller understanding of how viruses interact with their hosts if we are to devise effective preventive and therapeutic strategies to deal with them.

---

[1] Balter, M. (1998). On world AIDS day, a shadow looms over southern Africa. *Science, 282*, 1790.

[2] Cohen, J. (1997). Is an old virus up to new tricks? *Science, 277*, 312–313.

Source: Gibbons, A. (1993). Where are new diseases born? *Science, 261*, 680–681.

price paid for many of the material benefits of civilization we enjoy today. It remains to be seen just what the long-term effects on the human species as a whole will be. If the promise of genetic engineering offers hope of alleviating some of the misery and death that result from our own practices, it also raises the spectre of removing genetic variants that might turn out to be of future adaptive value, or of introducing variants that might turn out to make us immediately susceptible to new problems that we don't even know about today.

CHAPTER SUMMARY

In humans, most behavioural patterns are culturally learned or acquired. Other characteristics are determined by an interaction between genes and environment. The gene pools of populations contain various alternative alleles. When the environment changes, their gene pool confers the possibility for physical alteration to meet the change.

When a polymorphic species is separated into different faunal regions, it is usually polytypic; that is, populations differ in the frequency with which genetic variability is expressed. It appears that the human species has been polytypic at least since the time of *Homo erectus* and *H. ergaster*. Gene flow, however, has prevented diversification into multiple species.

Early anthropologists classified *H. sapiens* into subspecies, or races, based on geographic location and such phenotypic features as skin colour, body size, head shape, and hair texture. The presence of atypical individuals and the nonconcordance of traits continually challenged these racial classifications. No examples of pure racial types could be found. The visible traits were found to occur in a worldwide continuum. No definite grouping of distinct, discontinuous biological groups has been found in modern humans.

A biological race is a population of a species that differs in the frequency of genetic variants from other populations of the same species. Three observations must be made concerning this biological definition: (1) It is arbitrary; (2) it does not mean that any one race has exclusive possession of any particular allele(s); and (3) individuals of one race will not necessarily be distinguishable from those of another. As a means for understanding human variation, the concept of race has several limitations. First, race is an arbitrary category, making agreement on any particular classification impossible; second, humans are so complex genetically that often the genetic basis of traits on which racial studies are based is itself poorly understood; and, finally, race exists as a cultural as well as a biological category. Most anthropologists now view the race concept as useless for an understanding of human biological variation, preferring to study the distribution and significance of specific, genetically based characteristics, or else the characteristics of small breeding populations.

Biological anthropologists have determined that much of human physical variation appears related to climatic adaptation. People native to cold climates tend to have greater body bulk relative to their extremities than individuals who live in hot climates; the latter tend to be long and slender. Studies involving body build and climate are complicated by such other factors as the effects on physique of diet and of clothing.

In Canada and the United States, race is commonly thought of in terms of skin colour. Subject to tremendous variation, skin colour is a function of several factors: transparency or thickness of the skin, distribution of blood vessels, and amount of carotene and melanin in a given area of skin. Exposure to sunlight increases the amount of melanin, darkening the skin. Natural selection has favoured heavily pigmented skin as protection against the strong solar radiation of equatorial latitudes. In northern latitudes, natural selection has favoured relatively depigmented skins, which can utilize relatively weak solar radiation in the production of vitamin D. Selective mating, as well as geographic location, plays a part in skin colour distribution.

Racism can be viewed solely as a social problem. It is an emotional phenomenon best explained in terms of collective psychology. The racist individual reacts on the basis of social stereotypes and not established scientific facts.

Notwithstanding the impossibility of defining biologically valid human races, many people have assumed that there are behavioural differences among human races. The innate behavioural characteristics attributed by these people to race can be explained in terms of enculturation rather than biology. The intelligence tests outlined in this chapter that have been interpreted to indicate that European Americans are intellectually superior to African Americans, for example, are designed by European Americans for European Americans from similar backgrounds. It is not realistic to expect individuals who are not familiar with European American middle-class values to respond to items based on knowledge of these values. African and European Americans both, if they come from different types of backgrounds, are thus at a disadvantage. At present, it is not possible to separate the inherited components of intelligence from those that are culturally acquired. Furthermore, there is still no agreement on what intelligence really is, but it probably comprises several different talents and abilities.

Although the human species has come to rely on cultural rather than biological adaptation for survival, human gene pools still continue to change in response to external factors. Many of these changes are brought about by cultural practices; for example, the shipment of powdered milk to human populations that are low in the frequency of the allele for lactase retention into adulthood may contribute to the death of large numbers of people. Those who survive are most likely to be those with the allele for lactase retention. Unquestionably, this kind of selection is deleterious to those individuals who are "selected out" in this way. Just what the long-term effects will be on the human species as a whole remains to be seen.

QUESTIONS FOR CRITICAL THOUGHT

1. What problems arise when you consider how others may racially classify you?

2. New diseases threaten our well-being in Canada; for example, SARS, avian flu, and the West Nile virus. How has this reality affected our lifestyles? Have the political and medical establishments risen to the challenge of protecting the public and providing up-to-date information? How might biological anthropologists contribute to these issues?

3. Identify a few positive and negative consequences on society of the new research involving the human genome, stem cell research, and human cloning (if it ever happens).

INTERNET RESOURCES

AAA Statement on Race

www.aaanet.org/stmts/racepp.htm
Visit the American Anthropological Association website to read the discipline's statement on race. Also see how professional anthropologists work to bring their intellectual framework into the realm of public policy.

Eugenics in Canada

www.abheritage.ca/abpolitics/people/influ_eugenics .html
How eugenics impacted the life of an Alberta girl.

Classification and Genetic Variation

http://anthro.palomar.edu/vary/vary_2.htm
Presents models of classification based on biological differences rather than culturally defined stereotypes: typological, populational, and clinal models. This site is part of a larger home page that discusses distribution of blood types.

Human Cloning

http://news.bbc.co.uk/1/hi/sci/tech/1682591.stm
BBC article dated November 29, 2001, on Europe rejecting human cloning.

www.wired.com/medtech/health/news/2004/ 03/62695
Wired News dated March 2004, reviews Canada's stand on human cloning. The article contains other links related to bioethics.

Race and Intelligence

www.indiana.edu/~intell/bellcurve.shtml
Leading scientists' critiques of Hernstein and Murray's book, *The Bell Curve*. Learn more about the problems and biases built into race-based intelligence testing.

Anti-Racism in Canada

www.narcc.ca/about/index.html
A national, community-based, member-driven network that provides a strong, recognized, effective, and influential national voice against racism, racialization, and all other forms of related discrimination in Canada.

SUGGESTED READINGS

For a list of suggested readings, visit the textbook's website at www.humanevolution2.nelson.com.

"Absolute" or chronometric dates." In archaeology and palaeoanthropology, dates for archaeological materials based on solar years, centuries, or other units of absolute time.

Accelerator Mass Spectrometry. Also known as AMS dating, an innovation of regular mass spectrometry that determines the composition of a material by bombarding it with ions to separate and count the constituent atoms of a sample according to their mass. The quantity of carbon-14 can be directly measured using this technique.

Acheulean tradition. The toolmaking tradition of *H. erectus/ergaster* in Africa, Europe, and Southwest Asia in which handaxes were developed from the earlier Oldowan chopper.

Action theory. The theory that self-serving actions by forceful leaders play a role in civilization's emergence.

Adaptation. A process by which organisms achieve a beneficial adjustment to an available environment; also the results of that process—the characteristics of organisms that fit them to the particular set of conditions of the environment in which they are generally found.

Adaptive radiation. Rapid diversification of an evolving population as it adapts to a variety of available niches.

Affluent forager. Also known as complex hunter-gatherers, are nonagricultural, substantially sedentary people with hierarchical social organization and food storage.

Agency theory. In postprocessual archaeology, the view that the archaeological record results from the actions of individuals who are part of a culture in which their actions take place.

Alleles. Alternate forms of a single gene.

Altered fossils. Remains of plants and animals that lived in the past that have been altered, as by the replacement of organic material by calcium carbonate or silica.

Amino acid racemization dating. In archaeology and palaeoanthropology, a technique for chronometric dating that measures the ratio of right- to left-handed amino acids.

Analogies. In biology, structures that are superficially similar; the result of convergent evolution.

Ancestral trait. A characteristic that is shared widely, such as mammary glands in mammals, and is considered to have been shared by a common ancestor.

Anthropogenesis. The process whereby humans modify their environment, consciously or not.

Anthropology. The study of humankind in all times and places.

Anthropomorphism. The ascription of human attributes to nonhuman beings.

Applied anthropology. Applying the knowledge and methods of anthropology to solve practical problems.

Arboreal. Tree dwelling.

Archaeology. The study of material remains and cultural features, usually from the past, to describe and explain human behaviour.

Archaeozoology. In archaeology, the analysis and interpretation of archaeological animal remains.

Archaic cultures. See Epi-Palaeolithic, Mesolithic and Archaic New World cultures immediately after the Palaeoindian. Some were hunting and gathering while others had a few crops.

Ardipithecus ramidus. Probable early hominin; lived about 6.0 to 4.4 million years ago.

Artifact. Any object fashioned or altered by humans.

Aurignacian tradition. Toolmaking tradition in Europe and Western Asia at the beginning of the Upper Palaeolithic.

Australopithecus. The first well-known hominin; lived between 4.2 and 1 million years ago. Characterized by bipedal locomotion when on the ground, but with an apelike brain; includes at least five species: *afarensis, africanus, anamensis, boisei,* and *robustus.*

Baton method. The technique of stone tool manufacture performed by striking the raw material with a bone or antler "baton" to remove flakes.

Binocular vision. Vision with increased depth perception from two eyes set next to each other allowing their visual fields to overlap.

Biological anthropology. The systematic study of humans as biological organisms.

Blade technique. A technique of stone tool manufacture by which long, parallel-sided flakes are struck off the edges of a specially prepared core.

Brachiate. To use the arms to move from branch to branch, with the body hanging suspended beneath the arms.

Bronze Age. In the Old World, the period marked by the production of tools and ornaments of bronze; began about 3000 B.C. in China and Southwest Asia and about 500 years earlier in Southeast Asia.

Burins. Stone tools with chisel-like edges used for working bone and antler.

Catastrophism. The view that layers of fossils were evidence of new acts of divine creation.

Chromosome. In the cell nucleus, long strands of DNA combined with a protein that can be seen under the microscope.

Civilization. In anthropology, a type of society marked by the presence of cities, social classes, and the state.

Clavicle. The collarbone.

Codon. Three-base sequence of a gene that specifies production of an amino acid.

Cognitive capacity. A broad concept including intelligence, educability, concept formation, self-awareness, self-evaluation, reliability of performance under stress, attention span, sensitivity in discrimination, and creativity.

Cold-blooded. Animals whose body temperature rises or falls according to the temperature of the surrounding environment.

Convergence. A process by which unrelated populations develop similarities to one another.

Cranium. The brain case of the skull.

Cro-Magnons. Europeans (*Homo sapiens*) of the Upper Palaeolithic after about 36 000 years ago.

Cultural ecology. The perspective that uses ecological and environmental factors to explain cultural variation; culture is the primary means by which people adapt to their environment.

Culture. The often unconscious standards by which societies—structured groups of people—operate. These standards are socially learned rather than acquired through biological inheritance.

Culture-bound. Based on the assumptions and values of one's own culture.

Datum point. The starting, or reference, point for a grid system.

Dendrochronology. In archaeology, a method of chronometric dating based on the number of rings of growth found in a tree trunk.

Derived trait. A characteristic shared narrowly among organisms; it shows that organisms have a close evolutionary relationship.

Direct percussion method. A technique of stone tool manufacture performed by striking the raw material with a hammerstone or by striking raw material against a stone anvil to remove flakes.

Directional selection. Natural selection that favours a single allele; therefore, allele frequency continuously shifts in one direction.

Disruptive selection. Natural selection that simultaneously favours individuals at both extremes of the distribution.

Divergent or branching evolution. An evolutionary process in which an ancestral population gives rise to two or more descendant populations that differ from one another.

DNA. The genetic material deoxyribonucleic acid; a complex molecule with information to direct the synthesis of proteins. DNA molecules have the unique property of being able to produce exact copies of themselves.

Domestication. An evolutionary process whereby humans modify, either intentionally or unintentionally, the genetic makeup of a population of plants or animals, sometimes to the extent that members of the population are unable to survive and/or reproduce without human assistance.

Ecological niche. A species' way of life considered in the context of its environment, including other species found in that environment.

Electron spin resonance. In archaeology and palaeoanthropology, a technique for chronometric dating that measures the number of trapped electrons in bone or shell.

Endocast. A cast of the inside of a skull; helps determine the size and shape of the brain.

Engendered archaeology. Set in feminist theory, it examines the roles gender plays in understanding the past, including the impact of gender bias in the profession of archaeology.

Entoptic phenomena. Bright pulsating forms that are generated by the central nervous system and seen in states of trance.

Enzyme. Proteins that initiate and direct chemical reactions in an organism.

Epicanthic eye fold. A fold of skin at the inner corner of the eye that covers the true corner of the eye; common in Asiatic populations.

Epipalaeolithic, Mesolithic, and Archaic. Cultures at the end of the Palaeolithic that survived into early post-glacial times. They are usually marked by the manufacture and use of small blades and cores. Mesolithic normally refers to these cultures in Europe while Epipalaeolithic is normally specific to the Near East while Archaic is reserved for the New World. Sometimes both Epipalaeolithic and Mesolithic are used with reference to the Old World in general.

Estrus. In primate females, the time of sexual receptivity during which ovulation takes place.

Ethnographer. An anthropologist who studies cultures from a comparative or historical point of view, utilizing ethnographic accounts.

Ethnography. The systematic description of a particular culture based on firsthand observation.

Ethnohistory. The study of cultures of the recent past through oral and written histories; accounts left by explorers, missionaries, and traders; and through analysis of such records as land titles, birth and death records, and other archival materials.

Ethnology. Someone who analyzes ethnographic data.

Evolution. Descent with modification.

Fact. An observation verified by several observers skilled in the necessary techniques of observation.

Faunal region. A geographic region with its own distinctive assemblage of animal life, not precisely like that of other regions.

Feature. In archaeology, a place within a site that is treated separately from other places within the site.

Flotation. An archaeological technique employed to recover very tiny objects by immersion of soil samples in water to separate heavy from light particles.

Fluorine test. In archaeology or palaeoanthropology, a technique for relative dating based on the fact that the amount of fluorine in bones is proportional to their age.

Foramen magnum. A large opening in the skull through which the spinal cord passes and connects to the brain.

Forensic anthropology. A field of biological anthropology and archaeology that specializes in the identification of human skeletal remains for legal purposes.

Fossil locality. In palaeoanthropology, a place where fossils are found.

Fossil. The remains of a once-living organism, generally having lived more than 10 000 years ago.

Gender. The cultural construction of masculinity and femininity as well as third genders and androgynous identities and roles.

Gene flow. The introduction of alleles from the gene pool of one population into that of another.

Gene pool. The genetic variants available to a population.

Genera; genus. In the system of plant and animal classification, a group of like species.

Genes. Portions of DNA molecules that direct the synthesis of proteins. DNA molecules have the unique property of being able to produce exact copies of themselves.

Genetic code. The sequence of DNA bases that specifies production of a particular amino acid.

Genetic drift. Chance fluctuations of allele frequencies in the gene pool of a population.

Genome. The complete sequence of DNA for a species.

Genotype. The actual genetic makeup of an organism.

Genus Homo. Hominin genus characterized by expansion of brain, reduction of jaws, and reliance on cultural adaptation; includes at least six species: *Homo habilis, H. erectus, H. ergaster, H. heidelbergensis, H. neanderthalensis,* and *H. sapiens.*

Gracile Australopithecines. Smaller, more lightly built members of the genus *Australopithecus.*

Gradualism. evolutionary mode lthat suggests that species evolve from subspecies through the accumulation of differences in the gene pools of the separated groups.

Grid system. A system for recording data from an archaeological excavation.

Ground-penetrating radar. By transmitting electromagnetic pulses from surface antennas into the ground, and measuring the time lag between when the pulses are sent and when they are received back at the surface, patterns in soil density are recorded.

Haplotype. A set of closely linked genes on a chromosome that tends to be inherited together as a unit.

Hardy-Weinberg principle. Demonstrates algebraically that the percentage of individuals that are homozygous for the dominant allele, homozygous for the recessive allele, and heterozygous should remain constant from one generation to the next, provided that certain specified conditions are met.

Hemoglobin. The protein that carries oxygen in the red blood cells.

Heterozygous. Refers to a chromosome pair that bears different alleles for a single gene.

Historic archaeology. The study of the material remains of past societies that also left behind historical documentary evidence. This subfield of archaeology studies the emergence, transformation, and nature of the Modern World.

Historical linguistics. The study of language origins, language change, and the relationships between languages.

Holistic perspective. A fundamental principle of anthropology, that the various parts of culture must be viewed in the broadest possible context to understand their interconnections and interdependence.

Home range. The area within which a group of primates usually moves.

Homeobox genes. Regulatory genes that code for proteins that travel to other homeobox genes and activate or deactivate them at different times.

Hominin. Hominoid tribe to which all human species, including those that are extinct, are assigned.

Hominine. Member of the *Homininae*, the subfamily of Hominidae to which African apes, humans and their immediate ancestors belong.

Hominoid. A catarrhine primate superfamily that includes apes and humans.

Homo habilis. Earliest representative of the genus *Homo*; lived between 2.4 and 1.6 million years ago. Characterized by expansion and reorganization of the brain, compared to *Australopithecus*.

Homologies. In biology, structures possessed by two different organisms that arise in similar fashion and pass through similar stages during embryonic development.

Homozygous. Refers to a chromosome pair that bears identical alleles for a single gene.

Horticulture. Cultivation of crops carried out with hand tools such as digging sticks or hoes.

Human osteology. The study of human skeletal remains.

Hydraulic theory. The theory that sees civilization's emergence as the result of the construction of elaborate irrigation systems, the functioning of which required full-time managers whose control blossomed into the first governing body and elite social class.

Hypoglossal canal. The opening in the skull through which the tongue-controlling hypoglossal nerve passes.

Hypotheses. Tentative explanations of the relations among certain phenomena.

Informants. Members of a society in which the ethnographer works who help interpret what he or she sees taking place.

Intensive agriculture. Intensive farming of large plots of land, employing fertilizers, plows, and/or extensive irrigation.

Interspecies gene transfer. Transfer of DNA as when retroviruses insert DNA into the cells of one species from another.

Isolating mechanisms. Factors that separate breeding populations, thereby preventing gene flow, creating divergent subspecies and ultimately (if maintained) divergent species.

Lactase. An enzyme in the small intestine that enables humans to assimilate lactose.

Lactose. The primary constituent of fresh milk.

Law of competitive exclusion. When two closely related species compete for the same niche, one will outcompete the other, bringing about the latter's extinction.

Law of dominance and recessiveness. Certain alleles are able to mask the presence of others.

Law of independent assortment. Genes controlling different traits are inherited independently of one another.

Law of segregation. Variants of genes for a particular trait retain their separate identities through the generations.

Linear evolution. A sustained directional shift in a population's average characteristics.

Linguistic anthropology. The branch of cultural anthropology that studies human language.

Lower Palaeolithic. The first part of the Old Stone Age; its beginning is marked by the appearance 2.6 million years ago of Oldowan tools.

Low-level food producers. People who use management techniques to secure resources; may include nonintensive growing of domesticated organisms.

Magnetometer. A device for detecting subsurface patterns by measuring the variation in magnetic-field strength of the soil.

Maritime Archaic culture. An Archaic culture of Northeastern North America, centred on the Gulf of St. Lawrence, that emphasized the utilization of marine resources.

Meiosis. A kind of cell division that produces the sex cells, each of which has half the number of chromosomes, and hence genes, as the parent cell.

Melanin. The chemical responsible for dark skin pigmentation, which helps protect against damage from ultraviolet radiation.

Microliths (microblades). The small (usually less than a few centimetres long), narrow, parallel-sided flakes removed from microcores.

Middle Palaeolithic. The middle part of the Old Stone Age characterized by the emergence of archaic *H. sapiens* and the development of the Mousterian tradition of toolmaking.

Mitosis. A kind of cell division that produces new cells having exactly the same number of chromosome pairs, and hence genes, as the parent cell.

Mousterian tradition. Toolmaking tradition of the Neandertals and their contemporaries of Europe, Western Asia, and northern Africa, featuring flake tools that are lighter and smaller than earlier Levalloisian flake tools.

Multiregional hypothesis. Populations of archaic *H. sapiens* throughout the Old World evolved, at more or less the same time, into modern humans.

Mutation. Chance alteration of a gene that produces a new allele.

Natufian culture. An Epipalaeolithic culture of Israel, Lebanon, and Western Syria, between about 12 500 and 10 200 years ago.

Natural selection. The evolutionary process through which factors in the environment exert pressure that favours some individuals over others to produce the next generation.

Neolithic period. The New Stone Age; began about 11 000 years ago in Southwest Asia when the first domesticated plants appear; in East Asia the period refers to the time when pottery was used and begins 17 000 to 15 000 years ago.

Notochord. A rod-like structure of cartilage that, in vertebrates, is replaced by the vertebral column.

Oldowan tool tradition. The earliest identifiable stone tools.

Orrorin tugenensis. Possible hominin; lived 6 million years ago. *Kenyanthropus platyops.* Hominin contemporary with early Australopithecines; not certainly a separate species.

"Out of Africa" hypothesis. Modern humans evolved in one geographic region, expanding and replacing other populations.

Palaeaolithic. The Old Stone Age, characterized by manufacture and use of chipped stone tools.

Palaeoindians. The earliest inhabitants of North America.

Palaeoanthropologist. An anthropologist who studies human evolution from fossil remains.

Palaeoanthropology. The study of fossil remains with the goal of reconstructing human biological evolution.

Palaeoethnobotany. In archaeology, the analysis and interpretation of archaeological plant remains.

Palaeopathology. The study of disease in ancient populations, usually from evidence presented in bone.

Palynology. In archaeology and palaeoanthropology, a method of relative dating based on changes in fossil pollen over time.

Participant observation. In ethnography, the technique of learning a people's culture through direct participation in their everyday life for an extended period of time.

Pastoralists. People who rely on herds of domestic animals for their subsistence.

Pentadactyly. Possessing five digits (fingers and toes).

Phenotype. The physical appearance of an organism that may or may not reflect a particular genotype because the latter may or may not include recessive alleles.

Polygenetic inheritance. When two or more genes work together to effect a single phenotypic character.

Polymorphic. A species with alternative forms (alleles) of particular genes.

Polytypic. The expression of genetic variants in different frequencies in different populations of a species.

Population. In biology, a group of similar individuals that can and do interbreed.

Postprocessual archaeology. A critique of processual archaeology that rejects scientific explanations of the archaeological record. It represents a diverse perspective encompassing social and cognitive aspects of human behaviour.

Potassium-argon analysis. In archaeology and palaeoanthropology, a technique for chronometric dating that measures the ratio of radioactive potassium to argon in volcanic debris associated with human remains.

Pre-contact. The period before European arrival in the Americas.

Prehensile. Having the ability to grasp.

Prehistoric. A conventional term used to refer to the period of time before the appearance of written records. Does not deny the existence of history, merely of *written* history.

Prehistoric/precontact archaeology. The study of ancient cultures that did not possess writing systems to record their history.

Pressure flaking. A technique of stone tool manufacture in which a bone, antler, or wooden tool is used to press, rather than strike off, small flakes from a piece of flint or similar stone.

Primary origins. When hunters and gatherers transform organisms from wild to domesticated and take up agriculture.

Primates. The group of mammals that includes lemurs, lorises, tarsiers, monkeys, apes, and humans.

Primatology. The study of nonhuman primates, their biology, adaptation, and social behaviour.

Processual archaeology. A scientific approach to explaining the process of culture changes and adaptations.

Public archaeology. Any archaeological activity that interacts or has the potential to interact with the public.

Punctuated evolution. A new species appears after a relatively quick and dramatic change then lasts for a long time with little significant change.

Race. In biology, a subspecies; a population of a species that differs in allele frequencies from other such populations. Humans cannot be divided into racial categories that have any biological validity.

Racism. A doctrine of racial superiority by which one group asserts its superiority over another.

Radiocarbon analysis. In archaeology and palaeoanthropology, a technique for chronometric dating based on measuring the amount of radioactive carbon (C-14) left in organic materials found in archaeological sites.

Regulatory genes. Control the expression or activity of other genes.

Relative dating. In archaeology and palaeoanthropology, designating an event, object, or fossil as being older or younger than another.

Ribosomes. Structures in the cell where translation occurs.

RNA. Ribonucleic acid; similar to DNA but with uracil substituted for the base thymine. Carries instructions from DNA to produce amino acids for protein building.

Robust Australopithecines. Slightly larger and more robust than gracile members of genus *Australopithecus*, with larger, more powerful jaws.

Sagittal crest. A crest running from front to back on the top of the skull in the midline.

Sahelanthropus tchadensis. Probable hominin ancestor to Ardipithecus; lived 7 to 6 million years ago.

Scapula. The shoulder blade.

Secondary origins. When agriculture expands from its original region of origin by migration of farmers or by the adoption of an agricultural way of life by hunter-gatherers who are in contact with farmers.

Seriation. A method used to place artifacts in approximate chronological order based on the recognition of small-scale incremental changes in form or style. The method assumes that single artifacts or groups of artifacts that are most similar are closest to one another in time and space. Sequences based on seriation can be tied to absolute chronologies if one or more of the artifacts can be dated.

Settlement archaeology. Research designed to describe the arrangement of occupations in the landscape in order to understand how people organized themselves in particular settings.

Sexual dimorphism. Within a single species, the presence of marked anatomical differences between males and females.

Shellmound. An extensive deposit of refuse including quantities of shell left behind by people. These deposits include artifacts and it is not unusual to find burials in them.

Sickle-cell anemia. An inherited form of anemia caused by the red blood cells assuming a sickle or crescent shape.

Sinodont. The modern Northeast Asian populations typified by a high complexity of dental characteristics such as root number.

Site. In archaeology, a place containing remains of previous human activity.

Skeletal biology. In anthropology, the analysis and interpretation of human bones, normally from archaeological sites.

Sociocultural anthropology. The branch of anthropology that focuses on humans as a culture-making species.

Soil marks. Stains that show up on the surface of recently plowed fields that reveal an archaeological site.

Soil resistivity meter. A device that detects subsurface patterns by passing electrical current through the ground and measuring the resistance of the soil to the current.

Species. In biology, a population or group of populations that is capable of interbreeding but that is reproductively isolated from other such populations.

Stabilizing selection. Natural selection as it acts to promote stability, rather than change, in a population's gene pool.

Stereoscopic vision. Complete three-dimensional vision from binocular vision plus visual connections from each eye to both sides of the brain allowing nerve cells to integrate the images derived from each eye.

Stratified. Layered; said of archaeological sites where the remains lie in layers, one upon another.

Stratigraphy. In archaeology and palaeoanthropology, the most reliable method of relative dating by means of strata.

Structural genes. Code for proteins that contribute directly to the actual formation of a structure such as whether a person has brown or blue eyes.

Subsistence strategy. Decisions and actions that affect food and raw material procurement of a society.

Sundadont. Southeast Asian populations with generalized features, particularly less elaborate dental characteristics than in the Sinodont pattern.

Technology. The knowledge that people employ to make and use objects.

Theoretical perspective. In archaeology, the set of assumptions that form a model or theory.

Theory. In science, an explanation of natural phenomena, supported by a reliable body of data.

Thrifty genotype. Human genotype that permits efficient storage of fat to draw on in times of food shortage and conservation of glucose and nitrogen.

Tool. An object used to facilitate some task or activity. Although toolmaking involves intentional modification of the material of which it is made, tool use may involve objects either modified for some particular purpose or completely unmodified.

Tradition. In archaeology, a distinctive tool kit or technology that lasts a long time at one or more localities.

Transcription. Process of conversion of instructions from DNA into RNA.

Transhumance. Among pastoralists, the grazing of sheep and goats in low steppe lands in the winter and then moving to high pastures on the plateaus in the summer.

Translation. Process of conversion of RNA instructions into proteins.

Unaltered fossils. Remains of plants and animals that lived in the past and that have not been altered in any significant way.

Unconscious selection. The preservation of valued variants of a plant or animal species and the destruction of less valued ones, with no thought as to the long-range consequences.

Uniformitarianism. The view that forces shaping the contemporary world were no different in the past.

Upper Palaeolithic. The last part of the Old Stone Age, characterized by the emergence of more modern-looking hominins and an emphasis on the blade technique of toolmaking.

Warm-blooded. Animals that maintain a relatively constant body temperature.

Wedge-shaped microcore. A stone that is usually prepared in the shape of a biface, split along the long axis to produce a flat surface or striking platform from which microliths are struck.

BIBLIOGRAPHY

Adams, R. (2001). Scale and complexity in archaic states. *American Antiquity, 11,* 188.

Alemseged, Z., Spoor, F., Kimbel, W.H., Bobe, R., Geraads, D., Reed, D. & Wynn, J.G. (2006). A juvenile early hominin skeleton from Dikika, Ethiopia. *Nature, 443,* 296–301.

Allaby, A. & Allaby, M. (1999). *Dictionary of earth sciences.* Oxford: Oxford University Press.

Allen, J.S. & Cheer, S.M. (1996). The non-thrifty genotype. *Current Anthropology, 37,* 831–842.

Amábile-Cuevas, C.F. & Chicurel, M.E. (1993). Horizontal gene transfer. *American Scientist, 81,* 332–341.

Ambrose, S.H. (2001). Paleolithic technology and human evolution. *Science, 291.*

American Anthropological Association (1998). Code of ethics of the American Anthropological Association. *Anthropology Newsletter, 39,* 19–20.

American Anthropological Association (1998). Statement on "race." Available at www.aaanet.org/stmts/racepp.htm.

Andrews, L.B. & Nelkin, D. (1996). The bell curve: A statement. *Science, 271,* 13.

Ankel-Simons, F., Fleagle, J.G. & Chatrath, P.S. (1998). Femoral anatomy of *Aegyptopithecus zeuxis,* an early Oligocene anthropoid. *American Journal of Physical Anthropology, 106,* 413–424.

Anonymous. (1998). The First Americans, ca. 20,000 B.C. *Discover, 19,* 24.

Apland, B., Blake, E.W., Cosgrove, J.A., Gaunt, S., Greer, S., Mackie, A.P. Mackie, K.E., Straathof, D., Thorp, V. & Torffe, P.M. Owen Beattie. *Canadian Journal of Archaeology, 24,* 129–147.

Appenzeller, T. (1998). Art: Evolution or revolution? *Science, 282,* 1451–1454.

Ashmore, W. (Ed.). (1981). *Lowland Maya settlement patterns.* Albuquerque: University of New Mexico Press.

Asquith, P.J. & Fedigan, L.M. (1991). *The Monkeys of Arashiyama: 35 years of research in Japan and the West.* Albany: State University of New York Press.

Balter, M. (1998). On world AIDS day, a shadow looms over southern Africa. *Science, 282,* 1790.

Balter, M. (1998). Why settle down? The mystery of communities. *Science, 282,* 1442–1444.

Balter, M. (1999). A long season puts Çatalhöyük in context. *Science, 286,* 890–891.

Balter, M. (2001). Did plaster hold Neolithic society together? *Science, 294,* 2278–2281.

Balter, M. (2001). Fossil tangles roots of human family tree. *Science, 291,* 2289–2291.

Balter, M. (2001). In search of the first Europeans. *Science, 291,* 1724.

Balter, M. (2001). Scientists spar over claims of earliest human ancestor. *Science, 291,* 1460–1461.

Balter, M. (2002). From a modern human's brow—or doodling? *Science, 295,* 247–249.

Bamshad, M.J. & Olsen, S.E. (2003). Does race really exist? *Scientific American, 289,* 78–85.

Barham, L.S. (1998). Possible early pigment use in South-Central Africa. *Current Anthropology, 39,* 703–710.

Barr, R. (1999). Infant crying behavior and colic. In J.J. McKenna, E.O. Smith, & W. Trevathan (Eds.), *Evolutionary medicine.* New York: Oxford University Press. xvi, 480 p.

Barton, R.A. (2004). Binocularity and brain evolution in primates. *PNAS, 101,* 10113–10115.

Bar-Yosef, O. (1986). The walls of Jericho: An alternative interpretation. *Current Anthropology, 27,* 157–162.

Bar-Yosef, O., Vandermeesch, B., Arensburg, B., Belfer-Cohen, A., Goldberg, P., Laville, H., Meignen, L., Rak, Y., Speth, J.D., Tchernov, E., Tillier, A.M. & Weiner, S. (1992). The excavations in Kebara Cave, Mt. Carmel. *Current Anthropology, 33,* 497–550.

Beattie, O., Geiger, J. & Tanaka, S. (1992). *Buried in ice* (p. 64). Mississauga, ON: Random House of Canada.

Beattie, O.B. & Geiger, J. (1987). *Frozen in time: The fate of the Franklin expedition.* Saskatoon: Western Producer Prairie Books.

Beattie, O., Apland, B., Blake, E.W., Cosgrove, J.A., Gaunt, S., Greer, S., Mackie, A.P., Mackie, K.E., Straathof, D., Thorp, V. & Torffe, P.M. The Kwäday Dän Ts'ínchy discovery from a glacier in British Columbia. *Canadian Journal of Archaeology, 24,* 129–147.

Bednarik, R.G. (1995). Concept-mediated marking in the Lower Paleolithic. *Current Anthropology, 36,* 605–634.

Begun, D. (1992). Miocene fossil hominids and the chimp-human clade. *Science, 257,* 1929–1933.

Begun, D. (2004). The earliest hominids—is less more? *Science, 303,* 1478–1480.

Begun, D.R. (2003). Planet of the apes. *Scientific American, 289* (2), 74–83.

Begun, D.R. & Güleç, E. (1998). Restoration of the type and palate of *Ankarapithecus meteai*: Taxonomic, phylogenetic, and functional implications. *American Journal of Physical Anthropology, 105,* 279–314.

Behrensmeyer, A.K., Todd, N.E., Potts, R. & McBrinn, G. E. (1997). Late Pliocene faunal turnover in the Turkana basin, Kenya and Ethiopia. *Science, 278,* 1589–1594.

Berger, L.R. (2000). *In the footsteps of Eve: The mystery of human origins.* Washington, DC: National Geographic Society.

Bermúdez de Castro, J.M., Arsuaga, E., Carbonell, E., Rosas, A., Martinez, I. & Mosquera, M. (1997). A hominid from the Lower Pleistocene of Atapuerca, Spain: Possible ancestor to Neandertals and modern humans. *Science, 276,* 85–1395.

Berra, T.M. (1990). *Evolution and the myth of creationism.* Stanford, CA: Stanford University Press.

Black, D. (1928). Discovery of further hominid remains of lower Quaternary age from the Chou Kou Tien deposit. *Science, 67,* 136–137.

Bloch, J.I. & Boyer, D.M. (2002). Grasping primate origins. *Science,* 298, 1606–1610.

Blumer, M.A. & Byrne, R. (1991). The ecological genetics and domestication and the origins of agriculture. *Current Anthropology, 32,* 23–54.

Boehm, C. (2000). The evolution of moral communities. School of American Research, *2000 Annual Report,* p. 7.

Bonvillain, N. (2000). *Language, culture, and communication: The meaning of messages* (3rd ed.). Upper Saddle River, NJ: Prentice Hall.

Brace, C.L. (1997). Cro-Magnons Я us? *Anthropology Newsletter, 38,* 1, 4.

Brace, C.L. (1982). The roots of the race concept in physical anthropology. In F. Spencer (Ed.), *A History of American physical anthropology, 1930–1980.* New York: Academic Press.

Brace, C.L. (2000). *Evolution in an anthropological view.* Walnut Creek, CA: Altamira Press.

Branda, R.F. & Eatoil, J.W. (1978). Skin color and photolysis: An evolutionary hypothesis. *Science, 201,* 625–626.

Breuer, T., Ndoundou-Hockemba, M. & Fishlock, V. (2005). First observation of tool use in wild gorillas. *PLoS Biology, 3,* e380.

Bridges, P.S. (1989). Changes in activities with the shift to agriculture in the southeastern United States. *Current Anthropology, 30,* 385–394.

Brown, P., Sutikna, T., Morwood, M.J., Soejono, R.P., Jatmiko, Saptomo, E.W. & Due, R.A. (2004). A new small-bodied hominin from the Late Pleistocene of Flores, Indonesia. *Nature, 431,* 1055–1061.

Brumm, A., Aziz, F., van den Bergh, G.D., Morwood, M.J., Moore, M.W., Kurniawan, I., Hobbs, D.R. & Fullagar, R. (2006). Early stone technology on Flores and its implications for *Homo floresiensis. Nature, 441,* 624–628.

Brunet, M., Guy, F., Pilbeam, D., Mackaye, H.T., Likius, A., Ahounta, D., Beauvilain, A., Blondel, C., Bocherens, H., Boisserie, J.R. and others. (2002). A new hominid from the Upper Miocene of Chad, Central Africa. *Nature, 418,* 145–151.

Bull, J.J. & Wichman, H.A. (1998). A revolution in evolution. *Science, 281,* 1959.

Burke, A. (2004). The ecology of Neanderthals: Preface. *International Journal of Osteoarchaeology, 14,* 155–161.

Burke, A. (2000). Hunting in the Middle Palaeolithic. *International Journal of Osteoarchaeology, 10,* 281–285.

Carneiro, R.L. (1970). A theory of the origin of the state. *Science, 169,* 733–738.

Cartmill, M. (1992). New views on primate origins. *Evolutionary Anthropology: Issues, News, and Reviews, 1,* 105–111.

Cartmill, M. (1998). The gift of gab. *Discover 19,* 64.

Cavallo, J.A. (1990, February) Cat in the human cradle. *Natural History,* 52–61.

Chan, J.W.C. & Vernon, P.E. (1988). Individual differences among the peoples of China. In J.W. Berry (Ed.), *Human abilities in cultural context* (pp. 340–357). Cambridge: Cambridge University Press.

Chicurel, M. (2001). Can organisms speed their own evolution? *Science, 292,* 1824–1827.

Ciochon, R.L. & Fleagle, J.G. (1987). *Ramapithecus* and human origins. In R.L. Ciochon & J.G. Fleagle (Eds.), *Primate evolution and human origins.* Hawthorne, NY: Aldine de Gruyter.

Clark, G.A. (1997). Neandertal genetics. *Science, 277*, 1024.

Clark, G.A. (2002). Neandertal archaeology: Implications for our origins 104. *American Anthropologist, 104*, 50–67.

Coe, S.D. (1994). *America's first cuisines.* Austin, TX: University of Texas Press.

Coe, W.R. & Haviland, W.A. (1982). *Introduction to the archaeology of Tikal.* Philadelphia: University Museum.

Cohen M, (1995) "Anthropology and race: The bell curve phenomenon," *General Anthropology 2*, 3.

Cohen, J. (1997). Is an old virus up to new tricks? *Science, 277*, 312–313.

Cohen, M. & Armelagos, G. (Eds.). (1984). *Paleopathology at the origins of agriculture.* Orlando: Academic Press.

Colburn, T., Dumanoski, D. & Myers, J.P. (1996). Hormonal sabotage. *Natural History, 3*, 45–46.

Conkey, M. (1991). Contexts of action, contexts for power: Material culture and gender in the Magdalenian. In J.M. Gero and M.W. Conkey (Eds.), *Engendering archaeology: Women and prehistory* (p. 78). Oxford: Basil Blackwell.

Connor, M. (1996). The archaeology of contemporary mass graves. *SAA Bulletin, 14*(4), 6, 31.

Conroy, G.C. (1997). *Reconstructing human origins: A modern synthesis.* New York: W.W. Norton.

Coon C.S., Garn, S. & Birdsell, J. (1950). *Races: A study of the problems of race formation in man.* Springfield, IL: C.C. Thomas.

Cormack, J.L. (2003). Davidson Black and his role in Chinese palaeoanthropology. In C. Shen & S.G. Keates (Eds.), *Current research in Chinese palaeoanthropology* (pp. 9–19). British Archaeological Reports 11.

Cornwell, T. (1995, Nov. 10). Skeleton staff. *Times Higher Education,* p. 20.

Corruccini, R.S. (1992). Metrical reconsideration of the Skhul IV and IX and Border Cave I Crania in the context of modern human origins. *American Journal of Physical Anthropology, 87*, 433–445.

Cotter, J.L. (1978). Symposium on Role of Archaeology in Historical Research, Summary and Analysis. In R.L. Schuyler (Ed.), *Historical archaeology: a guide to substantive and theoretical contributions* (pp. 18–19). Farmingdale, NY: Baywood.

Cowgill, G.L. (1997). State and society at Teotihuacan, Mexico. *Annual Review of Anthropology, 26*, 129–161.

Crawford, G.W. & Lee, G.A. (2003). Agricultural origins in the Korean Peninsula. *Antiquity, 77*.

Crawford, G.W. & Shen, C. (1998). The origins of rice agriculture: Recent progress in East Asia. *Antiquity, 72*, 858–866.

Crawford, G.W. & Smith, D.G. (2002). Early Late Woodland in Southern Ontario: An update. In J. Hart & C. Rieth (Eds.), *Northeast subsistence-settlement change: A.D. 700–A.D. 1300* (pp. 117–133). Albany: New York State Museum.

Crawford, G.W. (1992). The transition to agriculture in Japan, In A.B. Gebauer & T.D. Price (Eds.), *Transitions to agriculture in prehistory, Monographs in world archaeology no. 4* (pp. 117–132). Madison, Wisconsin: Prehistory Press.

Crawford, G.W. (1997). Anthropogenesis in Prehistoric Northeastern Japan. In K. Gremillion (Ed.), *People, plants, and landscapes: Studies in Paleoethnobotany* (pp. 86–103). University of Alabama Press.

Crawford, G.W. (2005). Green River Archaic Paleoethnobotany. In W.M. Marquardt & P.J. Watson (Eds.), *Archaeology of the Middle Green River Area, Kentucky* (pp. 181–212). Gainesville: University of Florida Press.

Crawford, G.W. (2006). East Asian plant domestication. In M.T. Stark (Ed.) *Archaeology of Asia*, (pp. 77–95). Malden: Blackwell Publishing.

Culotta, E. (1992). A new take on anthropoid origins. *Science, 256*, 1516–1517.

Culotta, E. & Koshland, D.E., Jr. (1994). DNA repair works its way to the top. *Science, 266*, 1926.

Cuvier, G. (1812). *Recherches sur les ossemens fossiles de quadrupáedes; ou, L'on râetablit les caractáeres de plusieurs espáeces animaux que les râevolutions du globe paroissent avoir dáetruites.* Paris: Chez Deterville.

Cyranoski, D. (2002). Almost human. *Nature, 418*, 910–912.

Darvil, T. (2002). *The concise Oxford dictionary of archaeology.* Oxford Reference Online. Oxford University Press.

Darwin, C. (1859). *On the origin of species.* Cambridge, MA: Harvard University Press.

Darwin, C. (1870). *The descent of man, and selection in relation to sex* (p. 705). New York: Hurst.

de Waal, F. (1996). *Good natured: The origins of right and wrong in humans and other animals.* Cambridge, MA: Harvard University Press.

de Waal, F. (2001). Sing the song of evolution. *Natural History 110*, 76–77.

de Waal, F. (2001). *The ape and the sushi master.* New York: Basic Books.

de Waal, F., Kano, T. & Parish, A.R. (1998). Comments. *Current Anthropology, 39*, 407–408, 410–411, 413–414.

Dennell, R. & Roebroeks, W. (2005). An Asian perspective on early human dispersal from Africa. *Nature, 438*, 1099–1104.

Dennell, R., Rendell, H. & Hallwood, E. (1988). Early tool-making in Asia: Two-million-year-old artefacts in Pakistan. *Antiquity, 62*, 98–106.

Diamond, J. (1994). Race without color. *Discover, 15*(11): 83–89.

Diamond, J. (1996). Empire of uniformity. *Discover, 17*(3), 78–85.

Diamond, J. (1997). *Guns, germs and steel.* New York: Norton.

Diamond, J. (1998). Ants, crops, and history. *Science, 281*, 1974–1975.

Doist, R. (1997). Molecular evolution and scientific inquiry, misperceived. *American Scientist, 85,* 475.

Donnan, C.B. & Castillo, L.J. (1992). Finding the tomb of a Moche priestess. *Archaeology 45*, 38–42.

Driver, J. (1999). Raven skeletons from Paleoindian contexts, Charlie Lake Cave, British Columbia. *American Antiquity, 64.*

Drucker, P. (1966). Rank, wealth, and kinship in northwest coast society. In T. McFeat (Ed.), *Indians of the north Pacific coast* (pp. 134–146). Seattle: University of Washington Press.

Durant, J. C. (2000, April 23). Everybody into the gene pool. *New York Times Book Review,* 11–12.

Eighth Annual Young Scientist Conference. (n.d.). *Owen Beattie.* Retrieved October 16, 2000, from http://ftp.ei.edduc .ab.ca/ dept/ins/beattie/html.

Eldredge, N. & Gould, S.J. (1972). Punctuated equilibria: An alternative to phyletic gradualism. In T.M. Schopf (Ed.), *Models in palaeobiology* (pp. 82–115). San Francisco: Freeman Cooper.

Ellis, C. (2004). Understanding "Clovis" fluted point variability in the Northeast: A perspective from the Debert Site, Nova Scotia. *Canadian Journal of Archaeology, 28,* 205–253.

Elston, R.G. & Brantingham, P.J. (2002). Microlithic technology in Northeast Asia: A risk minimizing strategy of the Late Paleolithic and Early Holocene. In R.G. Elston & S.L. Kuhn (Eds.), *Thinking small: Global perspectives on microlithization* (pp. 103–116). Archaeological Papers of the American Anthropological Association Number 12.

Enard, W., Przeworski, M., Fisher, S.E., Lai, C.S., Wiebe, V., Kitano, T., Monaco, A.P. & Pääbo, S. (2002). Molecular evolution of FOXP2, a gene involved in speech and language. *Nature, 418,* 869–872.

Evenson, Brad. (2002). Canada to be at forefront of new genome research. *National Post.* Toronto.

Fagan, B.M. & Beck, C. (1996). *The Oxford companion to archaeology.* New York: Oxford University Press.

Fagan, B.M. (1995). The quest for the past. In L.L. Hasten (Ed.), *Annual editions 95/96, Archaeology* (p. 10). Guilford, CT: Dushkin.

Fagan, B.M. (1998). *People of the earth* (9th ed.). New York: Longman.

Falk, D. (1989). Ape-like endocast of "Ape Man Taung." *American Journal of Physical Anthropology, 80,* 335–339.

Falk, D. (1993). A good brain is hard to cool. *Natural History, 102,* 65.

Falk, D. (1993). Hominid paleoneurology. In R.L. Ciochon & J.G. Fleagle (Eds.). *The human evolution source book.* Englewood Cliffs, NJ: Prentice-Hall.

Feder, K.L. (1999). *Frauds, myths, and mysteries* (3rd ed.). Mountain View, CA: Mayfield.

Federoff, N.E. & Nowak, R.M. (1997). Man and his dog. *Science, 278,* 305.

Fedigan, L.M. (1982). *Primate paradigms: Sex roles and social bonds.* Montreal: Eden Press.

Fedigan, L.M. & Strum, S.C. (2000). *Primate encounters: Models of science, gender, and society.* Chicago: University of Chicago Press.

Fedje, D.W., Wigen, R.J., Mackie, Q., Lake, C. & Sumpter, I. (2001). Preliminary results from investigations at Kilgii Gwaay: An early Holocene archaeological site on Ellen Island, Haida Gwaii, British Columbia. *Canadian Journal of Archaeology, 25,* 98–120.

Fedorak, S. (1994). *Is archaeology relevant? An examination of the roles of archaeology in education.* Unpublished master's thesis, University of Saskatchewan.

Ferber, D. (2000). Superbugs on the hoof? *Science, 288,* 792–794.

Fernandez-Carriba, S. & Loeches, A. (2001). Fruit smearing by captive chimpanzees: A newly observed food-processing behavior. *Current Anthropology, 42,* 143–147.

Ferrie, H. (1997). An interview with C. Loring Brace. *Current Anthropology, 38,* 851–869.

Ferris, N. (2000). Warning—Steep grade ahead: Current directions in Canadian archaeology. *Canadian Journal of Archaeology, 24,* 182–186.

Fiedel, S.J. (2000). The peopling of the New World: Present evidence, new theories, and future directions. *Journal of Archaeological Research, 8,* 39–103.

First Nations and the Canadian Museums Association. (1992). *Turning the page: Forging new partnerships between museums and First Peoples.* Ottawa.

Fladmark, K.R. (1996). The prehistory of Charlie Lake Cave. In R.L. Carlson & L. Dalla Bona (Eds.), *Early human occupation in British Columbia* (pp. 11–20). Vancouver: UBC Press.

Flannery, K. (1973). Archaeology with a capital "S." In C.L. Redman (Ed.), *Research and theory in current archeology* (pp. 47–53). New York: J. Wiley and Sons.

Fleras, A. & Elliott, J.L. (2002). *Engaging diversity: Multiculturalism in Canada.* Toronto: Nelson Thomson Learning.

Folger, T. (1993). The naked and the bipedal. *Discover, 14*(11), 34–35.

Fox, R. (1968). *Encounter with anthropology.* New York: Dell.

Frake, C.O. (1992). Lessons of the Mayan sky. In A.F. Aveni (Ed.), *The sky in Mayan literature* (pp. 274–291). New York: Oxford University Press.

France, D.L. & Horn, A.D. (1992). *Lab manual and workbook for physical anthropology* (2nd ed.), New York: West.

Frayer, D.W. (1981). Body size, weapon use, and natural selection in the European Upper Paleolithic and Mesolithic. *American Anthropologist, 83,* 57–73.

Freeman, L.G. (1992). *Ambrona and Torralba: New evidence and interpretation* [paper]. 91st Annual Meeting of the American Anthropological Association, San Francisco.

Futuyama, D.J. (1995). *Science on trial: The case for evolution.* Sunderland: Sinauer Associates.

Gabunia, L., Vekua, A., Lordkipanidze, D., Swisher III, C.C., Ferring, R., Justus, A., Nioradze, M., Tvalchrelidze, M., Anton, S.C., Bosinski, G., Joris, O., de Lumley, M.A., Majsuradze, G., & Mouskhelishvili, A. (2000). Earliest Pleistocene hominid cranial remains from Dmanisi, Republic of Georgia: Taxonomy, geological setting, and age. *Science, 288,* 1019–1025.

Galdikas, B.M.F. (1995). *Reflections of Eden: My years with the orangutans of Borneo.* Boston: Little, Brown.

Gamble, C. (1986). *The Paleolithic settlement of Europe.* Cambridge: Cambridge University Press.

Gao, X., Qi, W., Shen, C. & Keates, S. (2005). New light on the earliest Hominid occupation on East Asia. *Current Anthropology, 46,* supplement, S115–S120.

GCS Research Society. (1996). Biruté Galdikas. Retrieved October 18, 2004, from the World Wide Web: http://www.science.ca/scientists/scientistprofile.php?pID=7.

Gebo, D.L., Dagosto, D., Beard, K.C., & Tao, Q. (2001). Middle Eocene primate tarsals from China: Implications for haplorhine evolution. *American Journal of Physical Anthropology, 116,* 83–107.

Gebo, D.L., MacLatchy, L., Kityo, R., Deino, A., Kingston, J. & Pilbeam, D. (1997). A hominoid genus from the early Miocene of Uganda. *Science, 276,* 401–404.

Geertz, C. (1984). Distinguished lecture: Anti-relativism. *American Anthropologist, 86,* 263–278.

Gero, J.M. (1991). Genderlithics: Women's roles in stone tool production. In J.M. Gero & M.W. Conkey (Eds.), *Engendering archaeology: Women and prehistory* (pp. 163–193). Oxford: Basil Blackwell.

Gibbons, A. (1993). Where are new diseases born? *Science, 261,* 680–681.

Gibbons, A. (1996). Did Neandertals lose an evolutionary "arms" race? *Science, 272,* 1586–1587.

Gibbons, A. (1997). A new face for human ancestors. *Science, 276,* 1331–1333.

Gibbons, A. (1997). Ideas on human origins evolve at anthropology gathering. *Science, 276,* 535–536.

Gibbons, A. (1998). Ancient island tools suggest *Homo erectus* was a seafarer. *Science, 279,* 1635–1637.

Gibbons, A. (2001). Studying humans—and their cousins and parasites. *Science, 292,* 627–629.

Gibbons, A. (2001). The riddle of coexistence. *Science, 291,* 1726.

Gibbons, A. & Culotta, E. (1997). Miocene primates go ape. *Science, 276,* 355–356.

Gilchrist, R. (1999). Gendered hierarchies? Labour, "prestige" and production. (pp. 31–53). *Gender and archaeology. Contesting the past.*

Glausiusz, J. (1995). Hidden benefits. *Discover, 16*(3), 30–31.

Glausiusz, J. (1995). Micro gets macro. *Discover, 16*(11), 40.

Goebel, T. & Aksenov, M. (1995). Accelerator radiocarbon dating of the Upper Paleolithic in Siberia. *Antiquity, 69,* 349–357.

Goodall, J. (1986). *The chimpanzees of Gombe: Patterns of behavior.* Cambridge, MA: Belknap Press.

Goodenough, W. (1990). Evolution of the human capacity for beliefs. *American Anthropologist, 92,* 597–612.

Goodman, M., Bartez, W.J., Hayasaka, K., Stanhope, M.J., Slightom, J. & Czelusniak, J. (1994). Molecular evidence on primate phylogeny from DNA sequences. *American Journal of Physical Anthropology, 94,* 3–24.

Gould, S.J. (1985). *The flamingo's smile: Reflections in natural history.* New York: Norton.

Gould, S.J. (1989). *Wonderful life.* New York: Norton.

Gould, S.J. (1991). *Bully for Brontosaurus.* New York: Norton.

Gould, S.J. (1996). *Full house: The spread of excellence from Plato to Darwin*. New York: Harmony Books.

Gould, S.J. (2000). What does the dreaded "E" word mean, anyway? *Natural History, 109*(1), 28–44.

Gramly, R. (1982). The Vail site: A Palaeo-Indian encampment in Maine. Buffalo: Buffalo Society of Natural Sciences, Bulletin Series, Volume 30.

Graves, J.L. (2001). *The emperor's new clothes: Biological theories of race at the millennium*. New Brunswick, NJ: Rutgers.

Green, R.E., Krause, J., Ptak, S.E., Briggs, A.W., Ronan, M.T., Simons, J.F., Du, L., Egholm, M., Rothberg, J.M., Paunovic, M., and others. (2006). Analysis of one million base pairs of Neanderthal DNA. *Nature, 444,* 330–336.

Grine, F.E. (1993). Australopithecine taxonomy and phylogeny: Historical background and recent interpretation. In R.L. Ciochon & J.G. Fleagle (Eds.), *The human evolution source book*. Englewood Cliffs, NJ: Prentice-Hall.

Grün, R. & Thorne, A. (1997). Dating the Ngandong humans, *Science, 276,* 1575.

Gunter, C. & Dhand, R. (2005). The chimpanzee genome. *Nature,* 437, 47.

Haile-Selassie, Y., Suwa, G. & White, T. (2004). Late Miocene teeth from Middle Awash, Ethiopia and early hominid dental evolution. *Science, 303,* 1503–1505.

Halverson, J. (1989). Review of *Altimira revisited and other essays on early art. American Antiquity,* 54, 883.

Harrison, G.G. (1975). Primary adult lactase deficiency: A problem in anthropological genetics. *American Anthropologist,* 77, 812–835.

Harrold, F.B. (1980). A comparative analysis of Eurasian palaeolithic burials. *World archaeology, 12,* 199.

Hartwig, W.C. & Doneski, K. (1998). Evolution of the Hominid hand and toolmaking behavior. *American Journal of Physical Anthropology, 106,* 401–402.

Hastorf, C. (1991). Gender, space, and food in prehistory. In J.M. Gero & M.W. Conkey (Eds.), *Engendering archaeology: Women and prehistory* (pp. 132–159). Oxford: Basil Blackwell.

Haviland, W.A. (1975). The ancient Maya and the evolution of urban society. *University of Colorado Museum of Anthropology, Miscellaneous Series,* no. 37.

Haviland, W.A. (1997). Cleansing young minds, or what should we be doing in introductory anthropology? In C.P. Kottak, J.J. White, R.H. Furlow, & P.C. Rice (Eds.), *The teaching of anthropology: Problems, issues, and decisions* (p. 35). Mountain View, CA: Mayfield.

Haviland, W.A. (2003). Settlement, society and demography at Tikal. In J. Sabloff (Ed.), *Tikal*. Santa Fe, NM: School of American Research.

Haviland, W.A. & Power, M.W. (1994). *The original Vermonters: Native inhabitants, past and present* (Rev. and expanded ed.). Hanover, NH: University Press of New England.

Haviland, W.A., et al. (1985). *Excavations in small residential groups of Tikal: Groups 4F-1 and 4F-2*. Philadelphia: University Museum.

Heckenberger, M.J., Kuikuro, A., Kuikuro, U.T., Russell, J.C., Schmidt, M., Fausto, C. & Franchetto, B. (2003). Amazonia 1492: Pristine forest or cultural parkland? *Science, 301,* 1710–1714.

Hedigan, E.J. (1995). *Applied anthropology in Canada: Understanding aboriginal issues*. Toronto: University of Toronto Press.

Heidenreich, C.E. (1971). *Huronia: A history and geography of the Huron Indians, 1600–1650*. Toronto: McClelland and Stewart.

Herrnstein, R.J. & Murray, C.A. (1994). *The bell curve: Intelligence and class structure in American life*. New York: Free Press.

HGMIS (Human Genome Management Information System). (2001). Human genome project FAQs. *Human Genome News, 11,* 4.

Holden, C. (1996). Missing link for miocene apes. *Science, 271,* 151.

Holden, C. (1998). No last word on language origins. *Science, 282,* 1455–1458.

Holden, C. (1999). A new look into Neandertal's noses. *Science, 285,* 31–33.

Hole, F. & Heizer, R.F. (1969). *An introduction to prehistoric archeology*. New York: Holt, Rinehart & Winston.

Holloway, R.L. (1981). The Indonesian *Homo erectus* brain endocast revisited. *American Journal of Physical Anthropology, 55,* 503–521.

Hood, D. (1964). *Davidson Black: A biography*. Toronto: University of Toronto Press.

Houle, A. (1999). The origin of platyrrhines: An evaluation of the Antarctic scenario and the floating island model. *American Journal of Physical Anthropology, 109:* 541–559.

Howells, W.W. (1983). Origins of the Chinese people: Interpretations of the recent evidence. In D.N. Keightly (Ed.), *The origins of the Chinese civilization*. Berkeley: University of California Press.

Ingmanson, E.J. (1998). Comment. *Current Anthropology 39*, 409–410.

Jack, L.A. (1995). The faces of Djed. *Rotunda, 28* (3).

Jacob, T., Indriati, E., Soejono, R.P., Hsu, K., Frayer, D.W., Eckhardt, R.B., Kuperavage, A.J., Thorne, A. & Henneberg, M. (2006). Pygmoid Australomelanesian *Homo sapiens* skeletal remains from Liang Bua, Flores: Population affinities and pathological abnormalities. *PNAS*, 103, 13421–13426.

Jacoby, R. & Glauberman, N. (Eds.) (1995). *The bell curve*. New York: Random House.

Jerkic, S.M. (2001). The infuence of James E. Anderson on Canadian Physical Anthropology. In L. Sawchuck & S. Pfeiffer (Eds.), *Out of the past: The history of human osteology at the University of Toronto (https://tspace.library.utoronto.ca/citd/Osteology/jerkic.html)*. Toronto: CITD Press, University of Toronto at Scarborough.

Jolly, C.J. & Plog, F. (1986). *Physical anthropology and archaeology* (4th ed.). New York: Knopf.

Jones, S., Martin, R. & Pilbeam, D. (Eds.). (1992). *The Cambridge encyclopedia of human evolution*. New York: Cambridge University Press.

Kaiser, J. (1994). A new theory of insect wing origins takes off. *Science, 266*, 363.

Karavani, I. and Smith, F.H. (2000). More on the Neanderthal problem: The Vindija case. *Current Anthropology, 41*, 838–840.

Kay, R.F. (1981). The nut-crackers—A new theory of the adaptations of the Ramapithecinae. *American Journal of Physical Anthropology, 55*, 141–151.

Kay, R.F., Ross, C. & Williams, B.A. (1997). Anthropoid origins. *Science, 275*, 797–804.

Keenleyside, D.L. (2001). Glimpses of Atlantic Canada's past. Retrieved November 30, 2002, from the World Wide Web: http://www.civilization.ca/academ/articles/keen1_3e.html.

Kelley, J.H. & Williamson, R.G. (1996). The positioning of archaeology within anthropology. *American Antiquity, 61*, 5–20.

Kelley, J.H. & Williamson, R.F. (1996). The positioning of archaeology within anthropology: A Canadian historical perspective. *American Antiquity, 61*, 5–20.

Killen, G. (1998). Toward a scientific archaeology: Daniel Wilson, David Boyle and the Canadian Institute. In D.H. Mitchell & P.J. Smith (Eds.), *Bringing back the past: Historical perspectives on Canadian archaeology* (pp. 15–24). Canadian Museum of Civilization, Mercury Series, Hull, Quebec.

Kirkpatrick, R.C. (2000). The evolution of human homosexual behavior. *Current Anthropology, 41*, 385–413.

Koufos, G. (1993). Mandible of *Ouranopithecus macedoniensis* (hominidae: primates) from a new Late Miocene locality in Macedonia (Greece). *American Journal of Physical Anthropology, 91*, 225–234.

Kramer, P.A. (1998). The costs of human locomotion: Maternal investment in child transport. *American Journal of Physical Anthropology, 107*, 71–85.

Kuhn S.L. & Stiner, M.C. (2006). What's a mother to do? *Current Anthropology, 47*, 953–980.

Kunzig, R. (1999). A tale of two obsessed archaeologists, one ancient city and nagging doubts about whether science can ever hope to reveal the past. *Discover, 20*(5), 84–92.

Kurtén, B. (1986). *How to deep freeze a mammoth*. New York: Columbia University Press.

Lafitau J.F., Fenton, W.N., Moore, E.L. & Champlain Society. (1974). *Customs of the American Indians compared with the customs of primitive times*. Toronto: Champlain Society.

Lahr, M.M. (1996). *The evolution of modern human diversity: A study of cranial variation*. New York: Cambridge University Press.

Lamarck, J.B. (1809). *Philosophie zoologique, ou, Exposition des considâerations relative áa l'histoire naturelle des animaux*. Paris: Chez Dentu [et] L'Auteur.

Lawler, A. (2001). Writing gets a rewrite. *Science, 292*, 2419.

LeGros Clark, W.E. (1966). *History of the primates* (5th ed.). Chicago: University of Chicago Press.

Leigh, S.R. & Park, P.B. (1998). Evolution of human growth prolongation. *American Journal of Physical Anthropology, 107*, 331–350.

Leonard, W.R. (2003). Food for thought. *Scientific American, 13* (2), 62–71.

Leonard, W.R. & Hegman, M. (1987). Evolution of P_3 morphology in *Australopithecus afarensis*. *American Journal of Physical Anthropology, 73*, 41–63.

Lessem, D. (1995–96). Interview with Biruté Galdikas. In E. Angeloni (Ed.), *Physical anthropology 95/96* (pp. 77–85). The Dushkin Publishing Group. Simon Fraser University.

Lestel, D. (1998). How chimpanzees have domesticated humans. *Anthropology Today, 14*, 12–15.

Lev-Yadun, S., Gopher, A., & Abbo, Shahal. (2000). The cradle of agriculture. *Science, 288*, 1602–1603.

Lewin, R. (1987). Debate over emergence of human tooth pattern. *Science, 235*, 749.

Lewin, R. (1987). Four legs bad, two legs good. *Science, 235,* 969.

Lewin, R. (1987). The earliest "humans" were more like apes. *Science, 236,* 1062–1063.

Lewin, R. (1993). Paleolithic paint job. *Discover, 14*(7) 64–70.

Lewontin, R.C., Rose, S. & Kamin, L. J. (1984). *Not in our genes.* New York: Pantheon.

Li, W.H. & Saunders, M.A. (2005). News & views: The chimpanzee and us. *Nature, 437,* 50–51.

Lordkipanidze, D., Vekua, A., Ferring, R., Rightmire, G.P., Agusti, J., Kiladze, G., Mouskhelishvili, A., Nioradze, M., Ponce de León, M.S., Tappen, M., & Zollikofer, C.P.E. (2005). The earliest toothless hominin skull. *Nature, 434,* 717–718.

Lorenzo, C., Carretero, J.M., Arsuaga, J.L., Gracia, A. & Martinez, I. (1998). Intrapopulational body size variation and cranial capacity variation in middle Pleistocene humans: The Sima de los Huesos sample (Sierra de Atapuerca, Spain). *American Journal of Physical Anthropology, 106,* 19–33.

Lounsbury, F.G. (1978). Iroquoian languages. In B.G. Trigger (Ed.), *Handbook of North American Indians: Northeast* (pp. 334–343). Washington: Smithsonian Institution.

Lovejoy, C.O. (1981). Origin of man. *Science, 211*(4480), 341–350.

Lowenstein, J.M. (1992). Genetic surprises. *Discover, 13*(12), 82–88.

Lu, L.D. (1998). The microblade tradition in China: Regional chronologies and significance in the transition to neolithic. *Asian Perspectives, 37,* 84–112.

Lyell, C. (1868). *Principles of geology.* New York: Appleton.

MacDonald, G. (1969). Debert: *A Palaeo-indian site in Central Nova Scotia.* Anthropology Papers, No. 16. Ottawa: National Museum of Man.

MacLarnon, A.M. & Hewitt, G.P. (1999). The evolution of human speech: The role of enhanced breathing control. *American Journal of Physical Anthropology, 109,* 341–363.

MacNeish, R.S. (1992). *The origins of agriculture and settled life.* Norman, OK: University of Oklahoma Press.

Marcus, J. & Flannery, K.V. (1996). *Zapotec civilization: How urban society evolved in Mexico's Oaxaca Valley.* New York: Thames & Hudson.

Marquardt, W.M. & Watson, P.J. (2005). *Archaeology of the Middle Green River Area, Kentucky.* Gainesville: University of Florida Press, pp. 181–212.

Marshack, A. (1976). Some implications of the Paleolithic symbolic evidence for the origin of language. *Current Anthropology, 17,* 274–282.

Marshack, A. (1989). Evolution of the human capacity: The symbolic evidence. *Yearbook of Physical Anthropology, 32,* 1–34.

Marshall, E. (2001). Preclovis sites fight for acceptance. *Science, 291,* 1732.

Marshall, M. (1990). Two tales from the Trukese taproom. In P.R. DeVita (Ed.), *The humbled anthropologist* (pp. 12–17). Belmont, CA: Wadsworth.

Matson, R.G. & Coupland, G.G. (1995). *The prehistory of the Northwest coast.* San Diego: Academic Press.

Matthew, W.D. (1915). Climate and evolution. *Annals of the New York Academy of Sciences, 24,* 171–318.

McCorriston, J. & Hole, F. (1991). The ecology of seasonal stress and the origins of agriculture in the Near East. *American Anthropologist, 93,* 46–69.

McDougall, I., Brown, F.H. & Fleagle, J.G. (2005). Stratigraphic placement and age of modern humans from Kibish, Ethiopia. *Nature, 433,* 733–736.

McGimsey, C.R. (1972). *Public archeology.* New York: Seminar Press.

McGrew, W.C. (1992). *Chimpanzee material culture: implications for human evolution.* Cambridge, UK: Cambridge University Press.

McGrew, W.C. (2000). Dental care in chimps. *Science, 288,* 1747.

McHenry, H.M. (1992). Body size and proportions in early hominids. *American Journal of Physical Anthropology, 87,* 407–431.

McIntosh, S.K. (1999). *Beyond chiefdoms: Pathways to complexity in Africa.* Cambridge, England: Cambridge University Press.

McKenna, J. (1997, October). Bedtime story, *Natural History, 50.*

McKenna, J.J., Smith, E.O. & Trevathan, W. (1999). *Evolutionary medicine.* New York: Oxford University Press.

Mellars, P. (1989). Major issues in the emergence of modern humans. *Current Anthropology, 30,* 349–385.

Meltzer, D., Fowler, D. & Sabloff, J. (Eds.). (1986). *American archaeology: Past and future.* Washington, DC: Smithsonian Institution Press.

Mercader, J., Barton, H., Gillespie, J., Harris, J., Kuhn, S., Tyler, R. & Boesch, C. (2007). 4,300-year-old chimpanzee sites and the origins of percussive stone technology. *PNAS*, 104, 3043–3048.

Michel, B., Guy, F., et al. (2002). A new hominid from the Upper Miocene of Chad, Central Africa. *Science, 418,* 145–152.

Miles, H.L.W. (1993). Language, and the orangutan: The old "person" of the forest. In P. Cavalieri & P. Singer (Eds.), *The great ape project* (pp. 42–57). New York: St. Martin's.

Miller, J.M.A. (2000). Craniofacial variation in *Homo habilis*: An analysis of the evidence for multiple species. *American Journal of Physical Anthropology, 112,* 103–128.

Mintz, S. (1996). A taste of history. In W.A. Haviland & R.J. Gordon (Eds.), *Talking about people* (2nd ed., pp. 79–82). Mountain View, CA: Mayfield.

Mintz, S. (2002). A taste of history. In W.A. Haviland and R.J. Gordon (Eds.), *Talking about people* (3rd ed., pp. 87–90). New York: McGraw Hill.

Minugh-Purvis, N. (1992). The inhabitants of Ice Age Europe. *Expedition, 34* (3), 33–34.

Moffat, A.S. (2002). New fossils and a glimpse of evolution. *Science, 295,* 613–615.

Montagu A. (1942). *Man's most dangerous myth: The fallacy of race* (p. 216). New York: Columbia University Press.

Montgomery, S. (1991). *Walking with the great apes.* Houghton Mifflin Company.

Moore, A.M.T., Hillman, G.C. & Legge, A.J. (2000). *Village on the Euphrates: From foraging to farming at Abu Hureyra.* New York: Oxford University Press.

Morbeck, M.E. (1999). Life history of Gombe chimpanzees: The inside view from the skeleton. In S.C. Strum, D.G. Lindburg, & D. Hamburg (Eds.), *The new physical anthropology* (pp. 18–31). Upper Saddle River, NJ: Prentice Hall.

Morgan, L.H. (1877). *Ancient society: or, Researches in the lines of human progress from savagery, through barbarism to civilization.* Chicago: C.H. Kerr.

Moscati, S. (1962). *The face of the ancient Orient.* New York: Doubleday.

Mydens, S. (2001). He's not hairy, he's my brother. *New York Times,* August 12, Section 4, p. 5.

Nafte, M. (2000). *Flesh and bone: An introduction to forensic anthropology.* Durham, NC: Carolina Academic Press.

Nance, C.R. (1997). Review of Haviland's *Cultural Anthropology* (p. 2).

Neer, R.M. (1975). The evolutionary significance of Vitamin D, skin pigment and ultraviolet light. *American Journal of Physical Anthropology, 43,* 409–416.

Nesse, R.M., Stearns, S.C. & Omenn, G.S. (2006). Medicine needs evolution. *Science,* 311.

Nichols, J. (1998). The first Americans, ca. 20,000 B.C. *Discover, 19,* 24.

Normile, D. (1998). Habit seen as playing larger role in shaping behavior. *Science, 279,* 1454.

Normile, D. (2001). Gene expression differs in human and chimp brains. *Science, 292,* 44–45.

Nunney, L. (1998). Are we selfish, are we nice, or are we nice because we are selfish? *Science, 281,* 1619.

Oliwenstein, L. (1995). New footsteps into walking debate. *Science, 269,* 476.

Olszewski, D.I. (1991). Comment. *Current Anthropology, 32,* 43.

Orangutan Foundation International. (1999). About our president, Dr. Biruté Galdikas. Retrieved October 5, 2007, from the World Wide Web: http://www.orangutan.org/aboutourpresident.php.

Otte, M. (2000). On the suggested bone flute from Slovenia. *Current Anthropology, 41,* 271–272.

Paradis, L.I. (1981). Guerrero and the Olmec. In E. Benson (Ed.), *The Olmec and their neighbors* (pp. 195–208). Washington, DC: Dumbarton Oaks.

Paradis, L.I. (1998). Tollan et les Toltèques, chacun sa vérité. *Anthropologie et Histoire, Actes du Colloque 4* (pp. 19–26). Montréal: Département d'anthropologie, Université de Montréal.

Paradis, L.I. (1999). Le soleil Aztèque était-il un vampire? *Frontières,* 11, 25–30.

Paradis, L.I. (2000). Guerrero region. In S.T. Evans & D.L. Webster (Eds.), *The archaeology of ancient Mexico and Central America: An encyclopedia.* New York: Garland Publishing.

Paradis, L.I. (2000). La mort blanche. *Actes du Colloque 5.* Montréal: Département d'Anthropologie, Université de Montréal.

Paradis, L.I. & Tolstoy, P. (1970). Early and Middle Preclassic cultures in the Basin of Mexico, *Science, 167,* 344–351.

415

Parés, J.M., Perez-Gonzalez, A., Weil, A.B. & Arsuaga, J.L. (2000). On the age of hominid fossils at the Sima de los Huesos, Sierra de Atapuerca, Spain: Paleomagnetic evidence. *American Journal of Physical Anthropology, 111,* 451–461.

Parish, A.R. (1998). Comment. *Current Anthropology, 39,* 413–414.

Parks Canada. (2000). Unearthing the law: Archaeological legislation on lands in Canada. Retrieved October 18, 2004, from the World Wide Web: http://www.pc.gc.ca/progs/pfa-fap/loi-law/index_e.asp.

Parnell, R. (1999). Gorilla exposé. *Natural History, 108*(8), 38–43.

Parra, E.J., Marcini, A., Jin, L., Akey, J., Martinson, J., Batzer, M., Cooper, R., Forrester, T., Allison, D., Deka, R., Ferrell, R.E. & Shriver, M.D. (1998). Estimating African American admixture proportions by use of population-specific alleles. *American Journal of Human Genetics, 63,* 1839–1895.

Pendergast, D. (1990). Up from the dust: The Central Lowlands Postclassic as seen from Laminai and Marco Gonzales. In F.S. Clancy & P.D. Harrison (Eds.), *Vision and revision in Maya studies* (pp. 169–177). Albuquerque: University of New Mexico Press.

Pendergast, D. & Graham, E. (1998). The history of excavations at Lamanai. Retrieved from the World Wide Web: http://www.yorku.ca/anthro/Belize/history.html.

Pickering, T.R., White, T.D., and Toth, N., (2000). Cutmarks on a Plio-Pleistocene Hominid from Sterkfontein, South Africa. *American Journal of Physical Anthropology, 111,* 579–584.

Pilbeam, D. (1986). *Human origins.* David Skamp Distinguished Lecture in Anthropology, Indiana University.

Pilbeam, D. (1987). Rethinking human origins. In R.L. Ciochon & J.G. Fleagle (Eds.), *Primate evolution and human origins* (pp. 436–443). Hawthorne, NY: Aldine de Gruyter.

Pimentel, D. (1991). Response. *Science, 252,* 358.

Piperno, D.R. (2001). On maize and the sunflower. *Science, 292,* 2260–2261.

Pitt, D. (1977). Comment. *Current Anthropology, 18,* 628.

Plattner, S. (1989). Markets and market places. In S. Plattner (Ed.), *Economic anthropology.* Stanford, CA: Stanford University Press.

Pope, G. (1989, October). Bamboo and human evolution. *Natural History, 10,* 48–57.

Pope, G.G. (1992). Craniofacial evidence for the origin of modern humans in China. *Yearbook of Physical Anthropology, 35,* 243–298.

Potts R., Behrensmeyer, A.K., Deino, A., Ditchfield, P. & Clark, J. (2004). Small Mid-Pleistocene hominin associated with East African Acheulean technology. *Science, 305,* 75–78.

Power, M.G. (1995). Gombe revisited: Are chimpanzees violent and hierarchical in the free state? *General Anthropology, 2,* 5–9.

Powis, T., Stanchly, N., White, C.D., Healy, P., Awe, J. & Longstaff, F. (1999). A reconstruction of Middle Preclassic Maya subsistence economy at Cahal Pech, Belize. *Antiquity, 73,* 377–393.

Pringle, H. (1997). Ice Age communities may be earliest known net hunters. *Science, 277,* 1203–1204.

Pringle, H. (1998). The slow birth of agriculture. *Science, 282,* 1449.

Progenix Corporation. (1998). *The history of ginseng in the United States.* Retrieved March 12, 2001, from the World Wide Web: http://progenixcorp.com/ushistory.html.

Puleston, D.E. (1983). *The settlement survey of Tikal.* Philadelphia: University Museum.

Rappaport, R.A. (1994). Commentary. *Anthropology Newsletters, 35,* 76.

Relethford, J.H. (2001). Absence of regional affinities of Neandertal DNA with living humans does not reject multiregional evolution. *American Journal of Physical Anthropology, 115,* 95–98.

Relethford, J.H. & Harpending, H.C. (1994). Craniometric variation, genetic theory, and modern human origins. *American Journal of Physical Anthropology, 95,* 249–270.

Rhine S. (1998). *Bone voyage: A journey in forensic anthropology.* Albuquerque: University of New Mexico Press.

Rice, D.S. & Rice, P.M. (1984). Lessons from the Maya. *Latin American Research Review, 19,* 24–28.

Rice, P. (2000). Paleoanthropology 2000—part 1. *General Anthropology, 7,* 11.

Richmond, B.G., Fleangle, J.K. & Swisher III, C.C. (1998). First Hominoid elbow from the miocene of Ethiopia and the evolution of the Catarrhine elbow. *American Journal of Physical Anthropology, 105,* 257–277.

Ridley, M. (1999). *Genome, the autobiography of a species in 23 chapters.* New York: HarperCollins.

Rightmire, G.P. (1990). *The evolution of Homo erectus: Comparative anatomical studies of an extinct human species.* Cambridge, England: Cambridge University Press.

Rightmire, G.P. (1998). Evidence from facial morphology for similarity of Asian and African representatives of *Homo erectus. American Journal of Physical Anthropology, 106,* 61–85.

Rightmire, G.P. (1998). Human evolution in the Middle Pleistocene. *Evolutionary Anthropology: Issues, News, and Reviews, 6,* 218–227.

Rindos, D. (1984). *The origins of agriculture: An evolutionary perspective.* Orlando, FL: Academic Press.

Rogers, J. (1994). Levels of the genealogical hierarchy and the problem of hominoid phylogeny. *American Journal of Physical Anthropology, 94,* 81–88.

Rogers, T.L. (1999). *The attribution of ancestry for European and Indian (South Asian) individuals within a forensic context.* Burnaby, BC: Simon Fraser University, Department of Archaeology.

Romer, A.S. (1945). *Vertebrate paleontology.* Chicago: University of Chicago Press.

Roosevelt, A.C. (1984). Population, health, and the evolution of subsistence: Conclusions from the conference. In M.N. Cohen & G.J. Armelagos (Eds.), *Paleopathology and the origins of agriculture.* Orlando, FL: Academic Press.

Rosas, A. (2001). Occurrence of Neandertal features from the Atapunerea-SH site. *American Journal of Physical Anthropology, 114,* 74–91.

Rosas, A. & Bermúdez de Castro, J.M. (1998). On the taxonomic affinities of the Dmanisi mandible (Georgia). *American Journal of Physical Anthropology, 107,* 145–162.

Russell, P. (1998). The Paleolithic mother-goddess: Fact or fiction? In K. Hays-Gilpin & D.S. Whitley (Eds.), *Reader in gender archaeology* (pp. 261–268). New York: Routledge.

Sanday, P.R. (1975). On the causes of IQ differences between groups and implications for social policy. In A. Montagu (Ed.), *Race and IQ.* London: Oxford.

Sassaman, K.E. (1998). Sexual division of labor. In K. Hays-Gilpin & D.S. Whitley (Eds.), *Reader in gender archaeology.* New York: Routledge.

Schadla-Hall, T. (1999). Editorial: Public Archaeology. *European Journal of Archaeology, 2,* 147–158.

Schepartz, L.A. (1993). Language and human origins. *Yearbook of Physical Anthropology, 36,* 91–126.

Schwartländer, B., Garnett, G., Walker, N., & Anderson, R. (2000). AIDS in a new millennium. *Science, 289,* 64–67.

Schwartz J.H. (1999). *Sudden origins: Fossils, genes, and the emergence of species.* New York: John Wiley and Sons.

Schwartz J.H. (2004). Getting to know *Homo erectus.* *Science, 305,* 53–54.

Schwartz J.H. (2005). *The red ape: Orangutans and human origins.* Cambridge, MA: Westview Press.

Selim, J. (2002). Out of left field. *Discover, 23,* 30–31.

Sellen, D.W. & Mace, R. (1997). Fertility and mode of substance: A phylogenetic analysis. *Current Anthropology, 38,* 878–889.

Service E.R. (1975). *Origins of the state and civilization: the process of cultural evolution.* New York: Norton.

Shapiro, H.L. (1981). Davidson Black: An appreciation. In B.A. Sigmon & J.S. Cybulski (Eds.), *Homo erectus: Papers in honor of Davidson Black* (pp. 21–26). Toronto: University of Toronto Press.

Shearer, R.R. & Gould, S.J. (1999). Of two minds and one nature. *Science, 286,* 1093.

Sheets, P.D. (1987). Dawn of a New Stone Age in eye surgery. In R.J. Sharer & W. Ashmore (Eds.), *Archaeology: Discovering our past* (p. 231). Palo Alto, CA: Mayfield.

Shen, C. (2000). The tool use-patterning at the Grand Banks Site of the Princess Point Complex, Southwestern Ontario. *Northeast Anthropology, 60,* 63–87.

Shen, C. (2001). *The Lithic production system of the Princess Point Complex during the transition to agriculture in Southwestern Ontario, Canada.* Oxford: BAR International Series.

Shipman, P. (1981). *Life history of a fossil: An introduction to taphonomy and paleoecology.* Cambridge, MA: Harvard University Press.

Shreeve, J. (1994). Terms of estrangement. *Discover, 15*(11), 56–63.

Shreeve, J. (1995). *The Neandertal enigma.* New York: Willliam Morrow.

Shreeve, J. (1995). *The Neandertal enigma: Solving the mystery of modern human origins.* New York: William Morrow.

Sillen, A. & Brain, C.K. (1990). Old flame. *Natural History, 4,* 6–10.

Simons, E.L. (1989). Human origins. *Science, 245,* 1343–1350.

Simons, E.L. (1995). Skulls and anterior teeth of *Catopithecus* (primates: anthropoidea) from the Eocene and anthropoid origins. *Science, 245,* 1885–1888.

Simonsen, B.O. (2002). *The Canadian Archaeological Association and the development of archaeology in Canada.* Retrieved November 30, 2002, from the World Wide Web: http://canadianarchaeology.com/history/-bjorn.lasso.

Sjoberg, G. (1960). *The preindustrial city.* New York: Free Press.

Smith, B.D. (1995). *The emergence of agriculture.* New York: Scientific American Library.

Smith, B.D. (2001). Low-level food production. *Journal of Archaeological Research, 9,* 1–43.

Smith, P.E.L. (1976). *Food production and its consequences*. Menlo Park, CA: Cummings Publishing.

Solis, R.S., Haas, J. & Creamer, W. (2001). Dating Caral, a preceramic site in the Supe valley on the central coast of Peru. *Science, 292,* 723–726.

Solomon, R. (2001). Genome's riddle. *New York Times,* February 20, p. D3.

Sørensen, M.L.S. (2000). *Gender archaeology*. Malden, MA: Blackwell Publishers.

Spence, M. (1981). Obsidian production and the state in Teotihuacan. *American Antiquity, 46,* 769–788.

Sperling, S. (2000). Ashley Montagu (1905–1999). *American Anthropologist, 102,* 584.

Spuhler, J.N. (1979). Continuities and discontinuities in anthropoid-hominid behavioral evolution: Bipedal locomotion and sexual reception. In N.A. Chagnon & W. Irons, (Eds.), *Evolutionary Biology and human social behavior* (pp. 454–461). North Scituate, MA: Duxbury Press.

Stahl, A.B. (1984). Hominid dietary selection before fire. *Current Anthropology, 25,* 151–168.

Stanford, C.G. (1998). The social behavior of chimpanzees and bonobos: Empirical evidence and shifting assumptions. *Current Anthropology, 39,* 399–420.

Stanford, D. & Bradley B. (1999). Constructing the Solutrean solution. http://www.clovisinthesoutheast.net/stanford.html.

Steward, J.H. (1955). *Theory of culture change: the methodology of multilinear evolution*. Urbana: University of Illinois Press.

Stiner, M.C., Munro, N.D., Surovell, T.A., Tchernov, E. & Bar-Yosef, O. (1999). Paleolithic population growth pulses evidenced by small annual exploitation. *Science, 283,* 190–194.

Stone, R. (1995). If the mercury soars, so may health hazards. *Science, 267,* 958.

Stringer, C. & Gamble, C. (1993). *In search of the Neanderthals*. New York: Thames and Hudson.

Stringer, C.B. & McKie, R. (1996). *African exodus: The origins of modern humanity*. London: Jonathan Cape.

Strum, S.C. & Fedigan L. (2000). *Primate encounters: Models of science, gender, and society*. Chicago: University of Chicago Press.

Strum, S.C. & Fedigan, L.M. (1999). Theory, method, gender, and culture: What changed our views of primate society? In S.C. Strum, D.G. Lindburg & D. Hamburg (Eds.), *The new physical anthropology*. Upper Saddle River, NJ: Prentice Hall.

Strum, S.C. (2000). E-mail exchanges. In S.C. Strum & L. Fedigan (Eds.), *Primate encounters: Models of science, gender, and society* (p. 319). Chicago: University of Chicago Press.

Syms, E.L. (1997). Increasing awareness and involvement of aboriginal people in their heritage preservation: Recent developments at the Manitoba Museum of Man and Nature. In G.P. Nicholas & T.D. Andrews (Eds.), *At a crossroads: Archaeology and First Nations peoples in Canada* (pp. 53–68). Burnaby B.C.: Archaeology Press.

Szathmáry, E.J.E. (2001). A comment on the series "A view on the Science of Physical Anthropology at the millennium." *American Journal of Physical Anthropology, 114,* 1–3.

Tardieu, C. (1998). Short adolescence in early hominids: Infantile and adolescent growth of the human femur. *American Journal of Physical Anthropology, 107,* 163–178.

Tattersall, I. (1995). *The last Neanderthal: The rise, success, and mysterious extinction of our closest human relatives*. New York: Macmillan.

Thomas, D.H. (1998). *Archaeology* (3rd. ed.). Fort Worth: Harcourt Brace.

Thomson, K.S. (1997). Natural selection and evolution's smoking gun. *American Scientist, 85,* 516–518.

Tobias, P.V. & von Konigswald, G.H.R. (1964). A comparison between the Olduvai hominines and those of Java and some implications for hominid phylogeny. *Nature, 204,* 515–518.

Togue, R.G. (1992). Sexual dimorphism in the human bony pelvis, with a consideration of the Neanderthal pelvis from Kebara Cave, Israel. *American Journal of Physical Anthropology, 88,* 1–21.

Trigger B.G. (2003). *Understanding early civilizations: A comparative study*. Cambridge: Cambridge University Press.

Trigger, B.G. (1989). Reflections on encounters with archaeology. In D.H. Mitchel & P.J. Smith (Eds.), *Bringing back the past: Historical perspectives on Canadian archaeology* (pp. 77–92). Canadian Museum of Civilization, Mercury Series, Hull, Quebec.

Trinkaus, E. & Shipman, P. (1992). *The Neandertals: Changing the image of mankind*. New York: Alfred A. Knopf.

Underhill, P.A., Shen, P., Lin, A.A., Jin, L., Passarino, G., Yang, W.H., Kauffman, E., Bonne-Tamir, B., Bertranpetit, J., Francalacci, P., and others. (2000). Y chromosome sequence variation and the history of human populations. *Nat Genet, 26,* 358–361.

University of Toronto. (2001). *A brief history of anthropology at the University of Toronto*. Retrieved June 20, 2001, from the World Wide Web: http://www.chass.utoronto.ca/anthroplogy/history.htm.

USDEHGP (U.S. Department of Energy Human Genome Project). (2001). *Genomics and its impact on medicine and society*. Retrieved June 30, 2007, from the World Wide Web: http://www.ornl.gov/hgmis/publicat/primer2001/index.html.

Vekus, A., Lordkipanidze, D., Rightmire, G.P., Agusti, J., Ferring, R., Maisuradze, G., Mouskhelishvili, A., Nioradze, M., Ponce de Leon, M., Tappen, M., Valchrelidze, M. & Zollikofer, C. (2002). A new skull of early *Homo* from Dmanisi, Georgia. *Science, 297,* 85–89.

Walrath, D.E. (2001). *Will the real human ancestor please stand up?* College of Medicine, University of Vermont.

Watson, P.J. & Kennedy, M.C. (1991). The development of horticulture in the Eastern Woodlands of North America: Women's role. In J.M. Gero & M.W. Conkey (Eds.), *Engendering archaeology: Women and prehistory* (pp. 255–275). Cambridge. England: Basil Blackwell.

Weatherford, J. (1988). *Indian givers: How the Indians of the Americas transformed the world*. New York: Fawcett Columbine.

Weiner, J.S. (1955). *The Piltdown forgery*. New York: Oxford University Press.

Weiner, J.S. (1955). *The Piltdown forgery*. Oxford: Oxford University Press.

Weiss, E., Wetterstrom, W., Nadel, D. & Bar-Yosef, O. (2004). The broad spectrum revisited: Evidence from plant remains. *PNAS*, 101, 9551–9555.

Wheeler, P. (1993). Human ancestors walked tall, stayed cool. *Natural History*, 102(8), 65–66.

Whelan, M.K. (1991). Gender and archaeology: Mortuary studies and the search for the origins of gender differentiation. In D. Walde & N.D. Willows, N.D. (Eds.), *The archaeology gender* (pp. 358–365). Proceedings of the 22nd Annual Chacmool Conference. Calgary: Archaeological Association of the University of Calgary.

White, C.D. (1997). Ancient diet at Lamanai and Pacbitun: Implications for the ecological model of collapse. In S.L. Whittington & D.M. Reed (Eds.), *Bones of the Maya: Studies of ancient skeletons* (pp. xi, 290). Washington, DC: Smithsonian Institution Press.

White, T. Suwa, G. & Asfaw, B. (1994). *Australopithecus ramidus*, a new species of early hominid from Aramis, Ethiopia. *Nature*, 371, 306–312.

White, T.D. & Toth, N. (2000). Cutmarks on a Plio-Pleistocene hominid from Sterkfontein, South Africa. *American Journal of Physical Anthropology*, 111, 579–584.

White, T.D., Asfwah, B., DeGusta, D., Gilbert, H., Richards, G.D., Suwa, G. & Howell, F.C. (2003). Pleistocene *Homo sapiens* from Middle Awash, Ethiopia. *Nature, 423*, 742–747.

Whiting, J.W.M., Sodergem, J.A. & Stigler, S.M. (1982). Winter temperature as a constraint to the migration of preindustrial peoples. *American Anthropologist, 84,* 289.

Whitten, A. & Boesch, C. (2001). Cultures of chimpanzees. *Scientific American, 284,* 63–67.

Williamson, R.F. (2000). Trends and issues in consulting archaeology. *Canadian Journal of Archaeology 24*, 158–162.

Wills, C. (1994). The skin we're in. *Discover, 15*, 77–81.

Wilson, D. (1851). *The archaeology and prehistoric annals of Scotland*. Edinburgh: Sutherland & Knox.

Wilson, D. (1884). *The Huron-Iroquois of Canada: A typical race of American aborigines*. Ottawa: Transactions of Royal Society of Canada.

Wilson, D. 1858. On the supposed prevalence of one cranial type throughout the American aborigines. Edinburgh: s.n.

Wittfogel, K.A. (1957). *Oriental despotism, a comparative study of total power*. New Haven, CT: Yale University Press.

Wolpoff, M. & Caspari, R. (1997). *Race and human evolution*. New York: Simon & Schuster. pp. 305–307

Wolpoff, M.H. (1993). Evolution in *Homo erectus*: The question of stasis. *Paleobiology* 10(4): 389–406.

Wolpoff, M.H. (1999). Review of Neandertals and modern humans in western Asia. *American Journal of Physical Anthropology, 109*, 418.

Wolpoff, M.H., Hawks, J., Frayer, D.W. & Hunley, K. (2001). Modern human ancestry at the peripheries: A test of the replacement theory. *Science, 291*, 293–297.

Wong, K. (1998, January). Ancestral quandary: Neanderthals not our ancestors? Not so fast. *Scientific American*, pp. 30–32.

Wood, B. (1991). *Koobi Fora research project*. Oxford [Eng.]; New York: Clarendon Press. v. 4.

Wood, B. & Collard, M. (1999). The human genus. *Science, 284,* 68.

Wood, B. & Aiello, L.C. (1998). Taxonomic and functional implications of mandibular scaling in early Hominines. *American Journal of Physical Anthropology, 105*, 523–538.

Wood, B., Wood, C. & Konigsberg, L. (1994). *Paranthropus boisei*: An example of evolutionary stasis? *American Journal of Physical Anthropology, 95*, 117–136.

Woodward, V. (1992). *Human heredity and society*. St. Paul, MN: West.

Young Alberta Book Society. (1998). *Owen Beattie*. Retrieved October 16, 2000, from the World Wide Web: http://www.culturenet.ucalgary.ca/yabs/beattieo.html.

Zeder, M.A. & Hesse, B. (2000). The initial domestication of goats (*Capra hircus*) in the Zagros mountains 10,000 years ago. *Science, 287,* 2254–2257.

Zeller, A. (1994). Evidence of structure in Macaque communication. In R.A. Gardner et al. (Eds.), *The ethological roots of culture* (pp. 15–39). Netherlands: Kluwer Academic Publishers.

Zeller, A. (1996). The interplay of kinship organisation and facial communication in the macaques. In J.E. Fa & D.G. Lindburg (Eds.), *Evolution and ecology of macaque societies* (pp. 527–550). Cambridge, England: Cambridge University Press.

Zeller, A. (2001) Pretending in monkeys. In R.W. Mitchell (Ed.), *Pretence in animals and children* (pp. 183–195). Cambridge, England: Cambridge University Press.

Zilhão, J. (2000). Fate of the Neandertals. *Archaeology, 53,* 30.

Zimmer, C. (1999). New date for the dawn of dream time. *Science, 284,* 1243–1246.

Zimmer, C. (2001). *Evolution: The triumph of an idea.* New York: HarperCollins.

Zohary, D. & Hopf, M. (1993). *Domestication of plants in the Old World* (2nd ed.). Oxford: Clarenden Press.

Abell, Paul, 163
Aboriginal Australians. *See* Australian aborigines
Aboriginal Canadians. *See* First Nations; Inuit
Aboriginal peoples of Americas
    change from foraging to agriculture, 324
    crops of, 313
    food production by, 305
    languages of, 282
    origins of, 282
    spread of, 281–285
    trade among, 359
Abu Hureyra (Syria), 308, 321
Accelerator mass spectrometry (AMS), 56–57
Acheulean tool tradition, 220–221, 224–225, 231, 238, 244, 256
Acorns, 305
Action theory, 361
Adaptation, 86, 88–91
    mutations and, 84–85
    and skin colour, 382–385
    survival and, 102
Adaptive radiation, 138, 140, 141, 144
Adena culture, 337
Aegyptopithecus, 144–145, 146
Aerial photography, 39
Afar region (Ethiopia), 163–164
Africa. *See also* East Africa; South Africa
    anatomically modern fossils in, 256
    archaic *H. sapiens* in, 243–244
    Australopithecus in, 163
    and descent of anatomically modern humans, 255, 258–259
    H. ergaster in, 211
    Middle Pleistocene fossils in, 236–238
    population sizes in, 258
African Americans
    and IQ tests, 386–387
    and sickle-cell anemia, 90
Agency theory, 23
Agriculture. *See also* Farmers/farming
    at Abu Hureyra, 321
    artistic development compared to, 273
    in Brazil, 345
    and changes in way of life, 301
    division of labour in, 328
    innovations in, 345–346
    intensive, 301, 327–328, 345
    in Korea, 318
    and physiological stress, 325–326
    and population growth, 323
    pottery and, 299
    primary origins of, 314

    and religion, 360
    and ritual activity, 323
    secondary shifts to, 314–315
    slash-and-burn, 344, 360
    in sub-Saharan Africa, 316
    at Tikal, 344
    tools, 322
    transition from hunting/gathering to, 314–320
Ainu people, 32, 282, 318
Alaska, land bridge to, 282–283
Alberta
    use of fire in, 305
    Head-Smashed-In Buffalo Jump, 54, 286 fig.
    Vermilion Lakes site, 40
Alleles, 76, 370–371
Altered fossils, 35–36
Altimira Cave (Spain), 277–278
Alva, Walter, 356
Ambrona (Spain), 228
Ambrose, Stanley, 250
Analogies, 66
Anatolia, hominoids and, 152
Anatomically modern humans (AMHs)
    Cro-Magnons as, 264
    origins of, 251–259
    replacing archaic *H.sapiens,* 256–257
    Upper Palaeolithic people as, 264
Ancestral traits, 103
Ancestry, forensic anthropology and, 10, 380–381
Andaman Islanders, 377
Anderson, James, 6, 7, 18
Andersson, J.G., 217
Animals
    adaptation by, 89
    dating of remains, 55–56
    domestication of, 304–306, 310–311, 321
    fossilization of, 36
    game, 245–246, 283–284, 296
    killing methods, 246
    in Mexico, 313
    reliance upon, 302
    in rock art, 274–275
    size of, 305
    skeletons, 304–305
    in South America, 313
    in Southwest Asia, 310
    from Wallace site, 51, 52 fig.
Ankarapithecus, 152
Antelopes, 179
Anthropogenesis, 300
Anthropoids, 104

Anthropology
    applied, 8–9, 16
    biological, 7, 8, 9–10, 13, 34, 370
    Canadian, 5–7
    comparison in, 24–25
    and contemporary life, 28–29
    contributions to other disciplines, 26–27
    cultural, 8, 24, 370
    defined, 4
    development of, 4–5
    discipline of, 8–17
    ethics and, 27–28
    forensic, 9–10, 47–48
    and humanities, 25–26
    linguistic, 8, 15
    medical, 16, 26
    molecular, 7
    and science, 8, 17, 19
    social, 8
    sociocultural, 8, 14–15
    travel and, 4
    university departments, 13
    urban, 26
Anthropomorphism, 66
Ants, 301
Apes, 115–117. *See also* Bonobos; Chimpanzees; Gorillas; Orangutans
    communication of, 203
    distribution of, 148
    in forests, 145
    and human origins, 147–154
    infancy and childhood of, 188
    intelligence of, 168
    "killer," 194
    and language, 123, 203
    Miocene, 145–147
    monkeys vs., 155
    Neandertals and, 240
    Oligocene, 143–145
    teeth of, 95
Arago (France), 237
Arashiyama Texas-Japan project, 119
Arborealism, 106. *See also* Forests
    of *Ardipithecus,* 174
    of Australopithecines, 168
    bipedalism and, 181
    brain and, 106
    food and, 140
    leaping and, 140, 141, 142, 143
    of orangutans, 155
    of primates, 106, 143, 155
Archaeology, 8, 9, 11–14, 34
    in China, 13, 22–23

MaXxImages.com **115**: bottom, Peter Drowne/Color-Pic, Inc. **116**: right, David Watts/Anthro-Photo **116**: top left, Miriam Silverstein/Animals, Animals/MaXxImages.com **117**: Adapted from Strum, Shirley C., & Linda Redigan (2000). Primate Encounters: Models of Sciene, Gender and Society. Chicago: The University of Chicago Press. **120**: top left, Anita de Laguna Haviland **121**: top left, Amy Parish/Anthro-Photo **126**: top, Bromhall/Animals, Animals/MaXxImages.com **129**: Whitten, A., & Boesch, C. (2001). Cultures of chimpanzes. Scientific American, 284(1), 63-67. Copyright © Scientific American, Inc. **130**: David Bygott/Kibuyu Partners

Chapter 5. 140: top, Gary Crawford **141**: bottom, Martin Harvey **142**: From Bloch and Boyer, SCIENCE 298, Fig 2, p. 1606-1610 (22 November 2002). Reprinted with permission from of AAAS. **144**: bottom, E.L. Simons/Duke Primate Center **145**: top, Ollie Ellison/Duke University **147**: ORIGINAL PUBLICATION: From "LUCY: The Beginnings of Humankind" ILLUSTRATION CREDIT: © 1981 Luba Dmytryk Gudz \ Brill Atlanta **148**: Walrath, D. E. (2001). Will the real human ancestor plese stand up? © by author, College of Medicine, University of Vermount. Reprinted courtesy of D.E. Walrath. **151**: top left, David L. Brill **151**: bottom left, From "Planet of the Apes" by David Begun, August 2003. Reprinted by permission of Scientific American. Copyright David Begun. **151**: left, From "Planet of the Apes" by David Begun, August 2003. Reprinted by permission of Scientific American. Copyright David Begun. **154**: Gary Crawford **155**: National Museums of Kenya

Chapter 6. 160: Tim White/David L. Brill, Atlanta **162**: ORIGINAL PUBLICATION: From "LUCY: The Beginnings of Humankind" ILLUSTRATION CREDIT: © 1981 Luba Dmytryk Gudz \ Brill Atlanta **165**: bottom right, David L. Brill by permission of Owen Lovejoy **168**: bottom right, William H. Kimbel, Ph.D., Institute of Human Origins **169**: bottom right, Des Bartlett/NGS image Collection **169**: top right, Lee R. Burger, PURE, University of Witwaterstand **170**: National Museums of Kenya **171**: Melville Bell Grosvenor/NGS Image Collection **172**: bottom left, 1994, Tim O. White/David Brill, Atlanta **172**: top, David L. Brill **173**: Nature, vol. 418, p. 147, © 2002 Nature Publishing Group **175**: Dr. Fred Spoor/National Museums of Kenya **177**: Dr. Rose Sevcik, Courtesy of The Language Research Center, Georgia State University **178**: John Giustina Photography, www.tazama.com **179**: Adapted from Folger, T. (1993). The naked and the bipedal. Discover, 14(11), 34-35.

Chapter 7. 192: top left, National Museums of Kenya **192**: top right, National Museums of Kenya **196**: center left, David L. Brill/The National Geographic **196**: center, David L. Brill/The National Geographic **196**: center right, David L. Brill/The National Geographic **196**: bottom left, David L. Brill/The National Geographic **196**: bottom right, David L. Brill/The National Geographic **197**: Adapted from Cavallo, J.A. (1990). Cat n the human cradle. Natural History, 54-56, 58-60.

Copyright © American Museum of Natural History. **198**: top, E.R. Degginger/Color-Pic, Inc. **200**: top, William A. Haviland **201**: top, Andy Freeberg **202**: top, Anita de Laguna Haviland **203**: top left, Mary Ann Fittipaldi **203**: top right, Mary Ann Fittipaldi

Chapter 8. 214: © John Reader/Photo Researchers **215**: top, Russell Ciochon, University of Iowa **216**: top, National Museums of Canada **219**: Figure 1 from Lordkipanidze D, Vekua A, Ferring R, Rightmire GP, Agusti J, Kiladze G, Mouskhelishvili A, Nioradze M, Ponce de León MS, Tappen M, & Zollikofer CPE (2005). The earliest toothless hominin skull. Nature, 434, 717-718. **221**: Gary Crawford **222**: Adapted from Pope, G.C., (1989). Bamboo and human evolution. Natural History, 10, 50-54. Copyright © American Museum of Natural History. **224**: Courtesy of Chen Shen **225**: top, 1985 David L. Brill **228**: top, 1985 David L. Brill **229**: bottom left, Kenneth Garrett/NGS Image Collection **229**: top right, Kenneth Garrett/NGS Image Collection **230**: top, Alexander Marshack

Chapter 9. 237: top, Javier Trueba/Madrid Scientific Films **238**: center right, © PhotoDisc/Getty Images **238**: bottom left, 1985 David L. Brill **241**: left, © Bettmann/Corbis **241**: right, © The Field Museum, John Weinstein **242**: 1985 David L. Brill **243**: top, Paul Jaronski, UM Photo Services **244**: top, Milford H. Wolpoff **245**: Gary Crawford **247**: © Erik Trinkaus **248**: top left, © Kenneth Garrett/National Geographic Image Collection **250**: top left, Alexander Marshack, New York University **250**: top right, Alexander Marshack, New York University **251**: top, University of Liege **255**: top right, Qafzeh Archives & Dr. B. Vandermeersch, Courtesy of Dr. Ofer Bar-Yosef **256**: top right, 2003 David L. Brill **257**: top, Sally McBrearty **258**: Wolpoff & Caspari, p. 205-207. From Raceand Human Eolution, copyright © 1996 by Milford Wolpoff and Rachel Caspari. Reprinted with the permission of Simon & Schuster, Inc.

Chapter 10. 264: bottom left, David L. Brill, artifact credit, Musée de l'Homme, Paris **266**: Figure 1 from Brown P, Sutikna T., Morwood M.J., Soejono R.P., Jatmiko, Saptomo E.W., & Due R.A. (2004). A new small-bodied hominin from the Late Pleistocene of Flores, Indonesia. Nature 431:1055-1061 **268**: top, Gary Crawford **269**: bottom, Gary Crawford **269**: **270**: center left, William A. Haviland/UVM Photo Service **270**: bottom, William A. Haviland/UVM Photo Service **272**: Zinman Institute of Archaeology, University of Haifa, Mt. Carmel, 31905, Israel, http://ohalo.haifa.ac.il/ **274**: top right, Alexander Marshack, New York University **275**: top, Gary Crawford **276**: © Jean Vertut **276-277**: By R. Lewin (1993). Paleolithic paint job. Discover, 14(7), 67-69. Copyright © 1993 The Walt Disney Co. Reprinted with permission of Discover Magazine. **278**: top left, Negative No. K15806, Courtesy Department of Library Sciences, American Museum of Natural History **278**: center left, Negative No. K15823, Courtesy Department of